# PROGRESS IN MEDICINAL CHEMISTRY

3

| | |
|---|---|
| ENGLAND: | BUTTERWORTH & CO. (PUBLISHERS) LTD.<br>LONDON: 88 Kingsway, W.C.2 |
| AFRICA: | BUTTERWORTH & CO. (AFRICA) LTD.<br>DURBAN: 33–35 Beach Grove |
| AUSTRALIA: | BUTTERWORTH & CO. (AUSTRALIA) LTD.<br>SYDNEY: 6–8 O'Connell Street<br>MELBOURNE: 473 Bourke Street<br>BRISBANE: 240 Queen Street |
| CANADA: | BUTTERWORTH & CO. (CANADA) LTD.<br>TORONTO: 1367 Danforth Avenue, 6 |
| NEW ZEALAND: | BUTTERWORTH & CO. (NEW ZEALAND) LTD.<br>WELLINGTON: 49/51 Ballance Street<br>AUCKLAND: 35 High Street |
| U.S.A.: | BUTTERWORTH INC.<br>WASHINGTON, D.C.: 7235 Wisconsin Avenue, 14 |

# PROGRESS IN MEDICINAL CHEMISTRY

## 3

*Edited by*

### G. P. ELLIS, B.Sc., Ph.D., F.R.I.C.

*Department of Chemistry and Biology, Welsh College
of Advanced Technology, Cardiff*

*and*

### G. B. WEST, B.Pharm., D.Sc., Ph.D.

*School of Pharmacy, University of London*

LONDON

**BUTTERWORTHS**

1963

Suggested U.D.C. number: 615.7:54

*Printed in Great Britain at the Pitman Press, Bath*

# PREFACE

THE present volume consists of seven reviews on a wide variety of chemical and biological topics, and follows the theme set by previous volumes. Each chapter is written by experts in their own fields and attempts have again been made, wherever possible, to link chemical structure with pharmacological activity.

The chapter on the chemical aspects of neuromuscular block is complementary to that on the pharmacology of neuromuscular transmission which appeared in Volume 2. The development of a potent, safe, short-acting muscle relaxant is now needed and appears possible in the near future. Trypanocides for human and veterinary use are reviewed in detail, with emphasis on the chemical aspects, and the need for a new drug to eliminate both tissue and blood forms of the parasite seems urgent.

In the last few years, many drugs with antitussive action have been introduced. Although medical opinion is not unanimous in its approval of their usefulness, a review of the chemistry and pharmacology of this field is valuable. Much progress has recently been made in analysing the properties of the *Rauwolfia* alkaloids and the present review summarizes the knowledge that has accumulated to date in this difficult field.

The highly specialized but essential application of statistics to the evaluation of pharmacological and toxicological results is discussed in detail and the many examples given should be useful to both pharmacologists and biological statisticians. The present-day knowledge of anticonvulsant action is far from complete and so is the armoury of drugs of this type. The chapter on this topic therefore has been difficult to compile but is nevertheless most valuable. Although few new local anaesthetics have been discovered in recent years, much chemical effort has been made in this direction, and an assessment of the present situation is given in the last chapter.

Again, we are grateful to reviewers and others for their encouragement and suggestions. We are also gratified to know that earlier volumes have been of use to postgraduate students in schools of pharmacy and of medicine as well as to other workers in pharmaceutical research. Our thanks are due to the staff of Butterworths and to the authors, societies and publishers for permission to use illustrations and tables which have appeared in previous publications.

G. P. ELLIS
G. B. WEST

*March*, 1963

# CONTENTS

# SOME CHEMICAL ASPECTS OF NEURO-MUSCULAR BLOCK

## J. B. STENLAKE

### INTRODUCTION

THE experiments of Claude Bernard and Pelouze[1-3], over a hundred years ago, not only established the rôle of the neuromuscular junction in neuro-muscular transmission, but also clearly demonstrated the already known paralytic action of crude curare extracts. Within a few years, Crum Brown and Fraser[4], prompted by the realization that curare extracts contained quaternary ammonium salts, examined the effects of other such compounds and showed that the methiodides of atropine, brucine, codeine, coniine, morphine, strychnine and thebaine, reproduce the paralytic action of curare extracts. Many other quaternary salts have since been studied in this way and neuromuscular blocking agents are now accepted as useful adjuncts to surgical anaesthesia. Drugs used for this purpose should be capable of pro-ducing a controlled neuromuscular block and should be free from undesirable side-reactions. Other important requirements are that their action should be readily reversible, and that the compounds should be rapidly eliminated from the system. The well-known limitations of the major neuromuscular blocking agents in various of these respects, and the search for more specific and more reliable drugs, have led, in recent years, to the examination of large numbers of synthetic and natural substances, mostly quaternary salts. A number of detailed factual reviews of various aspects of the literature in this field has appeared in the last few years[5-10a], but, with the exception of those by Taylor[11] and Cavallito[12,13], few attempts have been made to survey further the essential requirements of chemical structure for neuromuscular block.

### The Pharmacological Classification of Neuromuscular Blocking Agents

Bowman[14] has classified the various ways in which neuromuscular block may be achieved. These include: (a) depression of acetylcholine synthesis; (b) depression of acetylcholine release; (c) depression of motor end-plate sensitivity. Chemical agents which block transmission by methods (a) and (b) do so by reducing the output of the transmitter substance, acetylcholine. Such substances are outside the scope of the present article, which is con-cerned with compounds which reduce the effectiveness of released acetylcholine.

Broadly speaking these may be divided into two groups; the competitive blockers and the depolarizers. A competitive block is produced by compounds such as (+)-tubocurarine and gallamine, which compete with acetylcholine for its receptors, thereby preventing acetylcholine from exerting its depolarizing action. They do not interfere with the liberation of acetylcholine[15], but combine with the specific acetylcholine receptors in the motor end-plate, so that its potential is merely reduced and it is not depolarized. Subsequent stimulation of the nerve produces the usual release of acetylcholine, but, because the end-plate potential is reduced, the potential drop is too small to excite a response in the muscle. On the other hand, depolarizers such as decamethonium and suxamethonium resemble acetylcholine in their action on the motor end-plate region, causing electrical inexcitability which is much more prolonged than that produced by the natural transmitter agent[16,17]. A true acetylcholine-like action, however, is only produced by these compounds in some muscles of the cat and man. In other mammalian species, such as the monkey, dog, rabbit and hare, they exhibit a 'dual block', which at first is characteristic of depolarization, but later assumes characteristics of a competitive block[18]. In addition, compounds acting by 'dual block' cause a rapid decrease in the sensitivity of the muscle to repeated doses, a feature which is not characteristic of either depolarizers or of competitive blockers. Similar differences in the behaviour of the neuromuscular junction also exist between different muscles of the same species[19]. For example, decamethonium and suxamethonium exhibit a pure acetylcholine-like action at the junction of the cat tibialis muscle yet they block the cat soleus muscle by a 'dual mode of action'. Moreover, the balance between completion and depolarization may vary for any one drug with various muscles on which it shows 'dual action', and also between one drug and another on the same muscle. Thus, the action of suxamethonium is weighted in favour of depolarization, whilst that of decamethonium favours competition.

These refinements of the broad classification have only been established in recent years, and the necessarily extensive pharmacological examination required to achieve them has only been applied to a few compounds. By contrast, countless substances have been examined for motor end-plate activity, for which the literature only records a measure of potency on a single preparation, or at best gives some qualitative indication of whether the substance acts substantially as a competitive blocker or as a depolarizer. Detailed studies are important as they provide the basis for the present concepts of the receptor molecules and their reactions. Thus, the differences in response may be a reflection of differences in binding characteristics of the drug with the receptor molecule, and/or differences in the properties of the drug-receptor complex[19a]. The reversal of competitive block by neostigmine and similar substances also provides evidence of factors affecting drug-receptor binding, and studies of structure-action relationships in compounds reversing a neuromuscular block may well repay further investigation. Safe control of the block produced is a prime requirement of any blocking agent used as an adjunct to surgical anaesthesia, and the ready reversal of competitive block marks out this type of blocker as the most important group for the development of compounds useful to medicine.

With these facts in mind, the relationship between chemical structure and pharmacological action in this article has been restricted to broad issues. The emphasis is mainly on potency, and on the broad classification into competitive blockers and depolarizers.

## ESSENTIAL CHEMICAL REQUIREMENTS FOR MOTOR END-PLATE BLOCK

### The Onium Centre

It has been recognized since the early work of Crum Brown and Fraser[4] that the primary chemical requirement of a neuromuscular blocking agent is a strongly basic centre capable of permanent existence as a positively charged ion. The first compounds to be identified with this type of activity were quaternary ammonium salts, and, when acetylcholine (*I*) was also established as a quaternary ammonium salt, it was natural to expect that major developments would be derived from this group of compounds. The work of Hunt and Renshaw[20,21], and subsequently of Ing and Wright[22,23] established, however, that the property of neuromuscular block is not shown only by quaternary ammonium compounds. The analogous sulphonium (*II*), phosphonium (*III*), arsonium (*IV*) and stibonium (*V*) radicals which

$$CH_3 \cdot CO \cdot O \cdot CH_2 \cdot CH_2 \cdot \overset{+}{N}Me_3 \; Cl^- \qquad Me_3\overset{+}{S} \; X^- \qquad Me_4\overset{+}{P} \; X^-$$

$$(I) \qquad\qquad\qquad (II) \qquad\qquad (III)$$

$$Me_4\overset{+}{As} \; X^- \qquad Me_4\overset{+}{Sb} \; X^- \qquad Me_3\overset{+}{N} \cdot (CH_2)_{10} \cdot \overset{+}{N}Me_3 \; 2I^-$$

$$(IV) \qquad\qquad (V) \qquad\qquad\qquad (VI)$$

similarly carry a strong positive charge on the central atom, exhibit neuro-muscular blocking properties to a greater or lesser degree.

### Active Tertiary Bases

The absence of blocking properties in the corresponding precursor amines, sulphides, phosphines, arsines and stibines may be taken as further evidence of the primary effector rôle of the onium ion. Replacement of one of the quaternary ammonium groups of decamethonium (*VI*) by an amine group as in *N*,*N*-dimethyldecamethylenediamine monomethiodide (*VII*)[24] or by a hydrogen as in *N*,*N*-dimethyldecylamine methiodide (*VIII*)[25] produces a marked reduction in the degree and duration of activity. These compounds

$$Me_3\overset{+}{N} \cdot (CH_2)_{10} \cdot NH_2 \; I^- \qquad Me_3\overset{+}{N} \cdot (CH_2)_9 \cdot CH_3 \; I^-$$

$$(VII) \qquad\qquad\qquad (VIII)$$

also serve to emphasize the importance of a polyonium structure, a factor which is discussed in greater detail later in this chapter. Similarly, tertiary amines corresponding to gallamine (*IX*)[26], to a series of bisonium substituted triazines (*X*)[27], and to the bisonium substituted benzoquinones (*XI*)[28], are also less effective than the corresponding quaternary salts. However, the hydrochloride of the tertiary base, corresponding to the trisonium triazine derivative (*XII*) is almost as active as the quaternary salt in mice. Further, in the benzoquinone series (*XI*), the activity of tertiary bases has been related to the strength of the base, a fact which stresses the importance of a cationic centre.

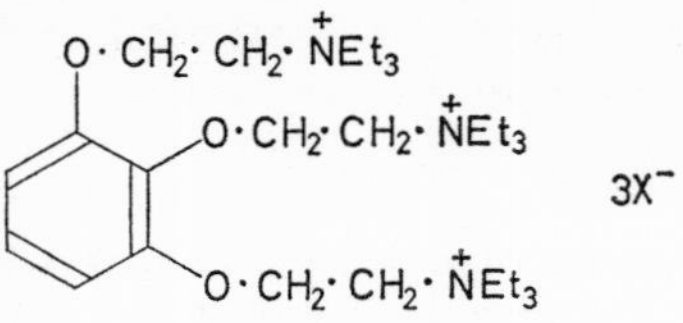

*(IX)*

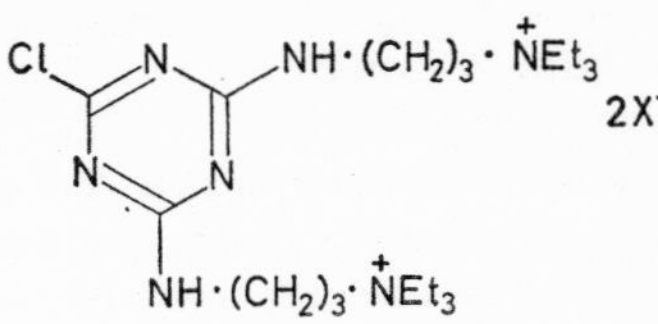

*(X)*

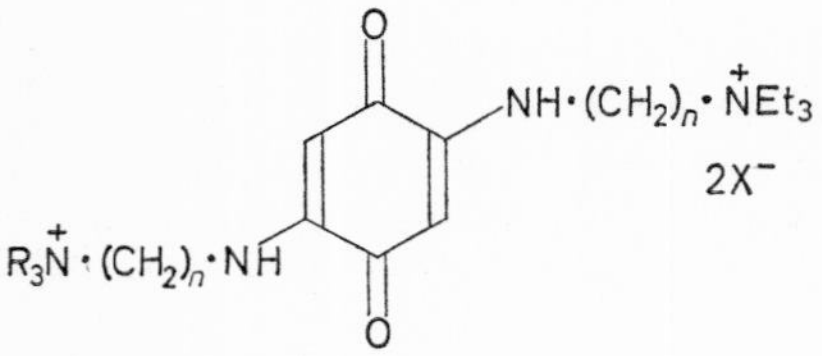

*(XI)*

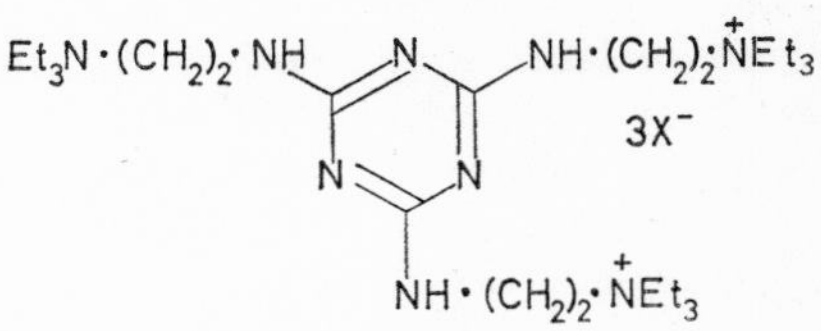

*(XII)*

## The Erythrina Alkaloids

The Erythrina alkaloids, a group of naturally occurring tertiary bases, also exhibit curare-like activity[29]. Chemically, they are of two groups; the tetrahydroisoquinoline derivatives *(XIII)* and *(XIV)*[30-33], and the lactone

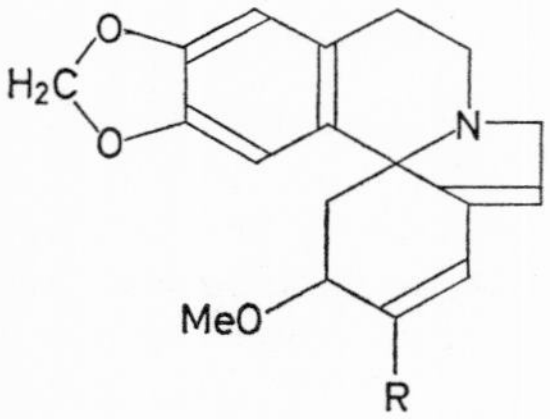

*(XIII)* R = H, Erythraline
R = OH, Erythratine

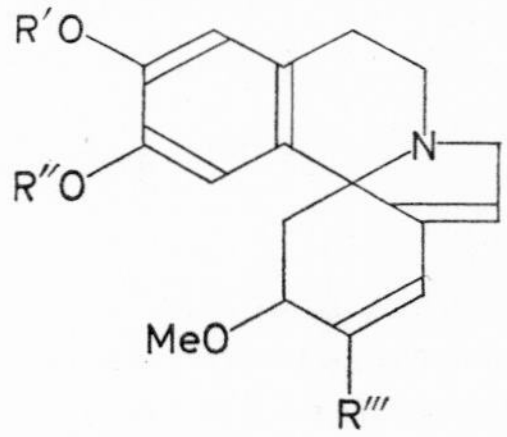

*(XIV)* R′ = P″= R‴= H, Erysopine
R′or R″=R‴=H, ⎱ Erysodine
               and
R″or R′ = Me ⎰ Erysovine
R′=R″= Me, R‴= OH, Erythratine

bases, α- and β-erythroidine *(XV)*[34]. Pharmacologically, the lactone bases are of greater interest than the tetrahydroisoquinoline alkaloids, although the most active lactone, dihydro-β-erythroidine *(XVI)* has only about one-third of the potency of (+)-tubocurarine on the rat diaphragm preparation[35] and one-twentieth of the potency of the latter on the cat muscle[36]. Although the activity of dihydro-β-erythroidine *(XVI)* is much less than that of (+)-tubocurarine in the cat, the onset of paralysis is about twenty times as fast[37]. Its action resembles that of (+)-tubocurarine in that it is reversed immediately by edrophonium and neostigmine, though rather more slowly by the latter anticholinesterase. Block is also partially antagonized by calcium ions, and increased by lowering the temperature of the preparation. Dihydro-β-erythroidine produces flaccid paralysis in chicks. Of the two

4

stereoisomeric tetrahydro-$\beta$-erythroidines $(XVII)$, $\beta$-tetrahydro-$\beta$-erythro-idine is about equipotent with dihydro-$\beta$-erythroidine in the frog[35], but the corresponding $\alpha$-isomer has greatly reduced potency (*Table 1.1*).

$\beta$-Erythroidine is effective when administered orally, and, contrary to the behaviour of other tertiary bases, its curarizing potency is markedly reduced on conversion to the methiodide[36]. It is possible that the curarizing action of the lactone alkaloids is explainable in terms of the comparatively

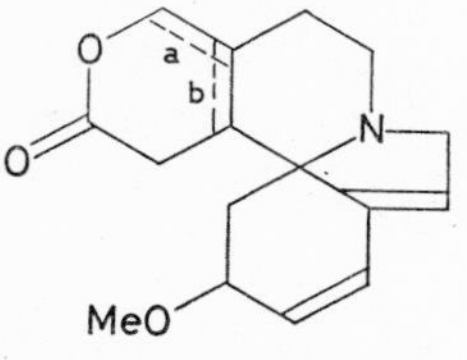

$(XV)$ $(a) = \alpha$-Erythroidine  
$(b) = \beta$-Erythroidine  
$(XVI)$ 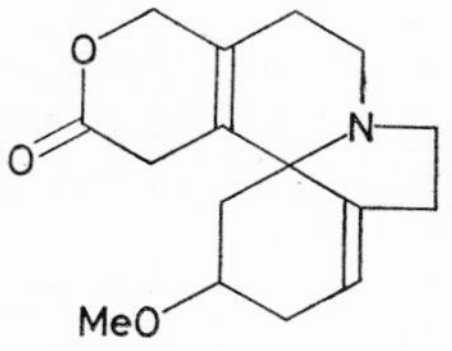  
$(XVII)$ 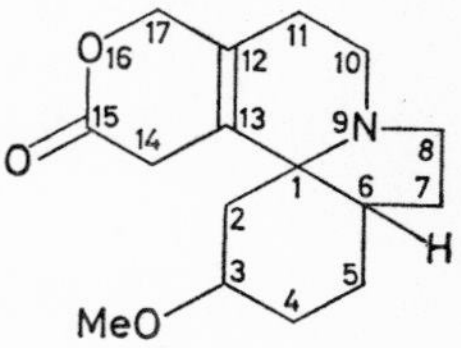

rigid ring structure, which holds the lactone carbonyl and amine functions in a fixed spacial arrangement, similar to that which obtains for the ester and basic groups of acetylcholine itself. Examination of models supports this suggestion. Conjugation of the 4,5 and 6,7 double bonds of $\beta$-erythroidine,

Table 1.1. Potency of $\beta$-erythroidine derivatives in frogs (lymph sac injection)[35]

| Alkaloid | Paralysing dose (mg/kg) |
|---|---|
| $\beta$-Erythroidine hydrochloride | 3–8 |
| $\beta$-Erythroidine methiodide | 200 |
| Dihydro-$\beta$-erythroidine hydrochloride | 0·6 |
| $\alpha$-Tetrahydro-$\beta$-erythroidine hydrobromide | 200 |
| $\beta$-Tetrahydro-$\beta$-erythroidine hydrobromide | 0·5 |
| (+)-Tubocurarine | 0·5–4·2 |

with the latter bond being $\beta$, $\gamma$ to the tertiary nitrogen, results in base-weakening[38]. Replacement of this conjugated unsaturation by a single double bond in the 5,6 position in dihydro-$\beta$-erythroidine, largely removes the influence of this double bond on the nitrogen, and the consequent base-strengthening contributes to the increased potency observed. Models of $\alpha$- and $\beta$-tetrahydro-$\beta$-erythroidines reveal major differences in the shape of these molecules, which may account for the marked difference in pharma-cological response. Three of the four rings (shaded) are approximately coplanar in structure $(XVIIIB)$, and the fourth spiro-ring is largely above the plane of the other three. In structure $(XVIIIA)$, on the other hand, only two rings are coplanar, and of the remaining two, one is above and the other below this plane. It is apparent, therefore, that although both lactone and amine groups are approximately coplanar in both isomers, only the isomer $B$ is capable of approaching (at the $\alpha$-face) an acetylcholine receptor sufficiently closely to permit interaction at both cationic and anionic centres.

The stereochemistry of the isomer A is such that the molecule could approach closely to either the cationic or the anionic centre, but not to both. The suggestion is made tentatively, and on the biological evidence only, that the structure of the most active isomer, $\beta$-tetrahydro-$\beta$-erythroidine, is represented by (*XVIIIB*), and this view is perhaps strengthened by the fact that the molecular shape of both $\beta$-erythroidine and of dihydro-$\beta$-erythroidine also approximate to that of (*XVIIIB*).

Synthetic methods[39-43] and X-ray crystallographic[44] evidence suggest that a 1,6-*cis*-structure is correct for the erythrinane derivatives obtained either by hydrogenation of the tetrahydroisoquinoline type erythrina alkaloids or by synthesis. The 3-hydroxy group is *cis* to the nitrogen. No

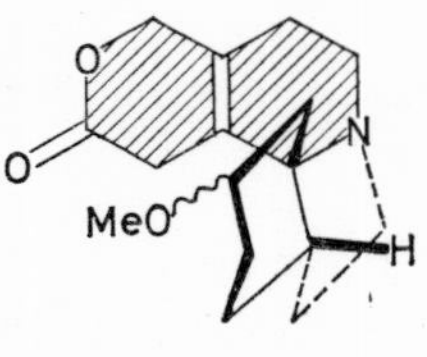

A
1,6 – cis

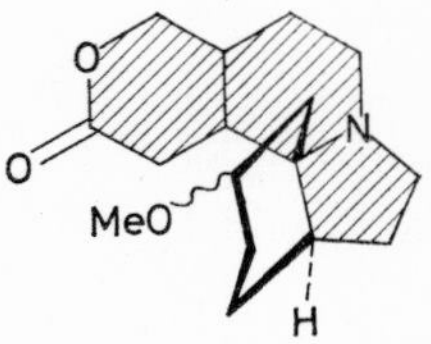

B
1,6 - trans

(*XVIII*)

relationship, however, has yet been established with the above tetrahydro-$\beta$-erythroidines, though 14,15,16,17-tetrahydro-16-oxa-erythrinane has been synthesized and resolved, and the laevorotatory enantimorph has been shown to be identical with anhydro-$\alpha$-hexahydrodesmethoxy-$\beta$-erythroidinol derived from $\beta$-erythroidine[45,46].

As tertiary bases, this group of alkaloids may be expected to pass tissue boundaries and reach the motor end-plate region more rapidly and more readily than a quaternary salt[47]; hence the more rapid onset of action with dihydro-$\beta$-erythroidine than with (+)-tubocurarine. The low potency of $\beta$-erythroidine methiodide, which has only been measured on the frog lymph sac preparation may, therefore, merely reflect a failure in tissue distribution, and consequently quaternary salts of the erythroidine lactone bases should be examined in other preparations.

## Pyrrolizidine alkaloids

More recently, attention has been drawn to a second group of tertiary base alkaloids which block transmission at the neuromuscular junction. Experiments on the rat phrenic nerve-diaphragm preparation and on the anterior tibial muscle of the cat[48] have shown that the pyrrolizidine alkaloids, heliotrine (*XIX*) and lasiocarpine (*XX*), block transmission by a mechanism which resembles that of decamethonium more closely than that of tubocurarine. Lasiocarpine is more potent than heliotropine on the rat phrenic nerve-diaphragm preparation, and it possesses a greater element of structural similarity to acetylcholine. The corresponding *N*-oxides are inactive, but related quaternary alkaloids do not appear to have been studied.

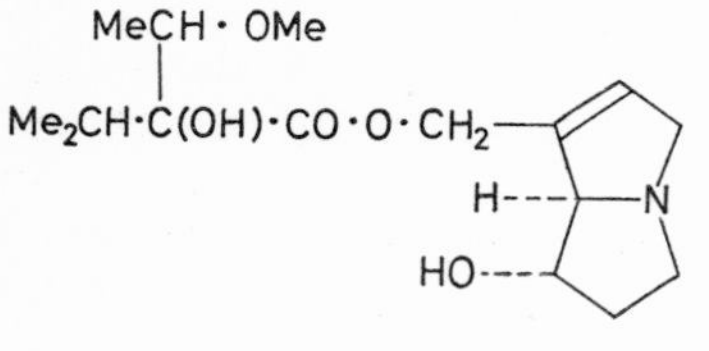

MeCH·OMe
|
Me$_2$CH·C(OH)·CO·O·CH$_2$

H---
HO---

*(XIX)*

MeCH·OMe
|
Me$_2$C(OH)·C(OH)·CO·O·CH$_2$

H----
MeCH=CMe·CO·O--

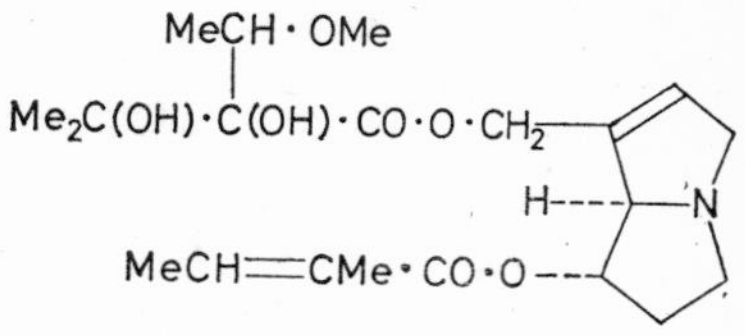

*(XX)*

*Miscellaneous non-quaternary bases*

Graham and James[49] have described a series of 2-halogenoalkylamines (*XXI*, R′ = Me, Et or Pr; R″ = H, Me, Et or Pr; X = Cl, Br or I) which exhibit decamethonium-like spastic paralysis in chicks. Maltoxin, a base

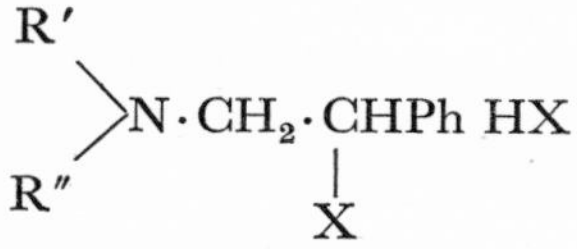

$$\begin{matrix} R' \\ \\ R'' \end{matrix}\Big\rangle N·CH_2·\overset{\displaystyle}{\underset{X}{CHPh}} HX$$

*(XXI)*

isolated from malt rootlets[50,51], has also been shown to have a decamethonium-like action on frog muscle[52,53]. Its action is antagonized by (+)-tubocurarine, but unaffected by eserine[53]. The base is aromatic, non-quaternary, as it forms a hydrochloride[50,51], and appears to act by depressing the sensitivity of the end-plate membrane[54].

Strong bases, such as guanidine, also effect neuromuscular transmission, raising the amplitude of the end-plate potential in the frog sciatic nerve-sartorius muscle preparation, as a result of an increase in the quantity of acetylcholine released[55]. Streptomycin, dihydrostreptomycin and neomycin, which are guanidine derivatives, also produce neuromuscular block, but only in large doses[56-63]. Partial block by streptomycin is reversed by neostigmine, but complete block is not reversed[56,58]. Neomycin block, on the other hand, is potentiated by ether, (+)-tubocurarine and sodium ions, and completely antagonized by neostigmine and by calcium ions[57,60-63].

## THE STRUCTURE AND ENVIRONMENT OF THE ONIUM GROUP

The importance of the onium group as a key structural feature of the great majority of neuromuscular blocking agents strongly suggests that the essential reaction is an ionic one, involving a complementary anionic centre on the receptor molecule. As yet, there is no way of distinguishing the requirements for the initial reaction between the drug and receptor from those of any subsequent reaction which may be essential to elicit the biological response. However, the marked variation in the response observed between one quaternary salt and another on a single tissue preparation, indicates that other factors in addition to ionization are important in determining the qualitative and quantitative characters of the response. Thus, there is evidence that both charge delocalization and steric factors modify ionic interaction between the drug and receptor, though it is seldom easy to disentangle the separate contributions of the two factors, since both are dependent on the nature of the onium group substituents. Moreover, the relative contributions of coulombic attraction and van der Waals's bonding are themselves dependent on the shape of the molecule and the steric requirements of the receptor surface. It is not surprising, therefore, that the optimum requirement of chemical structure to produce block is known to differ markedly from one test preparation to another, and that only limited generalizations are possible.

Holmes, Jenden and Taylor[64] showed that the ability of simple onium ions to block frog sartorius muscle is related to the charge density of the central onium ion. Their estimate of the charge distribution was based on the suggestion[65] that the positive charge of the ammonium ion, $[NH_4]^+$, is distributed approximately equally between the five atoms of the ion; and that in tetra-alkylammonium ions, $[R_4N]^+$, the distribution is further dependent on the relative electronegativity of the group R and the onium atom (X), and on the ionic radii of R and X. Thus, the relative order of charge density on the onium atom in the tetra-alkylammonium ions, corresponding to the electron-attracting power of the alkyl substituents, has been calculated to be $Me > Pr > Et$, which is in agreement with the order of the curarizing potency of tetramethylammonium, tetra-n-propylammonium and tetraethylammonium ions in the frog. Similar arguments, based on the dipole moments of the N—H ($\xrightarrow{1\cdot31}$), S—H ($\xrightarrow{0\cdot68}$), P—H ($\xrightarrow{0\cdot36}$) and As—H ($\xleftarrow{0\cdot10}$) bonds as criteria of charge distribution across the corresponding N—C, S—C, P—C and As—C bonds, led to the conclusion that curariform potency runs parallel to the charge density on the onium ion.

The limitation of such qualitative theoretical calculations is apparent from the fact that whereas it places $\overset{+}{Me_4N}$, $\overset{+}{Me_3S}$, $\overset{+}{Me_4P}$ and $\overset{+}{Me_4As}$ in this, the correct, order of descending potency, it fails to explain why the order of potency of tetraethylonium compounds $(\overset{+}{Et_4As} > \overset{+}{Et_4P} > \overset{+}{Et_3S} \equiv \overset{+}{Et_4N})$ and tetrapropylonium compounds $(Pr_4As \equiv \overset{+}{Pr_4P} > Pr_4N)$ are reversed, or why the tetrabutylphosphonium and tetrabutylammonium ions are approximately equipotent with the tetramethylammonium ion[23]. Alkyltrimethylammonium ions[23,66] are of a similar order of potency to the tetraalkylammonium ions; ethyltrimethylammonium is the least active, and the butyl-, hexyl- and octyltrimethylammonium ions are equipotent with tetramethylammonium. The importance of the test preparation is again shown by the fact that, in the cat, activity in this series reaches a maximum in butyltrimethylammonium, thereafter decreasing rapidly with increasing chain-length[67]. Külz[66], on the other hand, records a steady increase from $n = 2$ to $n = 8$ in the activity of the alkyltriethylammonium compounds. This increase in activity with chain length in these[68], and related polyonium compounds[69], may well be explained by the overriding influence of increasing van der Waals's bonding between drug and receptor, compared with a more or less constant contribution of coulombic forces as the series is ascended.

An explanation of the unusually low activity of the tetraethylammonium ion has also been put forward, based on its unusual conformation, which, in contrast to that of the tetra-n-propylammonium ion (*Figure 1.1A*)[70], is in the form of a nordic cross (*Figure 1.1B*)[71]. This conformation may lead to considerable shielding of the charge on the nitrogen[69]. Thomas and Starmer[68]

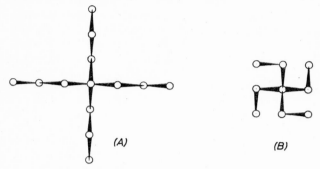

(A)     (B)

*Figure 1.1.* Conformation of tetra-alkylammonium ions

have advanced the theory that the major contribution to the total coulombic forces of attraction comes from the fractional charges distributed onto the α-carbon atoms of the ethyl substituents, and that the low activity of tetra-ethylammonium results from the fact that only two unhindered α-carbon atoms

(XXII)

(XXIII)

(XXIV)

may be directed towards a receptor surface at any one time. Experiments in the rat phrenic nerve-diaphragm preparation using tetraethylammonium (*XXII*), N,N-diethylpyrrolidinium (*XXIII*), and 1,1′-spirobipyrrolidinium (*XXIV*), in which rotation of the alkyl groups is increasingly restricted, and the α-carbon atoms increasingly available for binding, show the relative order of activity of the three compounds to be $1:1\cdot6:3\cdot1$. Recently tetraethyl-ammonium has been reported to promote acetylcholine release at nerve endings, a property which it shares with its hydroxy derivative, β-hydroxy-ethyltriethylammonium[72–74].

An adequate explanation of the increase in potency which occurs on replacement of methyl by ethyl substituents in quaternary salts of N-hetero-aromatic ring systems[23] has been put forward[11,64]. Thus, an electron drift towards the ring, which reduces charge density on the nitrogen in the

$N$-methylpyridinium ($XXV$) and $N$-methylquinolinium ($XXVI$) ions, does not occur in the corresponding $N$-ethyl compounds ($XXVII$) and ($XXVIII$). The redistribution of charge which occurs in the heteroaromatic ring of all such onium compounds is eliminated in the corresponding tetrahydro-quinolinium ions. In consequence, $N,N$-dimethyltetrahydroquinolinium ($XXIX$) and $N$-ethyl-$N$-methyltetrahydroquinolinium ($XXX$) are more potent than the compounds ($XXVI$) and ($XXVIII$) respectively, though compound ($XXIX$) is more potent than compound ($XXX$), in keeping with

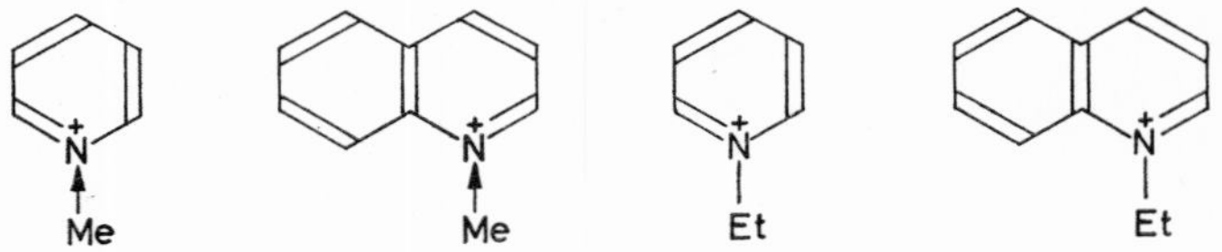

(XXV)　　　(XXVI)　　　(XXVII)　　　(XXVIII)

the predominantly aliphatic character of the onium substituents. The relative importance of charge distribution and steric factors cannot, however, be fully assessed from further consideration of these same molecules. Thus, although the non-planar tetrahydroquinolinium compounds ($XXIX$) and ($XXX$) are more potent than the corresponding planar quinolinium ions,

(XXIX)　　　(XXX)

no assumption about the steric requirements of the receptor molecule is possible, since two conclusions may be reached—either the receptor is flat and charge localization is more important than the shape of the drug molecule, or alternatively, the receptor is non-planar and charge localization and molecular shape of the drug molecule are additive properties, combining to give the greater activity in non-planar molecules. At present, there appears to be no evidence on which a decision between these two alternatives may be made, although Waser's[75] model of the cholinergic receptor (*Figure 1.2*) as a pore with an anionic wall, to which quaternary ammonium compounds are fixed, probably favours the latter.

That stereochemical factors cannot be ignored, however, is clear from recorded differences in the potency of $\alpha$- and $\beta$-isomers of the $N,N$-dialkyl-coniinium, $N,N$-dialkylconhydrinium, and $N$-methyl-($-$)-canadinium ions. Taylor[11] has commented on the difference in activity of the $N$-methyl-($-$)-canadinium isomers and, more recently, attention has again been drawn to the fact that the higher melting $\beta$-isomers are invariably more potent than the $\alpha$-isomers in both the coniinium and conhydrinium series (*Table 1.2*), although the actual potencies are low[76].

10

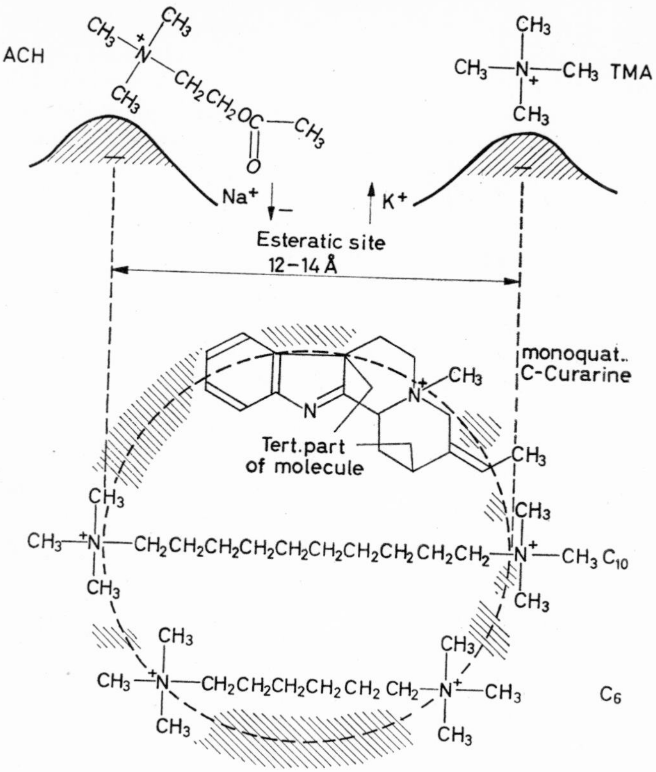

*Figure 1.2.* Model of a receptor pore in section and from above[75]. Anionic wall occupied by depolarizing acetylcholine (ACH) or tetramethylammonium (TMA), at the bottom permeation of sodium or potassium ions. The pore can be blocked by one bisquaternary or two monoquaternary curarine molecules, or by many smaller diamines such as hexamethonium ($C_6$). Depolarizing decamethonium ($C_{10}$) will leave enough room for ions to pass beside the molecule.

*Table 1.2.* Potencies of isomeric coniinium, conhydrinium and canadinium ions in the frog (lymph sac injection)[77,78]

| Isomer | M.p. | Paralysing dose (mg/kg) |
|---|---|---|
| α-N-Benzyl-N-ethylconiinium iodide | 180 | 43 |
| β-N-Benzyl-N-ethylconiinium iodide | 208 | 25 |
| α-N-Benzyl-N-propylconiinium iodide | 159 | 77 |
| β-N-Benzyl-N-propylconiinium iodide | 197 | 64 |
| α-N-Benzyl-N-butylconiinium iodide | 169 | 120 |
| β-N-Benzyl-N-butylconiinium iodide | 188 | 107 |
| α-N-Benzyl-N-isoamylconiinium iodide | 170 | 42 |
| β-N-Benzyl-N-isoamylconiinium iodide | 185 | 33 |
| α-N-Allyl-N-ethylconiinium iodide | 175 | 52 |
| β-N-Allyl-N-ethylconiinium iodide | 191 | 45 |
| α-N-Benzyl-N-ethylconhydrinium iodide | 163 | 65 |
| β-N-Benzyl-N-ethylconhydrinium iodide | 188 | 59 |
| α-N-Benzyl-N-propylconhydrinium iodide | 161 | 80 |
| β-N-Benzyl-N-propylconhydrinium iodide | 180 | 67 |
| α-N-Benzyl-N-isoamylconhydrinium iodide | 165 | 86 |
| β-N-Benzyl-N-isoamylconhydrinium iodide | 185 | 72 |

The isomeric pairs result from *cis—trans* isomerism. Each isomer may have a preferred conformation which is either (*XXXI*) or (*XXXII*) for the *cis*-structure (PhCH$_2$/Pr *cis*) and either (*XXXIII*) or (*XXXIV*) for the *trans*-isomer (PhCH$_2$/Pr *trans*). In the absence of other evidence to the contrary, it may be that the bis-equatorial structures (*XXXII*) and (*XXXIV*) represent the most probable conformation for the *cis* and *trans* isomers respectively. There is no evidence at the moment, however, on which to assign actual configurations to the groups of α- and β-isomers. Meanwhile, it is interesting

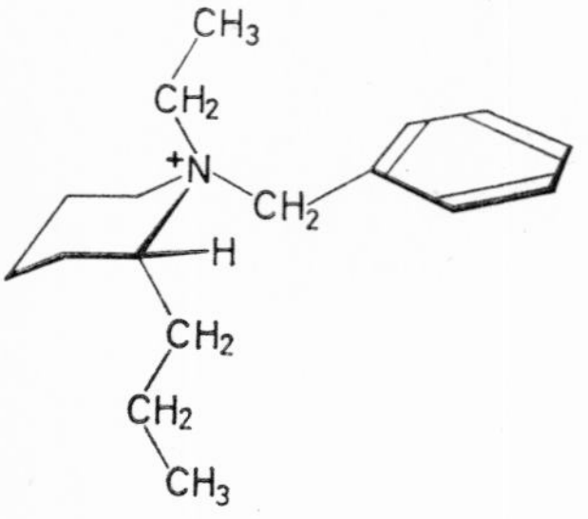

(*XXXI*)    or    PhCH$_2$/Pr *cis*    (*XXXII*)

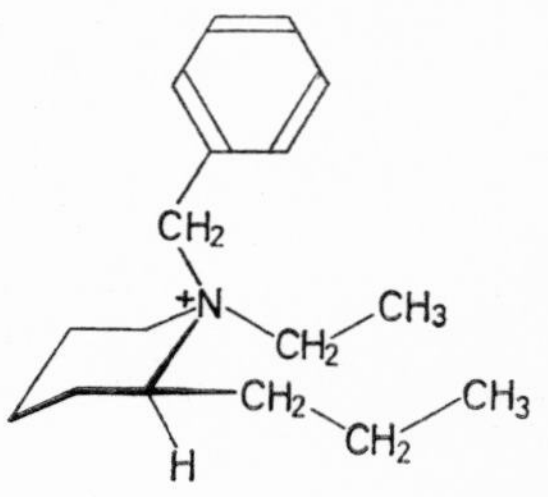

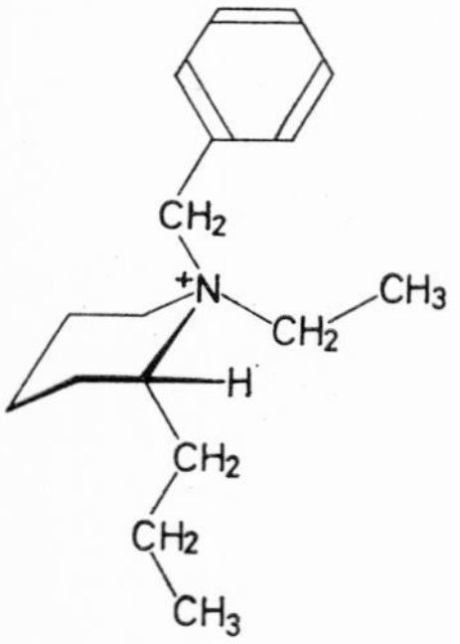

(*XXXIII*)    or    PhCH$_2$/Pr *trans*    (*XXXIV*)

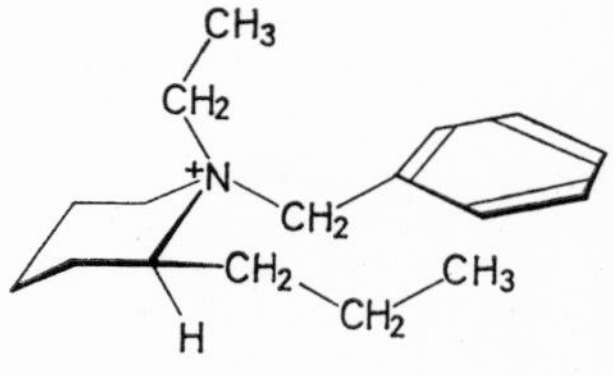

to observe that the conformation (*XXXIV*) offers a degree of co-planarity between the two rings which is not present in (*XXXII*), a difference in molecular shape which may well be linked with the observed difference in potency.

Structures have recently been established for a number of pure indolic monoquaternary bases isolated from calabash-curare and various *Strychnos* species, including the melinonines F (*XXXV*) and G (*XXXVI*) from *Strychnos melinoniana*[79]. Unfortunately, there is no record of any pharmacological examination of these planar aromatic structures, although the related tetrahydro base (*XXXVII*) has been shown to possess about one-fifth of the potency of (+)-tubocurarine in frogs[80].

Structures have also been established for melinonines A (*XXXVIII*) and B (*XXXIX*), which are without activity in frog toxicity tests[81], and for lochneram (*XL*) from calabash curare[82], which like melinonines F and G appears not to have been examined pharmacologically. Of the other monoquaternary curare alkaloids and derivatives, C-mavacurine (*XLI*) is

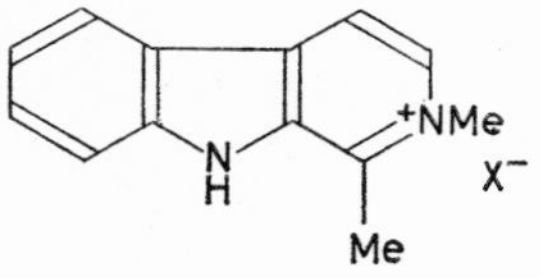

*(XXXV)*

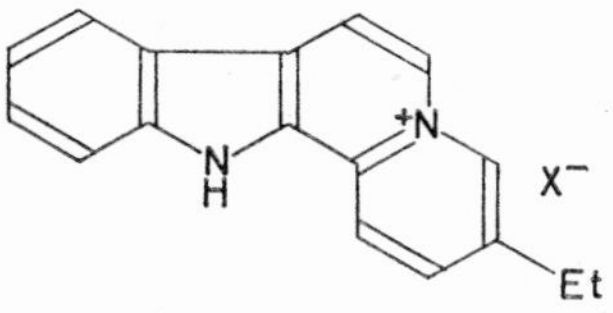

*(XXXVI)*

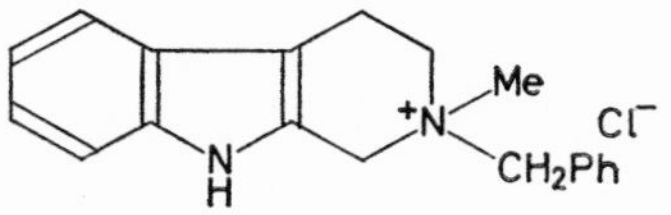

*(XXXVII)*

also inactive in frog toxicity tests[83], C-alkaloid Y (*XLII*)[84] has not been examined pharmacologically, and C-fluorocurine (*XLIII*)[85], Hemitoxiferine-I (*XLIV*)[86] and C-fluorocurarine (*XLV*)[85] produce mouse head drop in doses of 4·4, 1·14 and 1·8 mg/kg respectively. These structures, although

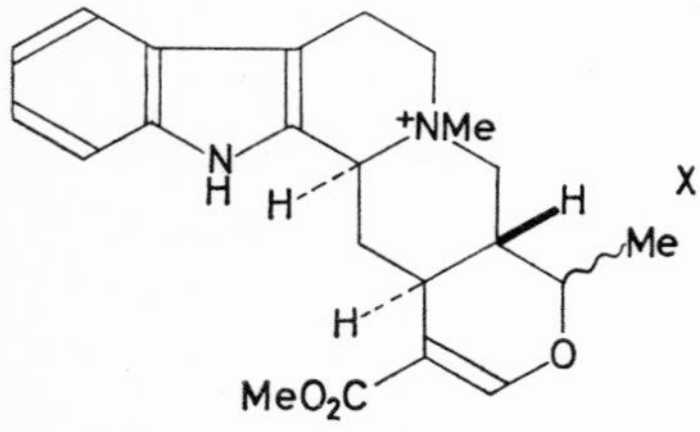

*(XXXVIII)*

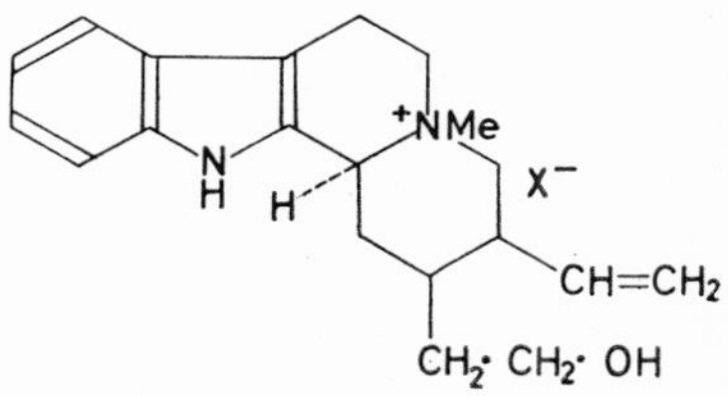

*(XXXIX)*

related, are significantly diverse, and hence throw little new light on structure-activity correlations, though they are more active than the yobyrine derivatives (*XLVI*) and (*XLVII*) which produce paralysis in the frog at 30 and 19 mg/kg respectively[87].

A group of inorganic complex ions has also been shown to block transmission at the neuromuscular junction in the rat diaphragm-phrenic nerve preparation[88], and to be antagonized by potassium ion, eserine and neostigmine. In a series of amine and ethylenediamine–derivatives of cobalt, $[Co(NH_3)_6]^{3+}$, $[Co(en)_3]^{3+}$, $[Co(NH_3)_5(NO_2)]^{2+}$, $[Co(NH_3)_4(NO_2)_2]^+$, $[Co(en)_2(NO_2)_2]^+$, and $[Co(NH_3)_2(NO_2)_4]^-$, only the cationic substances were active, and decreasing peripheral charge of the complex cation was associated with decreasing curariform activity. No difference in potency was observed between the optically active forms of $[Co(en)_3]^{3+}$. The larger complex cations derived from iron, nickel, cobalt, ruthenium and osmium, and the chelating agents 2,2'-bipyridine, $[\text{Metal}(\text{bipy})_3]^{2+}$, 1,10-phenanthroline, $[\text{Metal}(\text{phen})_3]^{2+}$ and 2,2',2"-terpyridine, $[\text{Metal}(\text{tripy})_2]^{2+}$

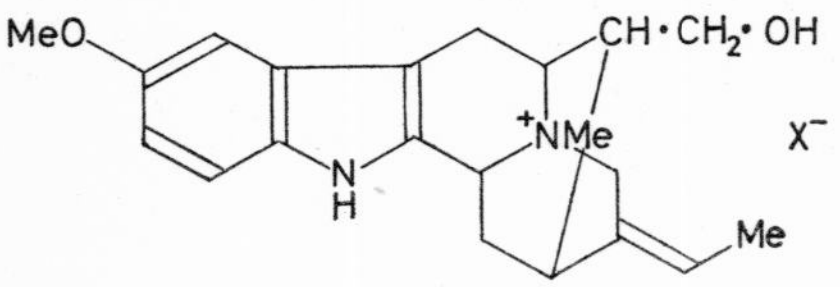

*(XL)*

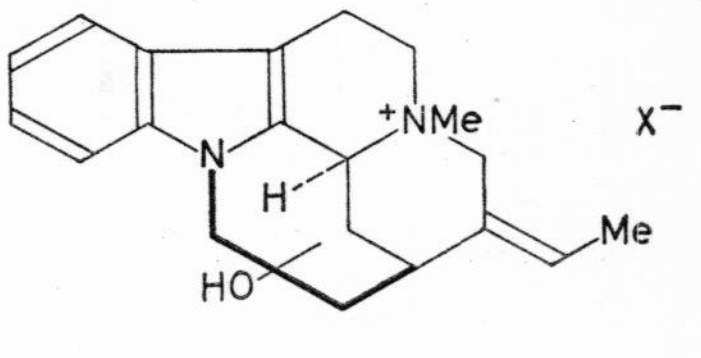

*(XLI)*

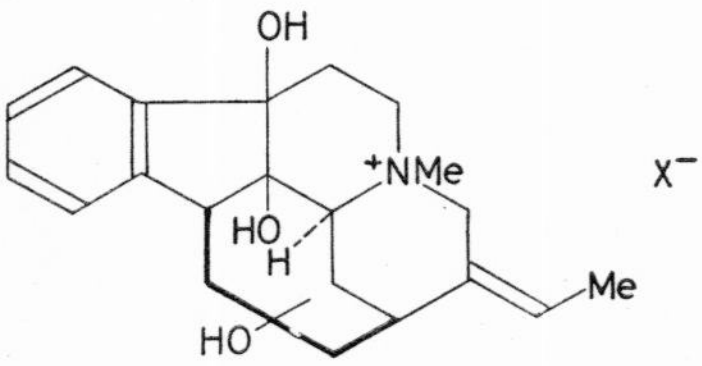

*(XLII)*

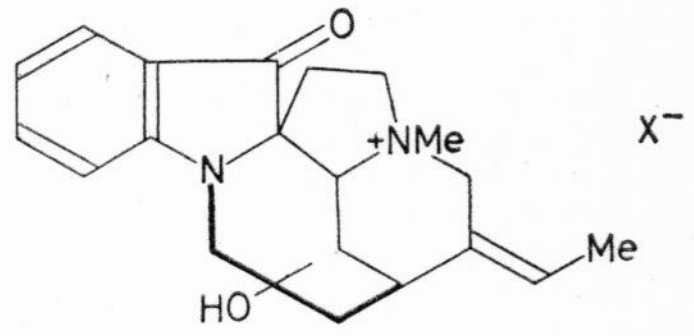

*(XLIII)*

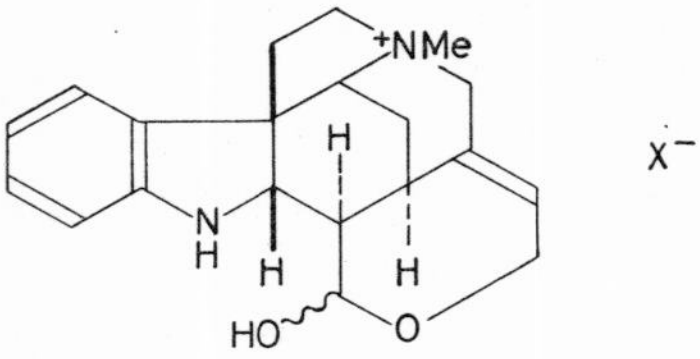

*(XLIV)*

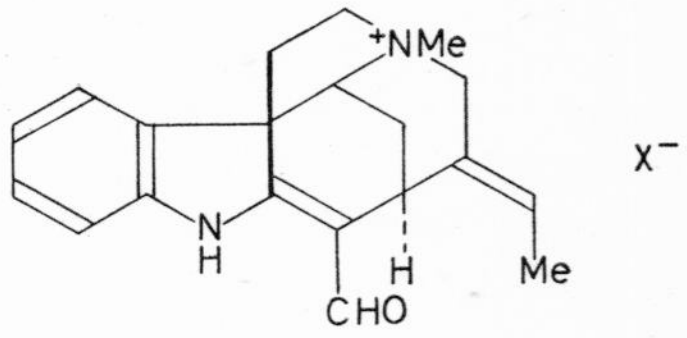

*(XLV)*

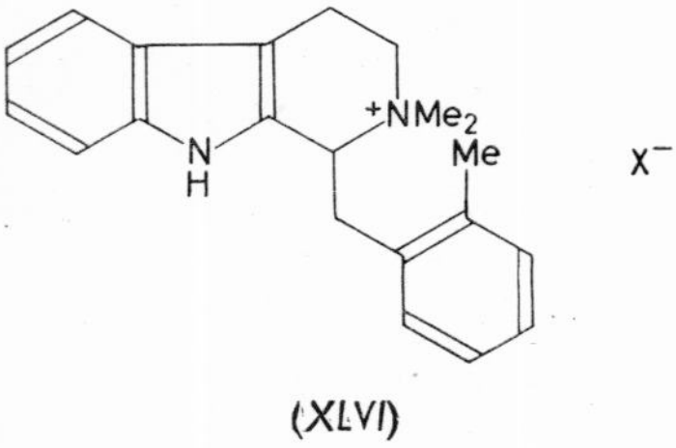

*(XLVI)*

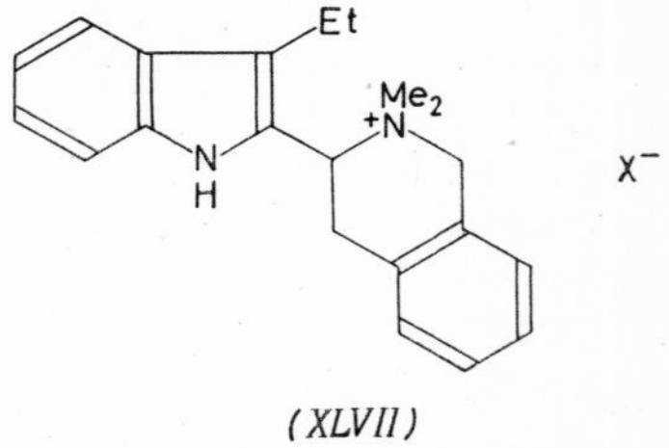

*(XLVII)*

resembled (+)-tubocurarine rather more closely than decamethonium both in potency, and in recovery time of the muscle preparation on washing out (*Table 1.3*). Compounds in this series have the same overall charge, but differ

14

in the distribution of charge over the ligand, and this appears to be reflected in the level of activity. The higher level of activity in this second series is

Table 1.3. Potencies of divalent neuromuscular blocking agents in the innervated rat diaphragm muscle[88]

| Compound | Molarity required to produce complete block in 3 mins. | Recovery time (mins.) |
|---|---|---|
| (+)-Tubocurarine chloride | $1 \cdot 2 \times 10^{-5}$ | 20–25 |
| $[Ru(tryp)_2]^{2+}2ClO_4^-$ | $2 \cdot 3 \times 10^{-4}$ | 16–24 |
| (±)-$[Ru(phen)_3]^{2+}2I^-$ | $3 \cdot 4 \times 10^{-4}$ | 14–22 |
| (±)-$[Ru(bipy)_3]^{2+}2I^-$ | $5 \cdot 6 \times 10^{-4}$ | 8–12 |
| $[Co(NH_3)_5NO_2]^{2+}2Cl^-$ | $2 \cdot 5 \times 10^{-3}$ | 4–7 |

attributed to the greater contribution from van der Waals' forces expected in larger molecules of this type based on hetero-aromatic systems. In this series too, pairs of optical isomers show a significant difference in curariform activity, (+)-$[Ru(phen)_3]^{2+}$, (+)-$[Ni(phen)_3]^{2+}$ and (+)-$[Os(phen)_3]^{2+}$

(XLVIII)

being 1·5–2 times more potent than the corresponding (−)-isomers on both the toad rectus abdominis and the rat diaphragm preparations. These 6–co-ordinate complexes have an octahedral configuration arising, not from asymmetry of a single atom but from asymmetry of the molecule as a whole (XLVIII), and the observed differences of activity between these optical isomers provide an interesting starting point for further study of the biological receptor surface.

In general, functional substitution in one or more of the alkyl groups of simple tetra-alkylammonium compounds does not lead to high neuro-

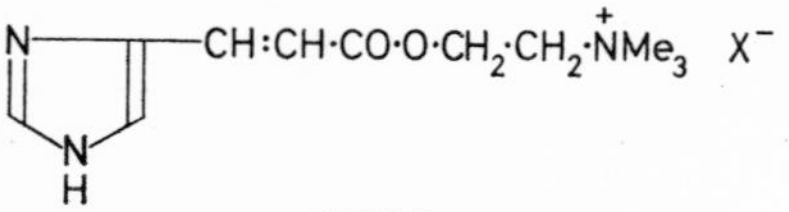

(XLIX)

(L)

muscular blocking potency. A number of compounds with structures based on that of acetylcholine have been shown to be active. These include the choline ester, urocanylcholine (murexine; XLIX), which is present in the hypobranchial glands of *Murex trunculus* and other snails of the Muricidae. Extracts of the glands have long been known to cause acetylcholine-like paralysis in both cold and warm blooded animals[89,90] and the active

15

principle has been identified by Erspamer[91–94] as urocanylcholine (*XLIX*). The pure substance produces a marked depolarizing type of neuromuscular block in the cat, dog and rabbit, which is qualitatively similar to, but weaker than that of, suxamethonium[95]; in the frog it has about one-tenth of the activity of suxamethonium[96]. Urocanylcholine is hydrolysed readily, and its dihydro derivative, 3-(4-imidazolyl)propionylcholine, even more readily by non-specific cholinesterases from human plasma, ox spleen, ox serum and guinea-pig liver[97]. It has also received a clinical trial[98].

A survey of other marine gastropods and molluscs[99] has led to the isolation of $\beta,\beta$-dimethylacryloylcholine (*L*, R = Me) from the southern oyster drill

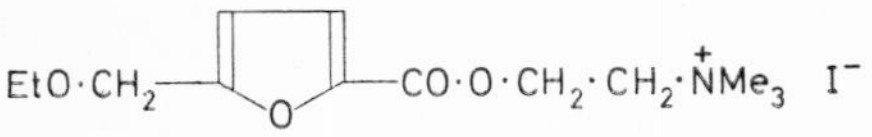

$$\text{EtO·CH}_2\text{—}\underset{O}{\boxed{\phantom{x}}}\text{—CO·O·CH}_2\text{·CH}_2\text{·}\overset{+}{N}\text{Me}_3 \quad I^-$$

*(LI)*

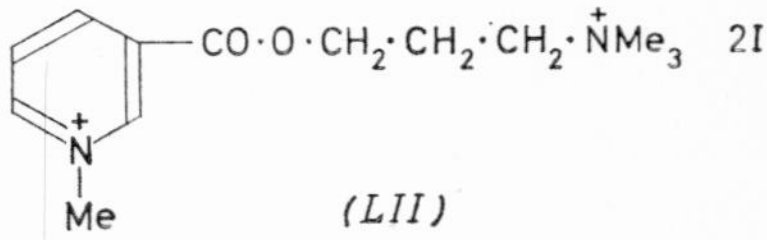

$$\boxed{\phantom{x}}\text{—CO·O·CH}_2\text{·CH}_2\text{·CH}_2\text{·}\overset{+}{N}\text{Me}_3 \quad 2I^-$$

*(LII)*

$$\boxed{\phantom{x}}\text{—CH}_2\text{·CO·O·CH}_2\text{·CH}_2\text{·}\overset{+}{N}\text{Me}_3 \quad 2I^-$$

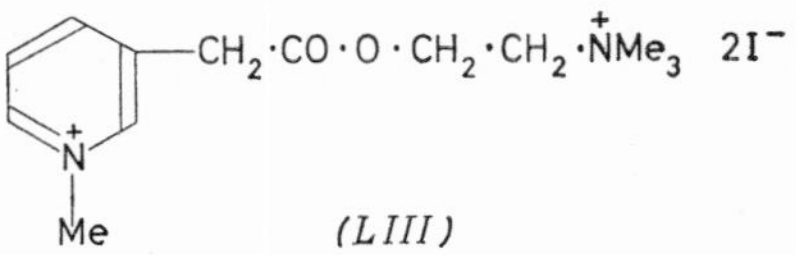

*(LIII)*

(*Thais fluoridana*) by Whittaker[100]. It has been shown to possess ganglion-stimulating and neuromuscular blocking properties[101]. Crotonoylcholine and pent-2-enoylcholine showed similar action, but were less potent[101]. The parent substance, acryloylcholine (*L*, R = H) has also been isolated from the common whelk, *Buccinum undatum*[102].

Tetrodoxin, a poison of the roe of the globe fish, blocks transmission in the rat phrenic nerve-diaphragm preparation, but is not antagonized by (+)-tubocurarine, decamethonium, acetylcholine, neostigmine or eserine[103,104]. Tetrodoxin shows similar effects on the tibial and soleus muscles of cats; the evidence suggests that there is some direct action on the muscle as well as neuromuscular block[105].

Other choline esters found to be active includes 5-ethoxymethyl-2-furoylcholine iodide (*LI*), which has been shown to depress neuromuscular conduction in cats and rabbits[106]. Nicotinoylcholine iodide methiodide has no effect on neuromuscular transmission, but nicotinoylhomocholine iodide methiodide (*LII*) and 3-pyridylacetylcholine iodide methiodide (*LIII*) block transmission on the cat sciatic nerve-gastrocnemius preparation in doses of 5–10 mg/kg[107]. Carbamic esters of choline and choline homologues have also been examined[107a,107b] and the compounds (*LIIIa*, R = H, R′ = Ph, *m*-BuOPh or 2-naphthyl; or R = R′ = Ph) have been shown to be as active as gallamine, though their action is not reversed by neostigmine[107b].

$$\text{RR′N·CO·O·CH}_2\text{·CH}_2\text{·}\overset{+}{N}\text{Et}_3 \quad X^-$$

*(LIIIa)*

16

Cyclopentyl-, cyclohexyl-trimethylammonium iodides, and their *cis*- and *trans*-2-hydroxy derivatives block the kitten phrenic nerve-diaphragm preparation, the non-hydroxylated compounds being the most potent and the *trans*-hydroxy derivatives the least potent[108]. A series of n-alkylatropinium and n-alkylbenzoylatropinium bromides possesses weak neuromuscular blocking potency when tested on the dog sciatic nerve-gastrocnemius muscle preparation[109]. Phenoxyethyldimethylbenzylammonium chloride also strongly inhibits transmission at the neuromuscular junction in the rabbit[110].

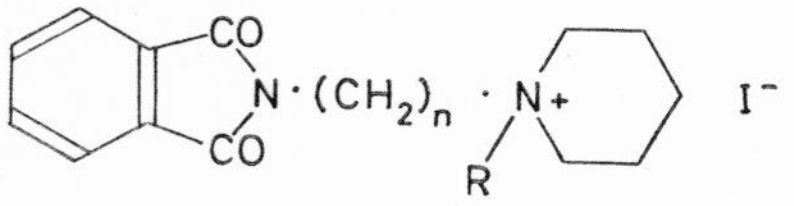

*(LIV)* 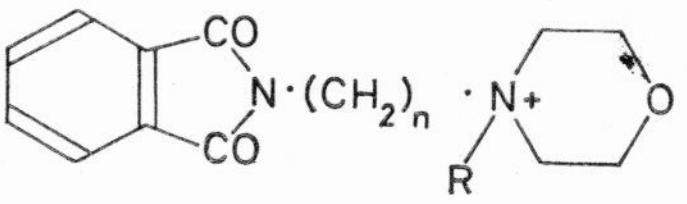                    *(LV)*

A series of monoquaternary *N*-($\omega$-phthalimidoalkyl)-*N*-alkylpiperidinium *(LIV)*[111] and *N*-$\omega$-phthalimidoalkyl)-*N*-alkylmorpholinium iodides *(LV)*[112] show increasing potency in the frog with increasing length of the methylene chain separating the quaternary nitrogen and the nitrogen of the phthalimide group. Maximum activity occurs in the piperidinium compounds

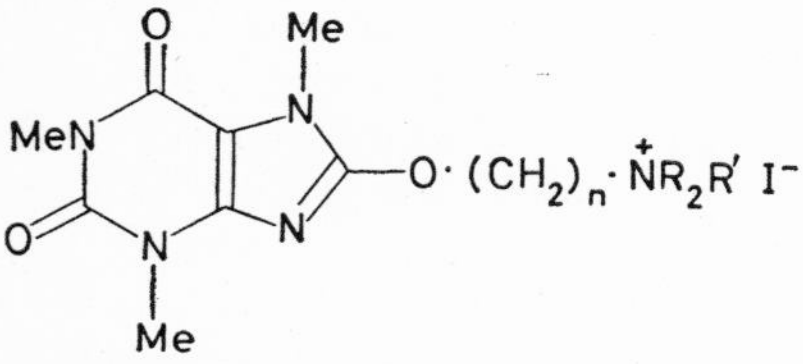

*(LVI)* 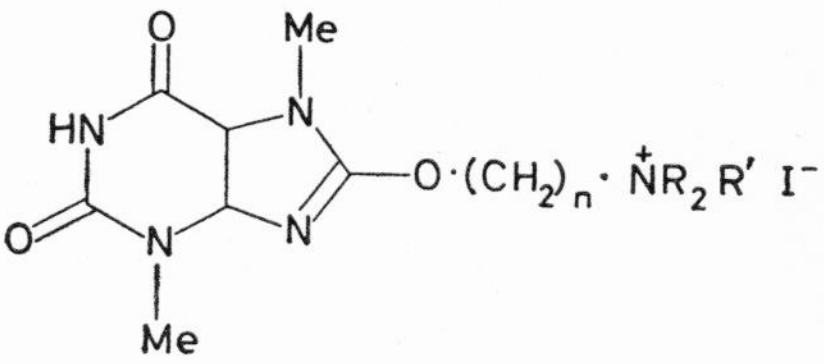                    *(LVII)*

with 7–9 methylene units, and is about one-tenth that of (+)-tubocurarine. *N*-Ethyl- and *N*-methyl-morpholinium compounds are two to three times less potent than the corresponding piperidinium compounds, no doubt due to the charge delocalizing influence of the oxygen function; the *N*-benzyl-morpholinium compounds, where n = 5 or 6 are, however, more active than their piperidinium counterparts. Other monoquaternary salts derived from 8-dialkylaminoalkoxycaffeines *(LVI)* show potencies which are between one-tenth and one-hundredth that of gallamine. The potencies are abolished in the corresponding theobromine compounds *(LVII)*[113], possibly as a result of zwitterion formation with the weakly acid 1-imino group, reducing the charge density on the nitrogen in the latter.

In the cat and dog, aneurine (thiamine), pyrithiamine, oxythiamine, and cocarboxylase in large doses have been reported to cause neuromuscular block[114–116] which is reversed by neostigmine[115]. The crude quaternary ammonium alkaloids of *Gonioma kamasse* E. may show depolarizing block on the isolated rat diaphragm-phrenic nerve preparation[115a].

## BIS-ONIUM COMPOUNDS

### Tubocurarine and Related Compounds

The four stereoisomers of tubocurarine ($LVIII$, R′ = Me; R″ = R‴ = H), show marked differences in neuromuscular blocking potency in the rabbit head drop and other tests. The configurational relationships of these isomers

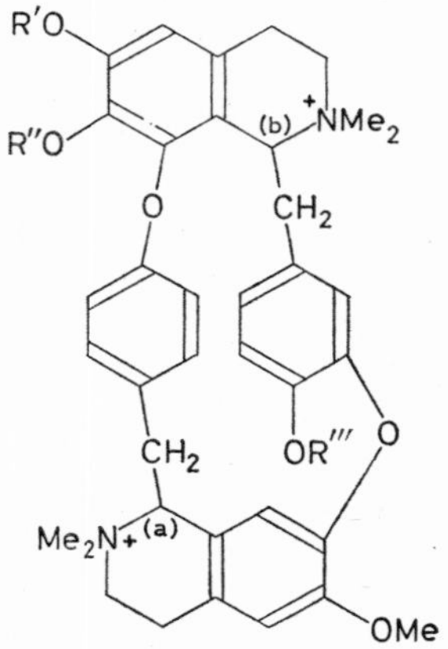

(LVIII)

follow from the work of Bick and Clezy[117], and these together with the observed potencies are summarized in *Table 1.4*.

Table 1.4. Relative potencies of tubocurarine isomers
(rat diaphragm test)[118,119]

| Isomer | Optical rotation (a) | (b) | Potency[118] |
|---|---|---|---|
| (+)-Tubocurarine | + | — | 1·0 |
| (−)-Tubocurarine | — | + | negligible |
| (+)-Curarine | + | + | 3·5 |
| (−)-Curarine | — | — | 1·3 |

Neither the absolute configuration of these isomers nor their conformation has been established, though an approach to the problem of conformational studies in this series, based on nuclear magnetic resonance spectra, has recently been described[120]. It is evident, however, that the molecule is not rigid, that significant variation of both conformation and inter-quaternary distance is possible between the isomers, and that this is probably relevant to the observed difference in potency[69].

The number and position of methoxyl substituents also appear to be significant. Thus (+)-chondocurarine ($LVIII$, R′ = R‴ = H; R″ = Me)[121], which has the same stereochemistry as (+)-tubocurarine, but differs only in the position of one methoxyl substituent, is about three times, and $O,O$-dimethyl-(+)-tubocurarine ($LVIII$, R′ = R″ = R‴ = Me), the total synthesis of which has recently been reported[121] about nine times as potent

18

as (+)-tubocurarine[118]. Similarly, $O,O$-dimethyl-(−)-curarine has more than twice the potency of (−)-curarine[118]. Comparable figures for (+)-curarine and its dimethyl ether are not available, though the latter has been reported to be about twice as potent as the former in the frog[122].

Cavallito[123] suggests that the lower activity of (+)-tubocurarine as compared with its dimethyl ether may be ascribed to zwitterion formation in the former, arising from the presence of the phenolic hydroxyl group in the molecule, and cites the work of Kalow[124] in support of this contention. This demonstrated a reduction in the potency of (+)-tubocurarine as pH increased, which was correlated with the dissociation of one phenolic

*Table 1.5.* Relative potencies of ethers derived from tubocurarine and its isomers (rat diaphragm test)[118]

| Compound | Structure (LVIII) | | | Rotation of optical centre | | Potency |
|---|---|---|---|---|---|---|
| | $R'$ | $R''$ | $R'''$ | (a) | (b) | |
| (+)-Tubocurarine | Me | H | H | + | − | 1·0 |
| $O,O$-Dimethyl-(+)-tubocurarine | Me | Me | Me | + | − | 8·7 |
| $O,O$-Diethyl-(+)-tubocurarine | Me | Et | Et | + | − | 1·9 |
| $O,O$-Di-n-butyl-(+)-tubocurarine | Me | n–Bu | n–Bu | + | − | 0·09 |
| $O,O$-Dibenzyl-(+)-tubocurarine | Me | $CH_2Ph$ | $CH_2Ph$ | + | − | 0·07 |
| (+)-Curarine | Me | H | H | + | + | 3·5 |
| $O,O$-Dimethyl-(+)-curarine | Me | Me | Me | + | + | — |
| (−)-Curarine | Me | H | H | − | − | 1·3 |
| $O,O$-Dimethyl-(−)-curarine | Me | Me | Me | − | − | 3·3 |
| (+)-Chondocurarine | H | Me | H | + | − | 2·9 |
| $N,N$-Diethylchondocurine | H | Me | H | + | − | 0·9 |
| $N,N$-Dibenzylchondocurine | H | Me | H | + | − | 0·17 |

hydroxyl group. This may be the reason for the greater potency of (+)-chondocurarine in which one of the free hydroxyl groups is removed, albeit by only one carbon atom, further from the influence of both onium groups. It fails, however, to explain the very low potency of the di-n-butyl and dibenzyl ethers of (+)-tubocurarine (*Table 1.5*). The marked increase of potency observed in a series of $N,N$-dimethyl-1,10-decamethylenebistetrahydroquinolinium (LIX) and -tetrahydroisoquinolinium di-iodides (LX) with increasing methoxyl substitution, also supports the view that the number and position of the methoxyl substituents in molecules of this type contribute directly to the activity of the molecule as a whole (*Table 1.6*)[125].

$O,O$-Dimethyl-(+)-tubocurarine has been evaluated clinically[126–129] and shown to be two to three times as potent as (+)-tubocurarine[130], but of shorter duration of action[131]. Its action is reversed by neostigmine. Studies by Dettbarn[132] indicated that $O,O$-dimethyl-(+)-tubocurarine chloride reversibly blocks conduction across the Ranvier node in a single nerve fibre preparation, but it is no more effective than (+)-tubocurarine, although the former has a slightly higher lipoid solubility than the latter. It appears unlikely, therefore, that $O,O$-dimethyl-(+)-tubocurarine owes its higher potency as a neuromuscular blocking agent to any difference in membrane permeability, though the work of Rosenberg and Ehrenpreis[133] on the squid giant axon indicates that this factor may also be important. Thus, although (+)-tubocurarine at a concentration of $1 \cdot 4 \times 10^{-2}$M fails to block conduction in the intact nerve, pre-treatment with *Naja naja* cobra venom and cetyltrimethylammonium bromide permits (+)-tubocurarine to penetrate the axon sheath to give a reversible block in concentrations as low as $5 \times 10^{-4}$M. Ehrenpreis[134] has also studied the binding of (+)-tubocurarine and its dimethyl ether with the acetylcholine receptor protein of electric

*Table 1.6.* Potencies of methoxytetrahydroquinolines and -tetrahydroisoquinolines (minimal effective dose in rabbits)[125]

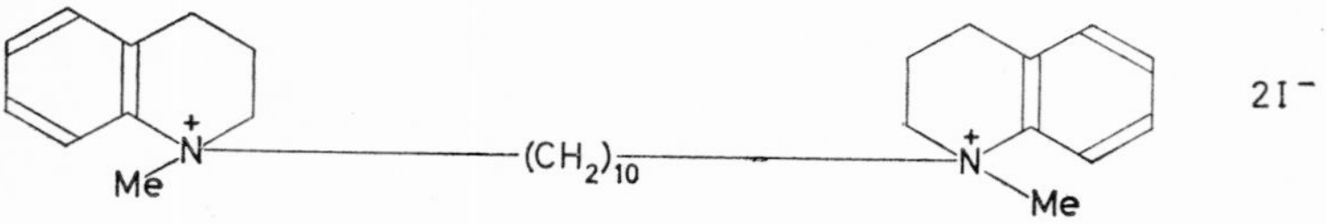

(LIX)

| Substituents | Dose (mg/kg) |
|---|---|
| None | 0·75 |
| 6-Methoxy- | 0·2 |
| 8-Methoxy- | 0·1 |

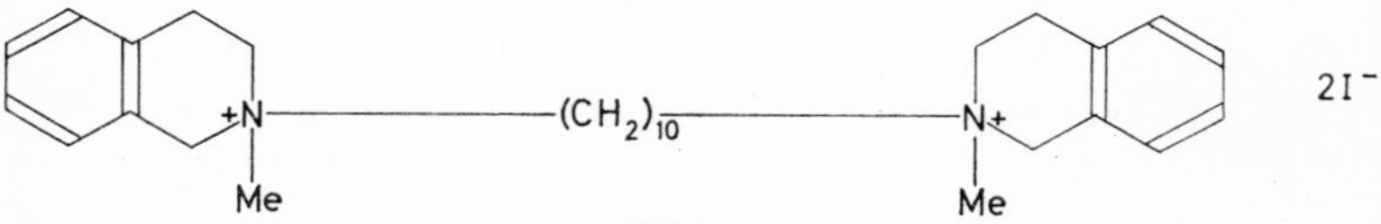

(LX)

| Substituents | Dose (mg/kg) |
|---|---|
| None | 0·75 |
| 6-Methoxy- | 0·2 |
| 6,7-Dimethoxy- | 0·05 |
| 6,7,8-Trimethoxy- | 0·02 |
| (+)-tubocurarine | 0·1 |

tissue of the electric eel (*Electrophorus electricus* L.). This protein fraction forms a precipitate with both substances, though the degree of binding is to some extent influenced by the pH of the medium (*Figure 1.3*). At pH 7·5, the affinity of the dimethyl ether is less than that of (+)-tubocurarine, but the reverse order of binding applies at pH 9·5, possibly due to the ionization of phenolic hydroxyl groups in the latter. The author concludes from this experiment and others which show that the precipitate is soluble in dilute acid and 1–2M urea, that precipitation involves H-bond formation. The failure to bind dimethyl-(+)-tubocurarine more readily than the parent substance is explained in terms of weaker blocking action on the intact electroplax[135], whilst it is suggested that the greater potency of the dimethyl ether as a blocking agent arises from its greater lipoid solubility. The action of (+)-tubocurarine at a concentration of 2 $\mu$g/ml on the intact electroplax is abolished when the calcium concentration is raised to 8 mм., and Ehrenpreis concludes that the curare binding site may include one or more phosphate groups.

The influence of alkoxyl substitution in the molecule of (+)-tubocurarine appears to be linked with the intensification of curare-like blocking drugs

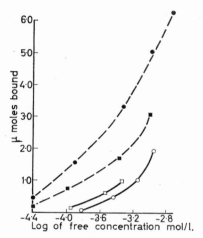

*Figure 1.3.* Comparative binding of tubocurarine and dimethyltubocurarine at pH 7·5 (phosphate) and pH 9·5 (borate); $\mu = 0.02$. ●, tubocurarine, pH 7·5; ■, dimethyltubocurarine, pH 7·5; O, tubocurarine, pH 9; □, dimethyltubocurarine, pH 9[134]

by diethyl ether[136–142]. Lewis and Muir[143] have studied the potentiating effect of a range of related aliphatic ethers on block by (+)-tubocurarine. All show the effect in some degree, though higher molecular weight ethers show a direct toxic action on the muscle. Other general anaesthetics, including chloroform[142,144], cyclopropane[140,142,145] and fluothane[142,146] also intensify block by (+)-tubocurarine, but are less powerful in their action. A number of other compounds including pentobarbitone[137,147,148], chlorothiazide[149] and other sulphonamide drugs (sulphanilic acid, sulphanilamide, naphthazosulphamide, noprylsulphamide, sulphathiourea, acetazolamide, probenecid and glybuthiazole)[150], and chlorpromazine[151,152] in large doses also increase the action of (+)-tubocurarine. Su and Lee[152] conclude that block by chlorpromazine resembles that of (+)-tubocurarine, since their effects are additive, and both are antagonized by eserine and neostigmine, although antagonism of chlorpromazine is not complete. There is evidence that chlorpromazine directly inhibits the muscle fibres. Pantothenic acid has also been reported to enhance the effects of (+)-tubocurarine in man[153].

In recent years, it has been shown that all the highly potent calabash curare alkaloids are also bisquaternary compounds[154], which may be separated from the low potency monoquaternary calabash alkaloids by their much lower mobility in partition chromatography. Structures have now been assigned to C-dihydrotoxiferine I (*LXI*, R = R′ = H)[155,156], C-alkaloid H (*LXI*, R = H, R′ = OH)[157], and toxiferine I (*LXI*, R = R′ = OH)[156,158,159], which produce mouse head-drop in doses of 30, 16

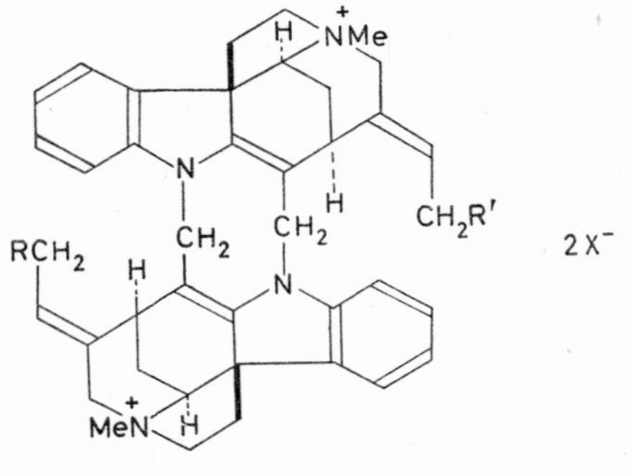

*(LXI)*

and 9 μg per kg respectively[85]. These three alkaloids, together with C-curarine I, are among the most potent of the calabash curare alkaloids so far reported, their activity being surpassed only by that of C-alkaloids E and G[85]. It may be significant that the potencies of C-dihydrotoxiferine I (*LXI*, R = R′ = H), C-alkaloid H (*LXI*, R = H, R′ = OH) and toxiferine I (*LXI*, R = R′ = OH) parallel the introduction of side-chain hydroxyl groups, and

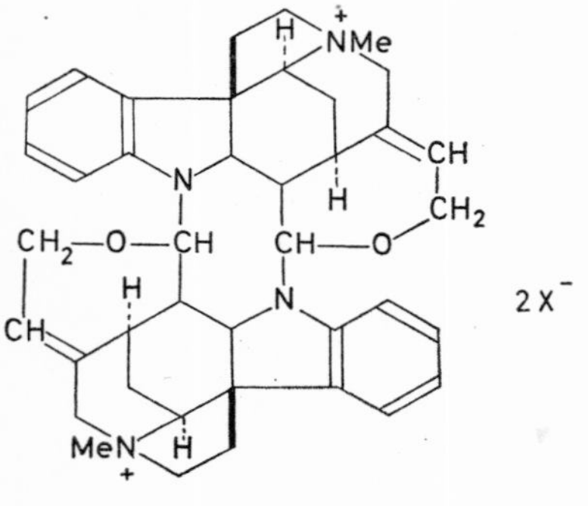

*(LXII)*

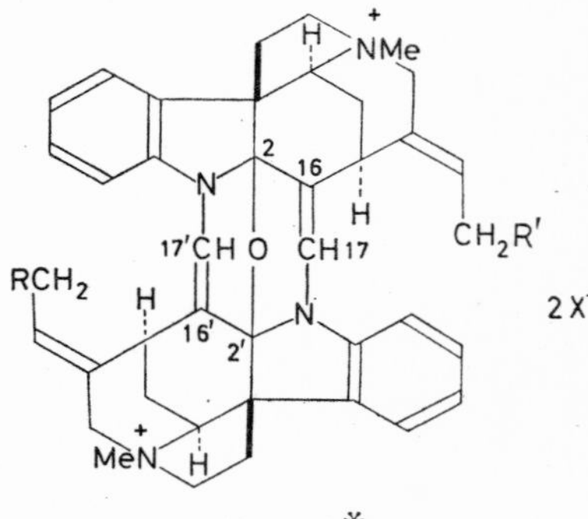

*(LXIII)* *

that when these are masked, as in caracurine V dimethochloride (*LXII*), activity disappears[160]. The presence of two new rings and the absence of the nuclear double bonds, however, affects the shape of the molecule and the relative orientation of oxygen and nitrogen substituents. Introduction of a further oxygen substituent on photo-oxidation of C-toxiferine and C-alkaloid H to yield C-alkaloid E (*LXIII*, R = R′ = OH; 0·3–4 μg/kg) and C-alkaloid G (*LXIII*, R = H, R′ = OH; 0·6–5 μg/kg)[160a] significantly increases potency in the mouse head-drop test, but there is no corresponding

* The isomeric structure with double bond in 2,16 and 2′,16′ positions, and a 17,17′ oxygen bridge is not excluded[160a].

22

increase in potency with C-curarine I (*LXIII*, R = R′ = H; 30 μg/kg) which is similarly derived from C-dihydrotoxiferine[85]. Structures have also been established for a number of other rather less potent calabash curare and *Strychnos* alkaloids (for references see Battersby and Hodson)[161], including that of C-alkaloid D[161a].

Meanwhile, Waser and Harbeck[162] have reported the first clinical trials of C-toxiferine I and C-curarine I. Relaxation for 20–40 minutes (sufficient for endotracheal intubation) was obtained with C-curarine I at doses of 10–15 mg and with C-toxiferine I at doses of 2 mg in patients anaesthetized with nitrous oxide and thiopentone[162]. Foldes, Wolfram and Sokoll[162a] have also reported clinical studies of C-toxiferine I, in which it is described as a potent long-acting non-depolarizing muscle relaxant. Its action is readily

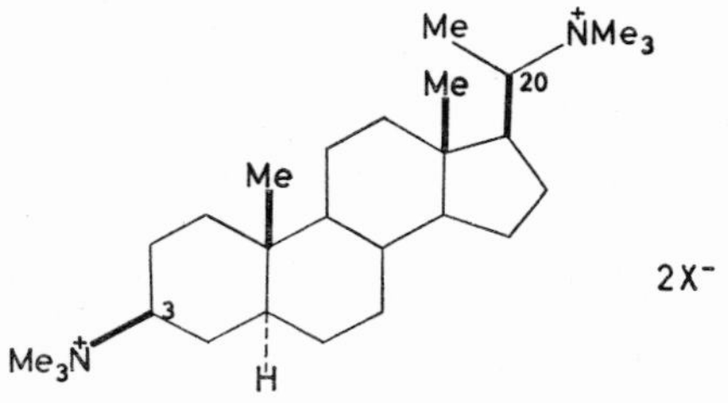

(*LXIV*)

reversed by anticholinesterases and is potentiated by halothane; it has a sparing effect on respiration. According to Paton and Perry[163], C-toxiferine I shows less species variation than other blocking agents. Waser[164] has used ¹⁴C labelled C-toxiferine to study the distribution of receptor sites in the rat diaphragm preparation.

A new class of bisquaternary curarizing alkaloids has been discovered with the isolation of the steroidal alkaloid malouetine (*LXIV*) from *Malouetis bequaertiana* E, Woodson[165]. Malouetine, although not the only alkaloid present, accounts for the whole of the curarizing properties of the plant material. It has about 75 per cent of the potency of (+)-tubocurarine in the rabbit head-drop test, and its action is readily reversed by neostigmine. On the cat soleus muscle, it is almost twice as potent as (+)-tubocurarine, but in the mouse, the two drugs are equipotent, whilst its toxicity is only a third of that of (+)-tubocurarine[166]. The 3β,20β-, 3α,20α- and 3α,20β-isomers of malouetine (3β,20α-) have been prepared by Goutarel[166a], but no potency ratios are given. The dimethiodides of the bisdiethylaminoethyl ethers of oestradiol and androst-5-ene-3,17-diol cause paralysis in the rabbit at a dose of 0·1 mg/kg; this is enhanced by eserine[166b].

*Polymethylene Compounds and their Chain-substituted Derivatives*

*Variations in the chain*

The study of the polymethylenebistrimethylammonium compounds (*LXV*) based on the bisbenzylisoquinoline structure of (+)-tubocurarine[119] led to the discovery of decamethonium (*LXV*, X = I, n = 10)[16,167,168].

23

Potency varies with chain length in this series, rising from a neglible level in pentamethonium and hexamethonium to a maximum in decamethonium,

$$Me_3\overset{+}{N}\cdot(CH_2)_n\cdot\overset{+}{N}Me_3\ 2X^-$$

$$(LXV)$$

$$Me_3\overset{+}{N}\cdot(CH_2)_2\cdot O\cdot CO\cdot CH_2\cdot CH_2\cdot CO\cdot O\cdot(CH_2)_2\cdot\overset{+}{N}Me_3\ 2X^-$$

$$(LXVI)$$

and thereafter, declining again. The low potency of the shorter chain compounds (LXV, n = 2, 3 and 4) has been attributed to onium group interaction, such compounds merely acting as doubly charged ions[169].

Although there is a formal structural analogy between decamethonium and (+)-tubocurarine, it is now well established that the two substances differ markedly in their behaviour at the neuromuscular junction, as described in the introduction to this chapter and by Bowman[14]. Shortening of the polymethylene chain also modifies the type of activity, so that pentamethonium (LXV, n = 5) and hexamethonium (LXV, n = 6) appear to act by competition rather than by depolarization[170–172]. This is also apparent from the observation that whereas decamethonium[173] and suxamethonium (succinyldicholine, Brevidil M, Anectine, Scoline, LXVI, X = Br or Cl)[174,175]

Table 1.7. Potencies of alkylene bisonium compounds[174,176]

| | $n$ | $m$ | Units in chain | Rabbit head-drop test[174,176] (mg/kg) |
|---|---|---|---|---|
| $Me_3\overset{+}{N}\cdot(CH_2)_n\cdot CO\cdot O\cdot(CH_2)_m\cdot\overset{+}{N}Me_3\ 2I^-$ (LXVII) | 2 | 2 | 6 | 70 |
| | 2 | 3 | 7 | 15 |
| | 2 | 4 | 8 | 1 |
| | 5 | 2 | 9 | 0·2 |
| $Me_3\overset{+}{N}\cdot(CH_2)_n\cdot O\cdot CO\cdot(CH_2)_m\cdot CO\cdot O\cdot(CH_2)_n\cdot\overset{+}{N}Me_3\ 2I^-$ (LXVIII) | 2 | 0 | 8 | 2 |
| | 2 | 2 | 10 | 0·2 |
| | 2 | 3 | 11 | 0·5 |
| | 2 | 4 | 12 | 0·5 |
| | 2 | 5 | 13 | 3 |
| | 2 | 8 | 16 | 5 |
| $Me_3\overset{+}{N}\cdot(CH_2)_n\cdot CO\cdot O\cdot(CH_2)_m\cdot O\cdot CO\cdot(CH_2)_n\cdot\overset{+}{N}Me_3\ 2I^-$ (LXIX) | 2 | 2 | 10 | 0·1 |
| | 2 | 4 | 12 | 0·3 |

are more potent than the corresponding ethonium compounds, penta- and hexaethonium are more potent than penta- and hexamethonium[171]. Replacement of the chain methylene units by ester links in structures (LXVII), (LXVIII) and reversed ester links in structure (LXIX) leads to compounds of the same type and with a similar pattern of activity. Maximum potency occurs in these compounds with the equivalent of a ten unit methylene chain (e.g. suxamethonium), and is similar to that of decamethonium (see

*Table 1.7*). (It must be remembered, however, that when potencies such as these are measured in terms of dose levels expressed in mg/kg, they ignore molecular weight differences, which may be significant if the potency differences are small.)

Suxamethonium (*LXVI*, X = Br or Cl)[174,177,178] is now used widely clinically[179-181] as a neuromuscular blocking agent, its action being depolarizing and not reversed by neostigmine. It owes its comparatively short and safe action to hydrolysis by acetylcholinesterase and plasma esterases, which split the molecule first to succinylmonocholine and ultimately to succinic acid and choline[182,183]—hydrolytic products of negligible neuromuscular blocking potency[183]. The action of suxamethonium may, however, be seriously prolonged, resulting in severe apnoea in cases where there is a deficiency of plasma esterases due to liver disease or other causes[184]. Another serious disadvantage of suxamethonium is the incidence of post-operative muscle pain[185,186]. As with (+)-tubocurarine, prolonged use of suxamethonium leads to histamine release[184,187], but whereas (+)-tubocurarine blocks autonomic ganglia to a significant degree, suxamethonium, in contrast, causes stimulation which may lead to mild hypertension[188].

Suxethonium (*LXX*, X = Br or I)[174] which resembles suxamethonium closely in its action, has also been used clinically[189]. It is

$$Me_2Et\overset{+}{N}\cdot(CH_2)_2\cdot O\cdot CO\cdot(CH_2)_2\cdot CO\cdot O\cdot(CH_2)_2\cdot\overset{+}{N}EtMe_2\ 2X^-$$

$$(LXX)$$

$$Me_3\overset{+}{N}\cdot(CH_2)_2\cdot O\cdot CO\cdot CHR\cdot CO\cdot O\cdot(CH_2)_2\cdot\overset{+}{N}Me_3\ 2Br^-$$

$$(LXXI)$$

significantly less potent than suxamethonium, is hydrolysed by plasma cholinesterase more readily[187], hence its duration of action is much shorter. Post-operative pain is said to be less with suxethonium than with suxamethonium[190]. Clinical trials of succinyldithia choline have recently been reported by Rizzi[190a].

A series of chain substituted bis-onium malonic ester derivatives (*LXXI*) and the corresponding 5-alkyl-4,6-dioxo- and 5-alkyl-4,6-dihydroxy-nonylenebistrimethylammonium di-iodides have also been described, and

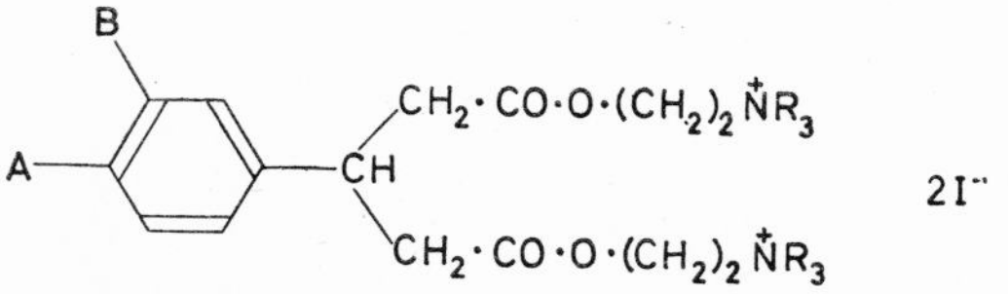

(*LXXIa*)

shown to be less potent than suxamethonium[191]. Bisquaternary ammonium derivatives (*LXXIa*, R = Me or Et; A and B = H, NO_2 or MeO) prepared from bisdialkyl-aminoalkyl esters of substituted β-phenylglutaric acids exhibit curare-like properties[191a].

Bischoline type esters (*LXXII*) and (*LXXIII*) derived from aromatic dibasic acids[192-195], however, exhibit their maximum potency at somewhat

Table 1.8. Potency of bisonium esters of aromatic acids

$$Me_3\overset{+}{N}\cdot(CH_2)_n\cdot O\cdot CO—⟨benzene⟩—CO\cdot O\cdot(CH_2)_n\cdot \overset{+}{N}Me_3 \quad 2X^-$$

(LXXII)

| $n$ | Units* in chain | Rabbit head-drop dose[192,] (mg/kg) |
|---|---|---|
| 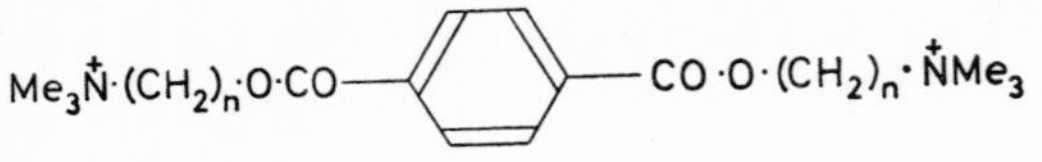 2 | 11 | 7 |
| 3 | 12 | 0·0 |

$$Me_3\overset{+}{N}\cdot(CH_2)_n\cdot O\cdot CO\cdot(CH_2)_m—⟨benzene⟩—CH_2\cdot CO\cdot O\cdot(CH_2)_n\cdot \overset{+}{N}Me_3 \quad 2X^-$$

(LXXIII)

| $n$ | $m$ | Units* in chain | Rabbit head-drop dose[19] (mg/kg) |
|---|---|---|---|
| 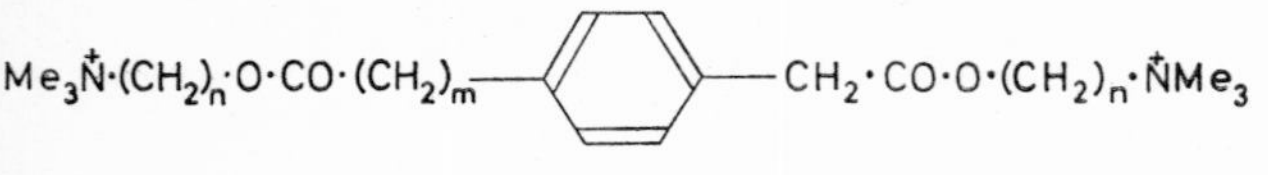 2 | 0 | 12 | 1 |
| 3 | 0 | 14 | 0·2 |
| 2 | 1 | 13 | 8 |
| 3 | 1 | 15 | 10 |

* Aromatic ring equivalent to three methylene groups.

greater interonium distances (*Table 1.8*), a property which they possess in common with a number of bischoline ethers (*LXXIV*), bisonium ethers (*LXXV*) and phenolic ethers (*LXXVI*) of the same type (*Table 1.9*).

Table 1.9. Potencies of bisonium ether compounds[196,197]

| | $n$ | Units in chain | Rabbit head-drop dose (mg/kg) |
|---|---|---|---|
| $Me_3\overset{+}{N}\cdot(CH_2)_2\cdot O\cdot(CH_2)_n\cdot O\cdot(CH_2)_2\cdot \overset{+}{N}Me_3 \quad 2I^-$ (LXXIV) | 2 | 8 | 50 |
| | 3 | 9 | — |
| | 4 | 10 | 1·5 |
| | 5 | 11 | 0·7 |
| | 10 | 16 | 0·8 |
| $Me_3\overset{+}{N}\cdot(CH_2)_n\cdot O\cdot(CH_2)_n\cdot \overset{+}{N}Me_3 \quad 2I^-$ (LXXV) | 2 | 5 | — |
| | 3 | 7 | — |
| | 4 | 9 | 1 |
| | 5 | 11 | 0·7 |
| | 6 | 13 | 0·9 |
| 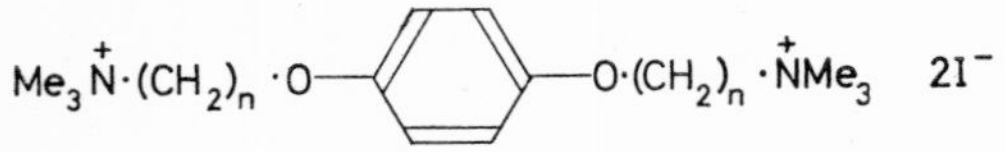 $Me_3\overset{+}{N}\cdot(CH_2)_n\cdot O—⟨benzene⟩—O\cdot(CH_2)_n\cdot \overset{+}{N}Me_3 \quad 2I^-$ (LXXVI) | 2 | 9 | 2 |
| | 3 | 11 | 1·5 |
| | 4 | 13 | 0·25 |
| | 5 | 15 | 0·25 |

Prodeconium bromide (dioxahexadecanium bromide, Prestonal, *LXXVII*), a derivative of the ether-linked compounds (*LXXIV*), has been introduced clinically as a short-acting muscle relaxant[198,199]. It is roughly equipotent with decamethonium, and produces a mixed block which resembles tubo-curarine rather than decamethonium.

$$Me_2\overset{+}{N}\cdot(CH_2)_2\cdot O\cdot(CH_2)_{10}\cdot O\cdot(CH_2)_2\cdot \overset{+}{N}Me_2 \quad 2Br^-$$
$$\overset{|}{CH_2\cdot CO\cdot OPr} \qquad\qquad \overset{|}{CH_2\cdot CO\cdot OPr}$$

(LXXVII)

The introduction of aromatic ester, in contrast to ether links, does not seriously modify the type of block produced. Thus, the esters (*LXXII*) and (*LXXIII*) in common with suxamethonium (*LXVI*), and succinylbis-α-methylcholine (*LXXVIII*)[200] are depolarizing agents, although, significantly,

$$\overset{+}{Me_3N} \cdot CHMe \cdot CH_2 \cdot O \cdot CO \cdot CH_2 \cdot CH_2 \cdot CO \cdot O \cdot CH_2 \cdot CHMe \cdot \overset{+}{NMe_3}$$

(*LXXVIII*)

$$\overset{+}{Me_3N} \cdot CH_2 \cdot CHMe \cdot O \cdot CO \cdot CH_2 \cdot CH_2 \cdot CO \cdot O \cdot CHMe \cdot CH_2 \cdot \overset{+}{NMe_3}$$

(*LXXIX*)

succinylbis-β-methylcholine (*LXXIX*) is much less potent and has been reported to have tubocurarine-like properties[201]. Further work with the optical isomers of the α- and β-methylcholine derivatives has confirmed the low potency of the latter in both the cat and the chick[202]. It has also provided the interesting observation that whereas the $(+)(+)$-$(-)(-)$- and $(+)(-)$-isomers of the α-methylcholine compound are decamethonium-like, and the $(+)(+)$- and $(-)(-)$- isomers of the β-methylcholine compound have tubocurarine-like properties, the $(+)(-)$-isomer of the latter is decamethonium-like[202]. The number and position of phenyl substituents in the phenylsuccinylcholine series also appears to be important. Thus, phenylsuccinyldicholine (*LXXX*, R' = R" = H) is decamethonium-like, but the diphenylsuccinyldicholines (*LXXX*, R' = H, R" = Ph) and (*LXXX*,

$$\overset{+}{Me_3N} \cdot CH_2 \cdot CPhR' \cdot O \cdot CO \cdot CH_2 \cdot CH_2 \cdot CO \cdot O \cdot CH \cdot R" \cdot CH_2 \cdot \overset{+}{NMe_3}$$

(*LXXX*)

R' = Ph, R" = H) are both tubocurarine-like[197,203]. These conclusions are supported by the fact that the potency ratio of bis(trimethylammonium) to bis(triethylammonium) analogues (Me₃/Et₃ index) is, typically, <1 for the tubocurarine-like succinylbis-β-methylcholine and >1 for suxamethonium and the esters (*LXXII*, n = 3, and *LXXIII*, n = 2, m = 1). Two new series of bisquaternary esters[204,205] have led to the development of the 2-diethylamino-ethoxyethyl α-phenyl-α-piperidinoacetate dimethiodide (*LXXXI*)[206], a short-acting tubocurarine-like blocking agent. Truxillonium, bis(4-pyridino-butyl) truxillate dimethiodide is reported to be some six to eight times as potent as $(+)$-tubocurarine in the cat[206a].

$$\overset{+}{N} \cdot CHPh \cdot CO \cdot O \cdot CH_2 \cdot CH_2 \cdot O \cdot CH_2 \cdot CH_2 \cdot \overset{+}{NEt_2} \cdot Me \quad 2I^-$$

Me

(*LXXXI*)

Substitution of methylene chain units of decamethonium by alicyclic rings in general reduces potency and modifies activity. Thus, the compounds (*LXXXII*)[207] and cyclomethone (*LXXXIII*)[208–210] are reported to have tubocurarine-like action. Cyclomethone has a short duration of action, and is antagonized by physostigmine; its effects are said, however, to resemble those of decamethonium more closely than those of $(+)$-tubocurarine[210]. On the other hand, incorporation of the onium group into saturated heterocyclic rings which form part of the interonium chain as in compounds (*LXXXIV*) and (*LXXXV*) does not significantly modify either potency or the type of block, although potency falls and the action becomes tubocurarine-like in

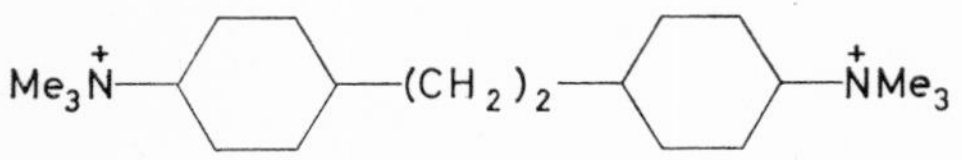

*(LXXXII)*

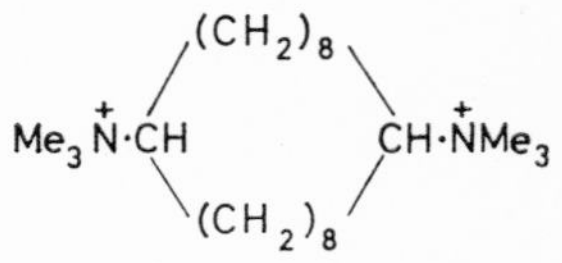

*(LXXXIII)*

the unsaturated ring analogue (*LXXXVI*). 9-(*p*-Methoxyphenyl)fluorene-2, 7-bistrimethylammonium (*LXXXVII*, $R = p\text{-MeO}\cdot C_6H_4$) and 2,7-bistrimethylammonium-9-(3,4-dimethoxyphenyl)fluorene-2,7-bistrimethylammonium di-iodide (*LXXXVII*, $R = 3,4\text{-}(MeO)_2\cdot C_6H_3$, $X = I$) on the other hand are more potent than tubocurarine[211].

A similar modification of properties appears also to occur in the aromatic ether linked compounds (*LXXVI*) already described and in the piperazine- and benzoquinone-linked compounds (*LXXXVIII*)[212], (*LXXXIX*)[213] and

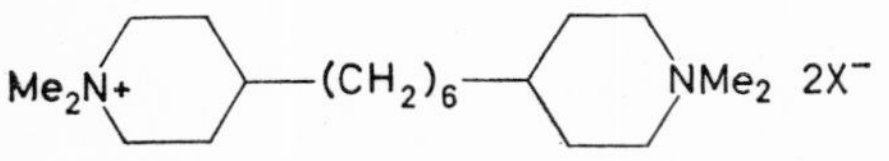

*(LXXXIV)*

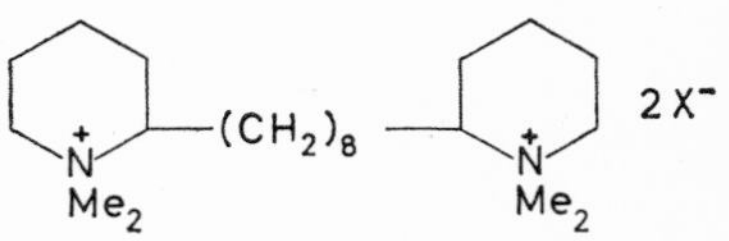

*(LXXXV)*

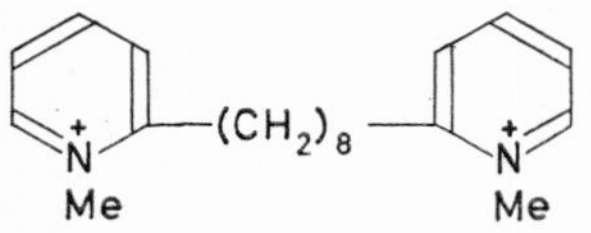

*(LXXXVI)*

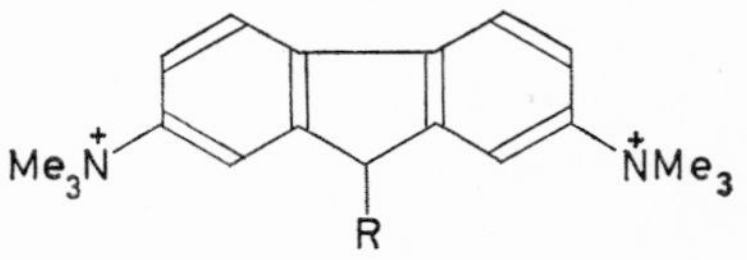

*(LXXXVII)*

$(XC)$[214,215] in which the $Me_3/Et_3$ indexes are $<1$. The piperazine compound (*LXXXVIII*, $R' = Et$, $R'' = PhCH_2$, $X = Br$) has been studied further and named Isocurine[216], and similarly the benzoquinone compound ($XC$, $R' = Et$, $R'' = PhCH_2$, $n = 3$, $X = Cl$) under the name of benzoquinonium chloride (Mytolon)[211-220]. The latter has been used clinically[138,220-223]. It produces a mixed block, which resembles tubocurarine rather than decamethonium, the block being only weakly antagonized by neostigmine[224].

Replacement of elements of the polymethylene chain by the —NH·CO·NH— and carbamoyl links also changes the pattern of activity in a manner similar to that seen with the aromatic ether compounds (*LXXVI*), maximum activity appearing in the longer chain compounds. In contrast to the ether-linked compounds, however, the general level of potency is retained in the biscarbamoyl compounds (*XCI*). Maximum potency (see *Table 1.10*) occurs in the sixteen unit chain compound, carbolonium

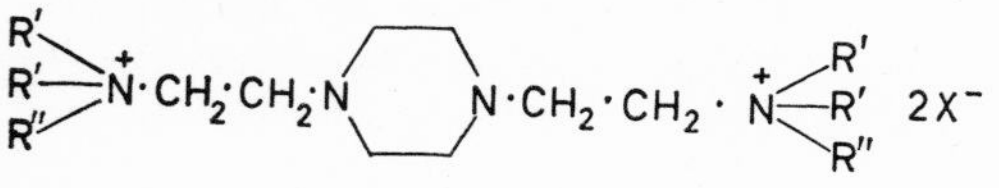

*(LXXXVIII)*

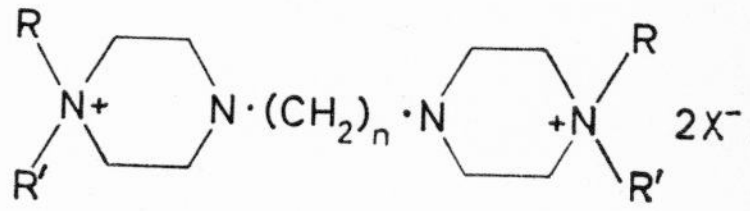

*(LXXXIX)*

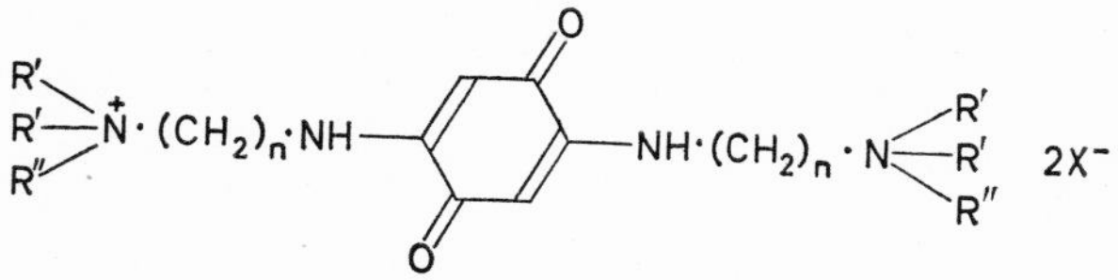

*(XC)*

(Imbretil, *XCI*, n = 6)[225-233], which has been used in surgical anaesthesia[234-240], and is roughly equipotent with decamethonium[241]. Carbolonium is not fully antagonized by neostigmine, and acts by depolarization.

*Table 1.10.* Potencies of carbolonium homologues[225-233]

| | $n$ | Units in chain | Rabbit head-drop dose (mg/kg) |
|---|---|---|---|
| $\overset{+}{Me_3N} \cdot (CH_2)_2 \cdot O \cdot CO \cdot NH \cdot (CH_2)_n \cdot NH \cdot CO \cdot O$ | 0 | 10 | 33 |
| | 1 | 11 | 0·8 |
| $\cdot (CH_2)_2 \cdot \overset{+}{N}Me_3 \quad 2X^-$ | 2 | 12 | 1 |
| (*XCI*) | 4 | 14 | 0·3 |
| | 5 | 15 | 0·1 |
| | 6 | 16 | 0·03 |
| | 10 | 20 | 0·09 |

*Variations in the end-groups*

The effect of substitution in the quaternary ammonium head of bis-onium compounds has been studied in considerable detail, and appears to depend in part on the interonium distance. As already discussed, replacement of *N*-methyl by *N*-ethyl substituents in decamethonium (*LXV*, n = 10), suxamethonium (*LXVI*), and a few closely related compounds, produces a decrease in potency. The relative order of activity is dependent to some extent on the test preparation. Thus, decamethylenebis(dimethylethyl-ammonium) iodide (*XCII*, n = 10, R = Me, R' = Et), has about one-eighth of the activity of decamethonium on the rat phrenic nerve-diaphragm preparation and about one-fifteenth on the quadriceps of the spinal rabbit[243]. Further substitution of *N*-methyl by *N*-ethyl groups does not influence potency on the rat diaphragm, but increases it on the rabbit quadriceps[242]. Decaethonium (*XCII*, n = 10, R = R' = Et) has weak tubocurarine-like

29

activity[171], so that replacement of *N*-methyl by *N*-ethyl substituents not only reduces activity, but changes its character. Rossum and Ariens[244] have also shown that in a series of compounds (*XCII*, n = 10, R = Me, R′ = alkyl), intrinsic activity *falls* with increasing alkyl chain length; but the depolarizing action of decamethonium changes, through the dipropyl derivative (*XCII*, n = 10, R = Me, R′ = Pr) which shows mixed competitive and depolarizing actions, to the diheptyl (*XCII*, n = 10, R = Me, R′ = $C_7H_{15}$) and higher alkyl compounds, which are competitive antagonists.

Incorporation of the onium groups into heterocyclic systems which do not form part of the interonium structure, provides an approach towards a tubocurarine-like structure, and in general results in a modification of properties in this direction. Aromatic-type heterocyclic systems, such as

(*XCII*)          (*XCIII*)

decamethylenebispyridinium (*XCIII*; $ED_{50}$ in the rabbit 10 mg/kg)[242], decamethylenebisquinolinium (*XCIV*), and decamethylenebisisoquinolinium (*XCV*) iodides, all markedly reduce potency; but introduction of methoxyl substituents into the bisquinolinium compound (*XCIV*) restores the level of activity. Potency is also markedly increased in the corresponding deca-methylenebistetrahydroquinolinium (*XCVI*), decamethylenebisdecahydro-quinolinium (*XCVII*), and decamethylenebistetrahydroisoquinolinium dimethiodides (*XCVIII*) which show evidence of tubocurarine-like activity, the compounds being antagonized by neostigmine[242]. Probably the most use-ful compound to emerge from this work is laudexium (laudolissin, *XCIX*)[249–254], prepared from the racemic form of laudanosine, which was found to be more active than tubocurarine in the cat, and rabbit[255]. The $ED_{50}$ dose of laudexium in the rabbit is 0·03 mg/kg[247,248]. Its action, like that of tubo-curarine, is readily reversed by neostigmine, but the relative species sensi-tivities are in the order, rabbit > cat > man > mouse > rat, which suggests that there remains some resemblance to decamethonium. On the other hand, it acts synergistically with ether and in man shows a lower tendency than (+)-tubocurarine to liberate histamine[255]. It has, however, a long duration of action and cases of re-curarization have been reported. The bisatropinium compounds (*C*)[256,257], appear to exhibit tubocurarine-like rather than decamethonium-like activity, since they produce flaccid paralysis in chicks[258,259]. Other analogous compounds of interest include a series of polymethylenebistheophyllinium bromides[260] and polymethylenebistheo-brominium bromides[261,262], which appear to show maximum curarizing potency in the decamethylene compounds. The replacement of *N*-methyl groups in suxamethonium (*LXVI*) by large saturated heterocyclic groups similarly modifies its depolarizing action as in the tetrahydroisoquinolinium (*CI*, n = m = 2)[263] and tropinium compounds (*CII*, m = 2–3, n = 1–6)[258]. In the latter compounds, activity reaches a maximum value in (*CII*, m = 2, n = 4) in which the interonium chain is equivalent to 12 methylene units.

This product (DF 596) is slightly more potent than tubocurarine in the dog and about half as potent in the cat; it is antagonized by neostigmine[258]. The compound (*CI*, n = 3, m = 0), $\gamma$-oxalolaudonium, has been examined

*Table 1.11.* Potency of compounds with heterocyclic onium groups[242,243,245-247]

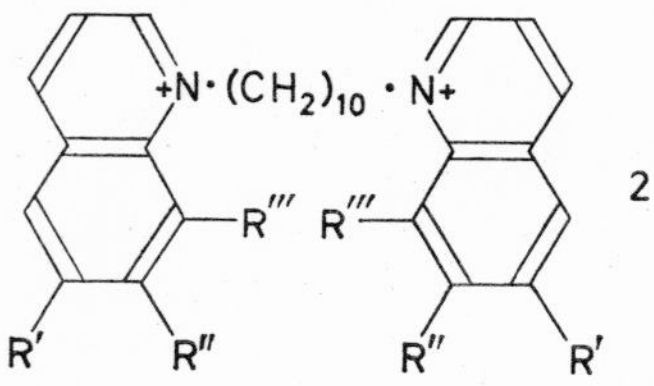

| | R' | R'' | R''' | Rabbit $ED_{50}$ (mg/kg) |
|---|---|---|---|---|
| (XCIV) | H | H | H | 4·5 |
| | MeO | H | H | 4·4 |
| | H | H | MeO | 0·2 |
| | H | H | EtO | >0·3 |
| | MeO | MeO | — | 0·15 |

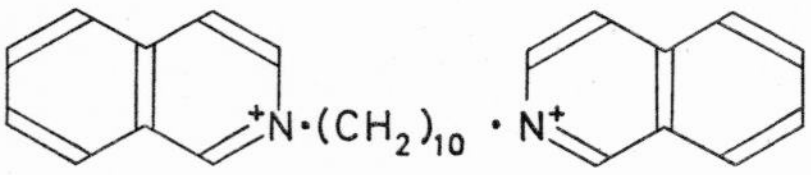

(XCV) — Rabbit $ED_{50}$ (mg/kg) — 4·0

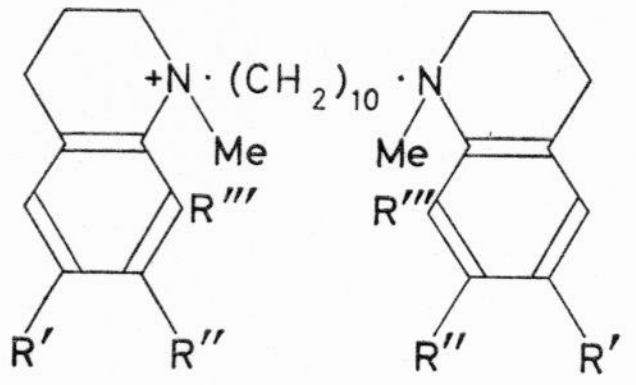

| | R' | R'' | R''' | Rabbit $ED_{50}$ (mg/kg) |
|---|---|---|---|---|
| (XCVI) | H | H | H | 0·75 |
| | MeO | H | H | 0·2 |
| | H | H | MeO | 0·1 |

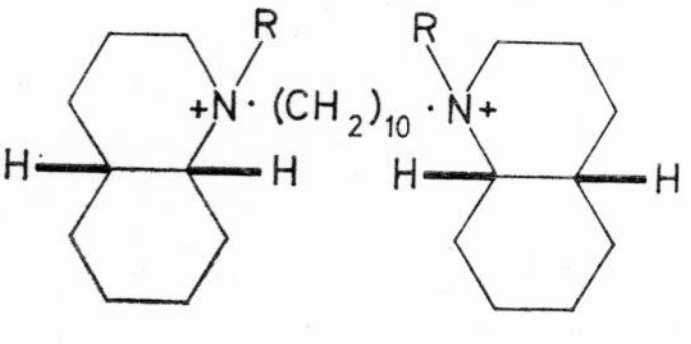

| | Ring Fusion | R | Rabbit $ED_{50}$ (mg/kg) |
|---|---|---|---|
| (XCVII) | cis | Me | 0·12 |
| | trans | Me | 0·1 |
| | trans | Et | 0·4 |

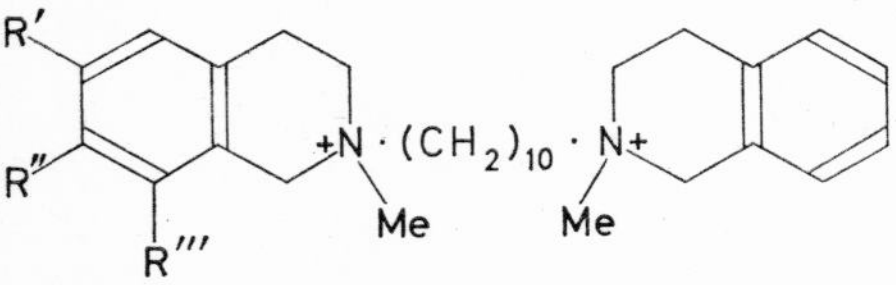

| | R' | R'' | R''' | Rabbit $ED_{50}$ (mg/kg) |
|---|---|---|---|---|
| (XCVIII) | H | H | H | 1·5 |
| | MeO | H | H | 0·2 |
| | MeO | MeO | H | 0·05 |
| | MeO | MeO | MeO | 0·02 |

\* Intravenous dose (mg/kg) paralysing 50 per cent of rabbits

in some detail[263a]. It produces a tubocurarine-like block in the cat, which is antagonized by neostigmine; and produces flaccid paralysis in small animals. Its potency is low, being only 1/30–1/40 that of suxamethonium, and the duration of block is about half that of equi-active doses of suxamethonium. $\gamma$-Oxalolaudonium does not produce ganglion block or histamine-release. Stability studies show that its potency in mice is reduced to about 30 per cent

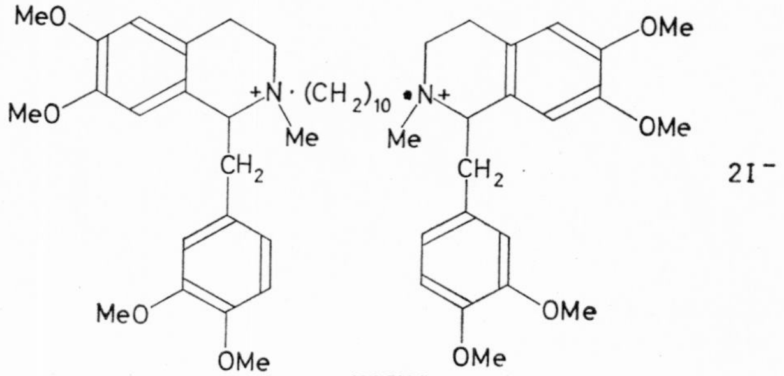

MeO — ... +N·(CH$_2$)$_{10}$·N+ ... OMe (XCIX) 2I$^-$

Me — N·(CH$_2$)$_{10}$·N — Me (C) 2I$^-$

PhCH·CO·O ... O·CO·CHPh
CH$_2$OH ... CH$_2$OH

+N·(CH$_2$)$_n$·O·CO·(CH$_2$)$_m$·CO·O·(CH$_2$)$_n$·N+ (CI) 2I$^-$

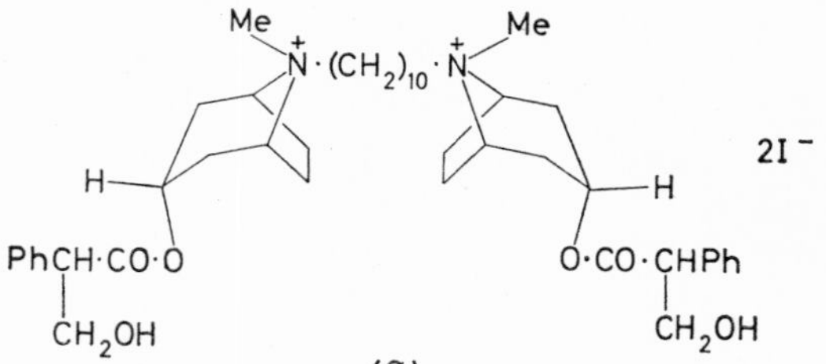

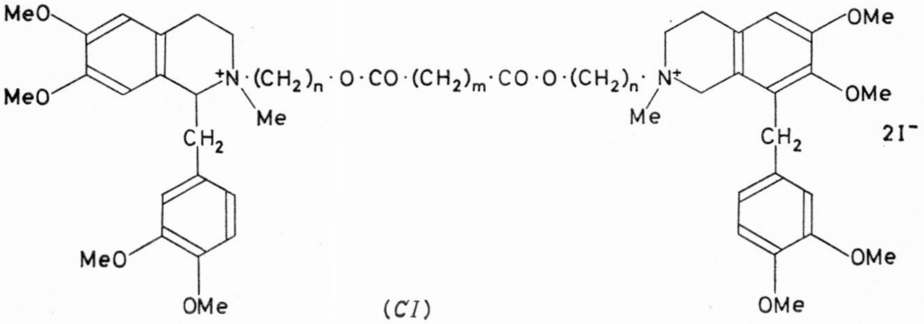

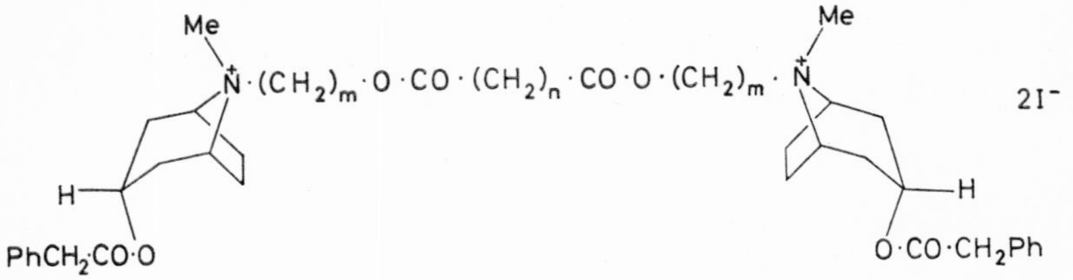

Me — N·(CH$_2$)$_m$·O·CO·(CH$_2$)$_n$·CO·O·(CH$_2$)$_m$·N — Me (CII) 2I$^-$

PhCH$_2$CO·O ... O·CO·CH$_2$Ph

in aqueous solution in 24 hours. Other chain-substituted, end-group modified bisquaternaries include succinylbistropanol methiodide[264] (CIII); the platynecine derivative, Diplacine (CIV)[265,266], the bispiperazinium

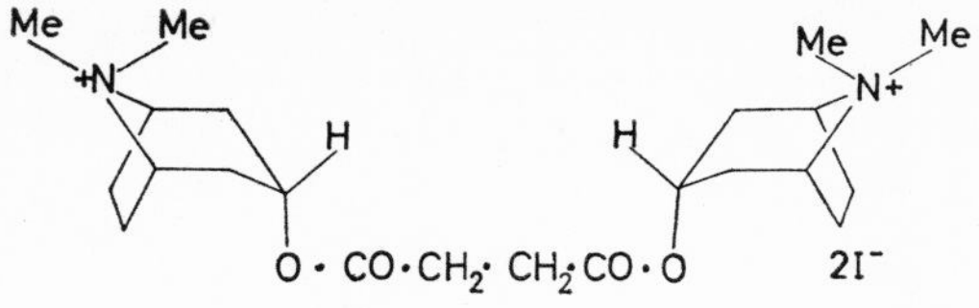

*(CIII)*

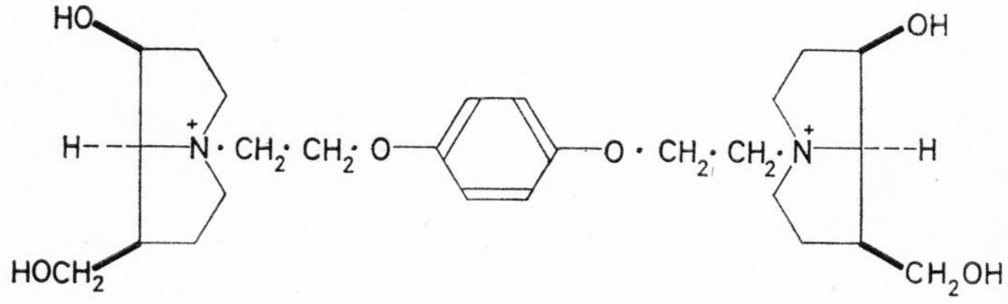

*(CIV)*

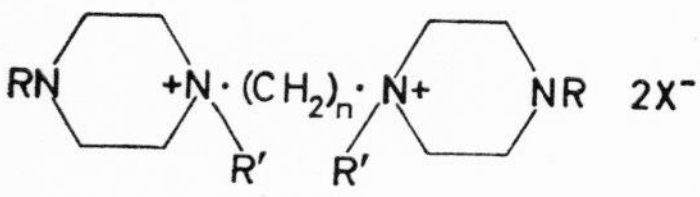

*(CV)* 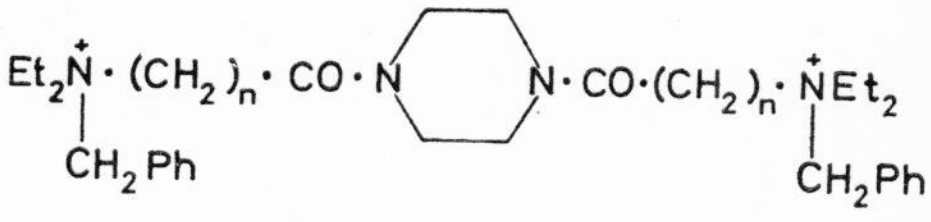                      *(CVI)*

$(CV)^{213}$, piperazine-substituted $(CVI; n = 1$ or $2)^{267}$, $(CVII)^{267}$, $(CVIII)^{267}$, and pyridazine-substituted compounds $(CIX)^{268}$; the *p*-phenylenebisquinolinium compounds $(CX)^{269}$, the polymethylenebisazabicyclo[3,3,1]nonanes

*Table 1.12.* Potency of piperazine bisonium compounds[267]

| | $R$ | $R'$ | Rabbit heat-drop dose (mg/kg) |
|---|---|---|---|
| $R'R_2\overset{+}{N}(CH_2)_2 \cdot O \cdot CO \cdot N \phantom{xxx} N \cdot CO \cdot O \cdot (CH_2)_2 \cdot \overset{+}{N}R_2R'$   2Br⁻ | | | |
| *(CVII)* | Me | Me | 1·25 |
| | Et | Et | 0·17 |
| | Et | PhCH₂ | 0·076 |
| | Me | PhCH₂ | 0·64 |
| $Et_2\overset{+}{N} \cdot (CH_2)_3 \cdot NH \cdot CO \cdot N \phantom{xx} N \cdot CO \cdot NH \cdot (CH_2)_3 \cdot \overset{+}{N}Et_2$   2Br⁻ | | | |
| R | | $R$ | |
| | | Et | 0·46 |
| *(CVIII)* | | PhCH₂ | 0·054 |

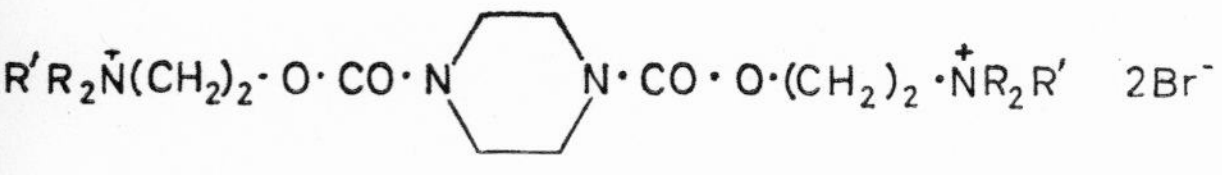

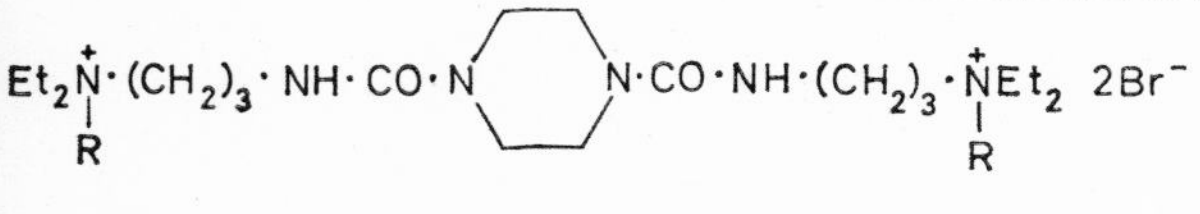

$(CXI)^{270-272}$ which exhibit maximum potency when $n = 4$; and the bisatropinium compounds $(CXII)$. In the bispiperidinium series, 2,2'-dodecamethylenebis(*N*,*N*-dimethylpiperidinium) iodide $(CXIII)$ is roughly equipotent with (+)-tubocurarine, though of short duration of action[273]. Maximum activity in a series of bis(3-hydroxydimethylpiperidinium)polymethylene

33

ethers (*CXIV*, n = 5, 6, 7, 8, 10, 12 and 14)[274] is shown in the dodecamethylene derivative (*CXIV*, n = 12), which is nearly equipotent with (+)-tubocurarine.

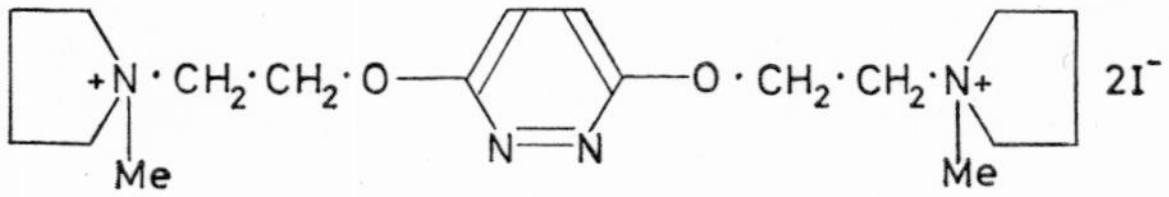

*(CIX)*

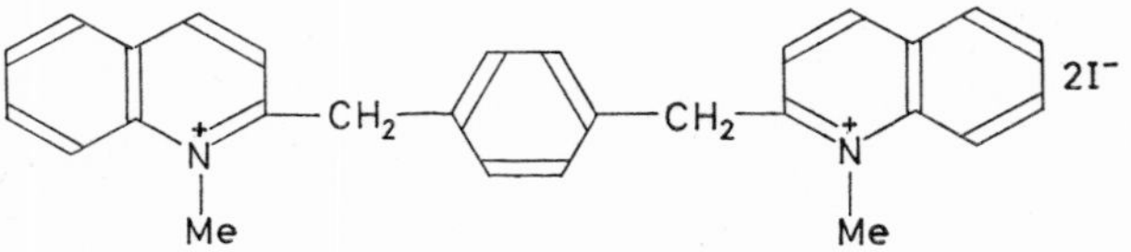

*(CX)*

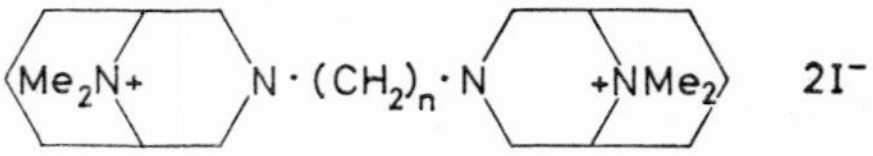

*(CXI)*

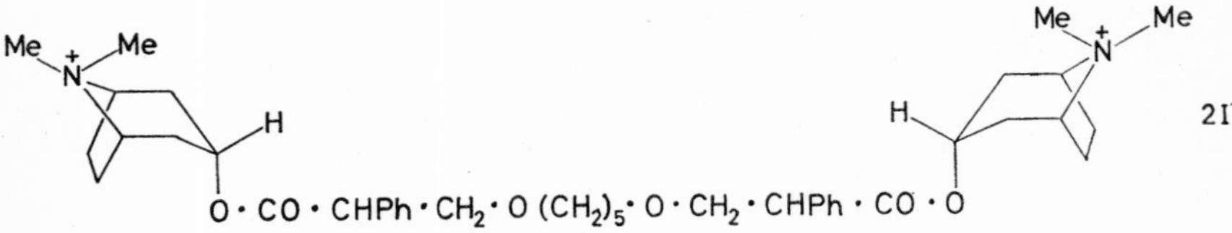

*(CXII)*

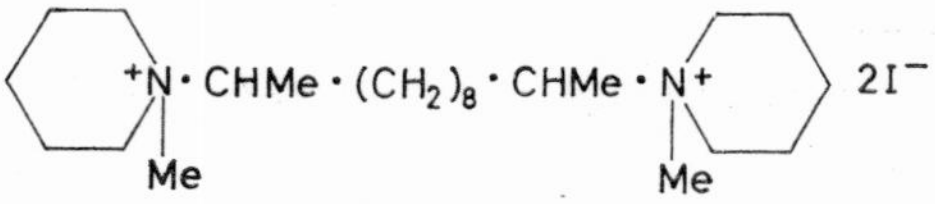

*(CXIII)*

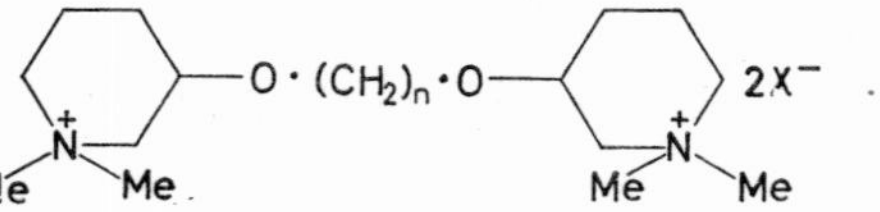

*(CXIV)*

The dodecamethylene- and the corresponding tetradecamethylene-compounds do not produce contracture in the avian muscles, though their less potent lower homologues do cause contracture[274].

In contrast to the behaviour of decamethonium and suxamethonium, the

34

short chain compounds such as penta- and hexa-methonium (*LXV*, n = 5 or 6) show an increase in potency on replacement of *N*-methyl by *N*-ethyl groups[275]. Replacement of *N*-methyl by saturated heterocyclic groups as in the piperidinium compounds (*CXV*, n = 6 and 7) also increases potency (in cat gastrocnemius, to about one-fifth that of tubocurarine); though by contrast, the corresponding morpholinium compounds (*CXVI*, n = 6 and 7)

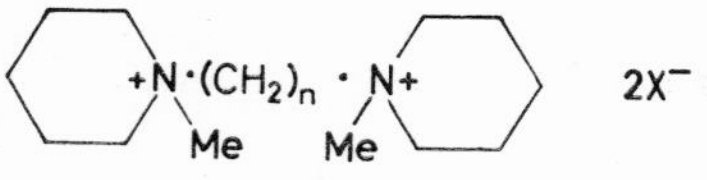

*(CXV)* 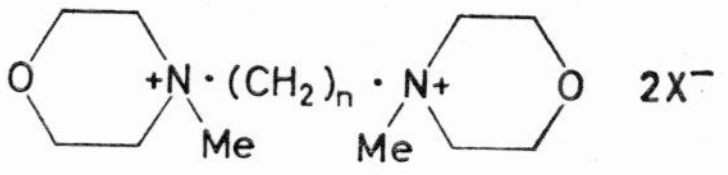                              *(CXVI)*

show negligible activity, presumably due to the charge delocalizing effect of the oxygen functions[276,277]. Surprisingly, the pyrrolidinium analogues (*CXVII*, n = 5, 6 and 7) are also inactive as neuromuscular blocking agents, although powerful ganglion blockers. On the other hand, decamethylene-bispyrrolidinium methiodide (*CXVII*, n = 10) is nearly equipotent with tubocurarine on the cat gastrocnemius preparation, showing a complex mode of action mainly resembling decamethonium[208,273]. Other compounds of this

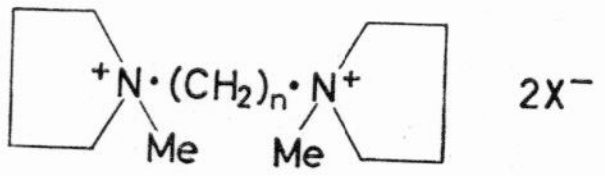

*(CXVII)* 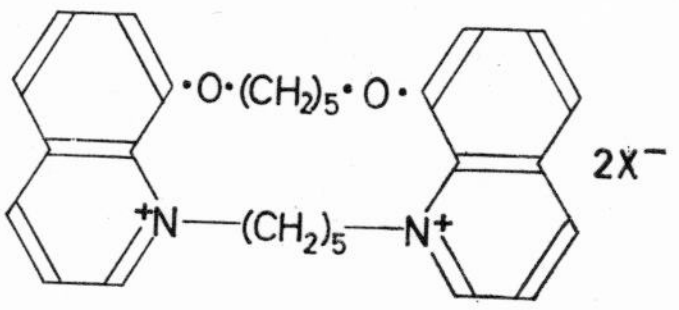                              *(CXVIII)*

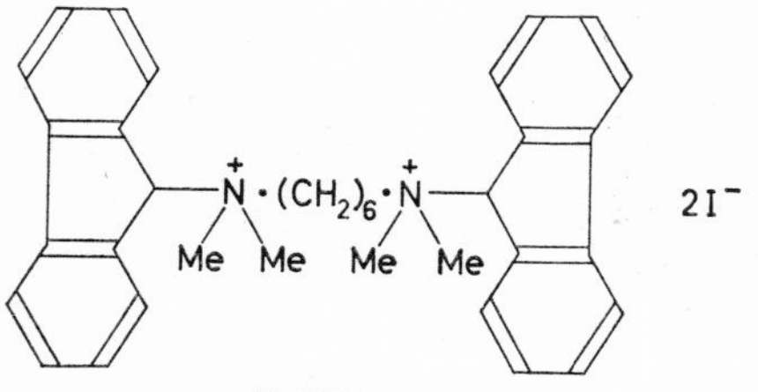

*(CXIX)*

type which have also been examined include the pentamethylenebisquino-linium methiodides (as *XCIV*)[278] and (*CXVIII*)[279]; hexamethylenebisatro-pinium and hexamethylenebisscopolinium methiodides[279]; pentamethylene-bisstychninium[280]; polymethylenebisphenazinium[281] and biscarbolinium[282] compounds; 1,4-xylylenebisbenzoyltropanolinium methiodide[283], and hexa-methylenebis-(9-fluorenyldimethylammonium) di-iodide (Hexafluorenium, Mylaxen, *CXIX*)[281]. The latter has been examined in dogs[284] and has been submitted to clinical trial[285,286]. It has, however, been reported to block the effects of pre-ganglionic stimulation of the vagus in the isolated guinea-pig heart preparation[287]. Hexafluorenium has also been shown to potentiate and prolong the neuromuscular blocking action of suxamethonium by inhibiting plasma cholinesterase[288].

## TRIS-ONIUM COMPOUNDS

Gallamine (Flaxedil; *CXX*, R = R′ = Et), which was synthesized by Bovet, Depierre and de Lestrange[289] in 1946, has been studied extensively and is now widely used clinically. It was based on a knowledge of neuromuscular block previously observed in aliphatic choline ethers[290,291], and the contribution of ether groups to the activity of (+)-tubocurarine, and a number of other bisquaternary ethers[292]. Potency, however, is greatly increased with the introduction of the third onium group, the three substances (*CXXII*, R = Et), (*CXXI*, R = Et) and (*CXX*, R = Et, R′ = Et), having relative potencies of 2, 25 and 100 on the rat diaphragm preparation[293]. Gallamine

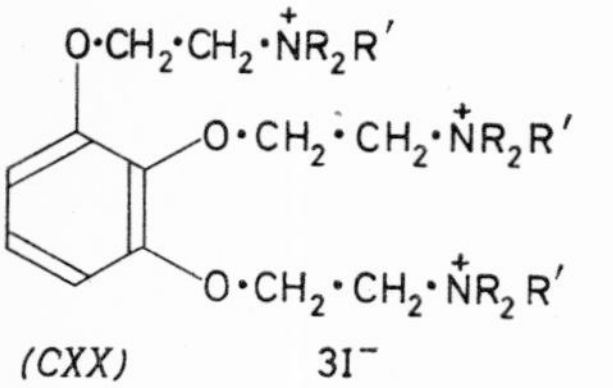

(CXX)    31⁻           (CXXI) 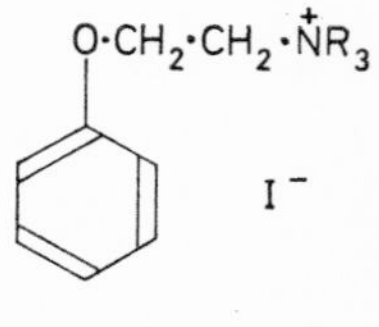           (CXXII)

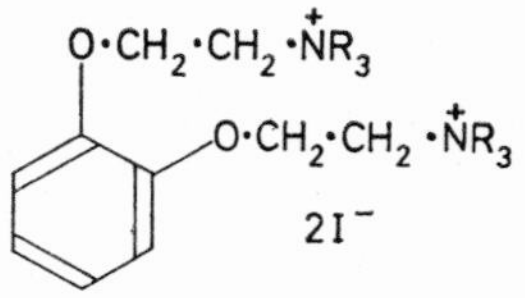

is (+)-tubocurarine-like in its action, being antagonized by neostigmine[289, 294], but it is significantly less potent than tubocurarine, having about one-fifth of the potency of the latter in man.

Studies of *N*-alkyl substitution in gallamine[290] have shown that successive replacement of *N*-ethyl by *N*-methyl substituents leads to a decrease in curariform potency, though this only becomes significant in the ethyl-dimethylaminoethoxy compound (*CXX*, R = Me, R′ = Et) and in the trimethylaminoethoxy compound (*CXX*, R = R′ = Me). In this respect, gallamine is similar in behaviour to hexaethonium in which the $Me_3/Et_3$ relative index of potency is also <1. It has recently been suggested that this probably follows from the staggered orientation of the positively charged oxyethyltriethylammonium groups in gallamine (*CXXIII*), which represents their most probable distribution as a result of the natural repulsion of like charges[69]. Such a staggered orientation places the onium groups on the apices of an equilateral triangle, the sides of which are approximately 9–10 Å in length, equivalent to the interonium distance in hexaethonium if the methylene chain is fully extended.

Kensler, Zirkle, Matallana and Condouris[295] have also examined a series of tris-onium compounds (*CXXIV*) where n = 2, 3 or 4 and R = Me or Et. Maximum potency occurs in the compound (*CXXIV*, n = 4, R = Et), which for reasons similar to those put forward above, has an analogous orientation and spacing of onium groups.

Similarly, the triethiodide (*CXXV*) derived from 4-hydroxyisophthalic acid has also been reported to have tubocurarine-like properties[296]. Chagus[297] has recently described experiments with $^{14}C$ labelled gallamine which show that it forms a labile complex with a macromolecular cellular component of the electric tissue of the electric eel when injected into the intact animal. The formation of the complex is dependent on the tissue concentration of the drug, and decurarization occurs when blood levels are lowered below a threshold value. The macromolecular cellular component which has been isolated contains a mucopolysaccharide which, in its purified form, has been shown to fix a constant number of different neuromuscular

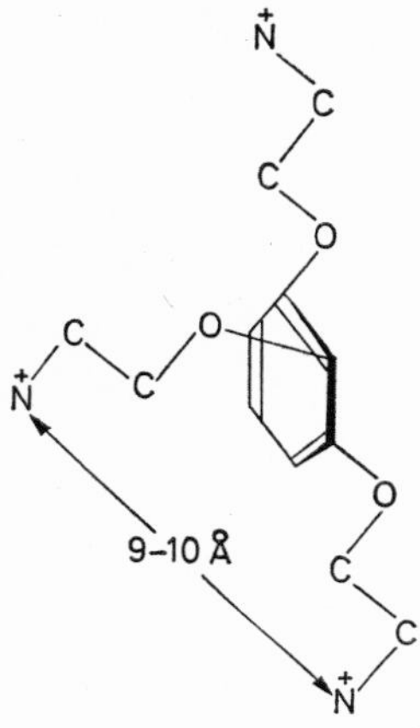

*(CXXIII)*

9–10 Å

blocking drugs (gallamine and dimethyl-(+)-isochondodendrine methiodide) per unit of dry weight. In a totally unrelated series of experiments, Bovet-Nitti[298] has found that the action of gallamine, in common with that of (+)-tubocurarine and a number of other tubocurarine-like drugs, is potentiated by the action of the substance SKF 525A (diethylaminoethyldiphenylpropyl acetate hydrochloride), suggesting that some reversible fixation of

$$\left[R_3 \overset{+}{N} \cdot (CH_2)_n\right]_3 CH \; 3Br^-$$

*(CXXIV)*

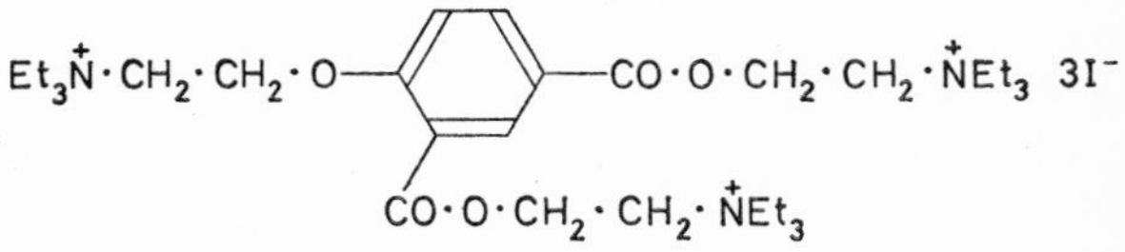

$$Et_3 \overset{+}{N} \cdot CH_2 \cdot CH_2 \cdot O - \!\!\!\left\langle\!\!\!\bigcirc\!\!\!\right\rangle\!\!\!- CO \cdot O \cdot CH_2 \cdot CH_2 \cdot \overset{+}{N}Et_3 \quad 3I^-$$

$$CO \cdot O \cdot CH_2 \cdot CH_2 \cdot \overset{+}{N}Et_3$$

*(CXXV)*

these drugs to undefined non-specific receptors occurs. More recently, Ahmad and Lewis[299] have studied the effect of gallamine on the flux of $^{47}Ca^{2+}$, $^{42}K^+$ and $^{24}Na^+$ in frog skeletal muscle. No significant change in uptake or release of these ions was observed in doses up to 8 mg/kg.

A similar pattern of activity to that observed in the gallamine series has also been noted in an extensive series of linear polyonium compounds prepared in recent years in the author's laboratories, which, together with the above observations, suggests that typical motor-end plates present a repeating arrangement of suitably spaced anionic receptors. The *NSN-*, *NNN*-trisonium compounds *(CXXVI)*[69,300] and *(CXXVII)*[301–303], the *NNNN*-tetra-onium compounds *(CXXVIII)*, the *NNSNN*-penta-onium compounds

(*CXXIX*) and the *NNNNN*-hexa-onium compound (*CXXX*) have been examined in the cat, rabbit, frog, mouse and chick. Ethonium compounds in which the onium groups are separated by 5 or 6 methylene groups are predominantly tubocurarine-like, whilst those in which the onium groups are separated by 10 methylene groups are decamethonium-like; compounds with intermediate interonium spacing (8 methylene groups) are transitional, and some transitional properties are evident in the *NNNN*-tetra-ethonium compounds (*CXXVIII*, $m = 6$, $n = 10$; $m = 8$, $n = 6$; and $m = 10$, $n = 6$) with

$$[R'R_2\overset{+}{N}\cdot(CH_2)_n\cdot\overset{+}{S}R'(CH_2)_n\cdot\overset{+}{N}R_2R']\ 3I^-$$
$$(CXXVI)$$

$$[R'R_2\overset{+}{N}\cdot(CH_2)_n\cdot\overset{+}{N}RR'\cdot(CH_2)_n\cdot\overset{+}{N}R_2R']\ 3I^-$$
$$(CXXVII)$$

$$[R'R_2\overset{+}{N}\cdot(CH_2)_m\cdot\overset{+}{N}RR'\cdot(CH_2)_n\cdot\overset{+}{N}RR'\cdot(CH_2)_n\cdot\overset{+}{N}R_2]\ 4I^-$$
$$(CXXVIII)$$

$$[Et_3\overset{+}{N}\cdot(CH_2)_6\cdot\overset{+}{N}Et_2\cdot(CH_2)_6\cdot\overset{+}{S}Et\cdot(CH_2)_6\cdot\overset{+}{N}Et_2\cdot(CH_2)_6\cdot\overset{+}{N}Et_3]\ 5I^-$$
$$(CXXIX)$$

$$\{Et_3\overset{+}{N}\cdot[(CH_2)_6\overset{+}{N}Et_2]_4(CH_2)_6\overset{+}{N}Et_3\}\ 6I^-$$
$$(CXXX)$$

mixed interonium spacings. Overall chain length is unimportant in determining the type of block, as shown by the groups of compounds shown in *Table 1.13* with similar overall chain length and contrasting types of action, the latter being determined solely by the interonium distance.

Potency among the hexamethylene-separated ethonium compounds increases broadly in line with the number of onium groups in the molecule (*Figure 1.4*) in the rabbit, cat, mouse and frog, though some anomalies are apparent. This increase in potency with increase in the number of onium groups in the molecule provides a further argument for a repeating arrangement of suitably spaced anionic receptors on the motor end-plate. The effect of onium group substitution in the hexamethylene-separated onium compounds varies markedly from one test animal to another. Potency is at a maximum in ethonium compounds in the cat and chick (*Figures 1.5* and *1.6*), though there is evidence of increasing potency with the introduction of butyl and larger substituents[69]. The reduction of potency on replacement of ethyl by methyl substituents in (*CXXVI*) and (*CXXVII*) is also accompanied by the appearance of decamethonium-like properties. The general pattern of activity shown by all the above hexamethylene-separated polyethonium compounds resembles closely that of hexaethonium, tridecaethonium, gallamine, and the tris-quaternary compounds[295] (*CXXIV*), and the common spacing element of inter-quaternary distance is no doubt significant.

*Table 1.13.* Comparison of chain-length and interonium distance of polyonium groups with the type of neuromuscular block exhibited
(TC = Tubocurarine, C10 = Decamethonium)

| Compound | Type of block | No. of atoms separating terminal onium groups |
|---|---|---|
| $Et_3\overset{+}{N}\cdot(CH_2)_6\cdot\overset{+}{N}Et_2\cdot(CH_2)_6\cdot\overset{+}{N}Et_2\cdot(CH_2)_6\cdot\overset{+}{N}Et_3$ | TC-like | 20 |
| $Et_3\overset{+}{N}\cdot(CH_2)_{10}\cdot\overset{+}{N}Et_2\cdot(CH_2)_{10}\cdot\overset{+}{N}Et_3$ | C10-like | 21 |
| $Et_3\overset{+}{N}\cdot(CH_2)_6\cdot\overset{+}{N}Et_2\cdot(CH_2)_8\cdot\overset{+}{N}Et_2\cdot(CH_2)_6\cdot\overset{+}{N}Et_3$ | TC-like | 22 |
| $Et_3\overset{+}{N}\cdot(CH_2)_8\cdot\overset{+}{N}Et_2\cdot(CH_2)_6\cdot\overset{+}{N}Et_2\cdot(CH_2)_8\cdot\overset{+}{N}Et_3$ | TC-like | 24 |
| $Et_3\overset{+}{N}\cdot(CH_2)_6\cdot\overset{+}{N}Et_2\cdot(CH_2)_{10}\cdot\overset{+}{N}Et_2\cdot(CH_2)_6\cdot\overset{+}{N}Et_3$ | TC-like | 24 |
| $Et_3\overset{+}{N}\cdot(CH_2)_8\cdot\overset{+}{N}Et_2\cdot(CH_2)_8\cdot\overset{+}{N}Et_2\cdot(CH_2)_6\cdot\overset{+}{N}Et_3$ | 'Transitional' | 26 |
| $Et_3\overset{+}{N}\cdot(CH_2)_6\cdot\overset{+}{N}Et_2\cdot(CH_2)_6\cdot SEt\cdot(CH_2)_6\cdot\overset{+}{N}Et_2\cdot(CH_2)_6\cdot\overset{+}{N}Et_3$ | TC-like | 27 |
| $Et_3\overset{+}{N}\cdot(CH_2)_{10}\cdot\overset{+}{N}Et_2\cdot(CH_2)_6\cdot\overset{+}{N}Et_2\cdot(CH_2)_{10}\cdot\overset{+}{N}Et_3$ | C10-like | 28 |
| $Et_3\overset{+}{N}\cdot(CH_2)_{10}\cdot\overset{+}{N}Et_2\cdot(CH_2)_{10}\cdot\overset{+}{N}Et_2\cdot(CH_2)_{10}\cdot\overset{+}{N}Et_3$ | C10-like | 32 |
| $Et_3\overset{+}{N}\cdot(CH_2)_6\cdot\overset{+}{N}Et_2\cdot(CH_2)_6\cdot\overset{+}{N}Et_2\cdot(CH_2)_6\cdot\overset{+}{N}Et_2\cdot$ $(CH_2)_6\cdot\overset{+}{N}Et_2\cdot(CH_2)_6\cdot\overset{+}{N}Et_3$ | TC-like | 34 |

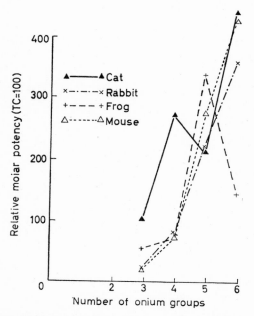

*Figure 1.4.* Relationship between relative potency and the number of onium groups

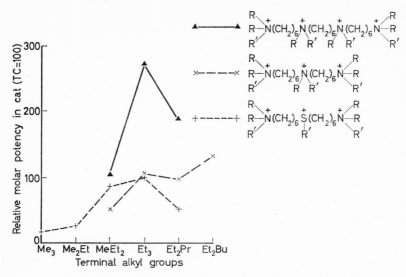

*Figure 1.5.* Relationship between relative potency in the cat and
*N*-substituents of the onium group

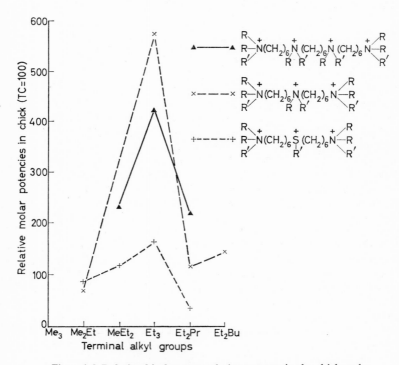

*Figure 1.6.* Relationship between relative potency in the chick and
*N*-substituents of the onium group

The influence of chain substitution has also been investigated in the simpler polyonium compounds. Replacement of a methylene group in the interonium polymethylene chain by an ether link, as in the compounds (CXXXI)[303–306] and (CXXXII)[305], produces a marked decrease in muscle-relaxing potency in the cat, rabbit, chick, mouse and frog. The compounds are all tubocurarine-like and, as with the corresponding polymethylene compounds, activity in general increases with the size of the N-alkyl substituents. The analogous bisonium ether compounds of Fakstorp and Pederson[307–309] (CXXXIII) are similarly of low potency[306]. The influence of the ether substituents on neuromuscular blocking potency is, therefore, in sharp contrast to its potentiating influence on ganglion-blocking activity[307–309]. Again, neuromuscular blocking potency is not greatly influenced by the minor structural changes within the series[306], which are so important in determining the level of activity of the same compounds as ganglion-blocking agents.

$$[R'R_2\overset{+}{N}\cdot(CH_2)_2\cdot O\cdot(CH_2)_2\cdot\overset{+}{N}RR'\cdot(CH_2)_2\cdot O\cdot(CH_2)_2\cdot\overset{+}{N}R_2R']\ 3I^-$$
$$(CXXXI)$$

$$[Et_2R\overset{+}{N}\cdot(CH_2)_6\cdot\overset{+}{N}RR'\cdot(CH_2)_2\cdot O\cdot(CH_2)_2\cdot\overset{+}{N}RR'\cdot(CH_2)_2\cdot\overset{+}{N}REt_2]\ 4I^-$$
$$(CXXXII)$$

$$\begin{bmatrix} R^1 \\ R^2-\overset{+}{N}\cdot(CH_2)n\cdot O\cdot(CH_2)m\cdot\overset{+}{N}-R^5 \\ R^3 \end{bmatrix}\ 2X^-$$
$$\begin{matrix} & R^4 \\ & R^6 \end{matrix}$$
$$(CXXXIII)$$

The lowering of potency observed with ether substitution into the chain of bis- and poly-onium compounds also contrasts with the potentiating effect of aromatic ether links in (+)-tubocurarine (XVIII) and its isomers, and in the decamethylenebis(tetrahydroquinolinium) and (tetrahydroisoquinolinium) compounds (XCVI) and (XCVIII). It seems likely, therefore, that ether substitution into aliphatic type compounds in proximity to the quaternary centres results in a reduction of the charge on the nitrogen, with a consequent lowered capacity to bind at the receptor surface. On the other hand, it is reasonable to suppose that the influence of methoxyl and other ether links in (+)-tubocurarine and related molecules is concentrated in the aromatic rings and tends, therefore, not to reduce the charge on the nitrogen in the same way.

Ester-linked trisonium compounds (CXXXIV) have also been prepared[310], of which the ethonium compounds have been shown to be short-acting non-depolarizing drugs. In general, they are less potent than (+)-tubocurarine. They are antagonized by neostigmine and edrophonium, and their action is prolonged by ether. The duration of block, particularly in the hen, is significantly less than for (+)-tubocurarine, and this is no doubt due to the rapid rate at which they are hydrolysed[311].

A number of much longer chain polyonium compounds have also been described by Schueler and Keasling[312]. These are polymeric mixtures (*CXXXV–CXXXVII*), so that only an average polymer length is known for each substance, and as a result of the method of polymerization, the terminal units of the polymer are dissimilar. The compounds exhibit high potencies, with long duration of action compared with that of the corresponding bisonium compounds to which the polymers are related. They all give flaccid paralysis and are antagonized by neostigmine, and thus appear to

*Table 1.14*. Potency of trisonium compounds containing ester groups[310]

$$[R_2R'\overset{+}{N}(CH_2)_2 \cdot O \cdot CO \cdot (CH_2)_n \cdot \overset{+}{N}EtR' \cdot (CH_2)_n \cdot CO \cdot O \cdot (CH_2)_2 \cdot \overset{+}{N}R_2R'] \ 3I^-$$
(*CXXXIV*)

| n | R | R' | Cat* | Hen* | Duration of action at 40–60% block in minutes | |
|---|---|---|---|---|---|---|
| | | | | | Cat | Hen |
| 2 | Et | Et | 7·0 | 2·3 | 10 | 5 |
| 2 | Et | Me | 5·9 | 7·8 | 14 | 5 |
| 2 | Me | Me | — | 1·7 | — | 4 |
| 1 | Et | Me | >50 | >50 | 8 | 4 |
| (+)-tubocurarine | | | 0·12 | 0·35 | 20 | 18 |

\* Dose (mg/kg) producing 50% paralysis of the gastrocnemius/sciatic preparation

*Table 1.15*. Potencies of long chain polyonium compounds[312]

| Compound | Average n | Inter-onium distance Å | Dose to effect 90% reduction of contraction height (chicken-gastrocnemius) (mg/kg) | Minutes to recovery of 90% of control contraction height |
|---|---|---|---|---|
| (*CXXXV*, R = Me) | 30 | 8 | 0·5 | >180 |
| (*CXXXV*, R = Et) | 22 | 8 | 0·5 | >180 |
| (*CXXXVI*) | 8 | 16 | 1·0 | >180 |
| (*CXXXVII*) | 37 | 15·8 | 0·2 | 90 |
| Decamethonium | — | 15·8 | 0·05 | 8 |

produce a competitive block. The increase in potency and duration of activity which is a general feature of all polyonium compounds strongly suggests that these substances are pharmacologically bi- or polyvalent. This possibly implies an array of receptors arranged in a lattice pattern as described by Taylor[11], but Barlow[313] favours combination of polyonium compounds at a single receptor unit with subsidiary action at an anchoring site or sites. Citing the enzyme studies of Dixon and Webb[314], the view is taken that specialized receptor structures are unlikely to be closely spaced on a tissue area so specialized as a muscle end-plate, and that the attachment of polyvalent structures therefore involves alternative, but chemically similar, points of attachment.

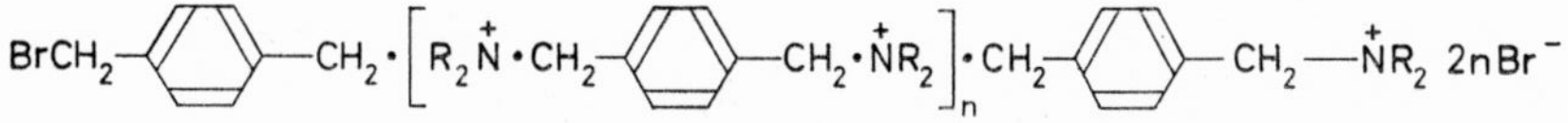

BrCH$_2$—⬡—CH$_2$·[R$_2$N$^+$·CH$_2$—⬡—CH$_2$·NR$_2^+$·CH$_2$]$_n$—⬡—CH$_2$—NR$_2^+$ 2nBr$^-$

*(CXXXV)*

BrCH$_2$—⬡—CH$_2$·CH$_2$—⬡—CH$_2$·[Et$_2$N$^+$·CH$_2$—⬡—CH$_2$·CH$_2$—⬡—CH$_2$·NEt$_2^+$]$_n$·CH$_2$—⬡—CH$_2$·CH$_2$—⬡—CH$_2$Br 2nBr$^-$

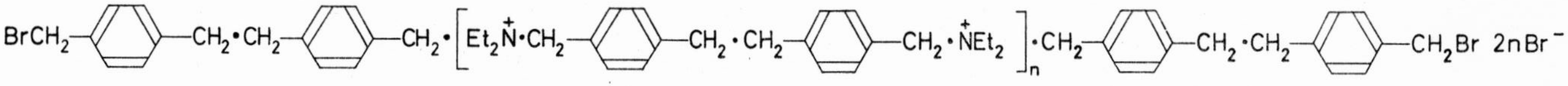

*(CXXXVI)*

Br(CH$_2$)$_{10}$[Me$_2$N$^+$·(CH$_2$)$_{10}$·NMe$_2$]$_n$·(CH$_2$)$_{10}$·NMe$_2$ 2nBr$^-$

*(CXXXVII)*

43

## CONCLUSIONS

Clinically, the outstanding need of the moment is for the development of a potent, safe, short-acting muscle relaxant. Studies of ester-linked bisonium compounds derived from suxamethonium have so far failed to produce drugs which combine high potency with short action, based on the action of choline- or other esterases, in such a way that the action of the drug is fully reversible by neostigmine and similar agents. The influence on reversibility of methyl branches in the polymethylene ester chain of suxamethonium, and the increase of potency generally obtained with polyonium compounds may provide useful leads. Of greater fundamental importance, however, are studies already in progress in a number of laboratories, relating the stereochemistry of neuromuscular blocking agents to their potency, reversibility and distribution within the animal body. To succeed, such studies must establish not only absolute stereochemical configuration, but also the most probable conformation of the molecule in the biological system in which it produces its effect. Many of the most interesting and most potent neuromuscular blocking agents have non-rigid molecules, and studies of the biological action of both completely rigid molecules, such as those based on the steroid nucleus, and on molecules of known conformation should provide fruitful areas of work ultimately leading to new advances.

## REFERENCES

1. BERNARD and PELOUZE *C.R. Acad. Sci., Paris* 1850, **31,** 533
2. BERNARD and PELOUZE *Union med.* 1850, **4,** 505
3. BERNARD *C.R. Acad. Sci., Paris* 1856, **43,** 825
4. CRUM BROWN and FRASER *Trans. roy. Soc. Edinb.* 1869, **25,** 151, 693
5. DE BEER *Ann. N.Y. Acad. Sci.* 1951, **54,** 362
6. BOVET *Ann. N.Y. Acad. Sci.* 1951, **54,** 407
7. BOVET *Curare and Curare-like Agents* (Ed. Bovet, Bovet-Nitti and Marini-Bettôlo): Elsevier, London, 1959, p. 252
8. BARLOW *Introduction to Chemical Pharmacology:* Methuen, London, 1955
9. WASER *J. Pharm., Lond.* 1960, **12,** 577
10. LEWIS *Ann. Rep. Prog. Appl. Chem.* 1960, **45,** 220
10a. D'ARCY and TAYLOR *J. Pharm., Lond.* 1962, **14,** 129, 193
11. TAYLOR *Pharmacol. Rev.* 1951, **3,** 412
12. CAVALLITO *Curare and Curare-like Agents* (Ed. Bovet, Bovet-Nitti and Marini-Bettôlo): Elsevier, London, 1959, p. 252
13. CAVALLITO and GRAY *Progress in Drug Research* Vol. II (Ed. Jucker): Birkhauser, Basle, 1960
14. BOWMAN *Progress in Medicinal Chemistry* Vol. 2 (Ed. Ellis and West): Butterworth, London, 1962, p. 88
15. DALE, FELDBERG and VOGT *J. Physiol.* 1936, **86,** 353
16. PATON and ZAIMIS *Brit. J. Pharmacol.* 1949, **4,** 381
17. BURNS and PATON *J. Physiol.* 1951, **115,** 41
18. ZAIMIS *J. Physiol.* 1953, **122,** 238
19. JEWELL and ZAIMIS *J. Physiol.* 1954, **124,** 417
19a. ARIENS *Arch. int. Pharmacodyn.* 1954, **99,** 32
20. HUNT and RENSHAW *J. Pharmacol.* 1925, **25,** 315
21. BENCOWITZ and RENSHAW *J. Amer. chem. Soc.* 1925, **47,** 1904
22. ING and WRIGHT *Proc. roy. Soc.* 1931, **109B,** 337

23. ING and WRIGHT *Proc. roy. Soc.* 1933, **114B,** 48
24. BARLOW, BLASCHKO, HIMMS and TRENDELENBURG *Brit. J. Pharmacol.* 1955, **10,** 116
25. DALLEMAGNE and PHILIPPOT *Arch. int. Pharmacodyn.* 1951, **87,** 127
26. ROBERTS, RIKER and ROY *Fed. Proc.* 1953, **12,** 361
27. CAVALLITO, SCHLIEPAR and O'DELL *J. org. Chem.* 1954, **19,** 826
28. CAVALLITO, SORIA and HOPPE *J. Amer. chem. Soc.* 1950, **72,** 2661
29. LEHMAN *Proc. Soc. exp. Biol., N.Y.* 1935, **33,** 501
30. FOLKERS and KONIUSZY *J. Amer. chem. Soc.* 1939, **61,** 1232
31. FOLKERS and KONIUSZY *J. Amer. chem. Soc.* 1940, **62,** 436
32. FOLKERS and KONIUSZY *J. Amer. chem. Soc.* 1940, **62,** 1677
33. FOLKERS, KONIUSZY and SHAVEL *J. Amer. chem. Soc.* 1944, **66,** 1083
34. FOLKERS and MAJOR *J. Amer. chem. Soc.* 1937, **59,** 1580
35. UNNA, KNIAZUK and GRESLIN *J. Pharmacol.* 1944, **80,** 39
36. SALAMA and WRIGHT *Brit. J. Pharmacol.* 1951, **6,** 459
37. HANNA, MACMILLAN and McHUGO *Arch. int. Pharmacodyn.* 1960, **124,** 445
38. SANGSTER *J. chem. Educ.* 1960, **34,** 454
39. MONDON, *Angew. Chem.* 1958, **70,** 406
40. MONDON *Liebigs Ann.* 1959, **628,** 123
41. MONDON *Chem. Ber.* 1959, **92,** 1461, 1472
42. PRELOG, LANGEMANN, RODIG and TERNBAH *Helv. chim. acta* 1959, **42,** 1301
43. MONDON and HANSEN *Tetrahedron Letters* 1960, No. 14, 5
44. NOWACKI, BÜRKI, BONSAM and JAGGI *Chimia* 1956, **10,** 254
45. BOEKELHEIDE, MÜLLER, JACK, GROSSNICKLE and CHANG *J. Amer. chem. Soc.* 1959, **81,** 3955
46. MÜLLER, GROSSNICKLE and BOEKELHEIDE *J. Amer. chem. Soc.* 1959, **81,** 3939
47. BRODIE and HOGBEN *J. Pharm., Lond.* 1957, **9,** 345
48. GALLAGHER and KOCH *Nature, Lond.* 1959, **183,** 1124
49. GRAHAM and JAMES *J. med. pharm. Chem.* 1961, **3,** 489
50. URAKAWA, HAYAMA, DEGUCHI and OHKUBO *Japan J. vet. Sci.* 1958, **20,** 187
51. URAKAWA, HAYAMA, DEGUCHI and OHKUBO *Japan J. Pharmacol.* 1959, **9,** 41
52. URAKAWA, DEGUCHI and OHKUBO *Japan. J. Pharmacol.* 1960, **9,** 130
53. URAKAWA, DEGUCHI and OHKUBO *Japan. J. pharmacol.* 1960, **10,** 1
54. URAKAWA, NARAHASHI, DEGUCHI and OHKUBO *Amer. J. Physiol.* 1960, **198,** 939
55. OTSUKA and ENDO *J. Pharmacol.* 1960, **128,** 273
56. BRAZIL and CORRADO *J. Pharmacol.* 1957, **120,** 452
57. CORRADO, RAMOS and ESCOBAR *Arch. int. Pharmacodyn.* 1959, **121,** 380
58. JINDAL and DESHPANDA *Brit. J. Pharmacol.* 1960, **15,** 506
59. BEZZI and GESSA *Nature, Lond.* 1959, **184,** Suppl. No. 12, 905
60. PITTINGER and LONG *Antibiot. and Chemother.* 1958, **8,** 198
61. PITTINGER, LONG and MILLER *Curr. Res. Anesth.* 1958, **37,** 276
62. FULCHIERO, TURCOTTE and MARTIN *Proc. Soc. exp. Biol., N.Y.* 1958, **99,** 537
63. FREYBURGER, WALLACH, SMUTS and VAN DEN BRINK *Antibiot. Med. clin. Ther.* 1959, **6,** 457
64. HOLMES, JENDEN and TAYLOR *Nature, Lond.* 1947, **159,** 86
65. PAULING *The Nature of the Chemical Bond* 3rd Edn. Oxford University Press, London, 1960
66. KÜLZ *Pflüg. Arch. ges. Physiol.* 1922, **195,** 623
67. DALLEMAGNE and PHILIPOTT *Arch. int. Pharmacodyn.* 1951, **87,** 127
68. THOMAS and STARMER *J. Pharm., Lond.* 1961, **13,** 752
69. CAREY, EDWARDS, LEWIS and STENLAKE *J. Pharm., Lond.* 1959, **11,** 70T
70. ZALKIN *Acta. cryst.* 1957, **10,** 557
71. WAIT and POWELL *J. chem. Soc.* 1958, 1872
72. STOVNER *Acta physiol. scand.* 1957, **40,** 275, 285; 1957, **41,** 370; 1958, **42,** 268

73. KOKETSU *Amer. J. Physiol.* 1958, **193,** 213
74. BOWMAN and RAND *Lancet* 1961, **1,** 480
75. WASER *Curare and Curare-like Agents* (Ed. Bovet, Bovet-Nitti and Marini-Bettôlo): Elsevier, London, 1959, p. 227
76. CRAIG *The Alkaloids* Vol. V. (Ed. Manske): Academic Press, New York, 1955, p. 265
77. HILDEBRANDT *Arch. exp. Path. Pharmak.* 1905, **53,** 76
78. SCHOLTZ and PAWLICKI *Ber. Dtsch. chem. Ges.* 1905, **38,** 1289
79. BÄCHLI VAMVACAS, SCHMID and KARRER *Helv. chim. acta* 1957, **40,** 1167
80. BOEKELHILDE and AINSWORTH *J. Amer. chem. Soc.* 1956, **72,** 2132
81. SCHLITTLER and HOHL *Helv. chim. acta* 1952, **35,** 29
82. ARNOLD, BERLAGE, BERNAUER, SCHMID and KARRER *Helv. chim. acta* 1958, **41,** 1505
83. WIELAND and MERZ *Chem. Ber.* 1952, **85,** 731
84. ASMIS, BÄCHLI, GIESBRECHT, KEBRLE, SCHMID and KARRER *Helv. chim. acta* 1954, **37,** 1968
85. KEBRLE, SCHMID, WASER and KARRER *Helv. chim. acta* 1953, **36,** 102
86. ASMIS, WASER, SCHMID and KARRER *Helv. chim. acta* 1955, **38,** 1661
87. KARRER and WASER *Helv. chim. acta* 1949, **32,** 409
88. DWYER, GYARFAS, WRIGHT and SHULMAN *Nature, Lond.* 1957, **179,** 425
89. DUBOIS *Arch. Zool. exp. gen.* 1909, **2,** 471
90. VINCENT and JULLIEN *C.R. Soc. Biol., Paris* 1938, **127,** 1506
91. ERSPAMER *Experientia* 1948, **4,** 226
92. ERSPAMER and BENATI *Biochem. Z.* 1953, **324,** 66
93. ERSPAMER and BENATI *Science* 1953, **117,** 161
94. PASINI, VERCELLONE and ERSPAMER *Liebigs Ann.* 1952, **578,** 6
95. ERSPAMER and GLÄSSER *Brit. J. Pharmacol.* 1957, **12,** 176
96. QUILLIAM *Brit. J. Pharmacol.* 1957, **12,** 320
97. GRELIS and TABACHNICK *Brit. J. Pharmacol.* 1957, **12,** 320
98. BLASI and LEONE *Minerva anestesiol.* 1955, **21,** 137
99. KEYL, MICHAELSON and WHITTAKER *J. Physiol.* 1957, **139,** 434
100. WHITTAKER *Biochem. J.* 1957, **66,** 35P
101. HOLMSTEDT and WHITTAKER *Brit. J. Pharmacol.* 1958, **13,** 308
102. WHITTAKER *Biochem. Pharmacol.* 1958, **1,** 342
103. KURIAKI and WADA *Japan J. Pharmacol.* 1957, **7,** 35
104. WADA *Nippon Yakurigaku Zasshi* 1957, **53,** 429
105. KUGA *Nippon Yakurigaku Zasshi* 1958, **54,** 1257
106. MASHKOVSKII and AVAKYAN *Farmakol. i. Toksikol.* 1959, **22,** 506
107. HOLMSTEDT, LARSSON and SUNDWALL *Biochem. Pharmacol.* 1960, **3,** 155
107a. HAZARD, CHEYMOL, CHABRIER, SEKERA and ECHE-FIALAIRE *Bull. Soc. chim. Fr.* 1961, 2087
107b. KOPACOVA and VRBRA *Čsl. Farm* 1961, **10,** 133
108. STANDAERT and FRIESS *J. Pharmacol.* 1960, **128,** 55
109. SOYKA and GYERMEK *J. med. pharm. Chem.* 1960, **2,** 361
110. OHASHI *Kanazawa Daigaku Yakugakuba Kenyu Nempo* 1960, **10,** 23
111. DONAHOE, SEIWALD, NEUMANN and KIMURA *J. org. Chem.* 1957, **22,** 68
112. DONAHOE, SEIWALD, NEUMANN and KIMURA *J. med. pharm. Chem.* 1961, **3,** 611
113. CHAKRAVARTY and JONES *J. Amer. pharm. Ass., Sci. Ed.* 1959, **48,** 607
114. GJONE *Acta pharm. tox., Kbh.* 1955, **11,** 55
115. CHEYMOL, BOURILLET, LEVASSORT and KERP *Arch. int. Pharmacodyn.* 1957, **111,** 36
115a. LOCK *J. Pharm., Lond.* 1961, **13,** 268
116. PALMA and HITCHCOCK *Anesthesiology* 1958, **19,** 762
117. BICK and CLEZY *J. chem. Soc.* 1953, 3893

118. HOLIDAY and VARNEY, quoted by Wintersteiner *Curare and Curare-like Agents* (Ed. Bovet, Bovet-Nitti and Marini-Bettôlo): Elsevier, London, 1959 p. 160
119. KING *Nature, Lond.* 1946, **158,** 515; *J. chem. Soc.* 1947, 936
120. BICK, HARLEY-MASON, SHEPPARD and VERNENGO *J. chem. Soc.* 1961, 1896
121. DUTCHER *J. Amer. chem. Soc.* 1952, **74,** 2221
121a. HELLMANN and ELSER *Liebigs Ann.* 1961, **639,** 77
121b. TOLKACHEV, VORONIN and PREOBRAZHENSKII *J. gen. Chem. U.S.S.R.* 1959, **29,** 1192
122. MARSH, SLEETH and TUCKER *J. Pharmacol.* 1948, **93,** 109
123. CAVALLITO *Curare and Curare-like Agents* (Ed. Bovet, Bovet-Nitti and Marini-Bettôlo): Elsevier, London, 1959, p. 292
124. KALOW *J. Pharmacol.* 1954, **110,** 433
125. COLLIER and TAYLOR *Nature, Lond.* 1949, **164,** 491; 1950, **165,** 602
126. STOELTING, GRAF and VIEIRAI *Proc. Soc. exp. Biol., N.Y.* 1948, **69,** 565
127. STOELTING, GRAF and VIEIRAI *Curr. Res. Anesth.* 1949, **28,** 130
128. DAVIS and KARP *Curr. Res. Anesth.* 1951, **30,** 47
129. HESSELSCHWERDT, RUSHIDA and CULLEN *Anesthesiology* 1951, **12,** 14
130. UNNA, PELIKAN, MACFARLANE, CAZORT, SADOVE, NELSON and DRUCKER *J. Pharmacol.* 1950, **98,** 318
131. PELIKAN, UNNA, MACFARLANE, CAZORT, SADOVE and NELSON *J. Pharmacol.* 1950, **99,** 215
132. DETTBARN *Nature, Lond.* 1960, **186,** 891
133. ROSENBERG and EHRENPREIS *Nature, Lond.* 1961, **190,** 729; *Biochem. Pharmacol.,* 1961, **8,** 192
134. EHRENPREIS *Biochim. Biophys. Acta* 1960, **44,** 561
135. ROSENBERG and HIGMAN *Biochim. Biophys. Acta* cited by Ehrenpreis[134]
136. CULLEN *Anesthesiology* 1944, **5,** 166
137. PICK and RICHARDS *J. Pharmacol.* 1947, **90,** 1
138. ARROWOOD *Anesthesiology* 1951, **12,** 753
139. SECKER *Acta pharm. tox., Kbh.* 1951, **7,** 83
140. FOLDES, MACHAJ, HUNT, McNALL and CARBERRY *J. Amer. med. Assoc.* 1952, **150,** 1559
141. DUNDEE, GREY and RIDING *Brit. J. Anaesth.* 1954, **26,** 13
142. WATLAND, LONG, PITTINGER and CULLEN *Anesthesiology* 1957, **18,** 883
143. LEWIS and MUIR *personal communications*
144. NAESS *Acta physiol. scand.* 1949, **19,** 187
145. LANG, KIMURA and UNNA *Arch. int. Pharmacodyn.* 1951, **85,** 257
146. JOHNSTONE *Brit. J. Anaesth.* 1956, **28,** 392
147. KRAATZ, GLUCKMAN and SHIELDS *J. Pharmacol.* 1953, **107,** 437
148. HUSTON, MARTIN and DILLE *Arch. int. Pharmacodyn.* 1947, **74,** 46
149. FERRARI, GESSA and SANGIORGI *Nature, Lond.* 1959, **184,** Suppl. 16, 1235
150. CHEYMOL and BOURILLET *J. Physiol., Paris,* 1959, **51,** 433
151. DYRBERG and HOUGS *Acta pharm. tox. Kbh.* 1958, **14,** 138
152. SU and LEE *Brit. J. Pharmacol.* 1960, **15,** 88
153. MORPURGO and SPINELLI *R.C. Accad. Lincei* 1957, **23,** 460 (from *Chem. Abstr.* 1958, **52,** 1308lb)
154. VON PHILIPSBORN, SCHMID and KARRER *Helv. chim. acta* 1956, **39,** 913
155. BERNAUER, SCHMID and KARRER *Helv. chim. acta* 1958, **41,** 1408
156. BERNAUER, BERLAGE, VON PHILIPSBORN, SCHMID and KARRER *Helv. chim. acta* 1958, **41,** 2293
157. BERLAGE, BERNAUER, SCHMID and KARRER *Helv. chim. acta* 1959, **42,** 2650
158. BATTERSBY and HODSON *Proc. chem. Soc., Lond.* 1958, 287
159. BATTERSBY and HODSON *J. chem. Soc.* 1960, 736
160. ASMIS, SCHMID and KARRER *Helv. chim. acta* 1954, **37,** 1983

160a. VON PHILIPSBORN, ARNOLD, NAGYRARI, BERNAUER, SCHMID and KARRER Helv. chim. acta 1960, **43,** 141
161. BATTERSBY and HODSON, Quart. Rev. chem. Soc., Lond. 1960, **14,** 77
161a. BATTERSBY, HODSON and YEOWELL Proc. chem. Soc., Lond. 1962, 412
    BATTERSBY, YEOWELL, JACKMAN, SCHROEDER, HESSE, HILTEBRAND, VON PHILIPSBORN, SCHMID and KARRER Proc. chem. Soc. 1962, 413
162. WASER and HARBECK Anaesthesist 1959, **8,** 193
162a. FOLDES, WOLFRAM and SOHOLL Anaethesist 1961, **10,** 210
163. PATON and PERRY Brit. J. Pharmacol. 1951, **6,** 299
164. WASER Curare and Curare-like Agents (Ed. Bovet, Bovet-Nitti and Marini-Bettôlo): Elsevier, London, 1959, p. 219
165. JANOT, LAINÉ and GOUTAREL Ann. pharm. franc. 1960, **18,** 673
166. QUEVAUVILLER and LAINÉ Ann. pharm. franc. 1960, **18,** 678
166a. GOUTAREL Tetrahedron 1961, **14,** 126
166b. CAVALLINI, FERRARI, MONTEGAZZA and MASSARINI Farm. sci. e. tec. Pavia, 1951, **6,** 815
167. BARLOW and ING Nature, Lond. 1948, **161,** 718; Brit. J. Pharmacol. 1948, **2,** 298
168. PATON and ZAIMIS Nature, Lond. 1948, **161,** 718
169. GRAY and O'DELL Nature, Lond. 1958, **181,** 634
170. PATON Brit. J. Anaesth. 1956, **28,** 470
171. THESLEFF and UNNA J. Pharmacol. 1954, **111,** 99
172. ZAIMIS J. Physiol. 1953, **122,** 238
173. BARLOW, ROBERTS and REID J. Pharm., Lond. 1953, **5,** 35
174. BOVET, BOVET-NITTI, GUARINO, LONGO and MOROTTO R.C. Ist. sup. Sanit. 1949, **12,** 106
175. ARIENS and DE GROOT Arch. int. Pharmacodyn. 1957, **9,** 1004
176. FUSCO, PALAZZO, CHIAVARELLI and BOVET Gazz. chim. ital. 1949, **79,** 836
177. HUNT and DE TAVEAU Brit. med. J. 1906, **ii,** 1788
178. PHILLIPS J. Amer. chem. Soc. 1949, **71,** 3264
179. BRÜCKE, GINZEL, KLUPP, PFAFFENSCHLAGER and WERNER Wien klin. Wschr. 1951, **63,** 464
180. THESLEFF, Nord. méd. 1951, **46,** 1045
181. MAYRHOFER and HASSFURTHER Wien. klin. Wschr. 1951, **63,** 885
182. WHITTAKER and WIJESUNDERA Biochem. J. 1952, **52,** 475
183. TSUJI and FOLDES Fed. Proc., 1953 **12,** 321, 374
184. FOLDES Muscle Relaxants in Anesthesiology: Thomas, Springfield, Illinois, 1957, p. 52
185. CHURCHILL-DAVIDSON Brit. med. J. 1954, **i,** 74
186. HEGARTY Brit. J. Anaesth. 1956, **28,** 209
187. PATON Anesthesiology 1959, **20,** 453
188. THESLEFF Acta physiol. scand. 1952, **26,** 103
189. VALDONI R.C. Ist. sup. Sanit. 1949, **12,** 255
190. HALE, ENDERBY Brit. J. Anaesth. 1959, **31,** 530
190a. RIZZL Acta anaesthid. scand. 1961, **5,** 89
191. BÜCHI, GYI and WASER Arzneimitt.-Forsch. 1960, **10,** 699
191a. SMITH and RYAN J. org. Chem. 1961, **26,** 3856
192. FUSCO, PALAZZO, CHIAVARELLI and BOVET Gazz. chim. ital. 1958, **88,** 1293
193. ROSNATI Gazz. chim. ital. 1957, **87,** 215
194. BARSTAD, SKRAMSTAD and ÖKSNE Arch. int. Pharmacodyn. 1959, **121,** 395
195. SCOGNAMIGLIO Arch. ital. sci. Farmacol. 1959, **9,** 191
196. LEVIS, PREAT and DANBY Arch. int. Pharmacodyn. 1953, **93,** 46
197. ROSNATI, ANGELINI-KOTHNY and BOVET Gazz. chim. ital. 1958, **88,** 1293
198. FREY Proc. World Congr. Anaesth. (1955, Schevingen) 1956, 262
199. HUNTER Anaesthesist 1959, **8,** 82

200. ROSNATI *Gazz. chim. ital.* 1950, **80,** 663
201. VANDERHAEGHE *Nature, Lond.* 1951, **167,** 527
202. LESSER *J. Pharm., Lond.* 1961, **13,** 703
203. ROSNATI and ANGELINI-KOTHNY *Gazz. chim. ital.,* 1958, **88,** 1284
204. NAJER, CHABRIER, GIUDICELLI and DUCHEMIN *Ann. pharm. franç.* 1960, **18,** 126
205. CHEYMOL, GIUDICELLI, CHABRIER and NAJER *Arch. int. Pharmacodyn.* 1960, **125,** 121
206. CHEYMOL, GIUDICELLI, CHABRIER and NAJER *C.R. Acad. Sci., Paris* 1959, **248,** 1723
206a. KHARKEVECH and KRAVCHUK *Farmakol. i. Toksikol.* 1961, **24,** 318
207. RANDALL, GIULIANO, KAPPELL and ALLEN *J. Pharmacol.* 1952, **105,** 7
208. LÜTTRINGHAUS, KERP and PREUGSCHAS *Arzneimitt.-Forsch.* 1957, **7,** 222
209. PROTIVA and BOROUIČKA *Czech. Pat.* 88,309
210. VOTAVA and METYSŎVÁ-SRANKOVA *Physiol. Bohemoslov.* 1955, **8,** 431
211. MEDEŞAN and STOICA *Commun. acad. rep. populare Romîne, Inst. biochim., Studii cercetări biochim.* 1960, **3,** 417
212. HAZARD, CHEYMOL, CHABRIER, CORTEGGIANI and NICOLAS *Arch. int. Pharmacodyn.* 1950, **84,** 237; *Bull. Soc. chim. Fr.,* 1951, **18,** 209
213. BOISSIER, RATOUIS, DUMONT and PAGNY *C.R. Acad. Sci., Paris* 1960, **251,** 3114
214. HOPPE *Curr. Res. Anesth.* 1951, **30,** 262
215. HOPPE, FUNNELL and LAPE *J. Pharmacol.* 1955, **115,** 106
216. PHILIPPOT and DALLEMAGNE *Arch. int. Pharmacodyn.* 1954, **96,** 485
217. CAVALLITO, SORIA and HOPPE *J. Amer. chem. Soc.* 1950, **72,** 2661
218. HOPPE *J. Pharmacol.* 1950, **100,** 333
219. HOPPE *Ann. N.Y. Acad. Sci.* 1951, **54,** 395
220. FOLDES *Ann. N.Y. Acad Sci..* 1951, **54,** 503
221. DUNDEE, GRAY and REES *Anaesthesia* 1952, **7,** 134
222. HUNTER *Anaesthesia* 1952, **7,** 145
223. GORDON *Anesthesiology* 1953, **14,** 73
224. BOWMAN *Brit. J. Pharmacol.* 1958, **13,** 521
225. CHEYMOL *Bull. Acad. nat. Méd.* 1953, **137,** 83
226. CHEYMOL, DELABY, CHABRIER, NAJER, and BOURILLET *Arch. int. Pharmacodyn.* 1954, **98,** 161
227. CHEYMOL, DELABY, NAJER and GRAY *C.R. Acad. Sci., Paris* 1952, **235,** 1711
228. DELABY, CHABRIER and NAJER *Bull. Soc. chim. Fr.* 1955, 1616
229. DELABY, CHABRIER and NAJER *Bull. Soc. chim. Fr.* 1956, 212
230. KLUPP, KRAUP, STORMAN and STUMPF *Arch. int. Pharmacodyn.* 1953, **96,** 161
231. KLUPP and KRAUP *Arch. int. Pharmacodyn.* 1954, **98,** 340
232. NAJER, CHABRIER and DELABY *Bull. Soc. chim. Fr.* 1956, 689
233. CHEYMOL, CHABRIER, GIUDICELLI, NAJER and BOURILLET *C.R. Acad. Sci., Paris* 1957, **245,** 2560
234. BRÜCKE and REIS *Wien. med. Wschr.* 1954, **104,** 283
235. HOLZER, WALTNER and WILLOMITZER *Wien. med. Wschr.* 1954, **104,** 637
236. REIS *Anaesthesist* 1955, **4,** 10
237. MAYRHOFER, REMES and SCHUSTER *Anaesthesist* 1955, **4,** 174
238. MEISSNER *Anaesthesist* 1957, **6,** 362
239. BERGMAN *Anaesthesist* 1958, **7,** 137
240. WIEMERS and OBERBECK *Brit. J. Anaesth.* 1960, **32,** 607
241. FOLDES, WOLFSON, TORRES-KAY and MONTE *Anesthesiology* 1959, **20,** 767
242. COLLIER and TAYLOR *Nature, Lond.* 1949, **164,** 491
243. BARLOW, ROBERTS and REID *J. Pharm., Lond.* 1953, **5,** 35
244. ROSSUM and ARIËNS *Arch. int. Pharmacodyn.* 1959, **118,** 393
245. TAYLOR *J. chem. Soc.* 1951, 1150
246. TAYLOR and COLLIER *Nature, Lond.* 1950, **165,** 603

247. COLLIER *Brit. J. Pharmacol.* 1952, **7**, 392
248. TAYLOR and COLLIER *Nature, Lond.* 1951, **167**, 692
249. BODMAN, MORTON and WYLIE *Lancet* 1952, **ii**, 517
250. BINNING *Anaesthesia* 1953, **8**, 268
251. LEDERMAN *Sinai Hosp. J.* 1953, **2**, 25
252. DUNDEE, GRAY and RIDING *Brit. J. Anaesth.* 1954, **26**, 13
253. WYANT and SADOVE *Curr. Res. Anesth.* 1954, **33**, 178
254. HUNTER *Brit. J. Anaesth.* 1955, **27**, 73
255. COLLIER and MACAULEY *Brit. J. Pharmacol.* 1952, **7**, 409
256. KIMURA, UNNA and PFEIFFER *J. Pharmacol.* 1949, **95**, 149
257. KIMURA and UNNA *J. Pharmacol.* 1950, **98**, 286
258. HAINING, JOHNSON and SMITH *Nature, Lond.* 1959, **183**, 542
259. HAINING, JOHNSON and SMITH *Brit. J. Pharmacol.* 1960, **15**, 71
260. MORIN *C.R. Soc. Biol. Paris* 1956, **150**, 164
261. MORIN *C.R. Soc. Biol. Paris* 1958, **152**, 273
262. MORIN *Thérapie* 1958, **13**, 713
263. COLLIER, GLADYCH, MACAULEY and TAYLOR *Nature, Lond.* 1959, **183**, 542
263a. BRITTAIN, COLLIER and D'ARCY *Brit. J. Pharmacol.* 1961, **17**, 116
    COLLIER, GLADYCH, MACAULEY and TAYLOR *Atti XI Congresso Societa Italiana di Anaestesiologia* 1958, 162
    COLLIER, GLADYCH, MACAULEY and TAYLOR *Nature, Lond.* 1958, **182**, 1424
264. NÁDOR and GYERMEK *Acta. Chim. Acad. Sci. Hung.* 1952, **2**, 369
265. KUZOVKOV, MASHKOVSKĬ, DANILOVA and MEN'SHIKOV *Doklady Akad. Nauk. U.S.S.R.* 1955, **103**, 251
266. MEN'SHIKOV, DANILOVA, KUZOVKOV and GARINA *Russ. Pat.* 1959, 118,205 (*Chem. Abstr.* 1959, **53**, 19313b)
267. HAZARD, CHEYMOL, CHABRIER, SEKERA and BOURILLET *C.R. Acad. Sci., Paris* 1960, **250**, 3533
268. BIEL *U.S. Pat.* 2,830,050, 1958
269. PODREBARAC and McEWAN *J. org. Chem.* 1961, **26**, 1165
270. MASHKOVSKII and MEDVEDEV *Farmakol. i. Toksikol.* 1960, **23**, 493
271. NIHITSKAYA, USOVSKAYA and RUBTSOV *Zhur. Obscheĭ. Khim.* 1960, **30**, 3306
272. RUBTSOV, MASHKOVSKII, NIKITSKAYA, MEDVEDEV and UROVSKAYA *J. med. pharm. Chem.* 1961. **3**, 441
273. KOMISSAROV *Farmakol. i. Toksikol.* 1960, **23**, 238
274. FISHER and KESLING *J. Amer. pharm. Assoc. Sci. Ed.* 1958, **47**, 438
275. WIEN and MASON *Brit. J. Pharmacol.* 1951, **6**, 611
276. MASON and WIEN *Brit. J. Pharmacol.* 1955. **10**, 124
277. PRAPAS *U.S. Pat.* 2, 946, 789
278. BOVET, COURVOISIER, DUCROT and HORCLOIS *Arch. int. Pharmacodyn.* 1949, **80**, 137
279. ECKFELD *J. Pharmacol.* 1959, **126**, 21
280. HAZARD, CHEYMOL, CHABRIER and DROUIN *J. Physiol., Paris* 1957, **49**, 198
281. CAVALLITO, GRAY and SPINNER *J. Amer. chem. Soc.* 1954. **76**, 1862
282. GRAY, SPINNER and CAVALLITO *J. Amer. chem. Soc.* 1954, **76**, 2792
283. NÁDOR and ISSEKUTZ *Acta Chim. Acad. Sci. Hung.* 1953, **3**, 71
284. MACRI *Proc. Soc. exp. Biol. N.Y.* 1954, **85**, 603
285. CORDARO and ARROWOOD *Curr. Res. Anesth.* 1955, **34**, 112
286. ARROWOOD and KAPLAN *Curr. Res. Anesth.* 1956. **35**, 412
287. DELLA BELLA, ROGNONI and GOPAL *J. Pharm., Lond.* 1961, **13**, 93
288. FOLDES, MOLLOY, ZSIGMOND and ZWARTZ *J. Pharmacol.* 1960, **129**, 400
289. BOVET, DEPIERRE and DE LESTRANGE *C.R. Acad. Sci., Paris* 1947, **225**, 74
290. RIKER and WESCOE *Ann. N.Y. Acad. Sci.* 1951, **54**, 373
291. SIMONART *J. Pharmacol.* 1914, **6**, 147

292. BOVET, COURVOISIER, DUCROT and HORCLOIS *C.R. Acad. Sci., Paris* 1946, **223,** 597
293. BÜLBRING and DEPIERRE *Brit. J. Pharmacol.* 1949, **4,** 22
294. MUSHIN, WIEN, MASON and LANGSTON *Lancet* 1949, **i,** 726
295. KENSLER, ZIRKLE, MATALLANA and CONDOURIS *J. Pharmacol.* 1954, **112,** 210
296. CARISSIMI, RAVENNA, MILLA, GRUMELLI and GRASSO *Farmaco* 1958, **13,** 231
297. CHAGAS *Curare and Curare-like Agents* (Ed. Bovet, Bovet-Nitti and Marini-Bettôlo): Elsevier, London, 1959, p. 252
298. BOVET-NITTI *Curare and Curare-like Agents* (Ed Bovet, Bovet-Nitti and Marini-Bettôlo): Elsevier, London, 1959, p. 232
299. AHMAD and LEWIS *J. Pharm., Lond.* 1961, **13,** 383
300. EDWARDS, LEWIS, STENLAKE and ZOHA *J. Pharm., Lond.* 1957, **9,** 1004
301. EDWARDS, LEWIS, STENLAKE and ZOHA *J. Pharm., Lond.* 1958, **10,** 106 *T*
302. EDWARDS, LEWIS, STENLAKE and ZOHA *J. Pharm., Lond.* 1958, **10,** 122 *T*
303. PROTIVA and PLIML *Coll. Czech. chem. Comm.* 1953, **18,** 836
304. VANĚČEK and VOTAVA *Physiol. Bohemsloven* 1955, **4,** 220
305. EDWARDS, LEWIS, McPHAIL, MUIR and STENLAKE *J. Pharm., Lond.* 1960, **12,** 137 *T*
306. LEWIS, McPHAIL, MUIR and STENLAKE *J. Pharm., Lond.* 1961, **13,** 543
307. FAKSTORP and PEDERSON *Acta pharm. tox., Kbh.* 1954, **10,** 7
308. FAKSTORP and PEDERSON *Acta pharm. tox., Kbh.* 1957, **13,** 359
309. FAKSTORP and PEDERSON *Acta pharm. tox., Kbh.* 1958, **14,** 148
310. CAREY, LEWIS, STENLAKE and WILLIAMS *J. Pharm., Lond.* 1961, **13,** 103 *T*
311. STENLAKE and WILLIAMS *unpublished work*
312. SCHUELER and KEASLING *J. Amer. pharm. Assoc., Sci. Ed.* 1956, **45,** 292
313. BARLOW *Steric Aspects of Drug Action, Biochem. Soc. Symposium*, No. 19, 1960, 46
314. DIXON and WEBB *Enzymes:* Longmans Green, London, 1958, p. 486

# 2

# THE CHEMOTHERAPY OF TRYPANOSOMIASIS

## L. P. WALLS

### INTRODUCTION

TRYPANOSOMAL infections occur in many parts of the world, but by far their most important consequences are for Africa, where they make a serious impact on her economy and the way of life of her people. In spite of the great advances in chemotherapy, in the use of insecticides, and in knowledge of the disease and its vectors, trypanosomiasis in its various forms still dominates much of the continent. The trypanosomes are protozoa; the single-celled nucleated organism moving in the body fluids of the infected host by means of undulations of an extension of the cell known as the flagellum. In all but one form of trypanosomiasis the parasites are transferred from host to host by an insect vector. The story of the development of trypanocides is a classic of chemotherapy.

It began over a hundred years ago with the recognition by David Livingstone[1] that the disease of cattle and draught animals, which as much as anything else made exploration of Africa so hazardous, was associated with the bite of the tsetse fly. Livingstone attributed the disease to the inoculation of a poison by the fly—the discovery of the trypanosome was to wait over 40 years—and, impressed by the debilitating nature of the disease, he and Braid[2] at about the same time proposed medication with inorganic arsenic on account of its tonic effect. The treatment, if not curative, proved to be beneficial and thus early was the tradition established that advances in chemotherapy are often stimulated by false premises. The discovery of the trypanosome in 1895 revealed the true nature of the disease, and indicated that arsenic was probably acting not as a tonic but as a killer of the causative parasites. The notion of chemotherapy for trypanosomiasis was thus conceived at a time made favourable by the awakening knowledge of microbiology and the rapid advances in organic chemistry. A most important discovery by Laveran and Mesnil in 1902[3] was that some trypanosome species could be routinely passaged in small laboratory animals that usually developed a fatal disease. It is still true today that the successful outcome of an investigation in chemotherapy depends largely on the existence of some such conditions. This is not to decry the importance of *in vitro* tests and the recent methods of tissue culture: these are important in showing anti-parasite properties in a drug; but those factors relating to the host, such as toxicity, metabolism, distribution and concentration of the drug, are so complex that only experiments in animals really decide whether a drug is worthy of trial. Soon after Laveran and Mesnil's significant discovery, Thomas[4] demonstrated, by means of experiments in mice, that a synthetic organic arsenical with the trade name Atoxyl had marked advances over inorganic arsenical preparations; it was less toxic but capable of eliminating the parasites. Thus the way was open for the type of chemotherapeutic investigation that is commonplace today; namely, the synthesis of organic compounds and their testing against the infecting parasite in small animals. This situation was exploited by Ehrlich and his collaborators in work that led to the synthesis of several organic arsenicals active in trypanosome and other infections. The discovery of the Bart reaction for the preparation of such compounds from primary aromatic amines ensured that Thomas's discovery was to be fully exploited.

## THE CAUSATIVE ORGANISMS

The genus *Trypanosoma* comprises several pathogenic species which are to a large extent host-specific, and also to some extent vector- and drug-specific. Morphologically the species can be divided into three main groups: the monomorphic group (*e.g.*, *Trypanosoma congolense*, *T. vivax*); the polymorphic group (so-called because the parasite assumes different sizes and shapes) which consists of the closely-related *T. gambiense*, *T. rhodesiense* and *T. brucei*, with the *T. evansi* sub-group; and *T. cruzi*, in which polymorphism takes an extreme form. In *T. cruzi* not only are various flagellated trypanosomal forms to be found, but also rounded, leishmanial forms, indistinguishable from protozoa of the related genus *Leishmania*. For this reason some taxonomists have placed *T. cruzi* in a new genus, and it is of considerable interest that its peculiar morphological lability is associated with marked differences from other species in its host relationships and in its susceptibility to drugs. In marked contrast to all other trypanosome infections, a satisfactory drug treatment for *T. cruzi* infections has yet to be discovered.

The monomorphic trypanosomes, *T. congolense* and *T. vivax*, infect cattle, the related *T. simiae* infects pigs, whereas the polymorphic *T. gambiense* and *T. rhodesiense* infect man, and the closely-related *T. brucei* is responsible for the disease of horses known to the explorers as nagana. These trypanosomes and the diseases they cause are confined to Africa. They are usually cyclically transmitted by tsetse flies, although the diseases of cattle are also transmitted mechanically both by tsetse and other flies. The polymorphic trypanosomes of the *T. evansi* sub-group are much more widely distributed and are transmitted by various flies. *T. equiperdum*, uniquely, causes a venereally-transmitted infection of horses and occurs in many parts of the world. *T. cruzi* occurs not in Africa but in Central and South America and is responsible for serious and widespread disease in man. Transmission is by reduviid bugs and may be caused by contamination with infected faeces, rather than by inoculation.

## TESTING DRUGS FOR TRYPANOCIDAL PROPERTIES

All the trypanosome species mentioned, with the exception of *T. simiae* and *T. vivax*, can be passaged in small laboratory animals, causing blood infections (trypanosomes inhabit the plasma not the erythrocytes as in malaria) which may be readily detected and assessed by microscopic examination of blood smears. Virulent strains can be obtained, except for *T. cruzi*, which kill the infected animal within some six days, offering an ideal situation for the testing of synthetic compounds for trypanocidal properties. The situation is indeed much more favourable than with malaria, where the parasites responsible for the disease in man cannot be adapted to small animals, and chemotherapeutic study is done perforce on related species.

In a typical experiment with *T. brucei* or *T. rhodesiense*, groups of 5 or 10 mice are inoculated intraperitoneally, each with a suspension of 0·5 ml of infected blood in glucose–saline containing say 12,000 trypanosomes per $\mu$l. Mice, showing trypanosomes in the peripheral blood on the following day, are injected subcutaneously with a solution or suspension in distilled water of the drug under test, at doses approaching the maximum tolerated. Further injections may be made on consecutive days if desired. The peripheral blood is then examined daily for trypanosomes for two or three weeks. For *T. congolense* a similar procedure is followed, but infected blood with 1000 trypanosomes per $\mu$l is used, and mice showing trypanosomes in the peripheral blood 2 to 5 days later are injected with the drug. Chemotherapeutic activity in the compound tested is signalled by a prolongation of the life of the mice compared with the untreated controls. Active compounds are then assayed in mice in more detail, usually alongside mice treated with a drug of established value. Graded doses are given and a table is constructed showing the number of mice surviving each day until the end of the experiment[5]. A further table shows the number of mice cleared during the test and the number clear on the last day, thus showing the likelihood of relapse[6]. A plot of the group expectations of life against the logarithm of the doses, enables the relative activities of the drugs to be assessed[7]. In addition to the species already named, *T. equiperdum* is frequently used in laboratory investigations.

This method gives satisfactory results with most of the trypanosomes responsible for diseases of man or of his domestic animals, and indicates whether a drug is worthy of consideration for clinical trial. It is desirable, however, that further experiments in larger animals, rabbits or even monkeys, be prosecuted, and chronic toxicity investigated before a drug is committed to trial in man.

This straightforward method of investigation is unfortunately not available for three important pathogenic trypanosome species. The chemotherapeutic investigation of *T. cruzi* infections is usually carried out in a somewhat different manner, which will be dealt with later. *T. vivax*, an important species infecting domestic animals, especially in West Africa, and *T. simiae*, the causative agent of a disease of pigs which is largely responsible for preventing the establishment of a valuable pig industry in Nigeria, have not yet been satisfactorily transmitted in small animals. The importance of *T. vivax* has led investigators to consider the question of host specificity which is such a feature of protozoal infections, in malaria as well as in trypanosomiasis. Working on the assumption that the blood of susceptible species contains a substance or substances (absent from the blood of immune species) essential to the multiplication of the trypanosomes, Desowitz[8] found that *T. vivax* may be established in rats if various constituents of bovine blood (albumin, $\gamma$-globulin and fibrinogen) are first injected. The degree of parasitaemia depends on the amount of these fractions injected, but the satisfactory investigation of potential drugs with this trypanosome has not yet been realized. *T. congolense* and *T. vivax* often occur together in cattle and, therefore, it is desirable to use a drug to which both are susceptible. Fortunately, drugs are frequently active to a greater or lesser extent against both organisms. *T. simiae* presents a similar, perhaps more difficult, problem because, although it belongs to the *T. congolense* group, laboratory results with other species do not clearly indicate the likelihood of activity against *T. simiae*. An infection may be established in rabbits but it is variable and unsuitable for the testing of drugs; in some animals the disease is acute, with early deaths, in some, chronic, with delayed deaths, and in others, slight and self-cured. A more consistent infection, which is suitable for chemotherapeutic trials, can be established in splenectomized rabbits, but cheapness and convenience can hardly be claimed for the method[9].

## HUMAN TRYPANOSOMIASIS IN AFRICA

Trypanosomiasis in man in Africa is confined to the tropical and sub-tropical parts of the continent. It is less important in many respects than the disease of domestic animals, because even under epidemic conditions only a small proportion of the human inhabitants is infected[10]; a circumstance due probably to the absence, in the wild fauna, of a substantial reservoir of trypanosomes liable to infect man. Moreover, man can move away from locations where the fly has become dangerous, and his ordinary agricultural and domestic pursuits involve the clearing of ground, with consequential driving away of the fly. The incidence of the disease varies considerably from year to year and since its spread is almost certainly from man to man through the fly intermediary, outbreaks in a given area can usually be traced to the passage of infected migrants. The trypanosome species that cause the disease are transmitted by the tsetse fly and occur only in Africa, the disease being much more important in the West than in the East. *T. gambiense* is widespread between latitudes 15° N and 15° S on the West Coast, and between latitudes 10° N and 10° S on the East Coast, mainly along rivers and on the shores of the great lakes. The chief vector is the riverine tsetse, *Glossina palpalis*. In its initial stages the most striking feature of the disease is the enlargment of the lymphatic glands and spleen, but soon the secondary stage, involvement of the central nervous system, intervenes, leading to a lethargic condition which has given the disease its well-known name 'sleeping sickness.' *T. rhodesiense* has a more limited distribution, mainly in districts round Lake Nyanza, the S.E. corner of Tanganyika and the N.E. parts of Mozambique. The chief vector here is the widely distributed *G. morsitans*. The disease it causes is much more serious than that caused by *T. gambiense*, and is more likely to have an early fatal outcome. It is less susceptible to drug treatment and the discovery of *T. rhodesiense* in new localities is a cause of present concern[11].

A range of synthetic drugs is available which readily cures early human trypanosomiasis; the real problem of treatment is posed by the late cases, true sleeping sickness, in which the central nervous system is affected. The *sine qua non* condition for a successful drug is that it shall penetrate the blood-brain barrier and continue to exert its trypanocidal action there[12]. Some clue to its effectiveness may be gauged by investigating the trypanocidal action of the cerebro-spinal fluid of the patient; but even then it is doubtful whether a complete indication is given of the effectiveness of a drug in sleeping sickness[13]. Lourie examined various drugs for their ability to penetrate the barrier and concluded that, in general, acidic substances have this ability, provided they are not of a colloidal nature, whereas basic substances have not[14].

## TRYPANOCIDES FOR HUMAN USE

### Organic Arsenical Compounds

Atoxyl (I), the first organic arsenical used in medicine, was still in use in 1945 in spite of the enormous amount of synthetic work that has been devoted to this topic; no doubt cost had been an important consideration.

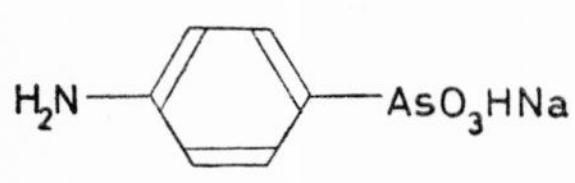

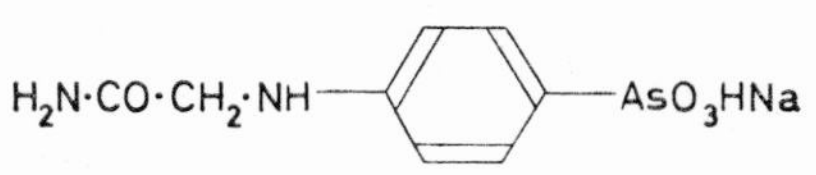

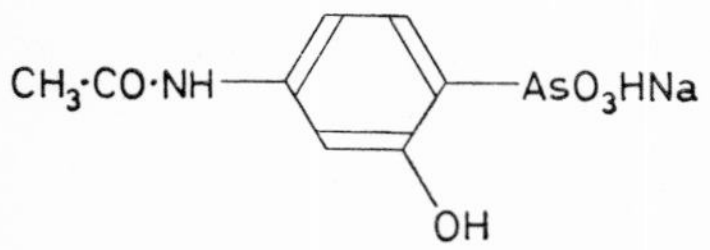

All organic arsenicals carry the risk of toxicity, the most serious being atrophy of the optic nerve. Therefore, later work has been concerned to discover compounds not only of greater activity but also of lower toxicity and with the ability to pass the blood-brain barrier. The discovery of tryparsamide (II) in 1919[15] represented a considerable advance, and this drug has been used for the treatment of thousands of patients. It is effective for the treatment of secondary T. gambiense disease, but has the great drawback of unpredictable toxicity. The ability of tryparsamide and related compounds to pass the blood-brain barrier was long regarded as a property peculiar to the quinquevalent arsenic compounds within the group of organic arsenicals, but this notion has not been substantiated by more recent work.

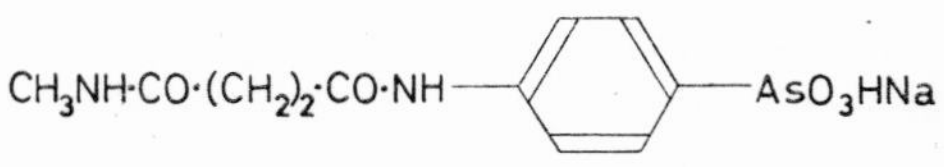

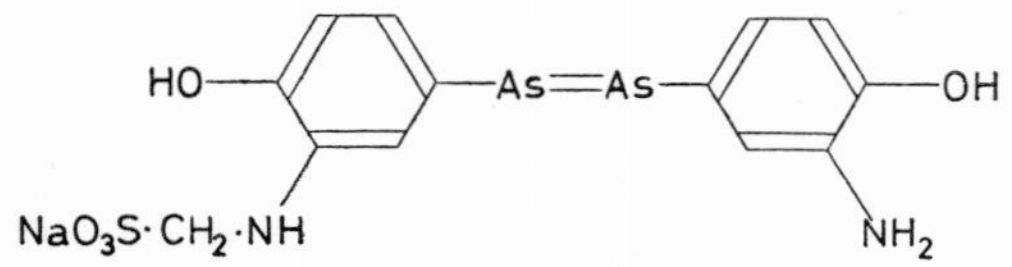

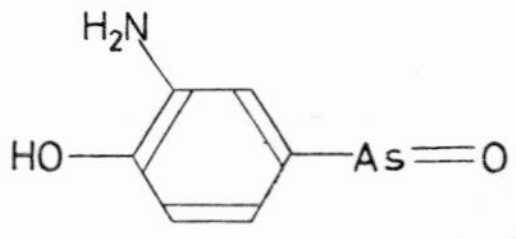

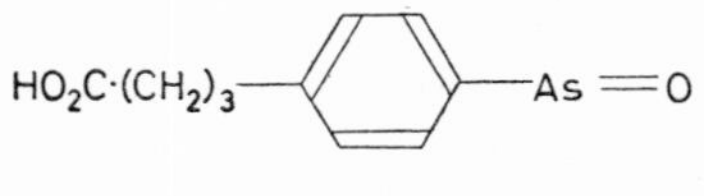

The clinical success scored by tryparsamide led to further synthetic work on organic arsenicals and more recently on organic antimonials, some of which have shown great promise in laboratory infections. The prototype molecule (*I*) has been variously modified by substitution in the benzene ring, by replacement or modification of the amino-group with a view to eliminating its basic character, and by modification of the arsonic acid radical. For example, substitution in the benzene ring and acylation of the amino-group afforded Orsanine or Fourneau 270 (*III*), preferred by French workers to tryparsamide. Neocryl (*IV*) was the result of more complex modification of the amino-group[16], and was at first thought to be less liable than tryparsamide to affect the optic nerve, but clinical trial demonstrated its ineffectiveness in the treatment of the late disease.

The idea of modification of the arsonic acid radical raises the question of the mode of action of these compounds. In spite of the clinical efficacy of tryparsamide it is, like other arsonic acids, inactive *in vitro*, and must be assumed, as postulated by Ehrlich for similar compounds, to be reduced after passage into the brain to an active tervalent compound, presumably the corresponding arsenoso-compound[17]. The tervalent arseno-compounds like neoarsphenamine (*V*), so long used for the treatment of syphilis, may have deserved more thorough trial in trypanosomiasis, but it is now considered that they also are inactive and require first to be oxidized *in vivo* to the active form, again presumably the arsenoso-compounds[18]. The evidence pointed therefore to the latter, hitherto dismissed as too toxic, as the most promising of the organic arsenicals and recent work has concentrated on them and substances related to them. Thus oxophenarsine (Mapharsen, Mapharside, *VI*) which is derived from neoarsphenamine, is effective in the treatment of trypanosomiasis as well as of syphilis. From a detailed study of the biological activity of the arsenosobenzenes has emerged the clinically valuable drug, Butarsen (*VII*)[19]. Substitution of arsenosobenzene with acidic groups usually results in compounds of low activity but Butarsen is the exception[20]. It appears to be less toxic than other arsenical drugs, is curative after relatively few injections and, most important, is active against trypanosome species resistant to other arsenicals; but it is ineffective in the late disease[21].

## Arsenicals with triazinyl and pyrimidinyl rings

The most noteworthy advance in the treatment of human trypanosomiasis since the discovery of tryparsamide is due to Friedheim, who replaced the amino-group of *p*-aminobenzenearsonic acid with a melamine radical[22]. The product, melarsen (*VIII*), and the corresponding arsenoso-compound, melarsen oxide, are superior to tryparsamide[23], but melarsen oxide is also as effective as tryparsamide in late cases, a surprising result that has been amply borne out by subsequent clinical experience[24].

The success with melarsen led to further synthetic work on this class of compound. The original method of preparation (from cyanuric chloride) is said to give mixtures, compounds with chloro- and hydroxy-groups in the triazine ring being present. This difficulty may be obviated by direct condensation of 4,6-diamino-2-chlorotriazine with *p*-aminobenzene-arsonic acid[25], and the same method was used to give compounds in which the benzene ring is substituted with hydroxyl, and in which the amino-groups of (*VIII*) are replaced by OH, $HO \cdot CH_2 \cdot CH_2 \cdot NH$ and $HO_2C \cdot CH_2 \cdot NH$. A later paper[26] describes similar compounds in which the triazine ring is replaced by pyrimidine ($IX$, $X = NH_2$, $Y = H$). The compounds are highly active but none is as good as melarsen or melarsen oxide. The pyrimidine compounds were studied in greater detail by Ainley and Davey[27], who introduced further substituents into the pyrimidine ring. The arsenoso-compound (corresponding to $IX$, $X = Y = NH_2$) has been outstanding, but preliminary results suggest that it is slightly inferior to melarsen oxide-BAL (see below)[28]. Activity was reduced when $Y = $ hydrogen or methyl, or when the primary amino-group was replaced by a secondary group. Quaternization of a pyrimidine

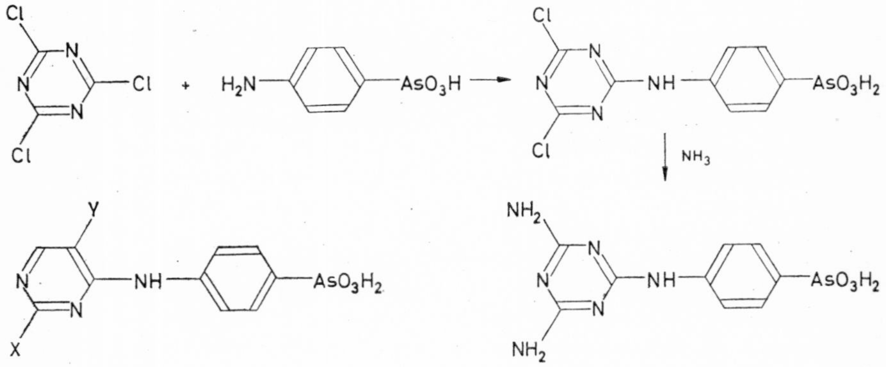

(IX)                                          (VIII)

nitrogen reduced activity, and so did union with the benzene ring at positions other than the 4-position. Water-soluble crystalline isethionates of the arsenoso-compounds have been prepared for injection.

*Organic arsenicals and BAL*

Ehrlich's original theory of receptors to account for chemotherapeutic action seemed admirably suited to the arsenicals; for it was assumed that the arsenoso-group, the ultimately active part of the molecule, combined with SH-groups of the essential proteins of the parasite. Prior combination of the arsenoso-compound with thiols would therefore modify the absorption, distribution and toxicity of the molecule. Early work on such compounds, the dithioarsenites ($R \cdot As(SR^1)_2$), has given discordant results, and for further study Cohen, King and Strangeways prepared carboxyl-substituted dithio-arsenites, of which the salts are soluble in water[29]. Several of these compounds have high activity, notably the dicysteinyl compound K 324. They are liable to dissociate in aqueous solution with the equilibrium shown on p. 59.

The activity of these compounds has thus been accommodated with the receptor theory, if this dissociation occurs *in vivo*. Cyclic compounds soluble in organic solvents were also prepared from dithiols, and compound K 352 was formed by the condensation of 4-acetamido-2-hydroxyarsenosobenzene and two molecules of the physiologically important peptide, glutathione. Although very promising in laboratory animals, K 324 and K 352 were too toxic in man[30]. The detoxifying action of BAL depends on a similar kind of combination, but with the formation of a stable ring $(X)$ and a compound less liable to dissociation. Early attempts to combine arsenic treatment with BAL led not only to the expected reduction in toxicity, but also to a loss of trypanocidal activity[31]. The problem is complex as shown by the fact that the water-soluble hydrochloride of oxophenarsine-BAL (BAL-OXO) $(X)$ is a potent trypanocide[32]. The corresponding compound from melarsen oxide, melarsoprol (Mel B, melarsen oxide-BAL and arsobal), is probably now the most effective treatment for late trypanosomiasis[33]. In early cases, a single injection of 3·6 mg/kg rapidly cures the blood infection, and for cerebral cases three daily injections of this dose usually suffice[33].

A possible interpretation of these results is that the SH-receptor theory is inadequate, and that a drug in the form of a stable cyclic dithioarsenite

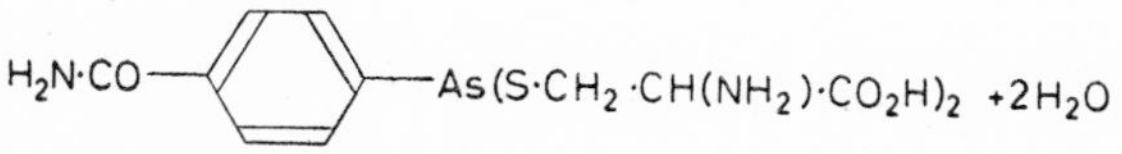

$$H_2N{\cdot}CO{-}\text{⟨benzene ring⟩}{-}As(S{\cdot}CH_2{\cdot}CH(NH_2){\cdot}CO_2H)_2 \ +2H_2O$$

K 324

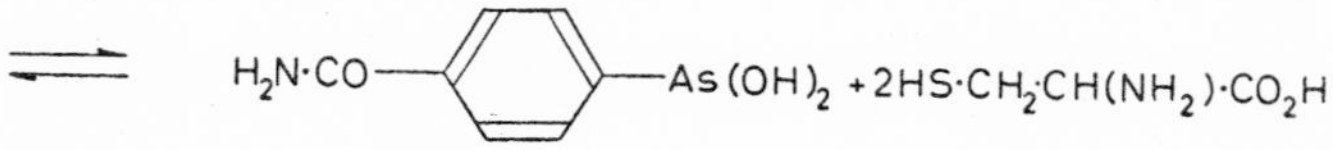

$$\rightleftharpoons \quad H_2N{\cdot}CO{-}\text{⟨benzene ring⟩}{-}As(OH)_2 \ +2HS{\cdot}CH_2CH(NH_2){\cdot}CO_2H$$

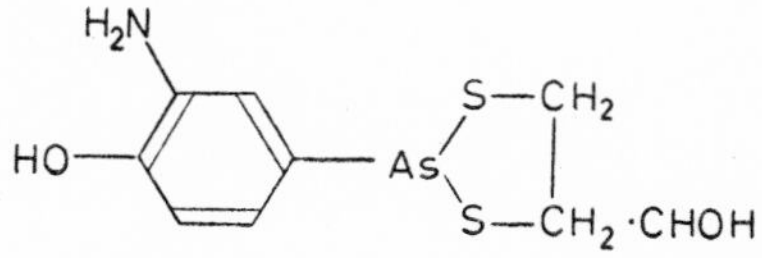

$$\begin{array}{c} H_2N \\ HO{-}\text{⟨benzene ring⟩}{-}As \begin{array}{c} S{-}CH_2 \\ | \\ S{-}CH_2{\cdot}CHOH \end{array} \end{array}$$

$(X)$

reaches the significant site on the parasite with minimum non-specific combination with proteins of the host. There is no doubt that the introduction of melarsoprol for the treatment of trypanosomiasis at all stages, even the hitherto incurable cerebral *T. rhodesiense* case, has been a major advance and that at a time when tryparsamide has become less and less effective owing to the emergence of resistant strains[34]. Melarsoprol is, however, a dangerous drug and great care is needed in its standardization[35] and its use in treatment; also it has the disadvantage of being injected in propylene glycol solution. Quite recently a water-soluble drug of the same class known as Mel W has been introduced[36], but preliminary clinical observation points to higher toxicity than for melarsoprol.

### Suramin (*Bayer 205, Germanin*)

The evolution of this remarkable substance in 1912 was based on the fact that the dyes, Trypan Red and Afridol-Violet, had slight trypanocidal action. Attempts to obtain compounds of higher activity by modification of the structure have resulted in loss of activity, recent examples being replacement of two of the amide groups by sulphonamide groups[37,38], and other more profound changes[39]. Besides its trypanocidal properties, suramin has a prophylactic action which may extend to three months, and which is not due to depot formation at the site of injection, but to slow excretion after intravenous injection. The persistence in the tissues may be attributed to the retention in the molecule of some of the structural characteristics of a complex dye. Suramin is ineffective in late trypanosomiasis, a shortcoming due to the inability of the large, probably colloidal, molecule to pass the blood-brain barrier. Nevertheless, its low toxicity and prophylactic action have enabled it to maintain its place in human and veterinary medicine to-day, fifty years after its introduction.

The high structure-specificity of suramin has led to much speculation on its mode of action. Jancsó attributed to it the power of sensitizing trypanosomes so that they attracted to themselves, and were destroyed by, the phagocytes of the reticulo-endothelial system[40]. When this system was blocked by splenectomy and intravenous injection of colloidal copper, suramin became much less effective. At the time this explanation received little attention, but more recently a similar one has been advanced to account for the antifilarial action of diethylcarbamazine (Hetrazan)[41] and for the schistosomicidal action of diaminodiphenoxyalkanes[42]. However, the action of the drug is more likely to be due to inhibition of vital enzyme systems of the parasite, and the superior action of suramin over other complex acid dyes may be attributed to a better molecular fit[38].

### Diamidines

This important class of trypanocide provides a notable example of how important discoveries in chemotherapy often follow incorrect assumptions. Trypanosomes are highly dependent on glucose metabolism, and depletion of the blood stream of the host of glucose by insulin, or even by hibernation, depresses the rate of multiplication of the parasites. The trypanocidal action of the hypoglycaemic drug Synthalin-B (XI) is, however, a direct one. Activity is retained by analogous compounds in which the guanidino-groups

$$NH$$
$$\|$$

are replaced by amino, isothiouronium ($-S-C-NH_2$), and better still, amidino groups[43]. It is among the aromatic diamidines that the most noteworthy activity has been found[44]. The three drugs stilbamidine (XII), propamidine (XIII, n = 3) and pentamidine (XIII, n = 5) have all been used clinically as the water-soluble isethionates, although stilbamidine has been largely abandoned on account of toxicity and loss of activity on storage. This loss is due to the action of sunlight which causes dimerization of the molecule[45]. Pentamidine is undoubtedly a most successful drug although, not unexpectedly for a basic substance, it has no action on late trypanosomiasis. To-day it is the favoured treatment for the recently infected patient and, by a short series of intramuscular injections of the readily-soluble isethionate, cure may be expected with few toxic symptoms or relapses, even when the infecting strain is arsenic-resistant. The discovery that pentamidine possesses valuable prophylactic properties is even more important[46]. Some protection may be secured, it has been claimed, by oral administration, but more reliable results are obtained by injection; and in the erstwhile French and Belgian African territories prophylaxis, colloquially known as pentamidinization, or lomidinization (after the synonym for the drug, Lomidine), has been practised on a vast scale. Recently there have been indications that the protection is becoming less effective. Prophylaxis on such a large scale always carries the risk that resistant strains tend in the course of time to become dominant, and with pentamidine prophylaxis there is some evidence of cryptic infections of low parasitaemia in protected persons[47]. A recent modification that holds considerable promise takes advantage of the prophylactic properties of both suramin and pentamidine by using a salt formed by these constituents. Consecutive injection of these substances into animals was found to annul to some extent

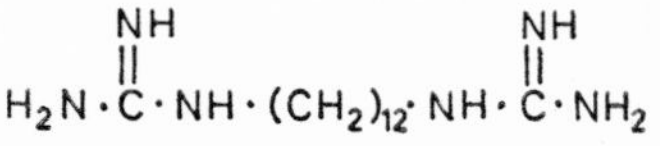

$$H_2N \cdot \overset{\overset{\displaystyle NH}{\|}}{C} \cdot NH \cdot (CH_2)_{12} \cdot NH \cdot \overset{\overset{\displaystyle NH}{\|}}{C} \cdot NH_2$$

*(XI)*

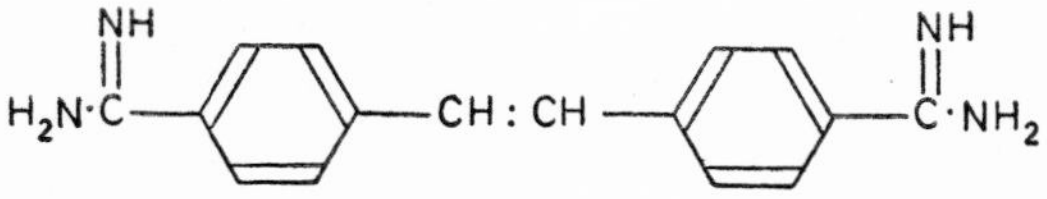

$$H_2N \cdot \overset{\overset{\displaystyle NH}{\|}}{C} - \bigcirc - CH:CH - \bigcirc - \overset{\overset{\displaystyle NH}{\|}}{C} \cdot NH_2$$

*(XII)*

$$H_2N \cdot \overset{\overset{\displaystyle NH}{\|}}{C} - \bigcirc - O \cdot (CH_2)_n \cdot O - \bigcirc - \overset{\overset{\displaystyle NH}{\|}}{C} \cdot NH_2$$

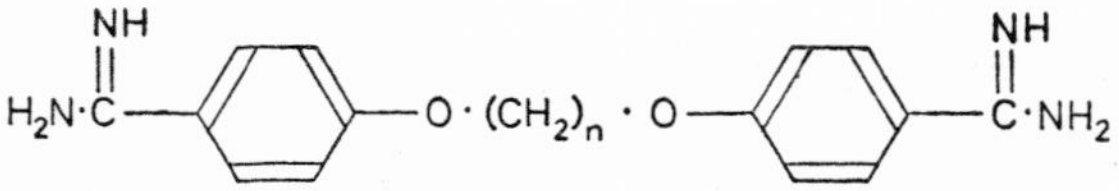

*(XIII)*

the toxic effects of either, whereas the chemotherapeutic effect of both was still exerted, and perhaps even enhanced[48]. Indeed, this new prophylactic has the advantages of great safety and prolonged effectiveness but the disadvantage of reaction at the injection site, no doubt due to its very low solubility[49].

An interesting recent announcement[50] is of an investigation of Berenil (4,4'-diamidinodiazoaminobenzene), best known as a drug for the treatment of *T. congolense* infections of domestic animals, for the treatment of early human trypanosomiasis. The results achieved were at least as good as those with pentamidine but there was no evidence of prophylaxis.

*Structure-activity relationships of the diamidines*

This subject has been studied in great detail since the publication of the synthesis of stilbamidine, propamidine and pentamidine[44]. Two amidino-groups are essential for high activity but the introduction of further amidino-groups into the propamidine molecule gives inactive compounds[51]. The amidino-groups must be attached directly to aromatic nuclei (*cf. XII* and *XIII*) and although most of the synthetic work has been on 4,4'-compounds, such 3,4'-compounds as have been made, fewer because more troublesome to synthesize, appear to be no less active, whereas the 3,3'-compounds are inactive.

61

*Replacement of the benzene rings*—Replacement by other nuclei has so far uniformly led to compounds of reduced or negligible activity. Among those reported have been the analogues of (*XII*) and (*XIII*) with furan[52], naphthalene[53] and pyridine rings[54].

*Incorporation of the benzene rings in a trinuclear system*—This has an equally unfavourable influence as in the phenanthrene compound (*XIV*)[55] (which

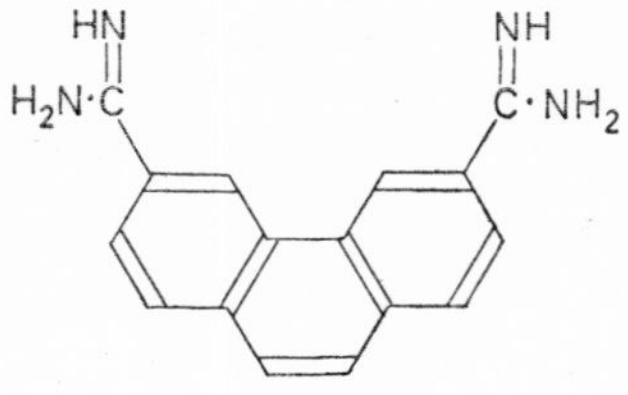

(*XIV*)

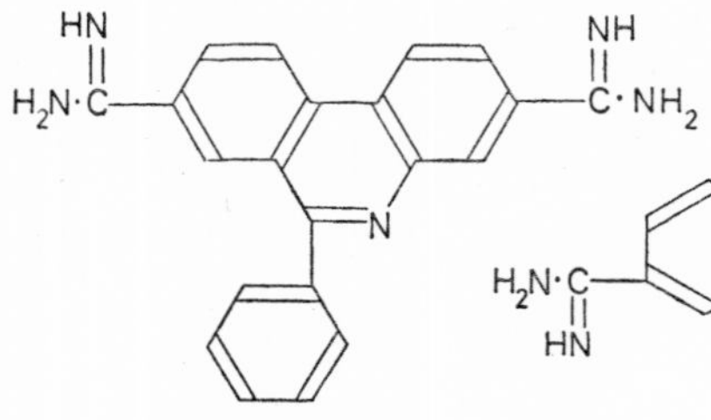

(*XV*)

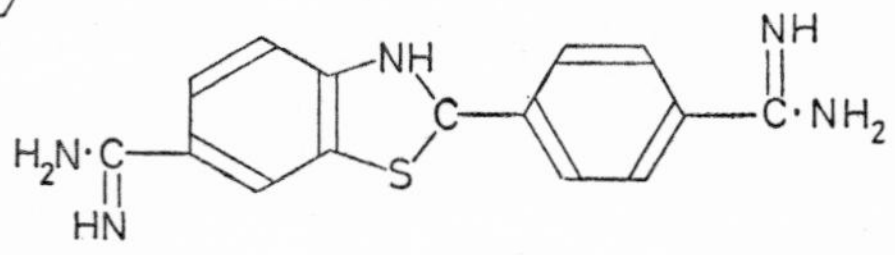

(*XVI*)

is however quite active against *T. congolense*[56]) and analogous carbazole and dibenzofuran compounds[57]. More surprisingly, the phenanthridine (*XV*) and its quaternary salt are also inactive[58] but the benzothiazole (*XVI*) has some activity[59].

*Substitution in the benzene rings*—Substitution in stilbamidine (*XII*) with 2,2′-dichloro, dihydroxy or dimethoxy affords compounds of equal or greater activity[60], but the two last-named substituents have little effect on the activity of pentamidine[61], whereas other groups (alkyl, halogen, nitro, amino) are dystherapeutic[62]. Substitution on the amidino-groups furnishes less active compounds[44].

*Replacement of amidino by other groups*—It is usually disadvantageous. The dicyanides from which the diamidines are prepared are inactive, as are the corresponding diamines. A series of diguanidines[63] provides an exception, the best compound (*XVII*) being active orally in mice but inferior to stilbamidine[64]. The diguanidine structurally analogous to stilbamidine has some

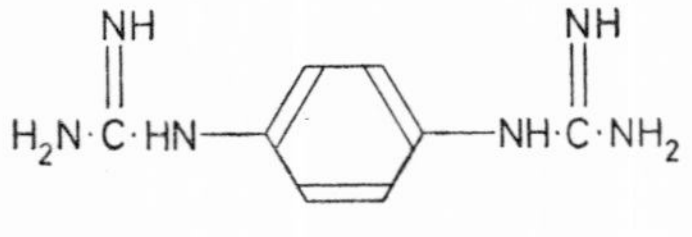

(*XVII*)

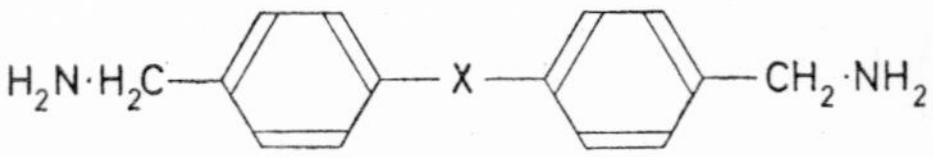

(*XVIII*)

activity, as also have the compounds in which —CH=CH— has been replaced by S, SO and $SO_2$[65]. The suggestion that the activity of the diamidines is due to the location at an optimum distance in the molecule of two highly ionized and mutually independent basic groups was tested by the preparation of compounds (*XVIII*), but these had no activity[66].

*Variation of the central chain*—This variation has produced the most interesting compounds of this series. Saturation of the double bond of stilbamidine (*XII*) does not reduce the activity and the $\alpha,\beta$-dimethyl homologue of (*XII*) is notable for possessing marked activity against *T. congolense* and *T. cruzi*[67]. The isomer of stilbamidine in which both benzamidine groups are attached to the same C-atom of ethylene is inactive[44]. Compounds with CO and CHOH in the chain are of low activity. The phenolic ethers (*cf. XIII*) are highly active when $n = 1$ to 10, but when the polymethylene chain of (*XIII*) was replaced by hydrocarbon chains containing double and triple bonds the resulting compounds proved to be much less active than the corresponding saturated compounds.[68]

The discovery of Berenil with high activity against *T. congolense* has changed the direction of chemical research in this field towards compounds with nitrogen in the chain. The more interesting compounds that have emerged are notable for *T. congolense* activity and will be dealt with in the section on animal trypanosomiasis.

## *Furans*

The first trypanocidal furan compounds to be discovered were the sulphonamide aldehyde bisulphite (*XIX*) and the corresponding sulphapyridine derivative[69]. Further investigation revealed that the activity resided in the furfural part of the molecule, and that the most active simple furan derivative is in fact furoic acid, to which furfural and furfuryl alcohol may be assumed to owe their activity after oxidation. Although cure of mice infected with *T. equiperdum* and *T. brucei* requires a series of doses of 10 mg/kg orally or subcutaneously, it is significant that arsenic-resistant strains are also sensitive, and trypanosomes made resistant to furoic acid remain sensitive to organic arsenicals. Thus a different point of attack on the trypanosomes from that of arsenic is assumed. The most important trypanocidal furans are derivatives of 5-nitrofurfuraldehyde[70], such as nitrofurazone (Furacin, *XX*, R = H) which is curative of *T. equiperdum* infection in mice with a single oral dose, but is not so effective against *T. rhodesiense*[71]. The 2-hydroxyethyl semicarbazone (*XX*, R = $CH_2 \cdot CH_2OH$) also has some activity in mice[72], and a patent claims activity for the thio-oxazolidone (*XXI*)[73]. In spite of rather indifferent laboratory results[74], nitrofurazone has secured a place in medicine as the only drug available for patients who have failed to respond to other forms of treatment and for them it may be life-saving[75]. The drug is given orally in doses of 1·5 to 2 g daily for 5 to 7 days and in successful cases clears the trypanosomes from the cerebro-spinal fluid. It is, however, a dangerous drug which sometimes causes neuritis, perhaps due to antagonism to thiamine, and, more seriously, drug-induced haemolysis of red cells in susceptible patients. This effect is akin to that caused by primaquine and occurs in patients with red blood cells deficient in the enzyme glucose-6-phosphate dehydrogenase. Unfortunately this deficiency is rather common in dark-skinned people and for generic reasons more common in men than in women. Since for reasons of occupation dark-skinned men are prone to trypanosomiasis, as many as 20 per cent of the patients may have this deficiency.

### Organic Antimonial Compounds

Friedheim has prepared a series of organic antimonials analogous to melarsen and its derivatives. The melarsen analogue (*XXII*, R = SbO$_3$HNa), prepared by a similar method[76], is a colourless substance and is polymerized on being heated with a 40 per cent aqueous solution of urea. The polymer

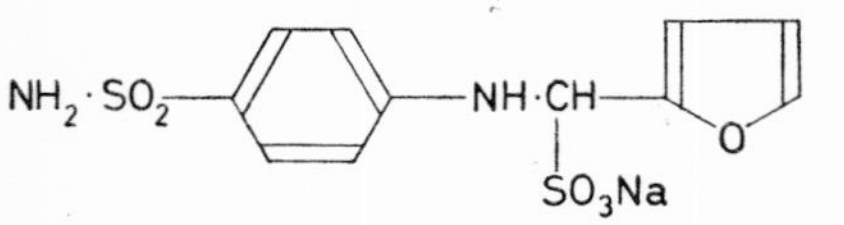

(XIX)

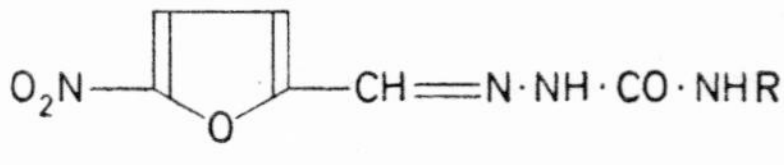

(XX)

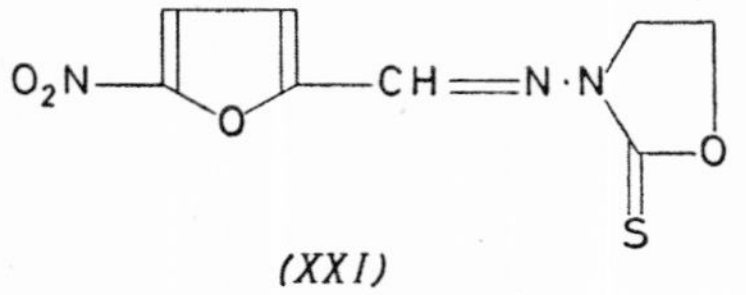

(XXI)

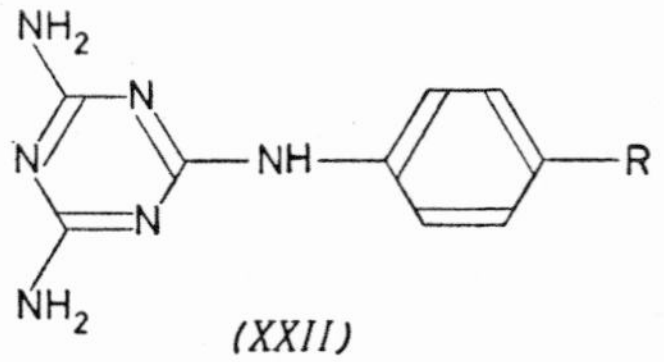

(XXII)

(MSb), which does not contain urea, forms a thixotropic gel in water and possesses remarkable prophylactic properties in mice, affording protection for considerably longer periods than suramin or pentamidine[23]. An antimonial of this type presents considerable problems of standardization[77] and neither this substance nor a dithioarsenite (*XXII*; R = Sb(S·CH$_2$·CO$_2$Na)$_2$) has been used in Africa on any considerable scale. Both substances cured patients of early and late trypanosomiasis. Friedheim claims that MSbB, a detoxicated compound formed from MSb and dimercaprol, is effective when given orally[78].

### Antibiotics

Although penicillin and the other well-known antibiotics are inactive against trypanosomes, prodigiosin (a pigment isolated from some strains of *Serratia marcescens*) had earlier been found to possess slight activity aginst *T. brucei* in mice[79]. Prodigiosin is a pyrryldipyrrylmethene and has recently been synthesized[80]. More important has been the discovery that puromycin (it was first called achromycin but that name has since been allotted to a tetracycline), an antibiotic from *Streptomyces albo-niger*, is active against *T. equiperdum* in mice, both orally and by injection[81]. Puromycin has no prophylactic action and is more effective against the *T. evansi* than the *T. brucei* group[82]. It is a purine derivative (*XXIII*) and its trypanocidal action is reversed by adenine and a number of other aminopurines[83]. An amino-nucleoside, 6-dimethylamino-9-(3-amino-3-deoxy-β-D-ribofuranosyl)purine (*XXIV*), which is obtained from puromycin by mild alkaline hydrolysis[84], has three to four times the trypanocidal activity of the parent substance.

The structure of the antibiotic was determined during an investigation which culminated in its total synthesis[85, 86]. By hydrolysis with alcoholic hydrochloric acid, three fragments were obtained and shown to be 6-dimethylamino-purine, O-methyl-L-tyrosine and 3-amino-3-deoxy-D-ribose[87, 88]. These conclusions were confirmed by synthesizing each component and deducing the position of glycosidation[89, 90]. Other amino-acids were condensed with the aminonucleoside (XXIV) and these also were trypanocidal, an observation which suggested that both they and puromycin are hydrolysed in the body

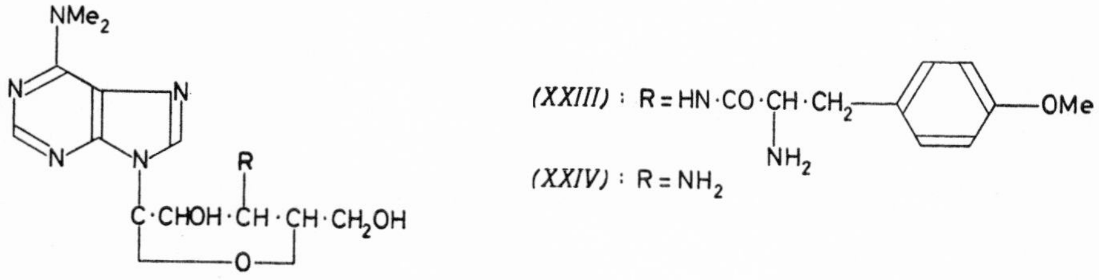

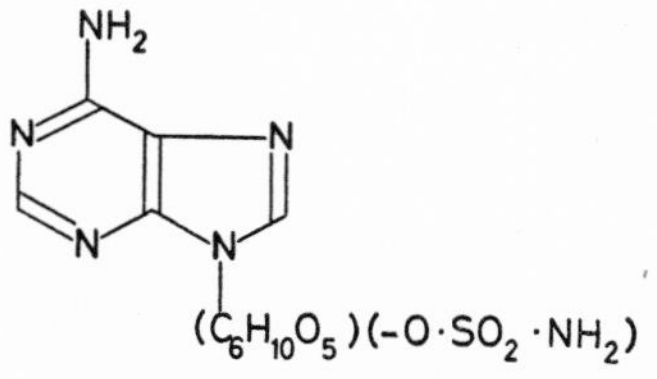

(XXIII) : R = HN·CO·CH·CH$_2$——⟨benzene⟩——OMe
        |
        NH$_2$

(XXIV) : R = NH$_2$

(C$_6$H$_{10}$O$_5$)(–O·SO$_2$·NH$_2$)

(XXV)

to the same active constituent (XXIV)[88]. The analogue of compound (XXIV), in which the dimethylamino-group has been replaced by a primary amino-group, has also been synthesized; this compound has only half the activity and thus it is unlikely that enzymic demethylation of compound (XXIV) is a factor in its activity[91]. Analogues of compound (XXIV) with other dialkylamino-groups have been prepared of which several, especially the diethylamino-homologue, are more active than the dimethylamino-compound (XXIV)[92]. When the nitrogen atom attached to C$_6$ is incorporated in a ring, or when one of the substituents of the amino-group is cyclohexyl, then compounds of lower activity result. The nucleoside corresponding to compound (XXIV) but with R = OH (and therefore structurally closer to adenosine) was also synthesized, but proved to be inactive[93].

Clinical trials of puromycin (Stylomycin) have been conducted on patients suffering from T. gambiense infection[94, 95]. Some cures were effected but the antibiotic is unlikely to be a useful drug on account of its delayed toxicity[96]. It shows no prophylactic activity.

Recently another antibiotic, nucleocidin, has been found to possess trypanocidal activity in mice and rats, but with a somewhat different species-spectrum from puromycin[97]. Nucleocidin is also an aminopurine, being hydrolysed to adenine by alcoholic hydrochloric acid. It has a similar ultra-violet absorption spectrum to adenosine and is therefore a 9-adenylglycoside:

a sulphur atom is present as a sulphonamide group and a partial structure ($XXV$) has been allotted to the antibiotic[98].

## VETERINARY TRYPANOSOMIASIS IN AFRICA

Trypanosome diseases of domestic animals in Africa are of two types, those caused by the polymorphic and those caused by the monomorphic trypanosomes. The nagana of the explorers was due to $T.$ $brucei$ which mainly affects equine species. Although it causes no disease in man it is closely related to $T.$ $gambiense$ and $T.$ $rhodesiense$. The polymorphic trypanosomes, $T.$ $evansi$ and $T.$ $equiperdum$, also cause disease of horses and camels, but these maladies are not confined to Africa. Much the most important trypanosome diseases of Africa are due to the monomorphic trypanosome $T.$ $congolense$ and closely related species such as $T.$ $simiae$ and $T.$ $vivax$, and these diseases are outstanding factors influencing life and livelihood. $T.$ $congolense$ and $T.$ $vivax$ mainly affect cattle, and cattle-rearing is vital to Africa. $T.$ $simiae$ infections are rapidly fatal to pigs, and pig-rearing could be an important factor in African economy, especially in Nigeria. The great importance of these trypanosomes is due to three main inter-related circumstances. First, they are not only transmitted cyclically by the wide-ranging $G.$ $morsitans$ and other tsetse species, but also mechanically by tsetse and other flies, particularly stomoxys and tabanidae species[99]. Secondly, these trypanosomes are very abundant in the blood of the natural fauna in whom they cause no apparent symptoms, and thus an inexhaustible reservoir of infection for susceptible domestic animals is available. This situation contrasts with that of $T.$ $rhodesiense$ which, after years of search, has only recently been found in a wild animal[100], and for which the relatively few chronic human infections are believed to serve as a reservoir. Thirdly the native, on whom ownership of cattle confers prestige, will vacate tsetse areas, or keep indigenous, inferior beasts that possess natural resistance[101]. Much of Africa offers good grazing land for cattle, but presence of fly means absence of cattle.

The tsetse problem has been tackled in ways other than by drug treatment of cattle. Realization that the natural fauna form a reservoir of infection led to large-scale destruction of game which in some areas, such as Rhodesia, had some success; but this policy is aesthetically objectionable and it is now realized that it simultaneously destroys one of Africa's greatest assets. Study of the habits of the various tsetse species shows that clearance of vegetation, particularly along the courses of rivers, prevents the fly from breeding. The scale of such operations is beyond human capacity, but closer study of the habits of the fly has led to a more discriminative approach to the problem known as obstructive clearing[102]. A notable example of reclamation of land from the fly may be found at Anchau in Nigeria[103]. The great development in insecticides since the war has provided a new means of attack on the source of trypanosomiasis. Insecticides effect complete eradication of the tsetse in circumscribed areas, as in Zululand, but in the main fly belts the high cost of spraying by aircraft and the difficulty in penetrating the forest canopy by this means render the method impracticable. Recourse has to be had therefore to drug treatment. A curative drug is important for the treatment of valuable animals and for those that have to trek occasionally through fly-country. If the drug is cheap, is unlikely to produce alarming local or systemic toxic signs and is easily administered (*e.g.* by a single subcutaneous or intramuscular injection), then it may be made available generally to native stock-holders. However, cattle are so prone to re-infection that a curative drug does not of itself make a major contribution to the problem of bovine trypanosomiasis. What is needed is a drug that not only possesses the qualities just listed but also affords, in one dose, protection to the treated animal for several months.

## TRYPANOCIDES FOR VETERINARY USE

### *Phenanthridinium Salts*

Up to 1940, the only treatment available for bovine trypanosomiasis was a course of intravenous injections of tartar emetic or a similarly complex antimonial, and this was used exclusively for valuable beasts belonging to large stock-owners. The discovery of the trypanocidal action of phenanthridinium salts opened up the prospect of mass treatment of cattle[104]. Acridinium salts had for long been known to possess chemotherapeutic properties including trypanocidal activity and it had seemed therefore worth while to investigate the chemically related phenanthridinium salts. The discovery of a versatile method of synthesis of phenanthridines[105] led to the important diamino-6-phenylphenanthridinium salts[106]. The characteristic of the trypanocidal activity of these salts is that they possess outstanding activity against *T. congolense*[107] and, as field trials subsequently proved, against *T. vivax*. The level of activity against the polymorphic trypanosomes such as *T. rhodesiense* is much lower. The first phenanthridinium salt to undergo field trials in Africa was phenidium chloride (*XXVI*) (8-amino-6-*p*-aminophenyl-5-methylphenanthridinium chloride),* and although it showed marked superiority over any previous drug, and was usually curative of bovine trypanosomiasis in one intramuscular or subcutaneous injection[108], it was quickly superseded by dimidium bromide (*XXVII*). This compound is even more active against *T. congolense* and is curative of cattle at 1 to 2 mg/kg[109]. Resistant strains of trypanosome have been encountered in cattle[110], although it is difficult to produce strains resistant to dimidium bromide in the laboratory[111]. Swelling near the injection site and temporary lameness are rather frequent consequences of injection of phenanthridinium compounds into cattle. More serious was the discovery that in some localities some animals treated with dimidium developed symptoms of photosensitization due to liver damage and these were often followed by death[112]. These symptoms have never been observed in laboratory animals nor in cattle in England[113], and their occurrence in Africa seems to depend markedly on geographical location. The drug was used on a large scale in the 1946 epidemic in Zululand and no cases of photosensitization resulted. The symptoms may be due to the association of drug treatment with some constituents of the pasture, or to the burden of

---

* This numeration is in accord with that now recommended by the I.U.P.A.C. and used by the Chemical Society. Originally these compounds were named according to the old Stelzner numeration, *e.g.*, phenidium chloride (*XXVI*) was named 7-amino-9-*p*-aminophenyl-10-methylphenanthridinium chloride.

a potent drug added to animals already suffering from impaired liver function[114]. When Evans treated 350,000 cattle in the Sudan with dimidium, he found these symptoms arose in animals on lush pasture and were alleviated by moving them to the more arid localities[115]; mortality attributed to the drug was of the order of 1 per cent but it has been higher in other regions.

The synthesis[116] of analogues of dimidium (*XXVII*) in which the *N*-methyl substituent was replaced by other groups (ethyl, allyl, propyl and higher homologues) gave a series of compounds of which the three first showed higher activity than dimidium bromide in laboratory infections[117]. The

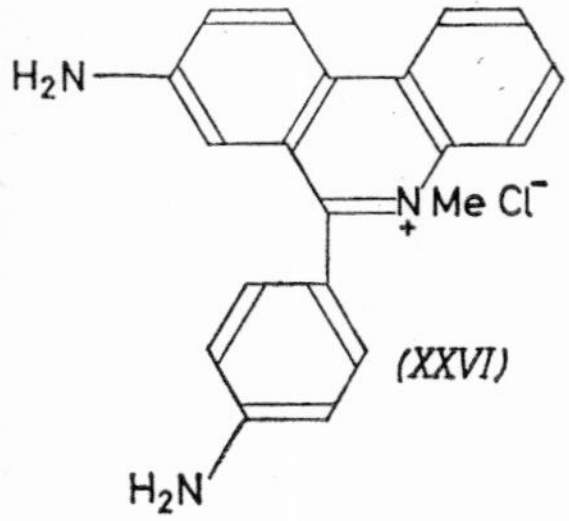

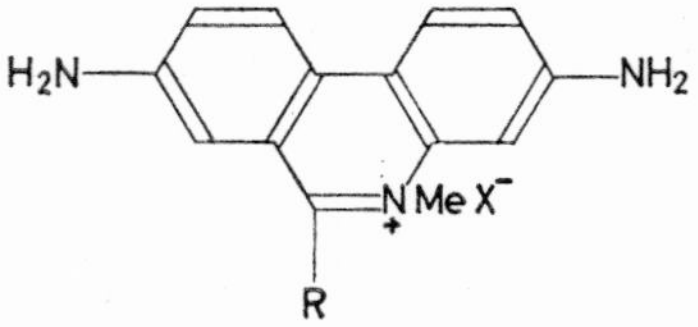

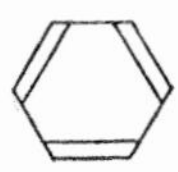

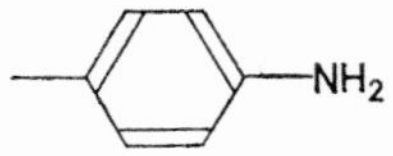

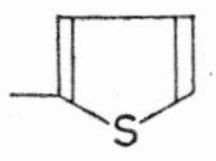

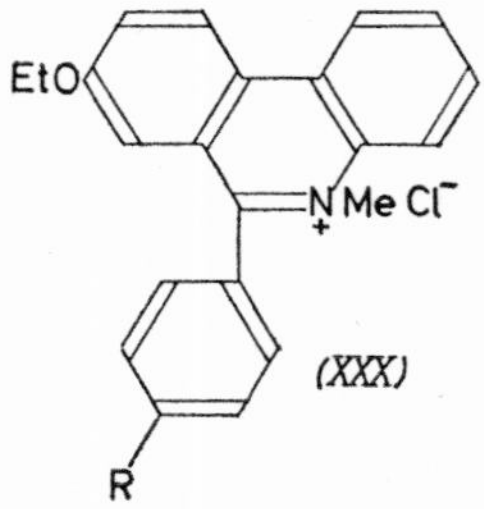

best compound, that with *N*-ethyl, now known as homidium (Ethidium), is several times more active against *T. congolense*, and the increase in activity against *T. brucei* and *T. gambiense* is even greater. A possible cause[116] is the considerable increase in the (small) proportion of pseudo-base in a solution of homidium at physiological pH compared with dimidium. The acute toxicity of homidium is similar to that of dimidium, but cattle treated with homidium in Africa have not shown signs of liver toxicity[118-120] although local reaction is sometimes serious[121]. The drug has a good margin of safety and, given in high dosage, often cures animals infected with trypanosome strains resistant to dimidium bromide[122]. The important difference between two such chemically similar compounds as dimidium and homidium in respect of toxicity has been attributed to different functions of the *N*-methyl and *N*-ethyl groups in the biological methylation processes of the host. The 6-substituent and the location of the amino-groups are also significant for liver toxicity, however; phenidium (*XXVI*) has never been incriminated and the liability to cause photosensitization symptoms in the dimidium group decreases in the following order: $(XXVIII) > (XXVII) \gg (XXIX)$. Homidium has largely replaced dimidium for the treatment of bovine trypanosomiasis.

*Structure-activity relationships of the phenanthridines*

The quaternary function (that is the N-alkyl group) and the 6-aryl group are essential to high activity[123], although the so-called isosteric thienyl[124] group may replace the 6-aryl group of dimidium (*XXVII*) to give a compound (*XXIX*) that is more active and less toxic[125]. Compounds analogous to dimidium but with R = hydrogen[126], methyl or benzoyl[127] are only slightly active, but substitution of the 6-phenyl group with nitro- and amino-groups furnishes highly active compounds curative of cattle but too dangerous for use[128]. Activity is lost when the primary amino-groups of dimidium are replaced by tertiary ones[124].

Compounds derived from phenidium (*XXVI*) by loss of either of the amino-groups have little activity; those in which the amino-group of the phenanthridine ring-system occupies other than the 8-position[129] differ from it in activity by the factors indicated in parenthesis:

$$9\text{-}NH_2 \ (2 \cdot 2) > 3\text{-}NH_2 \ (1 \cdot 5) > 8\text{-}NH_2 \ (1)$$

The 2- and 7-amino-compounds are only slightly active. The availability of intermediates and ease of synthesis determine the compounds which are used for the mass treatment of cattle, since low costs are essential. In this series, the 2- and 8-amino- and 3,8-diamino-compounds are much the most readily available; further consideration of the 3- and 9-compounds is discouraged by the complications of their synthesis. An exception to the generalization that two primary amino-groups, one of which must reside on the phenanthridine ring, are essential to high activity was found in 8-ethoxy compound (*XXX*, R = $NH_2$) which is more active than phenidium chloride (*XXVI*) in mouse infections[130].

Some other 8-alkoxy-compounds are also active, but most surprising was the discovery that a compound lacking an amino-group, namely the *p*-nitrophenyl analogue (*XXX*, R = $NO_2$), is as active as phenidium. The *p*-aminophenyl compound (*XXX*, R = $NH_2$) was given a brief trial in cattle but proved to be too toxic[128].

More profound modifications of the molecules of phenidium and dimidium result in loss of activity. Heterocyclic amino-quaternary salts with one ring less, whether isoquinolines, quinolines[131], quinazolines or cinnolines[132] possess little activity, as do the more distantly related quindolinium[133] and thiazolinium compounds[134]. Likewise the addition of a fused ring gives a compound with only very slight activity[135].

*Surfen C*

At much the same time as the phenanthridinium compounds were being investigated, Jensch[136] prepared a number of 4,6-diaminoquinaldines of which one, Surfen C (Congasin, *XXXI*), was highly active in *T. congolense* infections. It was tried out in cattle but was too variable in its action and too toxic to compete with the phenanthridine compounds[137].

The compound without the methyl groups of Surfen C is much less active[138], and compounds in which the melamine link between the two

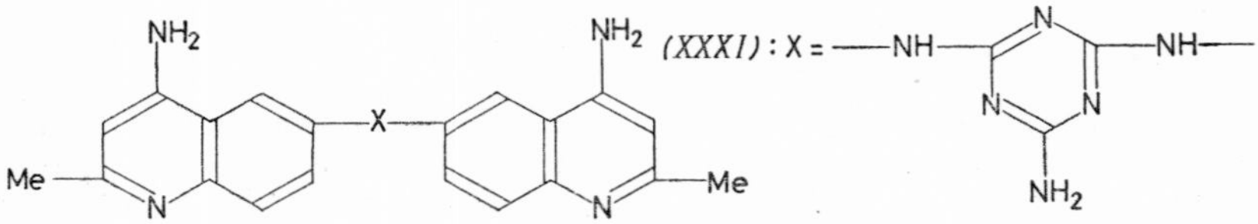

$(XXXII)$ : X = O · $(CH_2)_2$ · O

$(XXXIII)$ : X = NH · CO · $(CH_2)_4$ · CO · NH

4,6-diamino-quinaldine fragments is replaced by other groups as in compounds $(XXXII)$[139] and $(XXXIII)$[140] are active against polymorphic trypanosomes but not against $T.$ $congolense$.

## Quinapyramine

The preparation of analogues of the Surfens in which one 4,6-diamino-quinaldine radical was replaced by an aminopyrimidine gave compounds such as $(XXXIV)$ of low trypanocidal activity[141]. Quaternization of $(XXXIV)$

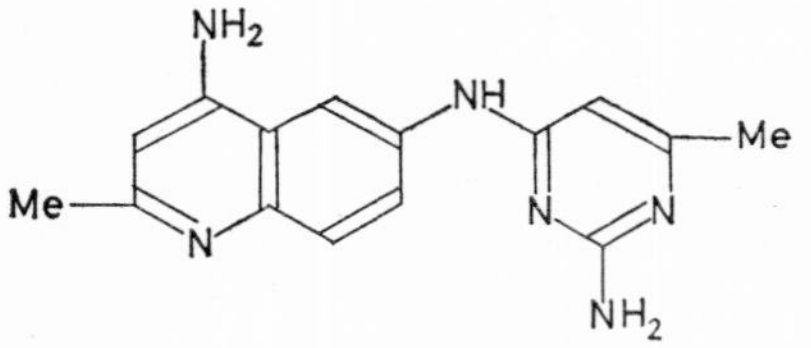

*(XXXIV)*

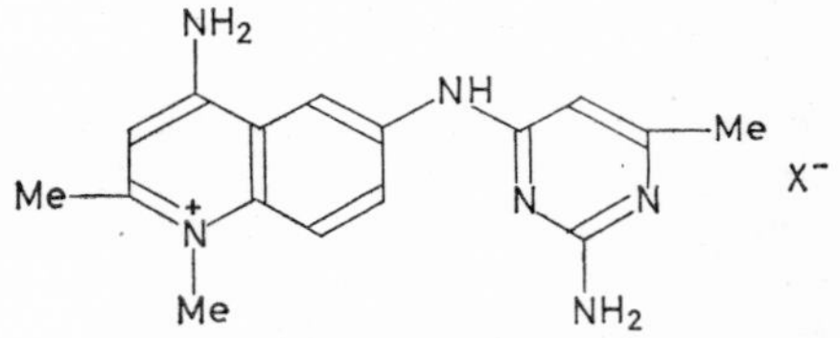

*(XXXV)*

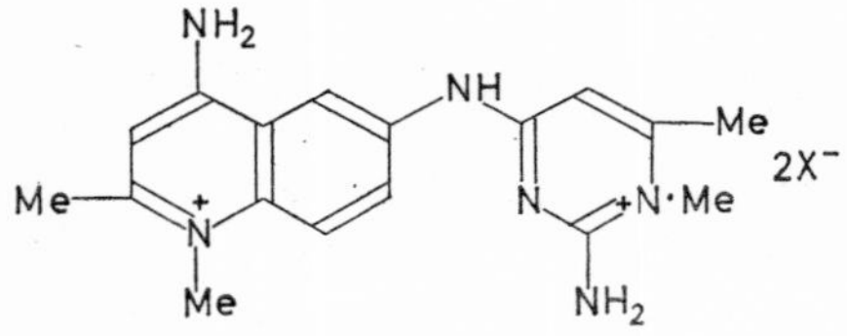

*(XXXVI)*

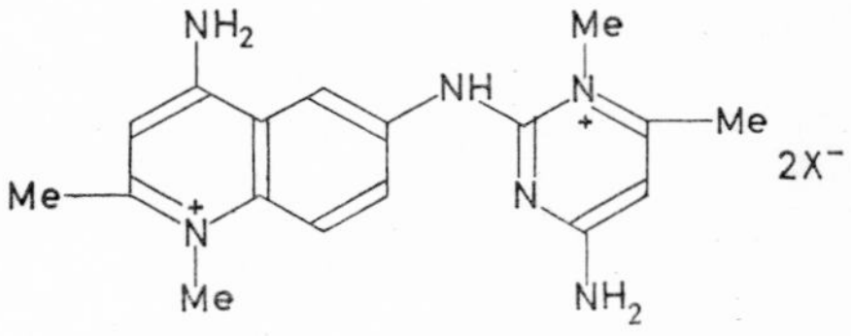

*(XXXVII)*

readily gave the quinaldinium salt $(XXXV)$ which is inactive, but crude specimens showed marked activity against $T.$ $congolense$ which was ultimately found to be due to the presence of traces of the diquaternary salt, quinapyramine (Antrycide, $XXXVI$, X = Cl$^-$ or MeSO$_4$$^-$)[142]. A satisfactory preparation of this latter compound was developed and its structure was confirmed by its synthesis through the condensation of the two authentic quaternary moieties. This drug has proved to be of great value in the treatment of bovine and other veterinary forms of trypanosomiasis[143]. It has activity against $T.$ $congolense$ similar to that of dimidium bromide but with a greater margin of safety, but it is less effective against $T.$ $vivax$ than against $T.$ $congolense$. The feature which distinguishes it from earlier trypanocides is its wide range of activity[144]; it is as effective against the polymorphic *T. equiperdum*, *T. evansi* and *T. equinum* as against *T. congolense*, somewhat less active against *T. rhodesiense*, *T. gambiense* and *T. brucei*, but inactive against *T. cruzi*. As a curative drug, quinapyramine is used as the water-soluble methylsulphate. The chloride, which is sparingly soluble in water, exhibits in mice a marked prophylactic action, due to formation of a reservoir of the drug under the skin at the injection site, and not to general retention of the drug in the tissues of the host, as occurs during the prophylactic action of suramin and pentamidine. Prophylactic action mediated by a similar mechanism (reservoir formation) is also shown in cattle[145] with quinapyramine-prophylactic (Antrycide Pro-salt), a mixture of the soluble methylsulphate and the sparingly soluble chloride[146]. Under experimental conditions, animals so treated by subcutaneous injection withstand a heavy challenge of *T. congolense*, and it was first thought that protection was afforded under natural conditions for the important period of six months, but probably a 2-monthly period is more realistic[147]. Such protection is of great value for trade cattle in transit through tsetse areas. Quinapyramine is a relatively safe drug and has marked advantages over the phenanthridinium drugs in its wide range of activity and in the mildness of the reaction at the injection site. Other important drugs have appeared since but these have supplemented rather than supplanted quinapyramine.

Difficulties have been encountered with quinapyramine, the two most important being the occasional 'break-through' of prophylaxis, perhaps due to cryptic infections, and the increasing occurrence of resistant strains. Drug resistance is the biggest current problem in trypanosomiasis of all kinds and when prophylaxis is practised it becomes of still greater importance; as the concentration of the prophylactic drug falls below a minimum level, an infection may establish itself in the presence of a low concentration of drug. Thus the conditions used in the laboratory for the production of resistant strains are simulated. Generally, strains resistant to quinapyramine are resistant to homidium, which likewise is a heterocyclic quaternary salt.

The extensive chemical work on the analogues of quinapyramine has been published mainly in the form of patents, but it appears that quinapyramine greatly exceeds its close chemical congeners in trypanocidal activity. The isomeric compound (*XXXVII*), and various compounds analogous to this and to quinapyramine but without the C-methyl groups, are much less active[148], as are the unquaternized and monoquaternized compounds of the class[141,142]. The Surfens were thought to owe their activity to their tautomeric potentialities as vinologues of amidines; when the quinaldine–nitrogen is quaternized as in quinapyramine these potentialities are lost, but ionic resonance similar in kind to that possessed by the active phenanthridinium salts is acquired.

## Cinnoline 528

Reference has already been made to studies on heterocyclic aminoquaternary salts possessing one ring less than the phenanthridinium drugs[132]. During the investigation of the aminocinnolines, it was observed that the crude products of reduction of 4-amino-1-methyl-6-nitrocinnolinium iodide and its 3-methyl homologue by iron powder had trypanocidal activity not possessed by the pure salts[149]. This activity was attributed to the presence of the azo-compound (*XXXVIII* or its homologue) as an impurity, a supposition that was confirmed by the synthesis of this compound, which proved to have moderate activity[150]. The compound corresponding to this azo-compound (*XXXVIII*) but with NHMe for each $NH_2$ was active[151] as also was the quinoline compound corresponding to (*XXXVIII*)[152]. The conclusion was reached that quinoline derivatives (*XXXIX*) and the corresponding cinnolines are likely to possess trypanocidal properties[153]. The effect of three

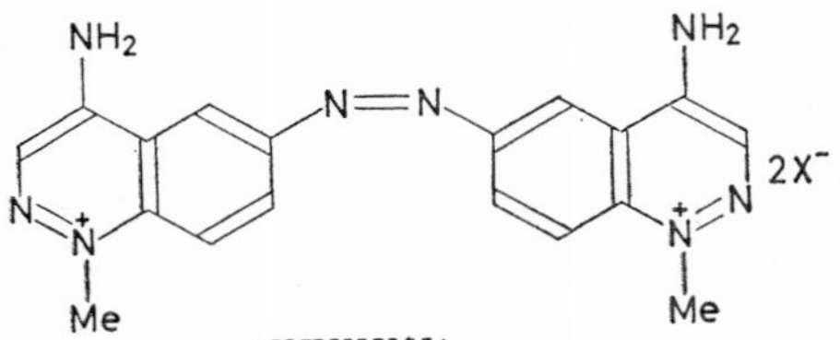

(*XXXVIII*) 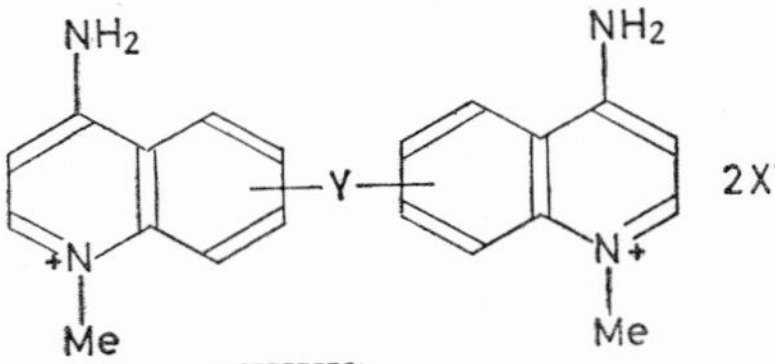          (*XXXIX*)

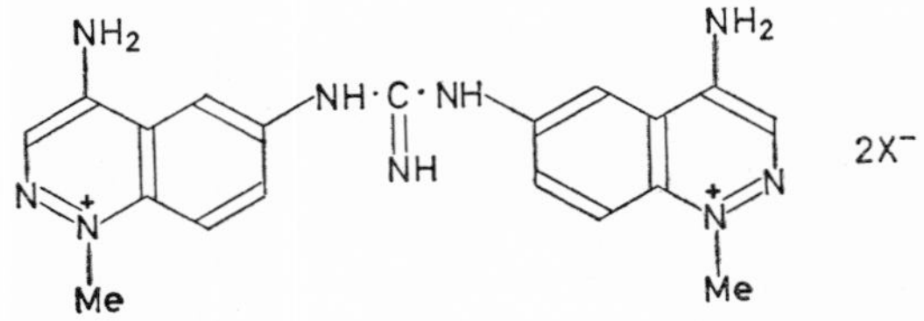

(*XL*)

different 'bridge' groups, Y, was investigated by condensing the appropriate amino-compounds or their quaternary salts with carbonyl chloride or thiocarbonyl chloride, and the thioureas obtained with the latter reagent were converted into guanidines. Reaction occurred exclusively on the 6-amino-group and of the quaternary salts ultimately obtained, the urea, thiourea and guanidine from 4,6-diamino-3-methylcinnoline, the thiourea and guanidine from 4,6-diaminoquinoline, and the thiourea from 4,6-diaminocinnoline were inactive. The ureas from 4,6-diaminoquinoline and 4,6-diaminocinnoline were slightly active but the guanidine (*XL*), Cinnoline 528, proved to be highly active against *T. congolense*[154], being approximately half as active and half as toxic as quinapyramine in mice. In a trial in cattle in Nigeria it cured *T. congolense* infections, but was less effective against *T. vivax* and had no worthwhile prophylactic properties[155].

### 4-Aminoquinaldium Salts

Certain 4-aminoquinolinium salts (*XLI*) and related compounds in which a general structural resemblance to the diamidines, Surfens, quinapyramine and Cinnoline 528 is discerned, possess notable antibacterial and other parasiticidal properties including slight action on *T. congolense* in mice[156]. The crude compound (*XLI*, n = 6) had greater trypanocidal activity than the pure salt, and as with quinapyramine and Cinnoline 528 this observation led to the discovery of a by-product contaminant of high activity[157]. Synthesis of possible compounds established the structure of the active product, Tozocide, as (*XLII*) for which a convenient preparative method was elaborated[158]. This compound was curative of trypanosomiasis of cattle but resistant strains proved to be cross-resistant to quinapyramine. Like Berenil, it gave a suraminate which was very effective in mice but of no value in cattle as a prophylactic[159].

### Diamidines

A feature of the diamidines has been their high activity against the polymorphic trypanosomes and relatively low activity against other species. An exception was the dimethylstilbamidine (*XLIII*) which is, however, less effective than the phenanthridinium compounds[56]. A major advance was the discovery of Berenil, 4,4'-diamidinodiazoaminobenzene (*XLIV*), which is highly effective in the treatment of *T. congolense* infections of cattle[160]. This substance is rather unstable but neutral, freshly-prepared solutions of its salt with an organic acid, *e.g.*, the diaceturate, are fairly stable. At a dosage of 2 mg/kg of this salt by intramuscular injection, cattle were cleared of infection within four days; no relapses or toxic effects were observed, and there were no serious reactions at the injection site. The drug is said to be effective also against *T. vivax* and *T. brucei*, but has no prophylactic action[161]. Berenil does not show cross-resistance to the quaternary trypanocides and is one of the most effective drugs for the treatment of cattle that develop trypanosomiasis after chemoprophylaxis[162]. Jensch comments that Berenil was developed from a consideration of the structure of the Surfens. He had earlier[163] given examples of potent trypanocides that had been obtained by the combination of such molecular fragments as

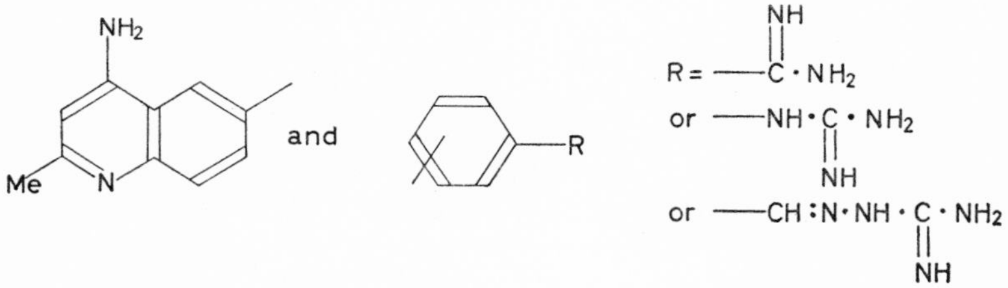

These fragments are all amidines, and not only these but the pyrimidine group of quinapyramine and phenanthridinium radicals have recently been variously combined to give potent trypanocides.

The discovery of Berenil led to further work on the diamidines. The tautomeric potentialities were simulated by replacing the bridge of (*XLIV*) by $NH \cdot CR=NH$ (R = Me, Et, Ph), giving compounds which are active, whereas the vinologous formamidines with $NH[CH=CH]_n \cdot CH=NH$ are not[164]. A striking example of a new compound formed by the union of molecular fragments of known trypanocides is (*XLV*) which has the central grouping of Congasin, and like that drug is highly active against *T. congolense*[165]. Compounds have recently been prepared which are related to both quinapyramine and Berenil. Several of them show high anti-protozoal activity, and one (*XLVI*) especially against *T. congolense*[166]. Di-*p,p'*-amidino-diphenylamine has only slight activity against *T. congolense*[44] but the

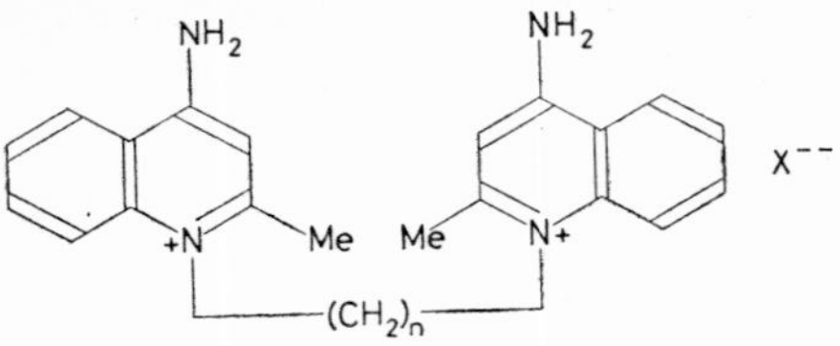

(XLI)

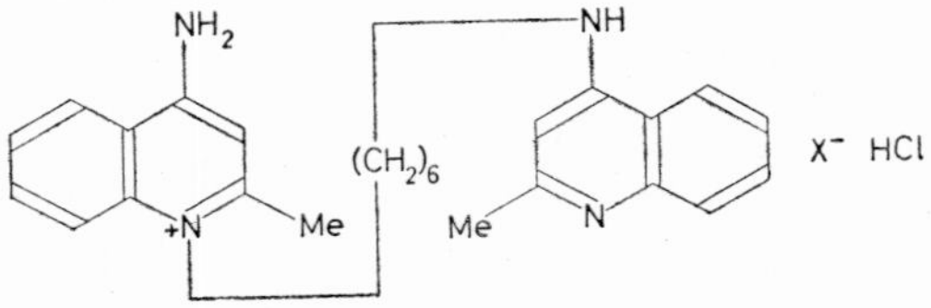

(XLII)

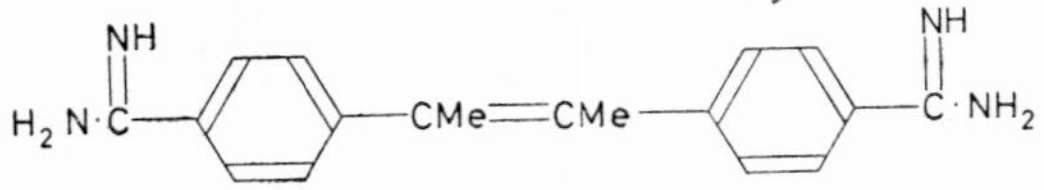

(XLIII)

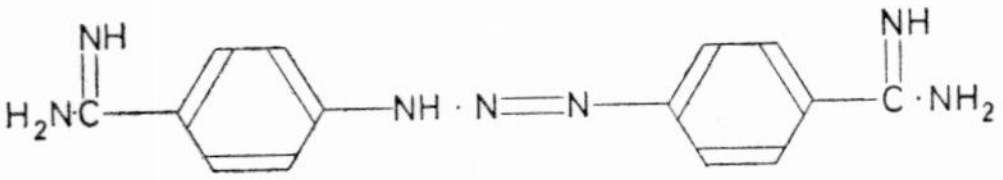

(XLIV)

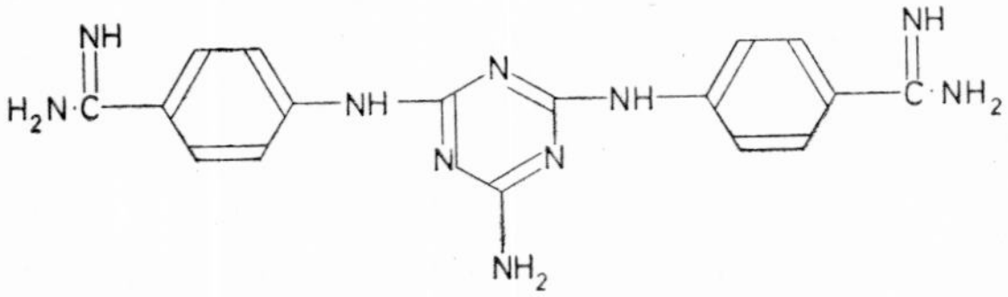

(XLV)

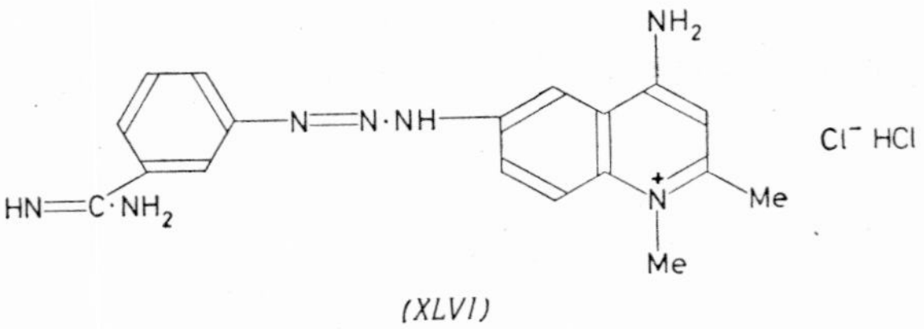

(XLVI)

introduction of ring-substituents gave rise to more active compounds of which the 2-methoxy-compound was the best; substitution on the central nitrogen atom had an unfavourable effect on activity[167].

### Phenanthridines with Prophylactic Properties

The result of combining molecular fragments of trypanocides was demonstrated most dramatically by Prothidium (*XLVII*) in which the pyrimidine

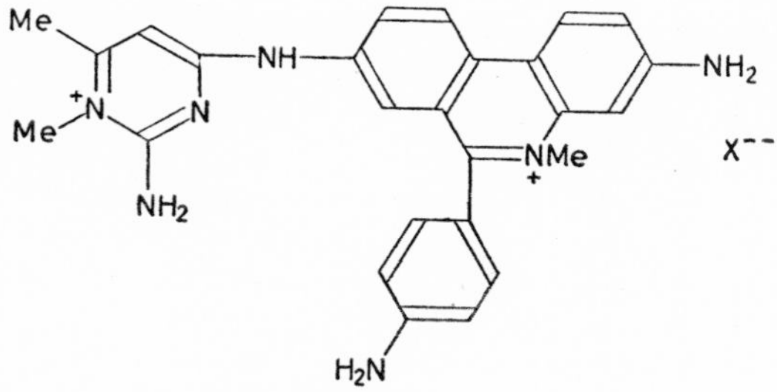

(XLVII)

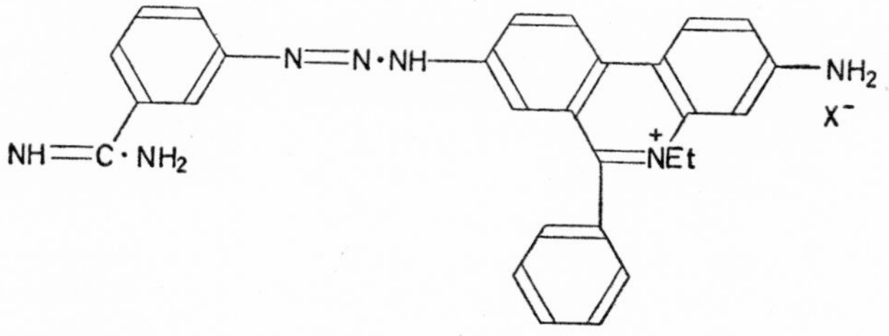

(XLVIII)

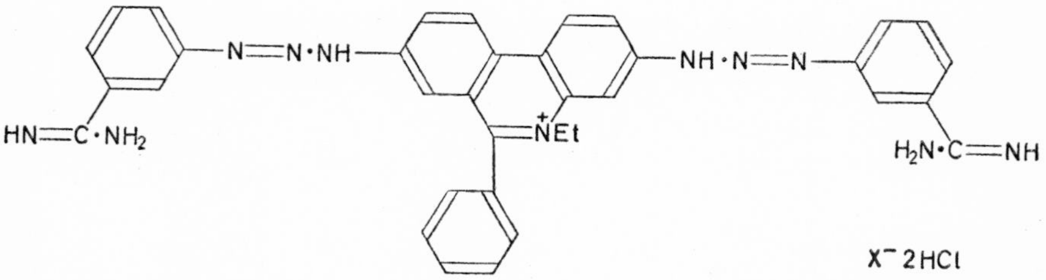

(XLIX)

ring of quinapyramine is attached to the amino-group of a phenanthridinium compound[168]. Analogues of (*XLVII*) were prepared, *inter alia* those with the pyrimidine ring in different positions[169], but these were less effective drugs. Prothidium is not only curative of bovine trypanosomiasis but a dose as low as 2 mg/kg protects cattle for as long as 6 months[170]. Prothidium is the most important prophylactic drug for African cattle, and the nature of its action is of great interest. The drug is an orange, water-soluble salt which after injection is rapidly concentrated in the parasites[171]. It was not detected in the blood of rats one hour after injection but was concentrated in the liver and kidneys for 7 days, during which time excretion in the bile was observed. Thus far it resembles other phenanthridinium compounds[172]. But, injection into cattle causes the location of a drug depot near the injection site where it can be detected 3 months after treatment. The mechanism of prophylaxis is therefore similar to that for quinapyramine-prophylactic. After Prothidium prophylaxis, the incubation period before a new infection becomes apparent may be as long as 50 days[173], and this circumstance no doubt explains the readiness with which resistant strains appear after chemoprophylaxis is undertaken.

The structure of Prothidium and quinapyramine suggested that the pyrimidine ring present in both molecules confers prophylactic properties, but recently active phenanthridinium salts related to Berenil have been prepared. The first prophylactic drug of this class was metamidium[174] which was prepared by the condensation of diazotized m-aminobenzamidine and homidium chloride. The product was first thought to be a mixture of the 3- and 8- (XLVIII) diazoamino-compounds, but whereas the active red salt, now known as isometamidium, has structure (XLVIII), the purple salt is an aminoazo-compound[175]. Isometamidium is likely to be of great value in Africa, for not only does it possess remarkable prophylactic properties, but it is active against trypanosome strains resistant to other drugs, even Prothidium[173]. The emergence of resistant strains has become the most serious problem in bovine trypanosomiasis now that the provision of suitable prophylactics has made continuous protection of cattle possible. Apart from troublesome reaction at the injection site which they sometimes cause, adequate curative drugs are now available and protection is readily afforded. But these successes lead to the spread of resistant strains, and a new drug such as isometamidium, which appears to differ from others in its range of activity, is of great value because of its ability to cure protected animals of break-through infections that are resistant to homidium and Berenil.

Recently a third prophylactic phenanthridine compound has been announced; when tetrazotized homidium cloride is condensed with 2 molecules of m-aminobenzamidine, the compound (XLIX, M & B 4596) is formed which protects mice infected with T. congolense and shows promise in cattle[176].

### The Suramin Complexes

About the same time as the discovery of Prothidium, a new approach to prophylaxis had been made at the West African Institute for Trypanosomiasis Research. It was argued that if the toxicity of homidium was reduced, as is that of pentamidine[48], by the simultaneous administration of suramin, then adequate dosage of homidium might be used for the treatment of animals infected with resistant strains. Simultaneous or prior treatment with suramin had little effect on the toxicity of homidium, so Williamson and Desowitz[177] prepared salts (or complexes as they regard them) of the anionic suramin with equivalent quantities of the cationic trypanocides, quinapyramine, homidium and Berenil. These complexes proved to be less toxic and more trypanocidal than the original drugs. As prepared by precipitation from aqueous solution they give viscous and thixotropic colloids which form depots at injection sites[178]. By this mechanism they exert considerable prophylaxis in mice, especially the Berenil complex, which protects mice for several weeks. Somewhat different results were obtained in zebu cattle[179]; the Berenil complex was of no value, the quinapyramine complex excelled quinapyramine-prophylactic, and the homidium complex at 5 mg/kg protected cattle for 216 days and at 10 mg/kg the protection was for 385 days. Unfortunately it has not yet been possible to take full advantage of this promise owing to the severe local reaction after injection[180]. Prothidium-suramin complex at 10 mg/kg protects cattle for about twice as long (285 days) as Prothidium itself at 2 mg/kg and first results suggest that the local reaction is less severe[171].

## Porcine trypanosomiasis

The severe and rapidly fatal disease of pigs due to *T. simiae* prevents the establishment of a large pig-industry in West Africa. Dimidium bromide shows some activity in pigs, and although quinapyramine is superior to dimidium[181], re-infected pigs are resistant to further treatment, suggesting that after 'cure' they had harboured a cryptic infection. Quinapyramine-prophylactic at high dosage (11·7 mg/kg) is curative, but the most successful drug is quinapyramine-suramin complex which also protects the animal for some 6 months[182].

## Equine trypanosomiasis

The traditional nagana, a dramatic disease of horses, camels, donkeys and mules, is due to infection with *T. brucei*, the most virulent of the trypanosome species, and is widespread in Africa from the Sudan to the borders of the Transvaal. *T. brucei* infects most mammals although man and apes are excepted, and is rapidly fatal for horses and camels. Cattle, sheep and goats are much less susceptible. The organic arsenicals are not very effective and the great standby has been suramin. For horses it is desirable that it be given jointly with tartar emetic[183]. Surfen C has some action on *T. brucei*[136] but more active compounds of this class are the aminoquinaldine derivatives[138] (*XXXII*) and (*XXXIII*)[139,140]. Pentamidine and other aromatic diamidines, especially Berenil, are active against *T. brucei* and offer an alternative to suramin. Quinapyramine is also effective although less so than against *T. congolense* and the so-called *T. evansi* group.

The *T. evansi* group of trypanosomes are not transmitted by tsetse but mechanically by other flies, chiefly of the stomoxys and tabanidae species. They cause diseases, chiefly of equine species, which are of wide distribution, being indeed of more importance in other parts of the world than in Africa. The disease is known as surra in Asia, and as mal de caderas in South America where the infecting species is *T. equinum*. The traditional remedy for *T. evansi* infections is suramin. In the Sudan where the infection is the only major disease of camels, the standard treatment is suramin (5 g in 50 ml of water), and relapses which may be due to strains resistant to suramin are treated with quinapyramine (2 g in 20 ml of water). Berenil is ineffective in relapses[184]. Spirotrypan, a complex organic arsenical, to which reference is made later, has effected cures of animals infected with *T. equinum*[185], but Butarsen is ineffective as a treatment for surra.

*T. equiperdum*, which is unique among trypanosomes in being transmitted venereally and not by an insect vector, is also world-wide in distribution, causing the disease known as dourine. Infections with *T. equiperdum* once caused serious loss of horses in Canada, but have since been eliminated from that country. Fortunately, infections due to this species are very susceptible to drug treatment, and cures may be effected with several organic arsenicals, suramin, pentamidine and quinapyramine.

Trypanosomiasis due to several species is of frequent occurrence in dogs in Africa and may be treated readily with the appropriate drug for the infecting species.

### Miscellaneous Trypanocides

The literature, particularly that referring to patents, frequently mentions compounds that have trypanocidal activity, usually of a low order, as shown by a delay in the death of infected mice. Some of these observations, however, are of considerable interest. Important, not only on account of their considerable activity in mice, but also because they differ so markedly in structure from the established trypanocides, are the dithiobiurets of which the best example (*L*, R = Ph, $R^1$ = Me) is

$$R\diagdown$$
$$\underset{R^1\diagup}{\phantom{x}}N \cdot CS \cdot NH \cdot CS \cdot NH_2 \quad (L)$$

curative of *T. congolense* infections in mice with a wide margin between curative and toxic dosage[186]. Analogous compounds (*L*, $R^1$ = H) in which R was phenyl, substituted *inter alia* with methoxyl, methyl, chloro or dimethylamino groups, showed activity[187]. Quaternary salts were prepared from those compounds in which the group R was basic, but these, and also compounds in which R was a heterocyclic radical, were inactive. The insolubility in water of the more active compounds, and the need for repeated injections to effect cure prejudiced hope of their success in the field.

Attention has recently been directed to another different and intrinsically interesting class of compound with trypanocidal activity, though of a low order[188]. Chlorophyllins, containing magnesium or copper (but not the corresponding non-metallic compounds), and haematoporphyrin delayed the death of mice infected with *T. congolense*, and on prolonged treatment sometimes effected cures. This action is inhibited by haemin and it is suggested that the activity depends on competition with haemin or some related growth factor.

Certain polymers are active in tubercular infections, and Goble and Singer, on the assumption that their antibacterial action was mediated through the reticuloendothelial system, investigated their effect on *T. congolense* infections in mice[189]. Some of these polymers showed activity, but since the same activity relationships between them hold also *in vitro* it is unlikely that their activity is due solely to their influence on phagocytosis.

The compound 6-azauracil[190], which has been shown to depend for its anti-tumour activity on its ability to interfere with pyrimidine synthesis by inhibiting the enzymic decarboxylation of orotidylic acid, prolongs the life of mice infected with *T. equiperdum*[191]. The dose required to exert an appreciable effect is so high that it is not possible to draw convincing conclusions from this result about the enzymic make-up of trypanosomes.

A series of remarkable organic arsenic-antimony compounds was described by Schmidt[192] (*e.g.* Sdt. 355) which were said to have high trypanocidal

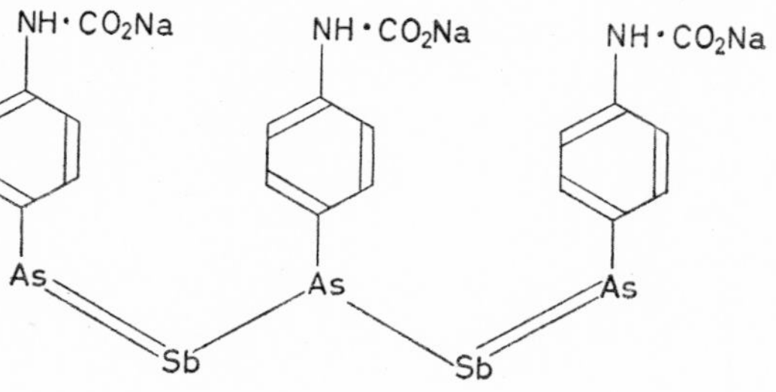

Sdt.355

activity. They are unstable compounds and there have been no reports of clinical trials.

## HUMAN TRYPANOSOMIASIS IN CENTRAL AND SOUTH AMERICA

Chagas's disease, which is common in Central and South America, is one due to infection with *T. cruzi* and is transmitted by reduviid bugs. The mode of transmission is believed to be by accidental ingestion of the faeces of infected bugs, or by contamination therewith of cuts or scars. The disease is therefore largely a problem of hygiene, and modern insecticides offer perhaps the most likely solution[193]. The extent of the problem may be appreciated by the fact that recent surveys in Brazil of *Triatoma infestans*, the common vector, have revealed infection rates of some 24 per cent, with over 80 per cent of the houses in some districts infested with the bugs[194]; an even more alarming situation has recently been found in South Peru[195]. The number of new cases seen annually is very high, 4,000 to 5,000 in Uruguay alone according to one authority[196], and the proportion of the population in Central and South American states showing infection, as revealed by complement fixation reactions, is commonly 24 per cent and may in some localities reach over 50 per cent. In 1955 an indigenous case was found in the United States[197]. The high incidence of the disease is probably due to the existence of a reservoir in animals, particularly armadillo. The disease is also encountered in dogs and rats.

Chagas's disease is not only very prevalent but it is also very serious. The primary infection is chiefly of children and the symptoms are fever, anaemia, and enlargement of the liver, spleen, lymphatic glands and especially of the thyroid. If the victim survives this acute phase, trypanosomes become very scanty in the blood but invade the tissues as the rounded leishmania-like so-called tissue forms. Probably multiplication takes place in every organ of the body, and in the chronic form, which is so common, the heart is frequently affected and the expectation of life of the victim is seriously reduced. This characteristic of multiplication in the tissues has caused some taxonomists to place the organism in a separate genus as *Schizotrypanum cruzi*.

*T. cruzi* is very resistant to drugs and the successful treatment of Chagas's disease remains one of the great challenges to chemotherapy. The resistance to drug treatment may be associated with the hypothesis that *T. cruzi*, unlike other trypanosome species, is relatively independent of enzymes with sulphydryl groups[198]. An unpromising situation is rendered more difficult by the organism's habit of invading the tissues of test animals just as it does in man, so that even if a test substance clears the peripheral blood of trypanosomes there is no certainty that the infection has been eradicated. *T. cruzi* may be grown in culture[199], in chick embryo[200] and in tissue culture, so that other ways of investigating drugs are available. *T. cruzi* is the most suitable organism to grow for the support of *Entamoeba histolytica* in cultures in the investigation of drugs for amoebicidal activity[201]. It is most impressive how rarely *T. cruzi* has been affected by drugs in these investigations, a circumstance that makes it particularly well-suited for this purpose.

The infection in mice, broadly speaking, resembles that in man. Young animals are more susceptible than adults. The disease kills a proportion of the mice at varying intervals after infection of upwards of 20 days, but the disease becomes chronic in some with irregular appearance of scanty parasites in the peripheral blood[202]. For test purposes 0·1 ml of diluted heart blood of an infected animal, containing about 100,000 trypanosomes, is injected into a mouse subcutaneously. Trypanosomes normally appear in the peripheral blood in 5 to 10 days but in view of the resistance of *T. cruzi* to drugs, treatment in the first instance is best given on the day of inoculation to detect minimal activity. Such compounds as show activity, by delaying or preventing the appearance of the trypanosomes in the peripheral blood, may then be further investigated by treating mice in which the blood infection has already been demonstrated, that is in the so-called established infection. Few compounds show worthwhile activity by the first test, and very few by the second. Three or four of the latter group have been tried clinically, but the usual experience is that they clear trypanosomes from the blood of patients but the tissue infection as determined by the xeno-diagnostic test persists. The trypanosomes multiply in the tissues so that when the tissue infection persists, parasites reappear in the blood, but in numbers too small to be readily detected. In the xeno-diagnostic test a 'clean' bug is caused to feed on the patient and if only a very few trypanosomes enter the insect's gut they multiply there and are readily detected in the faeces. Even in the untreated disease most of the trypanosomes eventually disappear from the blood-stream, and thus an examination of a blood smear does not give unqualified information about the therapeutic value of a drug.

## CHEMOTHERAPY OF CHAGAS'S DISEASE

The first synthetic compound that showed some promise in a clinical trial in Chagas's disease was Bayer 7602 (*N*,*N*'-bis(4-amino-2-methylquinolin-

6-yl)diallylmalonamide, Chagavlon, *LI*), a member of the Surfen group of drugs. Bayer 7602 shows good activity in the established infection in mice. Given on alternate days to a total of 60–100 mg/kg by intramuscular injection, a painful operation, it rapidly clears the trypanosomes from the blood in acute cases with improvement in the patient's condition[203,204], but the tissue infection is not eliminated, nor are chronic cases helped. Activity against *T. cruzi* is a general property of the substituted malonamides of

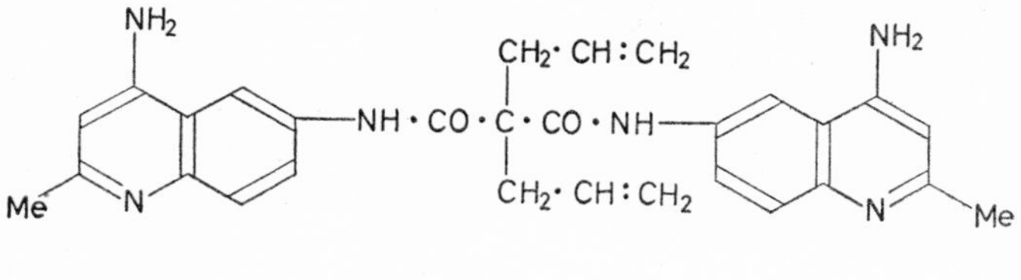

*(LI)*

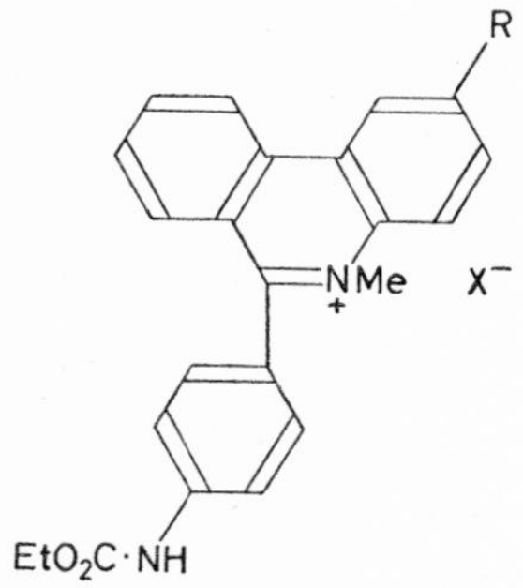

*(LII)*

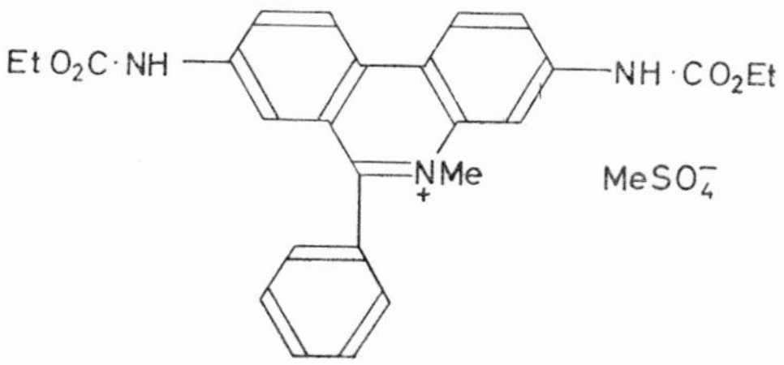

*(LIII)*

4,6-diaminoquinaldine[139], but not of other members of the Surfen class[140]. The corresponding malonamides of 4,6-diaminoquinoline are much less active[138] and quinapyramine is inactive.

Several members of the phenanthridinium group of trypanocides show activity against *T. cruzi* in mice when administered during the incubation period, and a few act on the established infection[202]. These compounds possess the urethano-group ($NH \cdot CO_2Et$) and activity does not parallel that against *T. congolense*. The first compound found to have an effect comparable with that of Bayer 7602 was the phenanthridinium compound (*LII*, R = $NH \cdot CO_2Et$), the isomer (*LIII*) being less active[205]. Two other compounds also have activity similar to that of Bayer 7602, namely the 2-aminophenanthridinium compound (*LII*, R = $NH_2$) and the isomeric 3-amino-compound. The former, which has been given the trivial name carbidium sulphate, has undergone clinical trial and the results in several patients were similar to those achieved with Bayer 7602; acute symptoms were rapidly relieved but the xeno-diagnostic test revealed that the tissue infection was not eradicated. Even minor variations in chemical structure led to compounds of greatly reduced activity[206].

Two arsenicals, one known as Bayer 9736[207] and the other as Spirotry-pan[208,209], also clear the bloodstream of trypanosomes but owing to the persistence of tissue forms, relapses occur. Spirotrypan is also active against

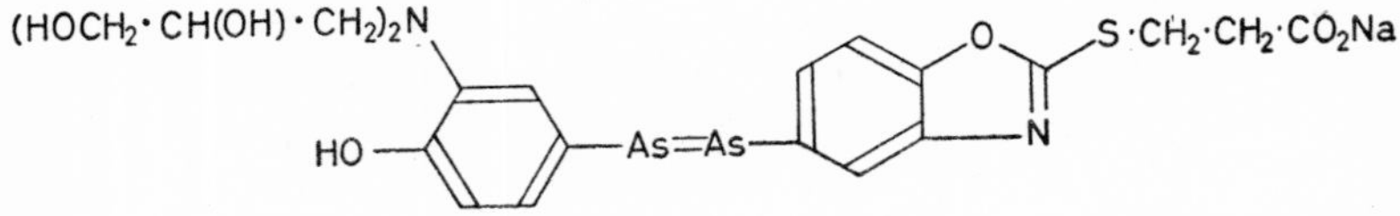

(LIV)

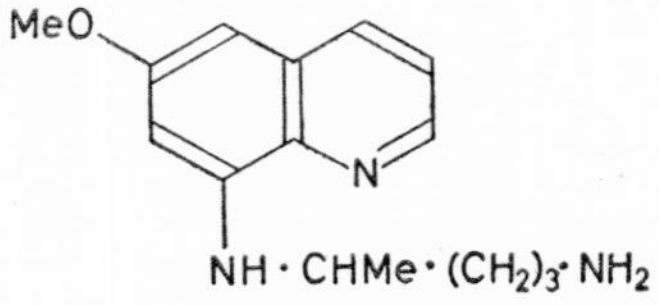

(LV)

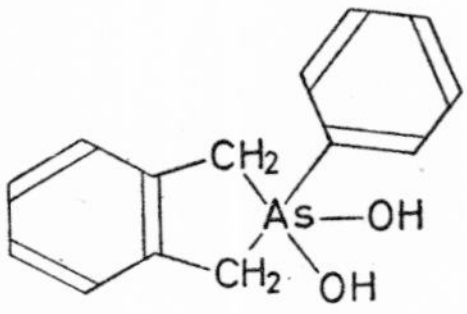

(LVI)

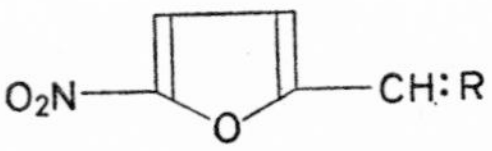

(LVII) R = N·NH·CO·NH·CO·NH$_2$
or N·NH·CO·CH$_2$·$\overset{+}{N}$Me$_3$ Cl$^-$
or CH·CH:N·NH·CO·NH$_2$

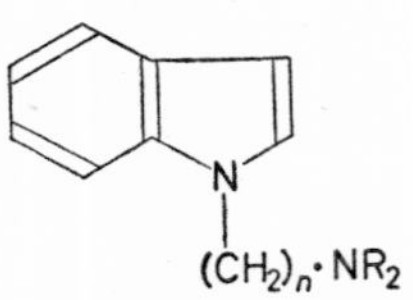

R = Me or Et
n = 2 or 3
(LVIII)

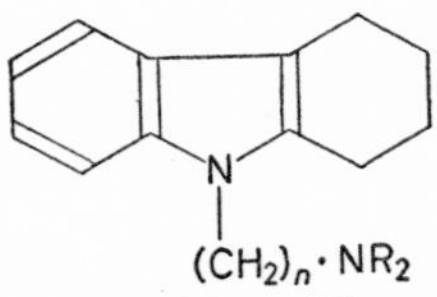

R = Me or Et
n = 2 or 3
(LIX)

other trypanosome species and like Bayer 9736, contains arsenic and sulphur; it is the unsymmetrical arseno-compound (LIV).

A more promising prospect appeared to open up when Goble found that the potent antimalarial primaquine (LV) and some other 8-aminoquinolines were effective against the established mouse infection[210]. These compounds are notable for their action on the exoerythrocytic forms of the parasite of benign tertian malaria which are known to be present in the liver. The dose effective against T. cruzi in mice is very high (20–30 mg/kg for 12 to 18 days) and proved to be toxic for dogs. A clinical trial of primaquine has also been reported; the drug was given by mouth and caused the parasites to disappear from the blood-stream of most patients, but no conclusions were reached on the effect on tissue forms[211]. The structure-activity relationships of this class of compound appear to follow the antimalarial activity rather closely[212], and the corresponding 6-quinolinols are inactive[213].

Among the few compounds that have been reported to possess some activity in the mouse infection is the diamidine (*XLIII*) which is also active against *T. congolense*[56]. Some isoarsindoles (*e.g. (LVI)*) are slightly active[214] and puromycin is active against the blood forms[215]. Many derivatives of 5-nitrofurfuraldehyde are active against *T. cruzi in vitro*, but only four compounds, (*LVII*) and nitrofurazone, have a suppressive action in the mouse infection and then at multiple high dosage[216]. A recent patent claims that certain indoles (*LVIII*) and tetrahydrocarbazoles (*LIX*) are 'especially' active against *T. cruzi*[217]. 2-Acetamido-5-nitrothiazole, when given orally to mice at 200 mg/kg, caused a decrease in mortality but the tissue forms were not affected, nor had the drug any protective action[218].

## CONCLUSIONS

The official publications of 1948 on trypanosomiasis[99,103,219] still form an excellent introduction to the subject as it relates to Africa. The work of the last fifteen years has gone far towards solving the major problems, both medical and veterinary. The successful treatment of the disease of man in Africa had already been established, and the more recent work has solved many of the problems arising from the diminished efficacy of tryparsamide and the increasing prevalence of the more rapidly fatal and less tractable disease due to *T. rhodesiense*. Progress has also been made, particularly in Central Africa, towards systematic prophylaxis. Even with the disease in man there are, however, no grounds for complacency[220], particularly in view of the political changes that are occurring in Africa and the growing shortage of skilled European staff. The new organic arsenicals have been of great value but they are dangerous drugs, and cases still arise that are resistant to them, and to the diamidines. There is urgent need for an entirely new and relatively safe drug. Prophylaxis carries its peculiar danger of aggravating the problem of drug-resistance, and has made little headway in East Africa. The most spectacular progress has been made in the treatment of the disease in cattle. At the time of the discovery of the phenanthridinium drugs, bovine trypanosomiasis may well have been the most important factor in the life of much of Africa and a problem seemingly incapable of a satisfactory solution. Now a sick animal may almost invariably be cured by a single injection of a drug, transit of animals through fly-belts may safely be undertaken, and the protection of animals for long periods is a possibility. Many problems still remain to be solved. Prophylaxis is so liable to provoke drug-resistance that in the present state of knowledge it almost looks as if new drugs must regularly be provided. Prophylaxis that depends on depot formation at the site of injection is frequently liable to cause necrosis and lameness. A new drug is urgently required in Northern Nigeria where the phenanthridinium compounds have not proved satisfactory[221]. Even more urgent is the need for a drug that is effective in the treatment of Chagas's disease, a drug that will eliminate tissue, as well as blood, forms of the parasite.

## THE CHEMOTHERAPY OF TRYPANOSOMIASIS

It can be readily appreciated that the great advances in the treatment of trypanosomiasis that have been made in recent years have all derived from the fundamental assumptions made by Ehrlich, on the validity of a chemotherapeutic approach to the treatment of diseases due to parasitic infection. Since then an enormous number of organic compounds has been screened against trypanosomes. As the number of chemical types has increased, the design of new drugs rests on a more solid foundation, so that in recent years remarkable results have accrued from the chemical manipulation of a limited number of complex radicals.

Apart from the striking improvements in the treatment of the disease in man, resulting from the use of the melamine arsenicals, modern chemotherapy of trypanosomiasis has developed mainly from the discovery of the aromatic diamidines and the phenanthridinium compounds. High activity is commonly associated in the quaternary salts with four aromatic rings (whether disposed as in dimidium or butterfly-fashion, as in Cinnoline 528) and at least two primary amino-groups. A similar disposition of aromatic rings occurs in the diamidines and in the Surfens, which may be regarded as their chemical analogues. Quinapyramine is, however, a diquaternary salt with three aromatic rings only, but its pyrimidine ring appears to confer prophylactic properties. When this ring or an amidinobenzene ring is present in a phenanthridinium salt, then, also, valuable prophylactic properties are likely to arise.

There are no indications yet that the improved understanding of the enzymic composition of the parasites and of the mode of action of known trypanocides is adequate to point to the synthesis of new and more effective drugs. Nevertheless, biochemical studies of the parasites and of the nature of drug resistance are fundamental to further progress. In recent years there has also been a great increase in the study of the immunological aspects of trypanosomiasis, a subject of great complexity. It is much too early even to speculate whether this work will ultimately make a contribution to the medical and veterinary problems of trypanosomiasis, but already it is yielding valuable information about the relationships between the tsetse fly and its various hosts.

## REFERENCES

1. LIVINGSTONE *Brit. med. J.* 1858, 360
2. BRAID *Brit. med. J.* 1858, 135
3. LAVERAN and MESNIL *Ann. Inst. Pasteur* 1902, **16,** 1
4. THOMAS *Brit. med. J.* 1905, **i,** 1140
5. BÜLBRING and BURN *Quart. J. Pharm.* 1938, **11,** 67
6. HAWKING *Quart. J. Pharm.* 1941, **14,** 337
7. GOODWIN *J. Pharmacol.* 1944, **81,** 224
8. DESOWITZ *Ann. trop. Med. Parasit.* 1954, **48,** 142
9. DESOWITZ and WATSON *Ann. trop. Med. Parasit.* 1953, **47,** 324
10. ANON *Brit. med. J.* 1948, **i,** 895
11. ORMEROD *Trans. R. Soc. trop. Med. Hyg.* 1961, **55,** 525
12. FRIEDEMANN *Physiol. Rev.* 1942, **22,** 125
13. HAWKING, HENNELLY and QUASTEL *J. Pharmacol.* 1937, **59,** 157
14. LOURIE *Trans. Faraday Soc.* 1943, **39,** 340

15. JACOBS and HEIDELBERGER *J. Amer. chem. Soc.* 1919, **41,** 1587
16. MORGAN and WALTON *J. chem. Soc.* 1931, 615
17. EHRLICH *Ber. dtsch. chem. Ges.* 1909, **42,** 27
18. EAGLE *J. Pharmacol.* 1939, **66,** 423
19. DOAK, STEINMANN and EAGLE *J. Amer. chem. Soc.* 1940, **62,** 3012
20. EAGLE and DOAK *Pharmacol. Rev.* 1951, **3,** 107
21. McLETCHIE *Trans. R. Soc. trop. Med. Hyg.* 1948, **41,** 445
22. FRIEDHEIM *J. Amer. chem. Soc.* 1944. **66,** 1775
23. ROLLO, WILLIAMSON and LOURIE *Ann. trop. Med. Parasit.* 1949, **43,** 194
24. BUTLER, DUGGAN and HUTCHINSON *Trans. R. Soc. trop. Med. Hyg.* 1957, **51,** 69
25. BANKS, GRUHZIT, TILLITSON and CONTROULIS *J. Amer. chem. Soc.* 1944, **66,** 1771
26. BANKS and CONTROULIS *J. Amer. chem. Soc.* 1946, **68,** 944
27. AINLEY and DAVEY *Brit. J. Pharmacol.* 1958, **13,** 244
28. BAKER *Brit. J. Pharmacol.* 1958, **13,** 436
29. COHEN, KING and STRANGEWAYS *J. chem. Soc.* 1931, 3043; 1932, 2505
30. MURGATROYD *Ann. trop. Med. Parasit.* 1937, **31,** 473
31. PETERS, STOCKEN and THOMPSON *Nature, Lond.* 1945, **156,** 616
32. FRIEDHEIM and VOGEL *Proc. Soc. exp. Biol. N.Y.* 1947, **64,** 418
33. U.S. Patent 2,659,723. *Chem. Abstr.* 1955, **49,** 1815: JONCHERE, GORNER and REYRAUD *Bull. Soc. Pat. exot.* 1953, **46,** 386
34. APTED *Trans. R. Soc. trop. Med. Hyg.* 1957, **51,** 75
35. LOURIE *Analyst* 1952, **77,** 175
36. FRIEDHEIM and DE JONGH *Trans. R. Soc. trop. Med. Hyg.* 1959, **53,** 262
37. SPINKS *Biochem. J.* 1948, **42,** 109
38. WILLS and WORMELL *Biochem. J.* 1950, **47,** 158
39. ADAMS, ASHLEY and BADER *J. chem. Soc.* 1956, 3739
40. JANCSO and JANCSO *Zbl. Bakt.* 1934, **132,** 257
41. HAWKING, SEWELL and THURSTON *Brit. J. Pharmacol.* 1950, **5,** 217
42. STANDEN *Trans. R. Soc. trop. Med. Hyg.* 1955, **49,** 421
43. KING, LOURIE and YORKE *Lancet* 1937, **ii,** 1360
44. ASHLEY, BARBER, EWINS, NEWBERY and SELF *J. chem. Soc.* 1942, 103
45. KIKUTH and MUDROW-REICHENOW *Z. ImmunForsch.* 1950, **107,** 139
46. LAUNOY *Ann. pharm. franç.* 1948, **6,** 357
47. GALL *Ann. trop. Med. Parasit.* 1954, **48,** 242
48. GUIMARAES and LOURIE *Brit. J. Pharmacol.* 1951, **6,** 514
49. SCHNEIDER and MONTEZIN *Bull. Soc. Pat. exot.* 1954, **47,** 249
50. *West African Institute of Trypanosomiasis Research, Ann. Rep.* 1960, Harrison and Sons, London, pp. 9, 14
51. BARBER and SLACK *J. chem. Soc.* 1947, 82
52. NEWTH and WIGGINS *J. chem. Soc.* 1947, 396
53. ASHLEY, GROVE and HENSHALL *J. chem. Soc.* 1948, 261
54. GREGORY, HOLT and SLACK *J. chem. Soc.* 1947, 87
55. BARBER and STICKINGS *J. chem. Soc.* 1945, 167
56. WIEN *Brit. J. Pharmacol.* 1946, **1,** 65
57. MOFFATT *J. chem. Soc.* 1951, 625
58. LIBMAN and SLACK *J. chem. Soc.* 1951, 2588
59. BOWER, STEPHENS and WIBBERLEY *J. chem. Soc.* 1950, 3341
60. ASHLEY and HARRIS *J. chem. Soc.* 1946, 567
61. DAVIS *J. chem. Soc.* 1958, 907
62. BERG and NEWBERY *J. chem. Soc.* 1949, 642
63. SAFIR, KUSHNER, BRANCONE and SUBBA ROW *J. org. Chem.* 1948, **13,** 924
64. HEWITT, GUMBLE, SAFIR, BRANCONE and SUBBA ROW *J. Pharmacol.* 1949, **96,** 305
65. SUGASAWA and IWAO *J. pharm. Soc. Japan* 1945, **65,** 5
66. ALBERT, MILLS and ROYER *J. chem. Soc.* 1947, 1452

67. BARBER, SLACK and WOOLMAN *J. chem. Soc.* 1943, 99
68. ASHLEY and MACDONALD *J. chem. Soc.* 1957, 1668
69. ZIERING and BUCK *Emil Barrer Jubilee Volume* Basle, 1946, p. 378
70. DODD *J. Pharmacol.* 1946, **86,** 311
71. BAKER *Brit. J. Pharmacol.* 1959, **14,** 408
72. COLE, FRICK, HODGES and DUXBURY *Antibiotics and Chemotherapy* 1953, **3,** 429
73. U.S. Patent 2,830,046; *Chem. Abstr.* 1958, **52,** 14697
74. PACKCHANIAN *Amer. J. trop. Med. Hyg.* 1955, **4,** 705
75. APTED *Trans. R. Soc. trop. Med. Hyg.* 1960, **54,** 225
76. FRIEDHEIM, VOGEL and BERMAN *J. Amer. chem. Soc.* 1947, **69,** 560
77. EDGE, HILL and STONE *Brit. J. Pharmacol.* 1954, **9,** 125
78. FRIEDHEIM *Ann. trop. Med. Parasit.* 1953, **47,** 350
79. FISCHL *Z. ImmunForsch.* 1935, **85,** 77
80. RAPOPORT and HOLDEN *J. Amer. chem. Soc.* 1962, **84,** 635
81. PORTER, HEWITT, HESSELTINE, KRUPKA, LOWERY, WALLACE, BOHONOS and WILLIAMS *Antibiotics and Chemotherapy* 1952, **2,** 409
82. TOBIE *Amer. J. trop. Med. Hyg.* 1954, **3,** 852
83. HEWITT, GUMBLE, WALLACE and WILLIAMS *Antibiotics and Chemotherapy* 1954, **4,** 1222
84. BAKER, JOSEPH and WILLIAMS *J. Amer. chem. Soc.* 1955, **77,** 1
85. BAKER, SCHAUB, JOSEPH and WILLIAMS *J. Amer. chem. Soc.* 1955, **77,** 12
86. BAKER and SCHAUB *J. Amer. chem. Soc.* 1955, **77,** 5900
87. WALLER, FRYTH, HUTCHINGS and WILLIAMS *J. Amer. chem. Soc.* 1953, **75,** 2025
88. BAKER, JOSEPH and WILLIAMS *J. Amer. chem. Soc.* 1954, **76,** 2838
89. BAKER, JOSEPH and SCHAUB *J. org. Chem.* 1954, **19,** 631, 638
90. BAKER and SCHAUB *J. org. Chem.* 1954, **19,** 646
91. BAKER, SCHAUB and KISSMAN *J. Amer. chem. Soc.* 1955, **77,** 5911
92. GOLDMAN, MARISCO and ANGIER *J. Amer. chem. Soc.* 1956, **78,** 4173
93. KISSMAN, PIDACKS and BAKER *J. Amer. chem. Soc.* 1955, **77,** 18
94. TRINCAO, FRANCO, NOGUEIRA, PINTO and MÜHLPFORDT *Amer. J. trop. Med. Hyg.* 1955, **4,** 13
95. TRINCAO, PINTO and FRANCO *Amer. J. trop. Med. Hyg.* 1956, **5,** 784
96. BAKER *Trans. R. Soc. trop. Med. Hyg.* 1957, **51,** 183
97. TOBIE *J. Parasit.* 1957, **43,** 291
98. WALLER, PATRICK, FULMER and MEYER *J. Amer. chem. Soc.* 1957, **79,** 1011
99. BUXTON *Trypanosomiasis in Eastern Africa:* H.M.S.O., London, 1948
100. ASHCROFT *Brit. med. J.* 1959, 173
101. CHANDLER *J. comp. Path.* 1958, **68,** 253
102. MULLIGAN *Trans. R. Soc. trop. Med. Hyg.* 1955, **49,** 203
103. NASH, *The Anchau Development and Settlement Scheme:* H.M.S.O., London, 1948
104. BROWNING, MORGAN, ROBB and WALLS *J. Path. Bact.* 1938, **46,** 203
105. MORGAN and WALLS *J. chem. Soc.* 1931, 2447
106. WALLS *J. chem. Soc.* 1945, 294
107. WALLS, BROWNING, CALVER and LECKIE *J. chem. Soc.* 1947, 67
108. HORNBY, EVANS and WILDE *J. comp. Path.* 1943, **53,** 269
109. CARMICHAEL and BELL *Vet. Rec.* 1944, **56,** 495
110. RANDALL and LAWES *Vet. Rec.* 1947, **59,** 221
111. BROWNING *Nature, Lond.* 1949, **163,** 590
112. RANDALL and BEVERIDGE *Vet. Rec.* 1946, **58,** 398
113. BROWNLEE, GOODWIN and WALLS *Vet. Rec.* 1947, **59,** 518
114. BURDIN and PLOWRIGHT *J. comp. Path.* 1952, **62,** 178
115. EVANS *Vet. Rec.* 1950, **62,** 59
116. WATKINS *J. chem. Soc.* 1952, 3059
117. WATKINS and WOOLFE *Nature, Lond.* 1952, **169,** 506

118. BURDIN and PLOWRIGHT *Nature, Lond.* 1952, **169,** 666
119. FORD, WILMSHURST and KARIB *Vet. Rec.* 1953, **65,** 907
120. ROBSON and WILDE *Vet. Rec.* 1953, **65,** 49
121. UNSWORTH *Ann. trop. Med. Parasit.* 1954, **48,** 229, 237
122. KARIB, FORD and WILMSHURST *J. comp. Path.* 1954, **64,** 187
123. BROWNLEE, GOSS, GOODWIN, WOODBINE and WALLS *Brit. J. Pharmacol.* 1950, **5,** 261
124. WALLS and WHITTAKER *J. chem. Soc.* 1950, 41
125. NEAL and KARIB *Brit. J. Pharmacol.* 1954, **9,** 37
126. DAVIS *J. chem. Soc.* 1956, 337
127. CALDWELL, COPP and WALLS *J. chem. Soc.* 1950, 2698
128. GOODWIN and UNSWORTH *Brit. J. Pharmacol.* 1952, **7,** 581
129. CALDWELL and WALLS *J. chem. Soc.* 1948, 188
130. COPP and WALLS *J. chem. Soc.* 1950, 311
131. McCOUBREY and MATHIESON *J. chem. Soc.* 1949, 696
132. KENNEFORD, LOURIE, MORLEY, SIMPSON, WILLIAMSON and WRIGHT *J. chem. Soc.* 1952, 2595
133. HOLT and PETROW *J. chem. Soc.* 1948, 919
134. STEPHENS and WIBBERLEY *J. chem. Soc.* 1950, 3336
135. COOK and MOFFATT *J. chem. Soc.* 1951, 2487
136. JENSCH *Angew. Chem.* 1937, **50,** 891
137. EVANS *J. comp. Path.* 1936, **49,** 160
138. JENSCH *Annalen* 1950, **568,** 73
139. PRATT and ARCHER *J. Amer. chem. Soc.* 1948, **70,** 4065
140. SCHOCK *J. Amer. chem. Soc.* 1957, **79,** 1672
141. BARRETT, CURD and HEPWORTH *J. chem. Soc.* 1953, 50
142. AINLEY, CURD, HEPWORTH, MURRAY and VASEY *J. chem. Soc.* 1953, 59
143. CURD and DAVEY *Nature, Lond.* 1949, **163,** 89
144. CURD and DAVEY *Brit. J. Pharmacol.* 1950, **5,** 25
145. DAVEY *Trans. R. Soc. trop. Med. Hyg.* 1950, **43,** 583
146. UNSWORTH and CHANDLER *Ann. trop. Med. Parasit.* 1952, **46,** 240
147. UNSWORTH and BIRKETT *Vet. Rec.* 1952, **64,** 351, 353
148. CURD and RICHARDSON *J. chem. Soc.* 1955, 1850
149. KENNEFORD, LOURIE, SIMPSON, WILLIAMSON and WRIGHT *Nature, Lond.* 1948, **161,** 603
150. McINTYRE and SIMPSON *J. chem. Soc.* 1952, 2606
151. McINTYRE and SIMPSON *J. chem. Soc.* 1952, 2615
152. MACEY and SIMPSON *J. chem. Soc.* 1952, 2602
153. MORLEY and SIMPSON *J. chem. Soc.* 1952, 2617
154. LOURIE, MORLEY, SIMPSON and WALKER *Brit. J. Pharmacol.* 1951, **6,** 643
155. CHANDLER *Brit. J. Pharmacol.* 1957, **12,** 44
156. AUSTIN, HUNT, POTTER and TAYLOR *J. Pharm., Lond.* 1957, **11,** 80
157. AUSTIN, COLLIER, POTTER, SMITH and TAYLOR *Nature, Lond.* 1957, **179,** 143
158. AUSTIN, POTTER and TAYLOR *J. chem. Soc.* 1958, 1489
159. TAYLOR—personal communication
160. JENSCH *Arzneimitt. Forschung* 1955, **5,** 634
161. MILNE, ROBSON and LIVEBANDIZA *Vet. Rec.* 1955, **67,** 280
162. SMITH and SCOTT *J. comp. Path.* 1961, **71,** 325
163. JENSCH *Angew. Chem.* 1948, **60,** 248
164. CRUNDWELL *J. chem. Soc.* 1956, 368
165. DAVIS *J. chem. Soc.* 1958, 907
166. BERG *J. chem. Soc.* 1961, 4041
167. EASSON *J. chem. Soc.* 1961, 1024
168. WATKINS and WOOLFE *Nature, Lond.* 1956, **178,** 368, 727

169. WATKINS *J. chem. Soc.* 1958, 1443
170. ROBSON and MILNE *Vet. Rec.* 1957, **69,** 564
171. TAYLOR *Brit. J. Pharmacol.* 1960. **15,** 230, 235
172. GOODWIN, GOSS and LOCK *Brit. J. Pharmacol.* 1950, **5,** 287
173. LYTTLE *J. comp. Path.* 1960, **70,** 18
174. WRAGG, WASHBURN, BROWN and HILL *Nature, Lond.* 1958, **182,** 1005
175. BERG *Nature, Lond.* 1960, **188,** 1106
176. BERG, BROWN, HILL and WRAGG *Nature, Lond.* 1961, **192,** 367
177. WILLIAMSON and DESOWITZ *Nature, Lond.* 1956, **177,** 1074
178. WILLIAMSON *Ann. trop. Med. Parasit.* 1957, **51,** 440
179. DESOWITZ *Ann. trop. Med. Parasit.* 1957, **51,** 457
180. STEPHEN *Ann. trop. Med. Parasit.* 1958, **52,** 417
181. WILSON *Nature, Lond.* 1949, **163,** 873
182. WATSON and WILLIAMSON *Ann. trop. Med. Parasit.* 1958, **52,** 72
183. STEWART *J. comp. Path.* 1935, **48,** 316
184. LEACH *J. comp. Path.* 1961, **71,** 109
185. JAHN and HÄUSSLER *Tierärztl. Umsch.* 1951, **6,** 131
186. WOOLFE *Brit. J. Pharmacol.* 1953, **8,** 420
187. FAIRFULL and PEAK *J. chem. Soc.* 1955, 796, 803
188. GOBLE and BOYD *Proc. Soc. exp. Biol. N.Y.* 1959, **100,** 745
189. GOBLE and SINGER *Ann. N.Y. Acad. Sci.* 1960, **88,** 149
190. BARLOW and WELCH *J. Amer. chem. Soc.* 1956, **78,** 1258
191. JAFFE *Biochem. Pharmacol.* 1961, **8,** 216
192. SCHMIDT *Med. u. Chemie* 1942, **4,** 164
193. DE BUSTAMENTE and DE CARVALHO *Rev. bras. Malariol.* 1957, **9,** 305
194. DIAZ *Rev. bras. Malariol.* 1954, **6,** 607
195. ANON *Nature, Lond.* 1961, **192,** 921
196. DIAZ *Brazil-med.* 1948, **62,** 217
197. WOODY and WOODY *J. Amer. med. Ass.* 1955, **159,** 676
198. VON BRAND and JOHNSON *J. cell. comp. Physiol.* 1947, **29,** 33
199. LITTLE and SUBBA ROW *J. Bact.* 1945, **50,** 57
200. GANAPATI *Nature, Lond.* 1948, **162,** 963
201. ANDERSON, JAMES, SWANMAN and NORENI *Exptl. Parasit.* 1952, **1,** 66
202. GOODWIN, GOSS, LOCK and WALLS *Brit. J. Pharmacol.* 1950, **5,** 277
203. MAZZA *Dtsch. tropen med. Z.* 1941, **45,** 577
204. MAZZA, BASSO and BASSO *Trop. Dis. Bull.* 1946, **43,** 720
205. BROWNING, CALVER, LECKIE and WALLS *Nature, Lond.* 1946, **157,** 263
206. WALLS *J. chem. Soc.* 1946, 1031; 1950, 3511
207. MAZZA, BASSO and BASSO *Trop. Dis. Bull.* 1943, **40,** 22
208. WAGNER and PEDAL *Arzneimitt.-Forsch.* 1954, **4,** 137
209. RIBIERO *Trop. Dis. Bull.* 1958, **55,** 1092
210. GOBLE *J. Parasit.* 1949, **35,** 375
211. RODRIGUEZ and PENALVER *Trop. Dis. Bull.* 1958, **55,** 991
212. GOBLE *Antibiotics and Chemotherapy* 1952, **2,** 265
213. GOBLE *J. Parasit.* 1954, **40,** 102
214. LYON and MANN *J. chem. Soc.* 1945, 30
215. HEWITT, WALLACE, GUMBLE, GILL and WILLIAMS *Amer. J. trop. Med. Hyg.* 1953, **2,** 254
216. PACKCHANIAN *Antibiotics and Chemotherapy* 1957, **7,** 13
217. G. P. 930, 988. *Chem. Abstr.* 1958, **52,** 17288
218. BRENER and PELLEGRINO *Rev. bras. Malariol.* 1958, **10,** 327
219. DAVEY *Trypanosomiasis in British West Africa:* H.M.S.O., London, 1948
220. APTED *Trans. R. Soc. trop. Med. Hyg.* 1962, **56,** 15
221. BROWN, HILL and HOLLAND *Brit. J. Pharmacol.* 1961, **17,** 396

# 3

# ANTITUSSIVE DRUGS

## C. I. CHAPPEL and C. VON SEEMANN

### INTRODUCTION

THE present review attempts to report progress in antitussive therapy achieved over the past twenty years. It is limited to those drugs which have a direct and specific action on the cough reflex, and includes the opium alkaloids, their synthetic derivatives and substitutes, and newer non-narcotic compounds. Such a classification eliminates adjuvant drugs such as expectorants[1-4] and antibiotics which are generally used in the treatment of cough accompanying respiratory disorders. A number of review articles on cough therapy and the management of cough have already been published[5-30], and the problem of addiction to antitussive drugs has been stressed[31-33]. Progress in this field has, however, been handicapped by the lack of simple and reliable methods for pharmacological testing[34], although greater insight into the pathophysiology of cough and the nervous pathways involved in the cough reflex has enabled the pharmacologist in some cases to determine by specific techniques the site of action of antitussive drugs.

### PATHOPHYSIOLOGY OF COUGH

#### Description of Cough

Cough may be defined as a series of phenomena of reflex or voluntary origin which combine to produce the rapid expulsion of air from the respiratory tract[35]. Preceding the expiratory thrust there is an inspiratory effort[36], and the degree of pulmonary expansion with inspiration is directly related to the magnitude of the succeeding expiration[35,37]. As lung expansion increases, so the inspiratory activity of the respiratory centre in the brain is more and more inhibited whilst increased stimulation of expiration develops. The link between inspiration and the subsequent expiration is probably through the Hering-Breuer reflex. When inspiration is complete, the glottis closes and remains closed as the expiratory phase begins. It then suddenly opens and the high intratracheal pressure reinforces the expiratory effort. The action of the glottis in this respect is not obligatory as cough may occur in animals breathing through a tracheotomy tube—the glottis acts rather to facilitate and synchronize the cough. The bronchi and trachea may also help to increase the resistance of the respiratory tract to the expired air. Irritation of the bronchi to produce cough also causes bronchoconstriction[38,39], and X-ray studies have shown marked narrowing of the lumen of the trachea in man during cough[40,41].

After inspiration and closure of the glottis, the expiratory phase of coughing begins. This is an active phenomenon involving contraction of the expiratory musculature of the thorax[42]. As the glottis is closed, a rapid and marked

89

increase in intrapleural pressure extending over the lung parenchyma results[43]. This high intrathoracic pressure exists only until the glottis opens and expiration begins. The increased pressure within the lung combines with the resistance offered by the respiratory tract, and results in expulsion of air at enormous velocity. Recent calculations place the linear velocity of the air within the trachea during cough near to the speed of sound[40].

The events described are typical of a single cough, but cough is often repetitive, consisting of a series of such events. Whereas the Hering-Breuer reflex represents the connection between inspiration and the succeeding expiration in a single cough, indiviudal cough spasms may be linked through Head's 'paradoxical reflex,' i.e. a strong expiration may lead to a stronger succeeding inspiration[44]. Thus a vicious circle may be established whereby involuntary coughing becomes a paroxysm of uncontrolled coughs.

*The cough reflex*

As involuntary cough is a reflex action, it follows that there exists a reflex arc consisting of receptor or sensory areas, an afferent branch transmitting the sensation to the brain, a central regulating mechanism, and an efferent branch passing from the brain to the muscle involved. Experimental production of cough consists of provoking this reflex at one or more points, while inhibition of cough is the result of a decrease in irritability or conduction at one or more parts of the reflex arc.

The sensory areas for cough are widely distributed in the mucous membrane of the upper respiratory tract. Dogs and rabbits[45] respond with strong coughs when the carina and division points of the main bronchi are stimulated. In the cat[38,39], the larynx is the most sensitive area, with the lower half of the trachea only slightly less sensitive. Physiological differences in the character of the cough in the cat produced by stimulation of different areas[46] may simulate the clinical cough in different disease states[47,48]. There appear to be three main types of receptors[49-51]: (1) the subepithelial endings which respond to mechanical or chemical stimuli, (2) smooth muscle spindles which are activated by pulmonary inflation or deflation (the stretch receptors), and (3) perichondrial receptors. The smooth muscle located in the large bronchi and trachea may be responsible for the Hering-Breuer deflation reflex or the paradoxical reflex of Head[38,52], whereas the rapidly adapting subepithelial endings are found most frequently in the lower half of the trachea and around the bifurcation[38]. According to Ernst[34], cough may be produced in cats with pleuritis by slight external pull on the trachea, and electrical stimulation of the visceral pleura of the dog has also been shown to cause coughing[53]. In man, congestion of the pulmonary circulation as a result of increased resistance in the systemic circulation[54], tactile stimulation of the external auditory passage[55], pressure on the liver and spleen[56], compression of the carotid sinus, and chemical stimulation of the carotid bodies are additional stimuli effective in producing cough[57].

The afferent branch of the cough reflex consists of: (1) the vagus nerve and its branches, with most of the vagal impulses originating in the stretch receptors of the lung[58], (2) the sensory innervation to the larynx which is supplied by the superior laryngeal nerve, (3) the glossopharyngeal nerve[44,59] which transmits nerve impulses from the ear, and (4) some sympathetic nerve trunks[60,61]. The efferent branch of the cough reflex consists of: (1) the motor nerves to the striated respiratory musculature, (2) the efferent vagal fibres which innervate the smooth muscle of the trachea and bronchi, (3) the phrenic nerve which controls the diaphragm, and (4) the recurrent nerve which closes the glottis.

The major gap in the knowledge of the physiology of cough lies in the central coordinating mechanism. A specific cough centre in the dorsolateral region of the medulla in the cat has been postulated[23,42,62]. However, it may be preferable to think of the central part of the reflex arc as a pathway involving the mechanisms which normally control respiration. Stimulation of the afferent part of the reflex pathway initiates the reflex whereas inhibition at any point by antitussive drugs depresses the remaining components of the reflex. The central reflex pathways may also be the site of coordination of the involuntary cough reflex with the higher centres. Nervous cough may be initiated by impulses from higher centres, while suppression of cough either voluntarily or through hypnosis may occur through such a mechanism[63].

## PHARMACOLOGICAL APPROACH TO COUGH

### Action on Sensory Zones

Nerve endings situated in the larynx and trachea may be blocked experimentally by painting the mucosa with local anaesthetic drugs[45,61,64,65], and these agents are used as sprays, e.g. in bronchoscopy to abolish the cough reflex[36]. Antitussives with a selective anaesthetic activity on the stretch receptors of the lung have been developed[66,67] and several authors have traced this effect[48,68–70]. Lobeline produces cough when given intravenously to man[57], and this action may be suppressed by pretreatment with hexamethonium[56]. Hexamethonium also inhibits cough produced in man by inhalation of an aerosol of acetylcholine[71,72].

### Action on Afferent Transmission

The afferent transmission of nerve impulses from the lung in the cough reflex resides mainly in the vagus[58], and to a lesser extent in sympathetic fibres from the stellate ganglion[60]. Transection of the vagi abolishes cough produced by chemical[45,60] or mechanical[61] stimulation of the trachea of the cat and rabbit. In the dog exposed to ammonia vapour[60], and sometimes in cats after mechanical stimulation of the trachea[61], thoracic sympathectomy may also be necessary to eliminate cough reflex completely. Unilateral vagotomy has been used in man as a surgical approach in intractable cough[73] but more experimental work is needed in this line.

### Action on Central Mechanisms

Morphine, codeine and their derivatives act on central respiratory mechanisms, and codeine is generally accepted as the prototype of antitussives having a central point of attack. Other drugs believed to act on central pathways are general anaesthetics[44], chloralose[61,74] and the barbiturates[75]. The central site remains the favourite target of the pharmacologist.

91

## Action on Efferent Transmission

In theory, drugs which reduce neural transmission, such as the neuro-muscular blocking agents, should be of value in the treatment of cough. However, in practical therapeutics several difficulties arise, the most important being respiratory paralysis. Papaverine suppresses cough induced by stimulation of the superior laryngeal nerve of the cat[76] but it is not known if this is related to its antispasmodic action.

## EVALUATION OF ANTITUSSIVE DRUGS

### Experimental Animals

The techniques that have been used are shown in *Tables 3.1* and *3.2*. Mayer and his co-workers[77], as well as Larsell[45] and Banister, Fegler and Hebb[60],

*Table 3.1.* Methods of producing experimental cough in animals by stimulation of the sensory zones

| Species | Anaesthetic used | Type of stimulation | References |
|---------|------------------|---------------------|------------|
| Dog | None | $H_2SO_4$ aerosol | 91, 96 |
| | | $NH_3$ vapour | 93–95 |
| | | Mechanical | 82, 97, 98 |
| | | Electrical | 100 |
| | Urethane | $H_2SO_4$ aerosol | 113 |
| | Chloroform | $NH_3$ vapour | 92 |
| | Chloralose | Electrical | 53, 99 |
| | | Mechanical | 115 |
| Cat | None | Mechanical | 34 |
| | Chloralose | $NH_3$ vapour | 60 |
| | | Mechanical | 81 |
| | Barbiturate | $NH_3$ vapour | 64, 65, 65*a* |
| | | Mechanical | 54, 64, 65, 65*a*, 114 |
| Guinea-pig | None | Mechanical | 88 |
| | | $H_2SO_4$ aerosol | 83 |
| | | $NH_3$ vapour | 84, 116 |
| | | $SO_2$ vapour | 86–88 |
| | | Antigen aerosol | 90 |
| | | Acrolein vapour | 117 |
| Rabbit | Barbiturate | $NH_3$ vapour | 60 |
| Rat | None | $SO_2$ vapour | 78, 79 |

found the rabbit to be the most sensitive animal for studies of a physiological nature on pulmonary reflexes. However, difficulties in maintaining rabbits in a uniform plane of anaesthesia and the tendency of these animals to sneeze rather than cough in response to chemical stimuli are reasons for their non-usage in routine antitussive testing. Difficulties in differentiating between coughs and sneezes have also been encountered in rats[78,79]. The cat under normal physiological conditions seldom coughs but is satisfactory for antitussive studies when anaesthetized[60,64,65,65*a*] or decerebrated[44,62,80]. It is the animal of choice for the provocation of cough by electrical stimulation of the superior laryngeal nerve. Further, Domenjoz[74] and May and Widdicombe[81] were able to produce cough by this means in the cat but not in the dog. On the other hand, Kasé[82] succeeded in the dog by stimulating a branch of the main nerve. A number of authors have used the guinea-pig in antitussive testing, producing cough by exposing the animal to chemical irritants[83-87] or by mechanical irritation of the trachea[88]. This animal has the great advantage of being readily available as a laboratory test animal, although large

*Table 3.2.* Methods of producing experimental cough in animals by electrical stimulation of afferent nerves or medulla

| Species | Anaesthetic | Nerve or medulla stimulated | References |
|---------|-------------|------------------------------|------------|
| Dog | None<br>Barbiturate | Cervical vagus<br>Superior laryngeal | 75, 101<br>82, 85 |
| Cat | Decerebrate<br>Barbiturate | Medulla<br>Medulla<br>Superior laryngeal | 62, 80<br>42<br>65a, 74, 76, 85, 102, 103 |
| Guinea-pig | Barbiturate | Superior laryngeal | 85 |

numbers are often required to give reliable data[89]. The guinea-pig has also been used for a study of cough during anaphylactic shock[90].

The dog is perhaps the animal most widely used for antitussive screening. This species has been utilized without anaesthesia for the study of cough produced by chemical[91,93-96] or mechanical[82,97,98] irritation of the respiratory mucosa. In the anaesthetized dog, experimental cough has been produced by mechanical stimulation of the mucosa of the trachea[85], and electrical stimulation of the visceral pleura[53], the tracheal mucosa[99,100], and the cervical vagus[75,82,101]. These animals are much less variable in their cough response on repeated exposure to a chemical irritant[96], than are other species and thus may be reliably used in studying the duration of action of antitussives[91].

### Anaesthesia

Generally, anaesthetics depress the vegetative reflexes, which include the cough reflex. Nevertheless, satisfactory results have been obtained, provided a superficial plane of anaesthesia is maintained. Often the threshold of stimulation required to elicit cough is affected by anaesthesia[102,103], so that such animals cannot be used for studies of duration of drug action. Decerebration appears to have a great advantage over anaesthesia for acute studies[62,80].

### Evaluation in Man

The final stage in the development of a new antitussive drug is the clinical evaluation. The critical question is whether to use patients suffering from pathological cough or individuals with an experimentally induced cough. During the past 10 years or so, a number of authors have studied methods of eliciting cough by artificial means (see *Table 3.3*). Although mechanical stimuli have been employed[118] most have used chemical stimuli[104,112,119,120], ammonia vapour being considered a reasonable agent. However, irritation of the nasal and laryngeal mucosa often resulted and later experiments have been carried out with a 10 per cent solution of citric acid in aerosol form; this does not irritate the mucosa. The cough produced by the intravenous injection of lobeline was developed in 1950, but some workers found that it failed to respond to opium alkaloids although hexamethonium was effective.

*Table 3.3.* Methods of producing experimental cough in man

| Type of stimulation | Year | Reference |
|---|---|---|
| Mechanical | 1922 | 118 |
| Ammonia | 1950–52 | 104–106 |
| Lobeline | 1950–51 | 56, 111 |
| Spray of ether or peppermint | 1952 | 119 |
| Acetylcholine aerosol | 1954 | 71, 72, 120, 112 |
| Paraldehyde | 1954 | 107 |
| Citric acid aerosol | 1954–57 | 108, 109, 110 |

### THERAPY OF COUGH

#### The Opium Alkaloids

Although there are reports[121–124] of the use of crude opium alkaloids in the treatment of cough, such preparations are now rarely used in medicine. In the following sections only those classes of opium alkaloids which have attained importance as antitussives will be discussed, *viz.* morphine, codeine and their close derivatives, and noscapine.

#### Morphine alkaloids and close derivatives

The chemistry of the morphine alkaloids, which may be considered as being derived from the morphinan skeleton (*I*), has been reviewed by Holmes[125], Holmes and Stork[126] and Stork[127].

*Morphine*—The alkaloid may be represented by formula (*II*, *R* = Me,

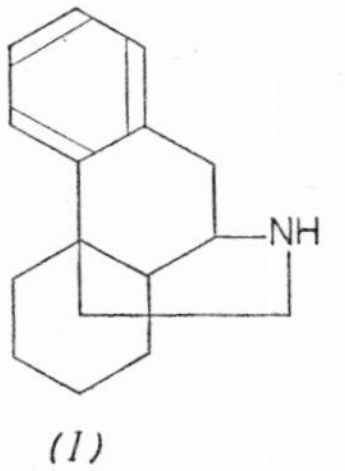

*(I)* 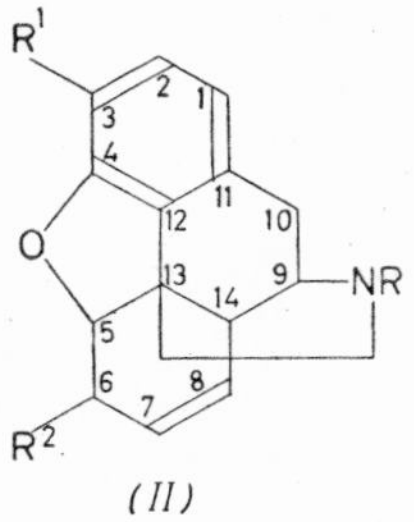                    *(II)*

$R^1 = R^2 = OH$) and may be designated as 3,6-dihydroxy-4,5-oxido-7,8-dehydro-*N*-methylmorphinan. For therapeutic purposes the salts of the naturally occurring laevorotatory base, especially the hydrochloride and the sulphate, are usually employed.

The pharmacology of morphine as an antitussive has been investigated thoroughly. Ernst[34] was one of the early workers to find that morphine in doses of 0·5 mg/kg s.c. inhibited the cough reflex in cats, and in a subsequent paper[128] he showed that codeine at 3 mg/kg s.c. also inhibited this cough reflex. Eichler and Smiatek[83], using a sulphuric acid aerosol to induce cough, later reported that doses of 1 mg/kg morphine s.c. reduced coughing in guinea-pigs. More recently, Friebel and Reichle[87], using a similar method, classified morphine among the drugs with predominantly analgetic and less pronounced antitussive activity. They also confirmed this finding in another series of experiments using rats as test animals[78]. The same authors[129] used morphine as the standard test substance in their comparison of the relative analgetic and antitussive activities in laboratory animals with the activities found in clinical trials. Green and Ward[85], using the experimental method of Domenjoz[74], besides methods involving cough induced by a sulphur dioxide aerosol, found the antitussive $ED_{50}$ value for morphine sulphate to be 0·4 mg/kg i.v. They also reported that this action was inhibited by nalorphine, and that, of the drugs tested by them, morphine had the most marked depressing effect upon respiration. Rosiere, Winder and Wax[93] later found that morphine sulphate was fourteen times more effective than codeine phosphate as an antitussive. Morphine (1 mg/kg i.m.) was also stated to inhibit experimental cough induced in dogs by faradic stimulation of the visceral pleura[53]. Morphine was inferior to methadone in preventing experimental cough induced by electrical stimulation of the tracheal mucosa of the anaesthetized cat[130]. Gross and Lebon[131] evaluated morphine by a method of experimental cough induced in the anaesthetized dog by means of faradic stimulation of the tracheal carina, and found that 0·5 mg/kg i.v. had no effect, whereas doubling this dose gave immediate cough suppression lasting for 20–30 minutes. Silvestrini and Maffii[132] found morphine to be a powerful antitussive in a number of different tests, especially in experiments using acrolein-induced cough in guinea-pigs, and classified it among the potent analgesics with antitussive activity. The antitussive $ED_{50}$ of morphine hydrochloride in guinea-pigs exposed to sulphur dioxide aerosol has been reported to be 5·9 mg/kg s.c., and 6·4 mg/kg i.p. in the same animals after mechanical irritation of the trachea[88]. Its dextrorotatory enantiomer is less active than the laevorotatory form, the $ED_{50}$ being reported as 10·4 mg/kg i.p.[133].

In human subjects, morphine is a potent cough suppressant[119]. Yet, in a double blind study, no significant differences in antitussive effects were found between morphine and placebo in experimental cough induced in a variety of ways in man[107,134]. Although the toxicity of morphine is low, its well-known depressant effect upon respiration may occasionally cause death. Wilson[135] has reported three fatalities in infants after administration of cough syrups containing morphine.

*Morphine-N-oxide (Genomorphine)*—It has been reported to be considerably more potent than morphine in inhibiting experimental cough in guinea-pigs[136], but it does not seem to have been accepted as an antitussive drug.

*Dihydromorphine (III, R = Me, R¹ = R² = OH)*—This compound was

95

found to be slightly more potent than morphine in inhibiting cough induced by sulphur dioxide in guinea-pigs, and considerably more potent in mechanically-induced cough[136]. Its dextrorotatory enantiomer has only about one-quarter of the antitussive activity of morphine[133].

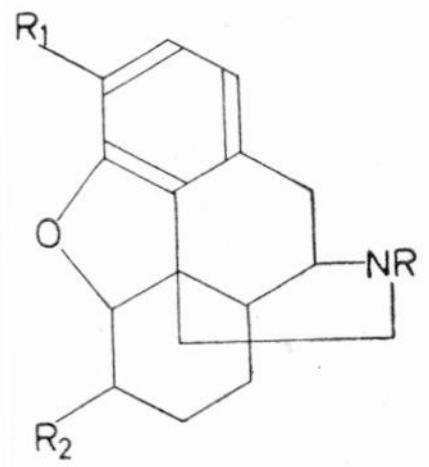

(III)

*Dihydromorphine-N-oxide*—It is somewhat less potent than morphine[136].

*Hydromorphone (dihydromorphinone, Dilaudid, III, R = Me, $R^1$ = OH, $R^2$ = ketonic oxygen)*—This drug was classified[87] among those possessing both analgetic and antitussive properties. It has been reported to be clinically inferior to noscapine[137], but to be very effective when administered rectally to infants and children in 1·25 mg doses[138]. Its dextrorotatory enantiomer has only about one-fifth of the antitussive activity of morphine[133].

*Nalorphine (N-allylnormorphine, II, R = CH$_2$·CH=CH$_2$, $R^1$ = $R^2$ = OH)*—This compound inhibits the antitussive effects of morphine[85] and those of codeine and methadone[130]. Its close chemical relative, *N*-propylnormorphine (*II*, R = Pr, $R^1$ = $R^2$ = OH) inhibits codeine[85]. Nevertheless, some success followed treatment with 20 mg doses of nalorphine in clinical trials[107,134].

## Codeine and close derivatives

Characterized by its chemical structure as morphine 3-methyl ether (*II*, R = Me, $R^1$ = OMe, $R^2$ = OH), codeine was regarded as the antitussive of choice for a considerable period of time. It was recently estimated that almost one-third of the total codeine production of the United States was used for the preparation of cough mixtures.

The pharmacology of codeine as an antitussive in animals was first investigated by Ernst[34]. He found that codeine inhibits the cough reflex in doses of 3 mg/kg s.c., and doses of 0·75 mg/kg s.c. are effective when given in association with 0·125 mg/kg morphine[128]. Later, Green and Ward[85] reported that the ED$_{50}$ of codeine (as the free base) was 4 mg/kg i.v. when tested by Domenjoz's method[74]. These authors found that its antitussive effect is abolished by n-propylnormorphine, and that cats rapidly become tolerant to its respiratory depressant effects. Codeine has been classified as one of the drugs with the highest antitussive and the lowest analgetic activities in guinea-pigs[87] and in rats[78]. Results obtained in rats and guinea-pigs compare reasonably well with those found in man[129]. Gross[139] reported that codeine at 1–2 mg/kg p.o. inhibited experimental cough induced in dogs either by faradic stimulation of the visceral pleura or by lobeline. The antitussive activity of codeine and its inhibition by nalorphine was also investigated by Huet[130]. Silvestrini and Maffii[132] found codeine to be about as potent as morphine in inhibiting acrolein-induced cough in guinea-pigs, slightly less active in cats after mechanical irritation, and considerably less active than morphine when tested by the method of Domenjoz[74]. Codeine (4 mg/kg i.v.) inhibits cough following electrical stimulation of the trachea in dogs, and its action becomes apparent only 30 minutes after administration and lasts for approximately 15 minutes[140]. Kohli, Gupta and Bhargava[141] found that the antitussive $ED_{50}$ of codeine, using the method of Domenjoz[74], was 1·5 mg/kg i.v., a result in close agreement with that obtained by other authors[75,132,142,143].

In human subjects, Hillis[119] found codeine as an antitussive to be no more effective than a placebo. In a double-blind study using ammonia gas, citric acid aerosol or paraldehyde i.v. to produce cough, no significant differences were observed between the efficacy of codeine and that of placebo[107,134]. But Höglund and Michaelsson[104] found that 10, 15, 20, and 30 mg of codeine raised the threshold value of cough produced by ammonia gas for 30, 58, 95, and 100 minutes respectively. Trendelenburg[106], using a similar method, found 20 mg codeine to be about as effective as 2·2 mg methadone, but he reported that it inhibited respiration and that 40 mg codeine produced bradycardia and 'a feeling of tightness'. In a double-blind evaluation of antitussives in healthy human subjects exposed to citric acid aerosol, codeine in 5, 10 and 20 mg doses was later found to be more effective than a placebo[144]. Doses of 15 mg codeine gave peak antitussive effects, during the first three hours after administration, equal to 2·5 mg methadone, with diminution of effects in the fourth hour[145]. A carefully screened group of healthy volunteers who were exposed to critic acid aerosol[144] received protection with 30 mg doses of codeine[146]. Codeine was also found to be more effective than morphine or normethadone in inhibiting cough induced in man by paraldehyde i.v.[124].

Clinical trials with doses of 10 and 25 mg of codeine in cases of pathologic cough showed a significant reduction in the frequency of cough[107]. In a second study[134] the same authors observed five patients over a period of 45 days of treatment with 10 mg codeine given four times per day orally: no objective differences between codeine and placebo were found, although the patients reported codeine as being superior. The authors concluded from the results of their first study[107] that the sense of well-being imparted in the patients by codeine accounts for part of its purported antitussive efficacy.

*Codeine-N-oxide*—In guinea-pigs this was found to be fourteen times more effective than codeine in inhibiting sulphur dioxide-induced cough, but only 1·6 times as effective in preventing cough following mechanical irritation[136]. The authors pointed out that it was a very weak analgesic and was less toxic than codeine, having less effect on blood pressure, respiration, heart rate, and intestinal peristalsis.

*Codeine Methobromide (Tecodine)*—The methobromide is an effective antitussive in dogs, about one-sixth as potent as methadone, but it possesses distinct respiratory depressant effects[147].

*Dihydrocodeine (Paracodin, Hydrocodin, III, R = Me, $R^1$ = OMe, $R^2$ = OH)*— This compound was studied by Friebel and Reichle[129], who found its antitussive effects in guinea-pigs to agree with results obtained in the clinic. It has been reported to be about four times as active as codeine in guinea-pigs, even its dextrorotatory enantiomer having about 73 per cent of the antitussive activity of codeine[136].

Clinical studies with a dihydrocodeine aerosol treatment in cases of postoperative cough, pulmonary tuberculosis, pulmonary tuberculosis complicated by bronchitis, and cases complicated by bronchial asthma gave good results[148]. Patients who were refractory to the common antitussive preparations showed a good response when treated with a composition containing 5 mg dihydrocodeine and 25 mg noscapine[149].

*Dihydrocodeine-N-oxide*—This possesses only very weak antitussive properties[136].

*Hydrocodone*—Well known for its narcotic properties, hydrocodone (Dihydrocodeinone, Dicodid, *III*, R = Me, R¹ = OMe, R² = O (ketonic oxygen)) was first studied as an antitussive by Ernst[34], who found it was more potent in the cat than codeine. Further pharmacological studies by Eichler and Smiatek[83] established that its antitussive activity in guinea-pigs is equal to that of morphine. It has been classified among the drugs with intermediate analgetic and antitussive activities[87,129] but Reichle and Friebel[78] found it to have more pronounced antitussive than analgetic activities in the rat. It is several times as active as, and with a longer duration of activity than, codeine in the dog[91,93], but slightly less active than morphine.

Human pharmacology studies showed it to be more than twice as active as codeine, with no side-effects being noted[106]. In a clinical trial Voiculescu and Neuman[150] stated that hydrocodone was centrally active. In recent years a preparation containing hydrocodone and phenyltoloxamine in the form of a resin complex (Tussionex) has been the subject of a number of clinical studies. Chan and Hays[151] found this combination to be more effective in dogs than hydrocodone alone, and much more potent than either dihydrocodeine or codeine. They reported satisfactory results in patients with respiratory disorders when treated with the equivalent of 5 mg hydrocodone twice a day; duration of antitussive effect was six to twelve hours. In a pharmacological study using normal subjects, Bickerman and Itkin[145] also found that the preparation gave sustained cough suppression over a period of seven hours. It is effective in children[152,153] but hydrocodone has habit-forming properties[152]. A double-blind clinical study carried out by Cass and Frederik[154] showed that doses of 'Tussionex' containing 10 mg hydrocodone were more effective than doses of 5 mg, and both were superior to placebo controls.

*Dihydrocodeinone Enol Acetate (Acedicon, Thebacon, IV)*—This compound was reported by Ernst[34] to be as potent as morphine as an antitussive in cats. In guinea-pigs, it has been variously described as having intermediate analgetic and antitussive activities[87], and also as being the most potent antitussive in guinea-pigs and in man[129]. Husen[155], in a recent clinical study on patients with pulmonary tuberculosis and other pulmonary diseases, used 7·5–15 mg per day, and reported satisfactory to excellent results in nearly every case. Duration of antitussive effects was 6 to 10 hours, with an onset of action 10 to 30 minutes after ingestion. Treatment lasted from several weeks to six months, during which time no development of tolerance was noted, and no cases of addiction were encountered.

98

*Oxycodone (dihydrohydroxycodeinone, Eucodal, Eukodal, V)*—This is among the drugs with intermediate analgetic and antitussive activities in guinea-pigs[87],

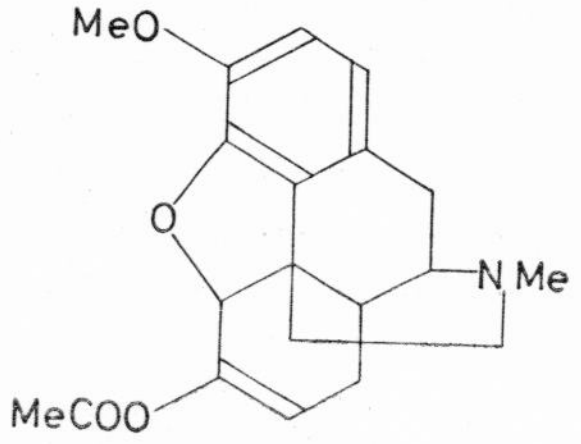

(IV)

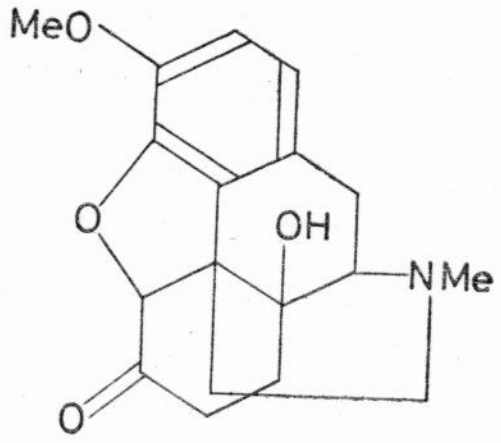

(V)

[129] but in rats its action is mainly analgetic rather than antitussive[78]. A comparison has been made between clinical results and those observed in mice, rats, and guinea-pigs[87,129].

*Ethylmorphine (Dionin, morphine 3-ethyl ether, II, R = Me, R¹ = OEt,*
$R^2 = OH$)—Classified among the compounds having closely associated analgetic and antitussive activities, it gave good agreement for antitussive data when tested in guinea-pig and man[87,129].

*Pholcodine*—Together with the corresponding dimethylaminoethyl, diethylaminoethyl, and piperidinoethyl ethers, pholcodine (3-(2-morpholinoethyl)

morphine, *II*, R = Me, R¹ = O·CH₂·CH₂·N ⟩O, R² = OH), was

first prepared by Chabrier, Giudicelli and Thuillier[111]. The title compound proved to have the most interesting properties. It has a low acute toxicity (LD₅₀ 535 mg/kg i.p., 1010 mg/kg orally, mouse), a low subacute chronic toxicity (50 mg/kg mouse for 30 days tolerated by most animals) and weak activity upon the central nervous system. As an antitussive, pholcodine inhibited lobeline-induced cough in oral doses of 80–100 mg. Clinical reports[111] indicated that it was effective in oral doses of 10–30 mg, with an onset of action 10–20 minutes after administration and a duration of effect of 1·5–4 hours, whilst daily intake of up to 120 mg caused no side-effects. A pharmacological study by May and Widdicombe[81] showed that it was three times as active as codeine and one half as potent as morphine in inhibiting expiratory effects due to mechanical irritation, but less active than either morphine or codeine in inhibiting inspiratory effects following inhalation of sulphur dioxide. Green and Ward[85] found that it was slightly more active than codeine in the cat, while Plisnier[156], using the same technique, reported it to be twice as potent as codeine, with a similar degree of hypotension as codeine and marked bronchospastic properties, but less than one-half the toxicity of codeine.

Snell and Armitage[157] reported that pholcodine was about as effective as heroin and significantly better than a placebo, in human subjects. Bickerman and Itkin[145] later found that it gave sustained cough suppression over a four-hour period, 10 mg being as effective as 15 mg codeine or 2·5 mg methadone. Pholcodine was also reported to be more active than morphine or normethadone in inhibiting cough induced in man by means of intravenous paraldehyde[124]. Ryde[158] conducted a clinical trial on patients mainly suffering from pulmonary tuberculosis, and obtained good results with the Swedish combined preparation Tussukon, containing pholcodine and a polysorbate preparation.

*Diacetylmorphine (diamorphine, heroin, II, R = Me, $R^1 = R^2 = OCOMe$)*—It has apparently been investigated as an antitussive only in human subjects. Hillis[119], in an experimental study on one volunteer, found it to be a potent cough suppressant, while other workers reported that it did not inhibit experimental cough[107,134].

The dangers of habituation or addiction inherent in the above group of drugs are well known and have recently been reviewed by Eddy, Halbach and Braenden[32]. It should be mentioned that Maller and Constantinescu[33] have reported on five cases of true addiction to antitussive preparations containing codeine, ethylmorphine, and heroin.

## Noscapine (Narcotine, Coscopine, Nicolane)

Noscapine, an alkaloid present in crude opium to the extent of 3–10 per cent, was discovered by Robiquet in 1817. Its structure was established by Marshall, Pyman and Robinson[159] as that of *l*-α-2-methyl-8-methoxy-6,7-methylenedioxy-1-(6,7-dimethoxy-3-phthalidyl)-1,2,3,4-tetrahydroisoquino-line *(VI)*.

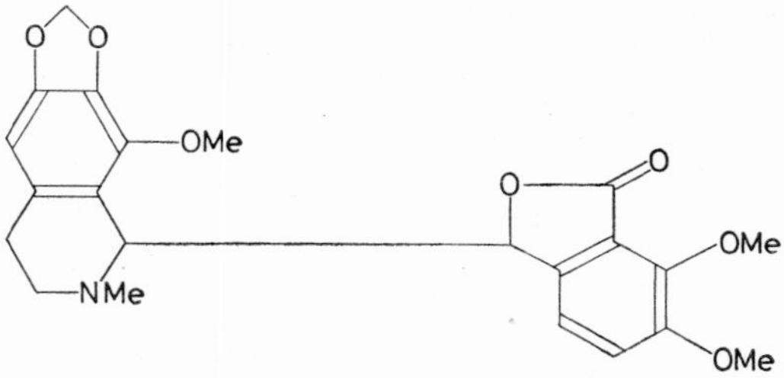

*(VI)*

Green and Ward[85] were among the first to investigate its pharmacology. Reichle and Friebel[78] thought it to be a potent, centrally active antitussive with little analgetic effects, and reported good agreement between data obtained for antitussive activities in rats, guinea-pigs, and man[129]. Van Dongen[160] tested noscapine by the method of Ernst[34] and reported it to be ineffective in inhibiting cough in doses of 1–5 mg/kg s.c., whilst higher doses caused undue excitation. The pharmacological results obtained up to the end of 1957 have been reviewed by Ervenius[161]. Silvestrini and Maffii[132] found that noscapine was effective in inhibiting experimental cough elicited with ammonia or with acrolein aerosol in guinea-pigs or elicited after inhalation of sulphuric acid aerosol in dogs, but less effective after mechanical stimulation. La Barre and Plisnier[162], who re-determined the antitussive $ED_{50}$ of noscapine by a modification of Domenjoz's method[74], found that it was more effective than codeine, which was apt to produce bronchospasm, whereas noscapine increased the vital capacity and acted as a bronchodilator. Doses of 1 mg/kg noscapine orally have also, however, been reported to cause little inhibition of cough[91].

In pharmacological experiments on human subjects, there are conflicting reports[107,144] on the effectiveness of noscapine. Clinical evaluations of the compound as an antitussive showed that 5–15 mg doses gave at most a 25 per cent reduction in the frequency of cough, but that patients evaluated it as better than a placebo[107,134]. Voiculescu and Neuman[150] included it in a study of a number of antitussives, but failed to give details of their results, while another study[137] showed that divided daily doses of 15–60 mg were effective in the majority of the patients, with no serious side-effects such as gastro-intestinal or respiratory complaints.

### Synthetic Compounds with Morphine-like Effects

*Pethidine (Meperidine, Demerol, Dolantin, VII, ethyl 1-methyl-4-phenylpiperidine-4-carboxylate)*—This was the first of many synthetic compounds with morphine-like effects to be synthesized over the last twenty years[163].

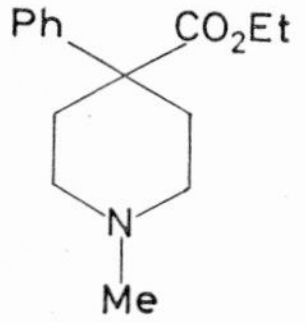

*(VII)*

Its chemical and pharmacological properties were first discussed by Eisleb and Schaumann[164], and it was investigated as an antitussive by Schaumann[165]. Using the method of Ernst[34], it was found to be active at 10 to 15 mg/kg s.c., but about 5 times less potent than morphine. Green and Ward[85] using the method of Domenjoz[74] found it to be less than half as active as morphine sulphate and about four times as active as codeine base. These authors also pointed out that, of all the drugs tested by them, this compound had the least depressant effect upon respiration. From a study of its analgetic and anti-tussive activities in guinea-pigs, it was shown that pethidine possesses mainly analgetic activity and little antitussive activity, while codeine was classified among the drugs with the highest antitussive activity[87]. Buschkem[166], investigating pethidine as a cough-preventative during intratracheal anaesthesia, found that the drug was comparatively inactive during the first 30 minutes after administration, but gave a significant reduction in cough frequency during the second 30 minutes.

*Ketobemidone (Cliradon, VIII, 4-(m-hydroxyphenyl)-1-methyl-4-piperidyl ethyl ketone)*—This is a close chemical relative of pethidine.

In guinea-pigs it possesses both analgetic and antitussive activities[87], whilst in rats it is more potent as an analgesic than as an antitussive[78]. The results in guinea-pigs are generally more comparable to those obtained in man than those obtained in the rat[129].

*Trimeperidine*—The Russian drug trimeperidine (Promedol, IX, 4-phenyl-4-propionyloxy-1,2,5-trimethylpiperidine), also chemically related to pethidine, was tested in dogs by a method involving electrical stimulation of the vagus. It was found to be about four times as active as codeine, but it depressed respiration[147].

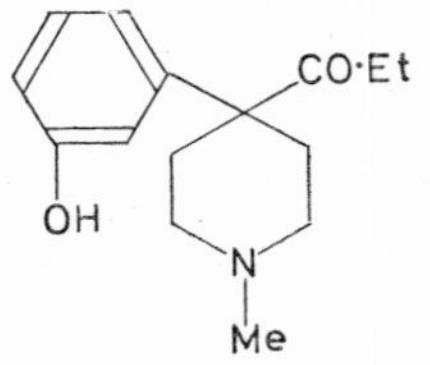

(VIII)

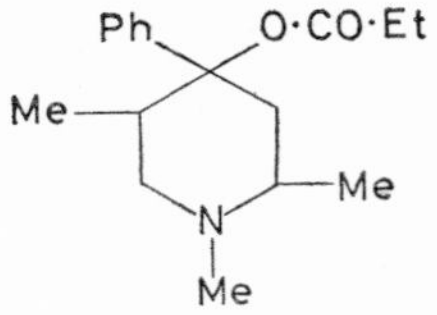

(IX)

*Methadone*—The drug methadone (Amidon, Amidone, Polamidon, Phenadone, X, 2-dimethylamino-4,4-diphenyl-5-heptanone) was first described by Eisleb[167] and his results were published by the Allies after the war[168].

$$Ph_2C \cdot CH_2 \cdot CHMe \cdot NMe_2$$
$$|$$
$$CO \cdot Et$$

(X)

It has been studied extensively as the racemate and in the form of its dextro and laevo optical enantiomers. Winter and Flataker[96] tested methadone as an antitussive, using unanaesthetized dogs, and found its *d*-enantiomer active in doses of 0·5 to 1 mg/kg after oral administration. Green and Ward[85] later found methadone hydrochloride to be active in cats when tested by the method of Domenjoz[74] in doses of 0·05 mg/kg. They stated that methadone had the highest antitussive activity of all the drugs tested in their series and they classified it as being eight times as active as morphine, twenty times as active as pethidine and eighty times more active than codeine. Its antitussive activity was inhibited by nalorphine. However, from tests in guinea-pigs using a sulphur dioxide aerosol induced cough, methadone was classified as a drug with mainly analgetic activities and comparatively little antitussive activity[87]. Reichle and Friebel[78] found *d*-methadone more effective as an antitussive than as an analgesic in rats. In unanaesthetized dogs, methadone was nine times more active than codeine[93]. Guseva[147] later found that methadone was about eight times as active as trimeperidine and about thirty times as active as codeine, with a longer duration of activity; but its depressant action upon respiration was such that it was recommended for clinical use only with some reservations. Huet[130] evaluated methadone by electrical stimulation of the tracheal mucous membrane of the anaesthetized cat, and found it to be better than morphine as a cough-suppressant. He also stated that nalorphine inhibited the antitussive activity of methadone, and confirmed the earlier results of Green and Ward[85]. The drug was also reported to have no influence upon the output of respiratory tract fluid in animals[169].

Methadone has been found to be a potent suppressant of experimentally induced cough in man[106,119]. The antitussive effect of 2·2 mg was approximately equal to that of 20 mg codeine phosphate or 7·5 mg dihydrocodeinone bitartrate[106]. The noted side-effects of methadone were sedation and euphoria in doses from 1–5 mg, and ataxia lasting for four to six hours with higher doses. Its antitussive effect, however, did not increase with doses higher than 5 mg. Contrary to other authors, Trendelenburg stated that methadone stimulated respiration[106]. Bickerman and Itkin[145] investigated methadone in a double-blind study, using cough produced experimentally in human subjects by means of citric acid aerosol. Using a dose of 2·5 mg, they classified methadone among the drugs with peak antitussive activity during the first three hours after administration. Of 43 children and infants treated with 1·5–2 mg every 3–4 hours for a variety of respiratory disorders, 65 per cent gave excellent and 30 per cent fair results, with only two failures due to intolerance[170]. Rasch[171] conducted a double-blind clinical study on 19 patients using placebo and 10 mg of d-methadone four times a day for 3–4 days, and showed that the drug was twice as effective as the placebo.

*Isomethadone*—An isomer of methadone, isomethadone (*XI*, 6-dimethylamino-4,4-diphenyl-5-methyl-3-hexanone) was first prepared[172] in 1948.

$$Ph_2C \cdot CHMe \cdot CH_2 \cdot NMe_2$$
$$|$$
$$CO \cdot Et$$

(*XI*)

Winter and Flataker[96] found that *l*-isomethadone had about forty times the analgetic activity of the *d*-enantiomer, which was found to be much more effective orally than by subcutaneous injection. The authors stated that *d*-isomethadone was an orally active antitussive in doses of 0·5–2 mg/kg. Reichle and Friebel[78] found both *d*- and *l*-isomethadone more effective as antitussive than as analgesics. Silvestrini and Maffii[132], using their method of inducing cough in guinea-pigs by means of an acrolein aerosol, found no relationship between the analgetic and antitussive activities of the substances tested by them; *l*-isomethadone had about four times the antitussive activity, and forty times the analgetic activity of its *d*-enantiomer.

*Dipipanone* (*Piperidylamidone, Pipadone, XII, 4,4-diphenyl-6-piperidinoheptan-3-one*)—The compound was synthesized by Ofner and Walton[173].

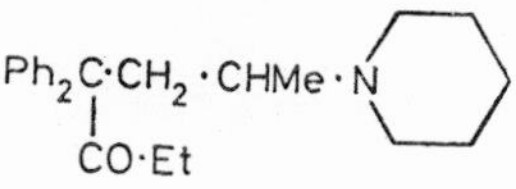

$$Ph_2C \cdot CH_2 \cdot CHMe \cdot N \bigcirc$$
$$|$$
$$CO \cdot Et$$

(*XII*)

It is distinguished from methadone by having a piperidino group in place of the dimethylamino group. Its pharmacology was investigated by Green and Ward[85], who found it to be forty times as active as codeine, and about half as active as methadone.

*Sulfamethadone* (*3-dimethylamino-1,1-diphenylbutyl ethyl sulphone, XIII*)—The sulphone analogue of methadone has an analgetic effect equal to that of methadone[174]. An improved method of synthesis has been described together with the resolution of the compound into its two optical antipodes[175]. The pharmacological properties of the two enantiomers were investigated by Luduena and Ananenko[176] who stated that the *l*-isomer was much more

$$Ph_2C \cdot CH_2 \cdot CHMe \cdot NMe_2$$
$$|$$
$$SO_2 \cdot Et$$

(*XIII*)

effective than the *d*-isomer and somewhat less analgetic than *l*-methadone. Side-effects encountered were depression of respiration, bradycardia and miosis. The drug is an effective antitussive in dogs[97] and has only slight analgetic activity[177].

*Racemorphan* (*Dromoran, Methorphinan, XIV, 3-hydroxy-N-methyl-morphinan*) —First described by Grewe[178,179], it is classified among the drugs with

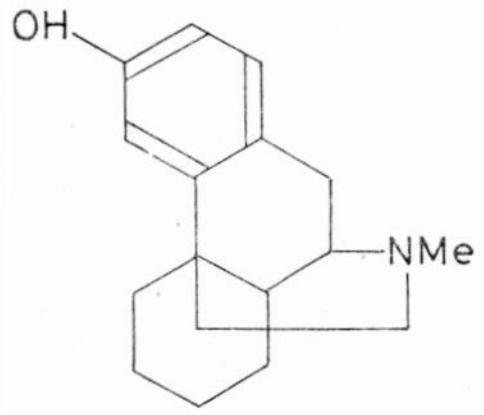

(*XIV*)

mainly analgetic and little antitussive activities[87]. Its analgetic activities in mice, rats and guinea-pigs have been compared with those found in man[129], and the results obtained in man were most closely comparable with those obtained in guinea-pigs. Comparison of the pharmacology of racemorphan and its *d*- and *l*-components showed that the *d*-enantiomer had negligible analgetic activity and less respiratory depressing activity than the *l*-enantiomer, and was less toxic. All three forms were stated to be moderately active as antitussives. The corresponding methyl ethers were found to have similar properties, but appeared to be less potent. The *d*-enantiomer of the methyl ether was stated to stimulate respiration and to be active as an antitussive agent[180]. Isbell and Fraser[181,182] investigated the actions and addiction liabilities of racemorphan and its derivatives in man, and stated that both the *l*-enantiomer (levorphanol, Dromoran (U.K.), Levo-Dromoran (U.S.A.)) and its methyl ether had the miotic and respiratory depressant activities of the racemate, and the *d*-enantiomers were inactive in those two tests. Both levorphanol and the *l*-form of its methyl ether were found to be highly addictive, although the *d*-enantiomers were stated to be free from addiction liabilities.

*Propoxyphene* (*XV, 4-dimethylamino-3-methyl-1,2-diphenyl-2-propionyloxybutane*) —First described by Pohland and Sullivan[183], it is capable of existing in two diastereoisomeric forms, of which the less soluble form has been called the α-isomer, and the more soluble one the β-isomer. In preliminary

104

experiments in rats, its α-isomer was stated to have approximately one-tenth the analgetic activity of methadone after s.c. administration. In anaesthetized dogs 1–2 mg i.v. or up to 20 mg s.c. were said to cause no respiratory depression. It was also stated that the β-diastereoisomer had no analgetic activity. Bickerman, German, Cohen and Itkin[144] studied the antitussive activities of dl-, d- and l-propoxyphene (presumably the α-diastereoisomer) in healthy human subjects using citric acid aerosol to induce

$$
\begin{array}{c}
\text{O} \cdot \text{CO} \cdot \text{Et} \\
| \\
\text{PhCH}_2 \cdot \text{C} \cdot \text{CHMe} \cdot \text{CH}_2 \cdot \text{NMe}_2 \\
| \\
\text{Ph}
\end{array}
$$

(XV)

cough, and they found that all the drugs tested were significantly better than a placebo. A dose of 32·5 mg of l-propoxyphene had an antitussive effect approximately equal to that of 15 mg of codeine. Silvestrini and Maffii[132] who investigated d- and l-propoxyphene using the guinea-pig acrolein aerosol test found that d- and l-enantiomers were of about equal potency as antitussives, but that the d-form was more effective as an analgesic.

It should be repeated at this point that all the drugs listed in the above paragraphs possess addictive liabilities, although propoxyphene is stated to be substantially less addictive than codeine. This problem has been thoroughly reviewed[32].

### Synthetic Antitussive Compounds

In this section the antitussive drugs obtained by total synthesis are discussed in the chronological order in which they appeared in the literature covered by this review.

*Piperidione (Sedulon, XVI, 3,3-diethylpiperidine-2,4-dione)*—This compound was first described in a German patent[184].

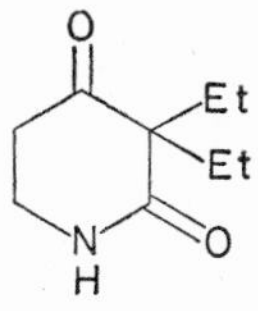

(XVI)

Hottinger[185] found that in mice and rabbits, piperidione was a drug with sedative and hypnotic activities, and a markedly low toxicity. When tested in 340 patients with various respiratory disorders, excellent results were reported in over 300 cases[185]. The drug in 100 mg doses is about as effective as an antitussive as 20 mg codeine, but many patients are distinctly sedated by this dose, and the drug inhibits respiration[106]. Jacobs[186] also evaluated the drug in 25 cases of advanced bilateral pulmonary tuberculosis and reported that all patients experienced relief.

*2-Amino-6-methylheptane (XVII)*—It was synthesized by Rohrmann and Shonle[187].

$$Me_2CH \cdot (CH_2)_3 \cdot CHMe \cdot NH_2$$
$$(XVII)$$

Ornston[188] treated 90 patients with minor respiratory disorders by means of a special inhaler, and reported 81 per cent success, with no evidence of irritation or addiction, but an occasional occurrence of nausea. Other workers[189,190] have also reported marked relief in about 70 per cent of patients with upper respiratory tract infections; but patients complained about the unpleasant odour or taste of the drug, which caused gagging, initial coughing, or a burning sensation in the throat and chest.

*Sodium Dibunate*—This compound (Sodium 2,6-di(t-butyl)naphthalene-sulphonate, Becantex, Becantyl, Linctussal, L-1633, *XVIII*) was first described as an industrial wetting agent[191]. Recent work[191a] indicates that sodium dibunate is a mixture of sodium 2,6- and 2,7-di(t-butyl)naphthalene-4-sulphonates.

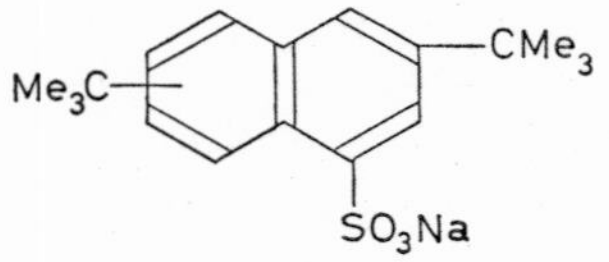

*(XVIII)*

It possesses antitussive activity in the dog, with little influence upon respiration volume but some increase in respiratory rate; it has low spasmolytic activity, and low toxicity[113]. There was however no dose-response relationship in guinea-pigs exposed to sulphur dioxide[87]. Salerno[192], using guinea-pigs similarly treated and cats and rabbits in which cough was elicited by electrical stimulation or by inhalation of saline-ether aerosol, reported that laryngeal cough was diminished with doses of about 1 mg/kg, and abolished with higher doses. As a centrally active antitussive it was not only effective in inhibiting cough at 10 mg/kg i.v., but it also raised the threshold value of stimulation[62].

Using the method of Domenjoz[74], its $ED_{50}$ in the cat has been estimated as 4·4 mg/kg i.v., with a duration of effect of 70 minutes after double this dose[141]. It is interesting to note that the antitussive activity of aromatic sulphonic acids is not limited to the above compound: in a structure-activity study[193], a comparison was made of sodium 2,6-di(t-butyl)naphthalene-sulphonate with the corresponding 2-t-butyl derivative and with *p*-toluenesulphonate. Using doses of 0·0436 millimoles/kg in the guinea pig to inhibit cough elicited with ammonia, all three substances gave about the same degree of reduction in cough frequency, and antitussive activity did not reside in the t-butyl group, nor in the naphthalene nucleus, but rather in the sulphonic acid moiety.

Clinical studies using a daily dose of 90–240 mg gave good results in reducing the frequency of coughing attacks[194], in cases of severe respiratory disease[195], and in reducing the frequency of cough in patients with neoplasms of the respiratory tract[196]. Simon[197] found 90–120 mg somewhat less effective in patients with pulmonary emphysema, but Cremoncini[198] achieved notable success with doses of 30–90 mg per day in infants and children, particularly in cases of pulmonary tuberculosis and of pertussis.

A molecular complex of the closely related 2,6-di(t-butyl) naphthalene-disulphonic acid with 1-dimethylamino-3,3-diphenylhexane-4-one (nor-methadone) was found to be about as active as codeine in the rat, and to have a similar therapeutic index[79]. A clinical trial carried out by Schmidt[199] gave satisfactory results, with no influence of the drug on blood pressure, haemo-gram, urine analysis, digestive functions, blood sugar levels, or appetite.

The closely related ethyl ester of 2,7-di(t-butyl)naphthalene-4-sulphonic acid (2,7 ethyl dibunate) has also been found to have antitussive activities[199a] in the cat[74] and in the dog or guinea-pig[84].

*Benzonatate*—The first description of benzonatate (nonaethyleneglycol monomethyl ether *p*-n-butylamino-benzoate, Benzononatine, Tessalon, KM 65, AGB) was in a series of U.S. patents issued to Matter[200]. These cover esters of polyethyleneglycol monoalkyl ethers with substituted *p*-amino-benzoic acids, of the general structure (*XIX*). In this formula, R represents

$$R(O \cdot CH_2 \cdot CH_2)_n \cdot O \cdot OC \underbrace{\phantom{xxxx}}_{} NHR'$$

*(XIX)*

hydrogen or a lower alkyl group of 1–6 carbon atoms, $n$ is an integer from 7–50 inclusive, and $R^1$ represents the n-butyl group, an alkyl group of 5–7 carbon atoms, or a cycloalkyl or oxa-alkyl radical with 4–7 carbon atoms. The title compound may be represented by formula *XIX* in which R = Me, $n = 9$, and $R^1 = $ n-butyl.

Bucher[66] stressed the importance of the pulmonary stretch receptors in the mechanism of cough, therefore with this in view, compounds which selectively anaesthetize pulmonary stretch receptors and tactile receptors were needed to be tested; at the same time it was realized that such com-pounds must be comparatively inactive against thermoreceptors which have their afferent pathways in thin nerve fibres of slow conductance. Accordingly chemical combinations of an efficient local anaesthetic group with a suitable substance possessing selective affinity for myelin were tried out[200]. *p*-(n-Butylamino)benzoic acid was selected for the former, with polyethylene-glycol monoalkyl ethers for the latter. A study of the relationship between chemical structure and biological activity was made using rabbits for deter-mining activity upon pulmonary stretch receptors, the guinea-pig ear test for influence upon tactile receptors, and the well-known mouse tail test for determining effects upon thermoreceptors. The parent substance amethocaine (Tetracaine, $\beta$-dimethylaminoethyl $p$-(n-butylamino)benzoate) was highly effective upon stretch receptors and thermoreceptors but had little effect upon tactile receptors. Investigating the compounds of formula $(XIX)$ in which R and $R^1$ were kept constant as methyl and n-butyl groups respectively, and $n$ was varied from 6 to 18, the desired maximal activities upon pulmonary stretch receptors and tactile receptors together with minimal activity upon thermoreceptors were found to occur with $n = 9$. Tests for antitussive activity of the compound with $n = 9$ in the cat by the method of Kroepfil[54] confirmed Bucher's hypothesis, the average threshold value for inhibition of coughing being found as 0·3 mg/kg.

Bucher's pharmacological investigations were confirmed by a clinical study of structure-activity relationships carried out by Herzog[67], who used similar compounds where $n$ equalled 6, 9 and 18. In a preliminary trial, the compound with $n = 18$ proved to be active, while the compound with $n = 6$ was incapable of inhibiting cough or of easing respiration, and the best results were again obtained with the compound where $n = 9$. The compounds were then evaluated in cases of pleurogenic and bronchogenic cough, and satisfactory results were obtained in over half of the cases. In these trials, the compound with $n = 9$ was found to be effective in doses of 5 mg i.v., 50–100 mg p.o., or 5–10 mg s.c. The onset of action was apparent within two minutes after i.v. injection, with an average duration of effect of about two hours, and was apparent five to ten minutes following s.c. or oral administration, with the effect lasting from two to ten hours. Particularly noticeable were the exceptionally low toxicity of the compound and the absence of cardiovascular side-effects, such as those encountered upon i.v. injection of procaine.

After the success of benzonatate $(XIX, n = 9, R = Me, R^1 = $ n-butyl) a series of compounds with the general structure $XX$ was synthesized[201] in which R represents hydrogen or a lower alkyl group, $R^1$ represents hydrogen, lower alkyl, or lower alkoxyalkyl, X stands for hydrogen, hydroxy, alkoxy, cycloalkoxy, alkoxyalkoxy, or a saturated oxacycloalkylalkoxy group, and Y represents an alkyl, cycloalkyl, oxacycloalkylalkyl, cycloalkylalkyl, or an alkoxyalkyl group, with $n$ being varied from $n = 7$ to $n = 17$.

$$R(O·CH_2CH)_n·O·OC—\overset{\displaystyle NHY}{\underset{\displaystyle X}{\bigcirc}}$$
$$\underset{R^1}{|}$$

*(XX)*

Although the above compounds were described as having antitussive and local anaesthetic activities which extended in some cases also to the pulmonary stretch receptors, none of them appear to have attained clinical importance. One of the difficulties in obtaining the compounds in the pure state has recently been resolved through an improved process for the preparation of pure polyalkylene glycol ethers[202]. One of those ethers, dodecylpolyethylene oxide ether (DOR 9/3), of the average composition

$C_{12}H_{25}(O \cdot C_2H_4)_n \cdot OH$ with $n =$ about 9, had been shown earlier to have important inhibitory effects upon pulmonary stretch receptors[203,204].

After the work of Bucher[66] and Herzog[67], benzonatate became probably the most thoroughly studied drug in the antitussive field. Bein and Bucher[70] compared the drug with a number of well-known local anaesthetics, anti-histaminics, and antispasmodics; they found it to have the highest activity of all drugs tested upon pulmonary stretch receptors and in conductance anaesthesia; they found also high activity in inhibiting central spinal polysynaptic reflexes, and moderate activities in infiltration and local anaesthesia. In a comparison of the drug with local anaesthetics, only benzonatate was active upon both pulmonary stretch receptors and contact receptors. Moreover, it is more potent as an antitussive in the cat than three of the five reference compounds[205]. Silvestrini and Maffii[132] found benzo-natate highly effective in inhibiting acrolein-induced cough in the guinea-pig, as well as in the cat by the method of Domenjoz[74], and somewhat effective in the dog, following faradic stimulation of the trachea. Guth and Goldenberg[115] investigated its activity in the trachea-clamping reflex in the dog, and discussed its probable mode of action.

The pharmacology of benzonatate in human subjects was studied by Marx[206], who investigated the influence of the drug upon respiratory dynamics in healthy subjects and patients with emphysematous bronchitis. He reported that it had no spasmolytic activity, no central respiratory depressant effect, and no influence upon resting respiration. Its action appeared to be peripheral, and it improved forced respiration in patients, causing an increase in respiratory reserve. Shane, Krzyski and Copp[110] found that 100 mg benzonatate was more than twice as active as 30 mg codeine in reducing frequency of cough. Tiffeneau's method[112] was used by Gregoire, Thibaudeau and Comeau[207] to show that benzonatate in doses of 10 mg i.v. reduced coughing. The first clinical study of benzonatate was published by Giuliano and Rossa[208], who reported major successes in coughs associated with various respiratory conditions. Later, Naegeli[209] reported success in cases of irritative and pleurogenic cough. Other favourable clinical investigations of the drug have been reported[150,207,210–219]. Success has also been obtained in the treatment of cough associated with pulmonary tuberculosis[209,219–222]. In infants and children suffering from various respira-tory diseases, daily doses of benzonatate (0·5–1·5 mg/kg i.m., or 4–10 mg/kg rectally, or 4–8 mg/kg orally) gave very satisfactory results, especially in cases of pertussis[223–226]. Equally satisfactory results in the treatment of pertussis were reported when the drug was given in the form of an aerosol in daily doses of 10–40 mg[227].

The drug was also used successfully in inhibiting cough associated with surgical procedures, such as extrapleural pneumothorax[228], tracheotomy[215], bronchospirometry, bronchoscopy, bronchography, laryngoscopy, and oesophagoscopy[207,229]. Husen[221], and also Suriani[230] found that it was ineffec-tive in bronchoscopy, but Diamant[231] used it to inhibit cough during surgical operations on the ear. In pulmonary emphysema, benzonatate caused an improvement in 40–80 per cent of patients[197,217,232], although Simon[233], in a double blind study on patients with asthmatic bronchitis, had found no significant differences between hydrocodone, benzonatate,

109

and a cough syrup containing ephedrine, ammonium chloride, and elixir terpin hydrate which has been used as the vehicle for the two drugs. The Council of the American Medical Association reviewed the literature on benzonatate, commenting on its peripheral and central action, on the low incidence of side-effects, the reported increase in depth and rate of respiration, and the low toxicity of the drug. The dosages suggested were 100 mg three to six times per day[234].

### Basic esters of C-substituted phenylacetic acids

*Caramiphen Ethanedisulphonate*—The free base of the above structure and its hydrochloride salt were first described as therapeutically useful compounds[235],

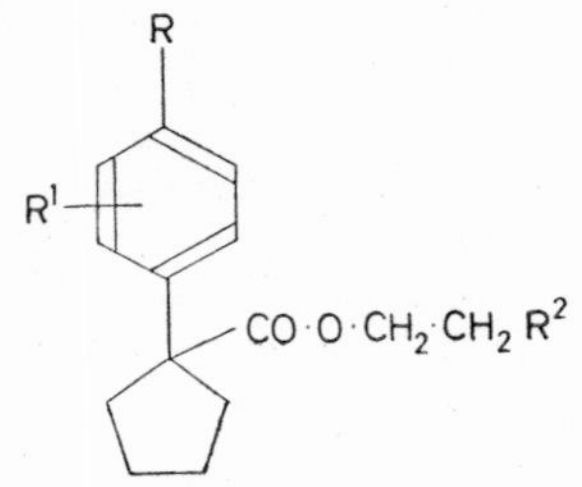

*(XXI)*

and the hydrochloride has since been widely used as a parasympatholytic agent (Panparnit, Parpanit). Subsequently, the structure was modified to include the isopropylmethylaminoethyl ester[236] and a series of compounds[237] represented by the above formula (*XXI*, R or R$^1$ = H, Me, OMe; R$^2$ = NEt$_2$, morpholino, or piperidino), but none of those compounds has attained clinical importance. The antitussive properties of the ethanedisulphonate salt[238] of the free base (Taoryl, Toryn, 2-diethylaminoethyl 1-phenylcyclopentanecarboxylate, *XXI*, R = R$^1$ = H, R$^2$ = NEt$_2$) were first recognized by Domenjoz[74]. Toner and Macko[103], using Domenjoz's method, found it to be less effective than codeine but with a longer duration of activity. The central effects of caramiphen were studied at doses of 2·5–6·0 mg/kg i.v., which reduced cough and had little influence upon respiration[62]. Huet[130] however found it to be ineffective as an antitussive, even in high doses. Bein and Bucher[70] reported that it was weakly active upon pulmonary stretch receptors, central spinal polysynaptic reflexes, and in conductance anaesthesia, and of very low activity in local and infiltration anaesthesia. On the other hand, Roth[239] reported it to have about 70 per cent of the activity of codeine.

Doses of 10 mg of caramiphen ethanedisulphonate inhibited cough for 3–5 hours in 60–70 per cent of patients with various respiratory disorders, and in over 80 per cent of cases of pertussis[240]. A double blind study on 26 patients in a tuberculosis sanatorium against placebo, codeine, and hydrocodone, showed that it was more effective than placebo but less effective than the two other drugs; doses of 30 mg per day caused drowsiness and dizziness in patients[241]. In a double-blind study on 120 patients, doses of 10 mg were less effective than 15 mg codeine[242]. Hudson[243] stated that large doses (60–80 mg) were useful when given shortly before bronchoscopy. In a series of 100 patients with dry or non-productive cough of long duration, Snyder[244] obtained relief in 88 cases after treatment with 40–60 mg per day, but he also observed 6 cases of mild nausea. The compound may have a sedative effect upon the bronchioles[245].

Two compounds which are chemically closely related to caramiphen should be briefly mentioned at this point. Both correspond to the general

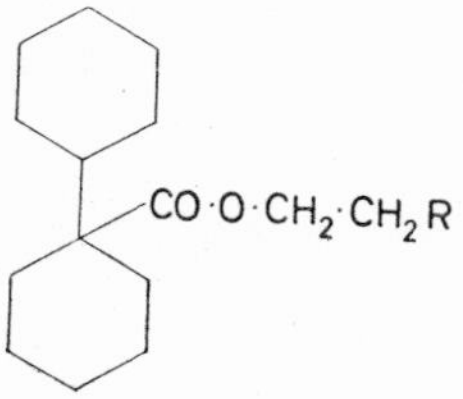

(XXII)

formula (XXII), which differs from that of caramiphen essentially in having the phenyl and the cyclopentyl groups of the latter replaced by two cyclohexyl rings.

*Dicyclomine* (*Bentyl, Bentylol, Merbentyl, Dicyclovérine, Wyovin, XXII, R = NEt₂*)—This is a well-known antispasmodic drug. Boissier[25], referring to unpublished work from his own laboratory, found that it possessed considerable antitussive properties.

*Dihexyvérine* (*Spasmodex, Metaspas, XXII, R = piperidino*)—Also well known as a powerful spasmolytic, it was included by Boissier[24] in his recent review of synthetic antitussives. He stated, without giving any details, that it possessed antitussive activity[25].

*Carbetapentane*—Structurally closely related to caramiphen (XXII), Carbetapentane (Toclase, Tuclase, Pentoxyvérine, Atussil, 2-(diethylaminoethoxy)ethyl 1-phenylcyclopentyl-1-carboxylate, XXIII: $R + R^1 = (CH_2)_4$,

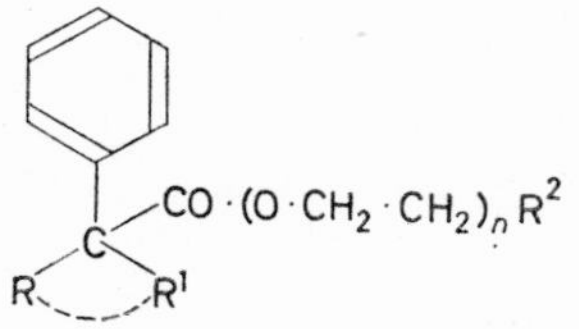

(XXIII)

$n = 2$, $R^2 = NEt_2$) differs from it only in having a 2-(diethylaminoethoxy)ethyl instead of a 2-diethylaminoethyl side chain. It was first described by Morren[246], who also synthesized a number of close analogues in which $n = 2$ and $R^2 = NEt_2$ were kept constant, viz. (XXIIIb): $R + R^1$

$= (CH_2)_2;$ $(XXIIIc):$ $R + R^1 = (CH_2)_5;$ $(XXIIId):$ $R \times R^1 = CH_2 \cdot CH_2 \cdot O \cdot CH_2 \cdot CH_2;$ $(XXIIIe);$ $R = Ph,$ $R^1 = H;$ $(XXIIIf):$ $R = $ cyclohexyl, $R^1 = H;$ $(XXIIIg):$ $R = $ 2-thienylmethyl, $R^1 = H;$ $(XXIIIh):$ $R = $ 2-furylmethyl, $R^1 = H.$ Some of the above compounds, together with a number of additional analogues corresponding to the general formula $(XXIII)$, and two additional compounds in which the 2-(diethylamino-ethoxy)ethyl group of carbetapentane is replaced by 3-diethylamino-1-methylpropyl $(XXIV)$ or by 1,3-bis(diethylamino)propyl $(XXV)$ groups respectively, were investigated for their antitussive activities[143]. Using the method of Domenjoz[74], and expressing the activities of the compounds as percentages of the antitussive activity of codeine, the results shown in *Table 3.4* were obtained:

*Table 3.4.* Antitussive activity of carbetapentane analogues

| Compound | $R + R^1$ | n | $R^2$ | Antitussive activity (codeine = 100) |
|---|---|---|---|---|
| XXIIIb | $(CH_2)_2$ | 2 | $NEt_2$ | <75 |
| XXIIIi | $(CH_2)_3$ | 2 | $NEt_2$ | <75 |
| XXIIIj | $(CH_2)_4$ | 2 | $NMe_2$ | 75 |
| XXIIIa | $(CH_2)_4$ | 2 | $NEt_2$ | 150 |
| XXIIIk | $(CH_2)_4$ | 3 | $NEt_2$ | <75 |
| XXIIIm | $(CH_2)_5$ | 2 | $NMe_2$ | 22·5–37·5 |
| XXIIIc | $(CH_2)_5$ | 2 | $NEt_2$ | <75 |
| XXIV | $(CH_2)_4$ | $CHMe \cdot (CH_2)_2 \cdot NEt_2$ | | <75 |
| XXV | $(CH_2)_4$ | $CH(CH_2 \cdot NEt_2)_2$ | | <75 |

From the above results, carbetapentane $(XXIIIa)$ was the compound of choice in this series. Moreover, it was found to be of low oral acute toxicity (230 mg/kg mouse, and 830 mg/kg rat) and of low 'chronic' toxicity: a group of mice survived daily oral doses of 100 mg/kg for 30 days. It caused a transient fall in blood pressure, it possessed a weak antispasmodic effect, but its local surface and infiltration anaesthetic effects were stated to be 2·4 times and three times those of procaine respectively[143]. Additional pharmacological studies[239] showed that the antitussive effect of the drug is 150 per cent that of codeine, with a similar duration of effect, when determined by Domenjoz's[74] method. Huet[130] found that the drug has negligible antitussive effects in dogs, but other workers[140], using a similar technique, reported that 1 mg/kg i.v. inhibited cough considerably more than 4 mg/kg i.v. of codeine.

The first clinical study of the drug was completed by Depoorter[247], who used daily doses of 30–100 mg. He stated that it was superior of codeine syrup and codeine plus morphine syrup in the treatment of cough due to mechanical irritation, that it gave excellent results in cases of productive cough, and that it was ineffective in cases of asthma. Parish[248], using daily doses of 25–180 mg in the form of tablets or syrup, also obtained excellent results, but noted five cases of slight drowsiness, two of allergic rash, and one of nausea in a series of 44 patients. Carbetapentane has also been recommended as an aid in anaesthetic procedures such as bronchoscopy[249,250] and bronchial catheterization[251]. Roth[239] found it useful in cases of bronchiectasis, bacillosis, pulmonary neoplasms, and also in asthma. Carter and Maley[252], using daily doses of up to 150 mg, found that cough was reduced or abolished in 91 per cent of 557 cases. Thus, carbetapentane is an antitussive drug of low toxicity and satisfactory efficacy, with a low incidence of side-effects, none of which appear to have been serious. Nevertheless, it was apparently withdrawn from the market in Britain in 1959, although it is still available in the U.S.A. and in Canada.

## Esters of C-substituted phenylacetic acids

Compounds have also been prepared, corresponding to the general formula $(XXVI)$, in which $R^1$ and $R^2$ are not linked with each other as in caramiphen or carbetapentane, but represent monovalent alkyl, aryl, or heterocyclic radicals and in which A represents an alkyl or alkoxyalkyl radical usually substituted with a basic group.

$$\begin{array}{c} R^1 \\ | \\ Ph \cdot C \cdot CO \cdot OA \\ | \\ R^2 \end{array}$$

$$(XXVI)$$

*2'-Diethylaminoethyl 1-Phenylbutyrate* $(XXVI, R^1 = Et, R^2 = H, A = CH_2 \cdot CH_2 \cdot NEt_2)$—It was first prepared by Halpern[253]. Engelhardt[254] found that the drug possessed much less spasmolytic activity than the corresponding diphenylacetate $(R^1 = Ph)$, while its bronchodilator activity was superior to that of ephedrine. The toxicity of the compound was exceptionally low. In tests for antitussive activity, 0·3 mg of the drug given intraduodenally were about as effective as 0·4 mg codeine, and it potentiated the antitussive effects of codeine. Hook[255] used the drug in the combination preparation 'Solgettes' on 150 patients with various upper respiratory tract infections; 92 of these patients reported themselves improved while only 5 reported side-effects.

*2'-n-Butoxyethyl 1-N-piperidinodiphenylacetate*—This compound $(XXVI, R^1 = Ph, R^2 = piperidino, A = CH_2 \cdot CH_2 \cdot OBu)$ was synthesized as one of a series of analogous compounds in which the terminal n-butyl group was replaced by methyl, ethyl, or n-hexyl groups[256]. It has apparently the highest antitussive activity in this series, with central sedative and local anaesthetic activities. As a spasmolytic agent it was found to have 65 per cent of the activity of papaverine. In a subsequent patent[257], it was described as being 2–3 times more effective as an antitussive than codeine. No clinical details have become available to date, but the compound is interesting from the structural point of view in having the basic group located in the acid moiety rather than in the alcohol side chain. Introduction of a second basic group, in the usual terminal position on the side chain, apparently destroys antitussive activity: the tertiary acid addition salts of the latter compounds have spasmolytic and central sedative properties, while the quaternary salts have curare-like activities[258–260].

113

*Esters of C-substituted diphenylacetic acids*

Compounds were prepared by Polezhaeva[261] corresponding to formula (*XXVI*) with $R^1$ = Ph, $R^2$ = H, Me, Et, OH, OPr, A = $CH_2 \cdot CH_2 \cdot NR^3_2$ or $CH_2 \cdot O \cdot CH_2 \cdot CH_2 \cdot NR^3_2$ or $CH_2 \cdot CH_2 \cdot O \cdot CH_2 \cdot CH_2 \cdot NR^3_2$ with $R^3$ = Me, Et, Pr, Bu, also thioesters of the same structure, *e.g.* $Ph_2CR^2 \cdot CO \cdot S \cdot CH_2 \cdot CH_2 \cdot NR^3_2$. They were then tested for antitussive activity by two methods[54,74]. One of the fifteen compounds prepared (2-diethylaminoethyl benzilate, *XXVI*, $R^1$ = Ph, $R^2$ = OH, A = $CH_2 \cdot CH_2 \cdot NEt_2$) was found to be more active than codeine or benactyzine, although later it was reported to be ineffective[141].

*Oxeladin*—This compound (Pectamol, 2′-(2-diethylaminoethoxy)ethyl 1,1-diethylphenylacetate, *XXVI*, $R^1$ = $R^2$ = Et, A = $CH_2 \cdot CH_2 \cdot O \cdot CH_2 \cdot CH_2 \cdot NEt_2$) was first prepared by Petrow, Stephenson and Wild[262]. Pharmacological studies were carried out by David, Leith-Ross and Vallance[263], who selected the compound as the most promising in a series in which the $NEt_2$ group had been varied to include NMeEt, NEtPr, $NBu_2$, $N(C_6H_{13})_2$, pyrrolidino, piperidino, and $\Delta^3$-piperideino groups. Its antitussive activity, determined by Domenjoz's method[74], was found to be about equal to that of carbetapentane, and slightly less than that of codeine. Its acute toxicity was similar to that of carbetapentane, both compounds being about 2–4 times as toxic as codeine. Oxeladin was also found to be about twice as active as procaine as an infiltration anaesthetic. Huet[130] reported that its antitussive effect was negligible, but Kohli, Gupta and Bhargava[141] found it to be slightly superior to codeine, with an $ED_{50}$ of 1·22 mg/kg i.v. In a clinical trial on 35 children, Roberts[264] reported success in 26 cases, 4 failures, and one case of allergic side-effects.

*Isoaminile*—The compound (Peracon, Dimyril, Z-495, 4-dimethylamino-2-isopropyl-2-phenylvaleronitrile, *XXVII*, R = $Pr^i$, A = $CH_2 \cdot CHMe$, B = $NMe_2$, $R^1$ = H) may be regarded as being somewhat related to the group of compounds discussed above, being formally derived from phenylacetonitrile ($\alpha$-isopropyl-$\alpha$-($\beta$-dimethylaminopropyl)phenylacetonitrile). An isomer

*(XXVII)*

of isoaminile in which A = $CHMe \cdot CH_2$ was first described, together with a number of closely analogous compounds in which R = 1-methylpropyl or $\alpha$-methylbenzyl, A = $CH_2 \cdot CH_2$, and B = dialkylamino or piperidino, with $R^1$ = hydrogen or *m*-methoxy[265–268]. These compounds were stated to be powerful analgesics with spasmolytic activity equal to that of papaverine. In addition, Rorig[269] synthesized a series of compounds which were stated to have diuretic activity. In these the phenyl group in (*XXVII*) was replaced by the *p*-methoxy- or the *p*-hydroxybenzyl group, with R = *p*-methoxy- or *p*-hydroxyphenyl, A = $CH_2 \cdot CH_2$, and B = $NEt_2$. Further, Moffett and

Aspergren[270] described another series of compounds with the general structure (*XXVII*) in which R = Ph, Pr$^1$, *m*- or *p*-ClC$_6$H$_4$, A = CH$_2 \cdot$ CH$_2$, and B = NEt$_2$, piperidino or substituted *N*-heterocycles, and found them to possess some anticholinergic activity. Basically substituted diphenylacetonitriles (*XXVII*, R = Ph, R$^1$ = H, A = CH$_2 \cdot$ CH$_2$, CH$_2 \cdot$ CHMe, or CHMe$\cdot$ CH$_2$, and B = NMe$_2$, NEt$_2$ or piperidino) had been characterized much earlier[271] as having atropine-like activities.

The antitussive activity of isoaminile was discovered by Krause[272], who used cough elicited by means of electrical stimulation of the tracheal mucosa of guinea-pigs under urethane anaesthesia. Its ED$_{50}$ was found to be 5·4mg/kg i.v. (codeine 7 mg/kg i.v.) Its analgetic activity was low, and respiration was slightly inhibited by doses of 5 mg/kg. Acute toxicity tests in mice gave LD$_{50}$ values of 65 mg/kg i.v., 240 mg/kg s.c., and 720 mg/kg p.o. In a test for subacute toxicity in mice, animals survived daily oral doses of 20 mg, but other workers[273] found liver damage in dogs and rats after daily oral doses of 20 mg/kg for 4 weeks. Isoaminile caused a transitory drop in blood pressure, did not potentiate barbiturate hypnosis, and was ineffective in preventing leptazole shock[274].

Christoffel and Kolberg[275] found the drug to be effective in human subjects in reducing cough induced by inhalation of 7·5 per cent citric acid aerosol. Clinical trials by the same authors[275] with daily doses of 90–320 mg showed that the drug became effective 15–20 minutes after oral administration, and that its effect lasted for 4–5 hours. No tolerance developed, and the drug was reported as being neither habit-forming nor addictive. Isoaminile was also reported to have no effects upon haemogram, urine analysis, blood pressure, liver function, nor respiratory function. Isoaminile as a cough suppressant gave good to excellent results in patients suffering from pulmonary tuberculosis and diseases of the respiratory tract[276–282]; undesirable side-effects were rare or absent.

In summing up the clinical evidence, isoaminile appears to be a useful antitussive drug, about as effective as codeine, and with a low incidence of side-effects.

*R-1132* (*4-(4-phenyl-4-ethoxycarbonylpiperidino)-2,2-diphenylbutyronitrile*)— Closely related to isoaminile, it may be represented by formula (*XXVII*) with

R = Ph, R$^1$ = H, A = CH$_2 \cdot$ CH$_2$, B = N

The compound was synthesized in 1959 together with 17 close congeners, in which the ester group in B and the length of the carbon chain in A was varied[283]. It was found to be among the most active compounds in inhibiting gastrointestinal motility in mice and in rats. Morris and Shane[284] stated that the drug had slight analgetic activity, and no parasympatholytic effects. They investigated its antitussive action in a double blind study on healthy volunteers by the citric acid aerosol method[109]. They found that 5 mg of R-1132 was about two-thirds as effective as 30 mg codeine in 17 subjects. Doses of 15 mg of R-1132 gave inhibition of cough in four subjects and reduction in two others, but two complained of side-effects, *viz.* dizziness, headaches, and lassitude.

*Chlophedianol*—The compound, chlophedianol (Detigon, Eletuss, Ulo, SL-501, 1-*o*-chlorophenyl-3-dimethylamino-1-phenylpropanol-1, *XXVIII*, R = *o*-ClC$_6$H$_4$, A = CH$_2 \cdot$CH$_2$, B = NMe$_2$) may be regarded as somewhat related to the above compounds of the general structure (*XXVII*) and may be formally derived by replacing the nitrile group in (*XXVII*) by a hydroxyl group:

$$\begin{array}{c} R \\ | \\ PhC \cdot A \cdot B \\ | \\ OH \end{array}$$

(*XXVIII*)

This class of compounds with R = alkyl, cycloalkyl, or aryl, A = CHR$^1 \cdot$CH$_2$ (R$^1$ = H, alkyl, or cycloalkyl), and B = dialkylamino, was first synthesized and described as antispasmodic[285] and the title compound was then found to have antitussive properties[286]. Gösswald[287] made a pharmacological study of some 65 compounds in the above series and selected 8 of them for detailed investigation of their antitussive activities. He obtained the results given in *Table 3.5* using guinea-pigs[109].

Table 3.5. Relative antitussive activities of compounds of structure *XXVIII* with A = CH$_2 \cdot$CH$_2$

| R | Ph | Ph | *o*-ClC$_6$H$_4$ | *m*-ClC$_6$H$_4$ | *p*-ClC$_6$H$_4$ | *o*-MeO$\cdot$C$_6$H$_4$ | *m*-MeO$\cdot$C$_6$H$_4$ | *p*-MeO$\cdot$C$_6$H$_4$ |
|---|---|---|---|---|---|---|---|---|
| B | NH$_2$ | NMe$_2$ | NMe$_2$ | NMe$_2$ | NMe$_2$ | NMe$_2$ | NMe$_2$ | NMe$_2$ |
| Relative Antitussive Activity | 0 | 60 | 100 | 0 | 20 | 20 | 20 | 40 |

The antitussive ED$_{50}$ of chlophedianol was found to be 20 mg/kg s.c. In experiments on dogs[101], the drug proved to be as potent as codeine in doses of 5 mg/kg p.o. or of 2 mg/kg s.c. In rabbits, chlophedianol had no influence upon respiration at 5 mg/kg i.v., while codeine or morphine at the same dose level caused definite depression. Guinea-pigs treated with 20 mg/kg s.c. daily for eight consecutive days showed no decrease of antitussive response. Its acute subcutaneous, intravenous, and oral toxicity in dogs, cats, rabbits, guinea-pigs, rats, and mice was found to be generally lower than that of codeine[274,288]. Boyd and Boyd[289] found that chlophedianol diminished the output of respiratory tract fluid in rabbits and in cats, and produced at the same time a decrease in the incidence of mucous pledgets. There are many favourable clinical reports of the use of chlophedianol as an antitussive[288,290-298] in patients suffering from bronchopneumonia, chronic cough, pulmonary neoplasms, and in postoperative conditions.

Summarizing the above results, the drug appears to be a useful antitussive, effective in doses of 20–30 mg given 3–5 times per day, with a duration of effect of a single dose of 3–5 hours and a low incidence of side-effects.

*Tussukal* (*Tusucal, Tussilax*)—This is a preparation of the adrenergic *p*-hydroxyephedrine (Suprifen, 10 mg), with the active antitussive ingredient, 40 mg of the preparation Hoe 10682 (4964 U; 1,1-diphenyl-2-piperidino-propanol-1, *XXVIII*, R = Ph, A = CHMe, B = piperidino). It differs from chlophedianol with respect to three points: the basic group B is piperidino instead of dimethylamino; its position is shifted from the 3- to the 2-position in the propanol chain; and R is a phenyl instead of an *o*-chlorophenyl group. Hoe 10682 was first prepared by Stein and Lindner[299], who also described a series of related compounds in which R is a phenyl group substituted with halogen, hydroxy, lower alkyl, lower alkoxy, or benzyloxy groups, and in which B represents a pyrrolidino, piperidino, 2-methyl-piperidino, morpholino, or a tetrahydroisoquinolino radical. This series was subsequently extended by Lindner and Stein[300] who made a detailed study of the relationship between antitussive activity, toxicity, and chemical structure, using an antitussive testing technique similar to that of Domenjoz[74]. Compounds with the general structure (*XXIX*) were investigated.

$$R^1—\underset{\underset{R^2R^6}{|\ \ |}}{\overset{\overset{R^3R^4}{|\ \ |}}{C}}·CR^5$$

(*XXIX*)

The parent compound, Hoe 10682 ($R^1 = R^2$ = Ph, $R^3$ = OH, $R^4$ = piperidino, $R^5$ = Me, $R^6$ = H), was arbitrarily assigned the antitussive activity = 1 and the toxicity = 1, and the following groups of compounds were described:

(*a*) With $R^1$, $R^3$, $R^4$, $R^5$ and $R^6$ representing the same groups as in Hoe 10682, and substituting the phenyl group $R^2$ with mono- or di-hydroxy, mono- or di-lower alkoxy, chloro, or lower alkyl radicals, or replacing it by a 3-pyridyl, cyclohexyl, *p*-biphenylyl, lower alkyl, or a benzyl group, 20 compounds were obtained of which only the one with $R^2$ = *p*-biphenylyl had a higher antitussive activity, but also a much higher toxicity, than Hoe 10682.

(*b*) In a second group of 10 compounds the OH group $R^3$ was esterified to include 8 different esters and 2 compounds in which the OH group had been replaced by the diethylamino or piperidino group. The *p*-amino-benzoate of Hoe 10682 proved to have four times the antitussive activity of the parent compound, with a similar toxicity.

(*c*) Only the basic group $R^4$ was varied in this group of 13 compounds, to include mono- and di-lower alkylamino, pyrrolidino, 2-methylpiperidino, morpholino, tetrahydroisoquinolino, and cycloalkylamino radicals; but none of those compounds exceeded Hoe 10682 in antitussive activity.

(*d*) Finally, 21 compounds were described in which first $R^5$ or $R^6$ were varied alone, or together with one, two, or three of the other groups in formula (*XXIX*). In the best two compounds, $R^1$, $R^2$, $R^5$ and $R^6$ were the same as in Hoe 10682, with the OH group in $R^3$ being esterified with *p*-amino-benzoic acid. The compound with $R^4$ = dimethylamino had twice the antitussive activity of the parent compound, and that with $R^4$ = diethyl-aminomethyl had four times the activity, while both had the same toxicity as Hoe 10682. However, some of the compounds which had the highest activities upon i.v. injection were found to be no more active than the parent compound upon oral administration, and further investigations were therefore restricted to that compound.

The antitussive $ED_{50}$ of Hoe 10682 was reported[300] to be 2 mg/kg i.v., or about one-half the potency of codeine. No difference in activity was found between the racemate and the optically active enantiomers of the compound. It had no analgetic activity in doses as high as 200 mg/kg s.c.; while it had no effect upon respiration in intact rabbits or cats, it caused a slight depression in anaesthetized animals. Toxic doses were found to cause convulsions, and no sedative action was noted. The drug caused slight and transient effects upon circulation, had a low degree of activity upon the autonomic nervous system, and little influence upon intestinal motility. It had considerable local anaesthetic activity, about four times that of procaine. Acute oral toxicity was found to be low ($LD_{50}$: 750 mg/kg mouse). Sub-acute toxicity tests extended over 6 weeks in rats with doses of 10 mg/kg p.o., given for five days per week, showed normal growth curves. However, guinea-pigs given the same dose s.c. over six weeks showed some evidence of liver damage. Boissier[274] also found the antitussive $ED_{50}$ of the drug in guinea-pigs challenged with sulphuric acid aerosol to be similar to that of codeine (22 and 20 mg/kg i.p., respectively); he reported it to have about one-third the antitussive activity of codeine in cats by Domenjoz's method[74]. A closely related compound in which the piperidino group had been replaced by the diethyl-amino radical was found to be inactive.

In a double blind study in normal human subjects challenged with citric acid aerosol against placebo, codeine and a number of other antitussives, a 60 mg dose of Hoe 10682 was about as effective as 15–30 mg codeine[145]. Clinical trials with the drug in various diseases of the respiratory system showed that the majority of patients were significantly improved[301, 302]; there was no indication that the drug was habit-forming or addictive.

Summarizing the above pharmacological and clinical data, Hoe 10682 appears to be a useful antitussive, with about one-quarter to one-half the potency of codeine, but additional clinical data are needed for a more complete evaluation.

*KAT-256*—This compound (Silomat, 1-*p*-chlorophenyl-2,3-dimethyl-4-dimethylaminobutanol-2, *XXX*, $R^1 = R^2 = R^5 = R^6 = $ Me, $R^3 = $ H, $R^4 = p$-Cl, $n = 1$) may also be regarded as being somewhat related to the compounds of the general structure (*XXVIII*) in which the phenyl radical has been replaced by a *p*-chlorobenzyl group, with R = Me, A = CHMe· $CH_2$, and B = $NMe_2$.

A series of some 300 basically substituted arylalkanols corresponding to formula (*XXX*) was synthesized by Berg[303] with the following variants: $R^1$ represented a lower alkyl group and $R^2$ was hydrogen, a lower alkyl group, an aryl or an aralkyl group including substituted aryl or aralkyl groups; $R^3$ and $R^4$, not necessarily identical, represented hydrogen, halogen, or alkyl, lower alkoxy, or tertiary amino groups; $R^5$ and $R^6$ were lower alkyl groups, or represented, together with the nitrogen atom, a pyrrolidino, piperidino, or morpholino group; and $n$ was 1 or 2. The series included both the racemates and the optically active enantiomers of some of the compounds.

The antitussive properties of the title compound were first recognized by Engelhorn[304], who found it to be about as effective as codeine by injection in a number of different animal tests. It was found to have little analgetic activity, and it reduced analgesia produced by codeine. Doses of 10 mg/kg i.p. caused transient sedation in cats, and 40–80 mg/kg s.c. some excitation in rats, while 3–6 mg/kg i.p. potentiated the effects of barbiturates in mice. The compound had no local anaesthetic and no bronchodilator activities,

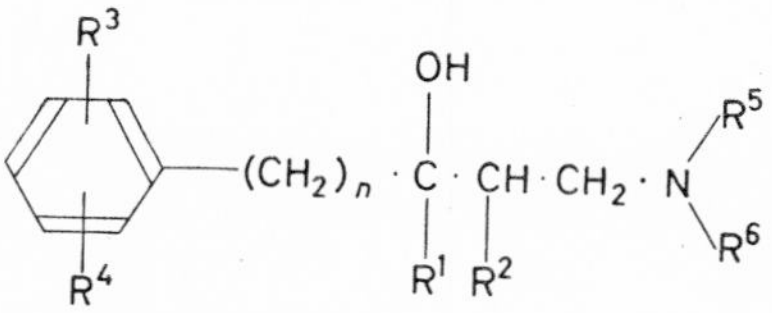

*(XXX)*

and apparently no action upon pulmonary stretch receptors, nor upon afferent or efferent pathways of the cough reflex. This indicated the central antitussive action of KAT-256. The drug was also found to stimulate respiration, and to antagonize the respiratory depressant activity of morphine. The acute toxicity of the drug following i.p., s.c., or oral administration to mice was similar to that of codeine. Chronic toxicity tests in rats treated with 50 mg/kg p.o. over a period of six months showed no pathological changes upon gross or histological examination.

Riebel[305] evaluated the drug clinically in 91 patients with pulmonary tuberculosis or bronchitis, as well as in cases of irritative cough following bronchoscopy, bronchography, or pneumothorax. Treatment consisted in 2–3 daily doses of 30–40 mg, supplemented by a single dose of 120 mg at night in very severe cases. Results obtained indicated that the drug was about as effective as codeine, but the absence of side-effects such as respiratory depression, drowsiness, nausea, allergic reactions, constipation, or influences upon circulation, were noted. Prolonged treatment gave no indications of development of tolerance nor of habituation. Expectoration was not inhibited, and careful spirometric investigation on 50 patients showed no adverse influences of the drug upon respiration.

Summing up the clinical and pharmacological evidence, KAT-256 (Silomat) appears at the present preliminary stage to be a promising antitussive drug, about as effective as codeine.

*Thiophene derivatives*

Thiophene derivatives related to the general structure (*XXVIII*), *i.e.* basically substituted 1,1-di-(2-thienyl)alkan-1-ols (*XXXI*) and their corresponding alk-1-enes (*XXXII*) obtained by dehydration, were synthesized by Adamson[306] with R = H, Me, Et, Pr, and NR$^1$R$^2$ representing NH$_2$, NHEt, NHBu, NMe$_2$, NEt$_2$, NPr$_2$, NMe·CH$_2$Ph, pyrrolidino, piperidino, or morpholino groups.

The carbinols (*XXXI*) were described as having antispasmodic and local anaesthetic activities, and the alkenylamines (*XXXII*), were, moreover, found to be powerful analgesics, with the order of potency of morphine[307]; the *dextro* enantiomers being more potent than the laevo forms[308]. Compounds of type (*XXXI*) in which the hydroxyl and amino groups are separated by only two carbon atoms have also been synthesized[309]. Antitussive properties were discovered in 1955 in some of the above compounds as follows:

*Thiambutene*—Green and Ward[85] reported thiambutene (3-diethylamino-1,1-di-(2-thienyl)but-1-ene, *XXXII*, R = Me, NR$^1$R$^2$ = NEt$_2$) to have an antitussive ED$_{50}$ of 0·2 mg/kg by Domenjoz's method[74]. The drug was stated to have an addiction liability similar to that of morphine[310].

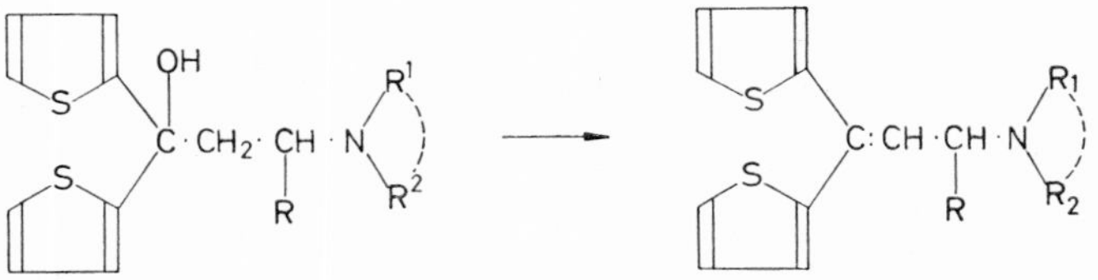

(*XXXI*)                 (*XXXII*)

*Ohton*—The 3-dimethylamino analogue of Thiambutene (*XXXII*, R = Me, NR$^1$R$^2$ = NMe$_2$), was studied by Kase[97] in dogs and found to inhibit 60 per cent of cough at doses of 3 mg/kg for 60 consecutive days, while 0·8 mg/kg morphine inhibited cough by 90 per cent on the first day, but had no more effect on the tenth day. The drug appeared to cause addiction[311].

*3-Piperidino-1,1-di(2-thienyl)but-1-ene*—The 3-piperidino analogue of Thiambutene (*XXXII*, R = Me, NR$^1$R$^2$ = piperidino) was stated to be a potent antitussive drug[312]. Its *d*-enantiomer had five times the antitussive and twice the analgetic activity of the *l*-form[313]. In a clinical trial on 113 patients with pulmonary tuberculosis or bronchitis, a 6 mg dose of the race-mate or 3 mg of the *d*-form proved to be about as effective as a 20 mg dose of codeine[314].

*Pipendyl methane (4-di-(2-thienyl)methylene-1-ethyl-piperidine*—This compound is related to compounds of the general structure (*XXXII*), *e.g.* to 4-diethyl-amino-1,1-di-(2-thienyl)but-1-ene in which one of the two ethyl groups on

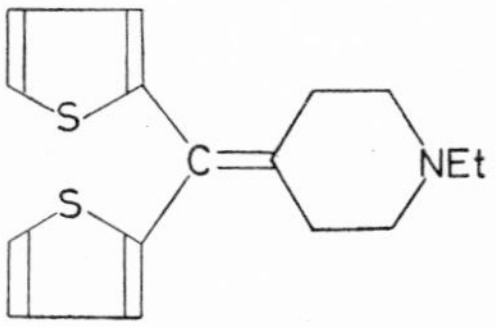

(*XXXIII*)

the nitrogen had been linked back to carbon atom 2. Its structure might be represented by formula (*XXXIII*). It was claimed as one of a series of closely related compounds with antispasmodic, antihistaminic, and analgetic activities[315]. When 40–60 mg per day of the drug was given to 16 patients suffering from pulmonary tuberculosis, marked improvement was obtained in 10 patients but higher doses caused undesirable side effects[316].

*3-Di-(2-thienyl)methylene-1-methylpiperidine (AT-327)*—A lower homologue of Pipendyl Methane in which the point of attachment has been shifted from the 4- to the 3-position on the piperidine nucleus, it was found to be more potent than codeine as an antitussive in dogs, about equipotent in cats, and less toxic than codeine in mice[317]. Favourable results were also obtained in a clinical trial in 45 patients. The drug was examined in 31 patients with pulmonary tuberculosis and found to be a satisfactory antitussive with almost no side effects[318].

Kasé and Yuizono[319] carried out an extensive structure-activity study in a series of 53 compounds analogous to analgesics, to related non-analgesic structures, to chlorpromazine derivatives, and to adrenergic amines, including a number of compounds of the general structures (*XXXI*) and (*XXXII*) with at least two compounds in each class containing piperidino groups. The compounds were tested for antitussive effects in dogs, cats, and mice. All compounds containing piperidino groups, with the exception of those related to adrenergic amines, were found to possess antitussive activity independent of analgetic potency.

*N-β-(1,2-Diphenylethoxy)ethyl-N-trimethylammonium bromide (Lysobex, Sedobex, TDBr)*—This may also be regarded as being somewhat related to compounds of the general structure (*XXVIII*) in which R represents $CH_2Ph$, A-B is replaced by hydrogen, and in which the OH group is etherified with a basically substituted ethyl group; moreover, the basic group has been quaternized. The title compound may be represented by formula (*XXXIV*) ($R^1 = R^2 = R^3 = Me$, $X = Br$):

$$PhCH \cdot O \cdot CH_2 \cdot CH_2 \cdot \overset{\overset{\displaystyle CH_2Ph}{|}}{\underset{\underset{\displaystyle R^3}{|}}{N^+R^2}}, X^-$$

(*XXXIV*)

Compounds in which $R^1$, $R^2$ and $R^3$ represent lower alkyl radicals, or $R^1$ and $R^2$ together represent pyrrolidino, piperidino, or morpholino groups, with $R^3 = Me$, and with X representing an anion, were synthesized by Suter and Kündig[320] and described as antitussives. The title compound was stated to have an unusually favourable therapeutic index, to be free from side-effects, and to be neither habit-forming nor addictive. Plisnier[321] found the compound to be about one-third more toxic than codeine, but to be three times as potent as an antitussive when tested by Domenjoz's method[74]. Studies in the chloralosed dog[322] showed that the drug had neither bronchodilator nor bronchoconstrictive action, and that it had no spasmolytic action following challenge with histamine or acetylcholine. Its therapeutic index was reported to be 2·16 compared to 1 for codeine phosphate.

The drug has been demonstrated to be useful as an antitussive in patients with various respiratory disorders[323], following surgical procedures[324] and in patients with various diseases of the respiratory tract[325].

Additional clinical data are necessary for a more complete evaluation of the drug, which appears to be an effective antitussive. It is interesting to note that this is one of the few instances in which a quaternary ammonium salt has been found to possess important antitussive activity: such activity in compounds possessing tertiary amino groups has usually been found to be destroyed, or at least greatly reduced, after quaternization (*cf.* 65*a*).

*Amides*

*Dextromoramide*—This compound (*d*-N-(3-methyl-2,2-diphenyl-4-morpholinobutyryl)pyrrolidine, pyrrolamidol, R.875, Jetrium, Palfium) may be regarded as related to the above compounds of the general structure

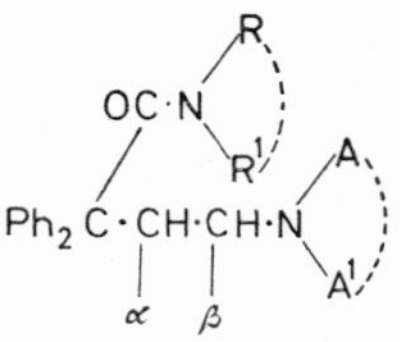

*(XXXV)*

(*XXVIII*), in which the OH radical had been replaced by an amide group, with R = Ph, A = $CHMe \cdot CH_2$, and B = morpholino. It was first described by Janssen[326], who synthesized over 100 compounds with the general structure (*XXXV*). Janssen found dextromoramide, the *d*-enantiomer of the compound with $NRR^1$ = pyrrolidino, $\alpha$ = Me, $\beta$ = H, and $NAA^1$ = morpholino to be the most potent analgesic in that series, many times more active than pethidine, morphine, or methadone in animals. It was twice as active as the corresponding racemate, which in turn appeared to be three times as active as morphine in preliminary experiments on human subjects. The drug inhibited cough following endotracheal intubation[327], and produced satisfactory results at 0·5 mg doses, and excellent results with 1 mg doses, given orally 4–6 times per day to patients with various respiratory diseases[328]. Additional clinical studies, especially with regard to the possible addictive properties of the drug, are required for a final evaluation.

*N-1′,1′,3′,3′-Tetramethylbutyl-2-diethylaminoacetamide* (*TR-310*)—It was first prepared by Malen and Boissier[329] in a series of 25 substituted amides of basically substituted acetic acids. This series was prepared to prove that the aromatic nucleus of lignocaine (lidocaine, Xylocaine) may be replaced by suitably selected aliphatic radicals without loss of local anaesthetic activity. The compounds may be represented by the general formula (*XXXVI*) in which $R^1$ and $R^2$ represent

$$R^1R^2N \cdot (CH_2)_n \cdot CHR^3 \cdot CO \cdot NHR^4$$

*(XXXVI)*

lower alkyl groups or together with N represent a nitrogen-containing heterocyclic radical, *n* stands for zero or one, $R^3$ for hydrogen or lower alkyl, and $R^4$ represents a tertiary alkyl group. The compounds have local anaesthetic, analgetic, convulsant, spasmolytic, and pressor properties. The series was subsequently extended to include 26 additional compounds in

122

which $R^4$ is a tertiary aliphatic radical with up to 14 carbon atoms in a chain, or a cycloaliphatic group; these compounds have local anaesthetic, analgetic, and antispasmodic activities[330]. In one structure-activity study[331] it was found that the 1,1,3,3-tetramethylbutyl group $(CMe_2 \cdot CH_2 \cdot CMe_3)$ in position $R^4$ gave the highest values for local anaesthetic activity, which was further enhanced by the 2-methylpiperidino group in the position of $R^1R^2N$. In a subsequent series of four papers[332-335] a detailed study of the pharmacological properties of most of the above compounds was made. Also included were a number of compounds in which $R^3$ represents ethyl or propyl radicals or in which $R^4$ represents straight-chain aliphatic radicals up to 12 carbon atoms, and a series of compounds in which the basic group was attached not to the acid moiety but to the amide nitrogen, *e.g.* of the formula $RCO \cdot NH \cdot CH_2 \cdot CH_2 \cdot NEt_2$; R in this instance represents straight-chain alkyl radicals up to 15 carbon atoms. All the above compounds have local anaesthetic and antispasmodic properties and some of them also have analgetic activity.

The antitussive activity of the title compound (*XXXVI*, $R^1 = R^2 = Et$, $n = 0$, $R^3 = H$, $R^4 = CMe_2 \cdot CH_2 \cdot CMe_3$) was studied[24] by means of Kasé's[97], de Vleeschhouwer's[113], and Domenjoz's[74] methods and found to be slightly superior to that of codeine and about equal to that of carbetapentane. The drug was stated to have spasmolytic, local anaesthetic, and analgetic properties, and no depressant effects upon respiration. Its toxicity appeared to be low ($LD_{50}$ mouse i.p. 260 mg/kg[331]), but it was stated to be convulsant in high doses. No clinical studies of the drug appear to have been published to date.

*Methaqualone*—The compound (Metolquizolone, Melsedin, Tuazole, QZ-2, 2-methyl-3-*o*-tolyl-4-quinazolone, *XXXVII*, R = Me, $R^1 = o$-tolyl, $R^2 = H$) which may be regarded as a cyclic amide, was first synthesized as a potential analgesic by Kacker and Zaheer[336] in a series of compounds of the general

*(XXXVII)*

formula (*XXXVII*) in which R represented hydrogen or lower alkyl, $R^1$ phenyl or substituted aryl, and $R^2$ hydrogen. The synthesis followed a general method previously used to prepare similar compounds including a number in which $R^2$ stood for chlorine in the 6-position[337]. The hypnotic activity of some of the above compounds was discovered by Gujral, Saxena and Tiwari[338], who found the title compound superior to ethylphenylbarbituric acid. Some of the pharmacological actions of the drug were studied including its low acute toxicity ($LD_{50}$ mouse, oral 1 g/kg, i.p. 200–300 mg/kg; rat, oral 0·5 g/kg)[339]. A dose of 100 mg/kg given orally five times per week for six weeks was non-toxic to rats. The compound caused loss of righting reflex in mice at doses of 90–100 mg/kg, inhibited the stimulant actions of leptazole, picrotoxin, amphetamine, caffeine, or Meratran, and potentiated the depressant effects of Mebubarbital, methylpentynol, reserpine, or chlorpromazine. The central depressant effects of the drug were confirmed in a clinical study[340] which showed that 150 mg doses of the drug gave hypnotic effects which were superior in 54 out of 100 patients to those obtained with other hypnotics. Similar results were reported by Parsons and Thomson[341] who found that a dose of 150 mg of the drug was as effective as 200 mg cyclobarbitone.

The antitussive effects of methaqualone were discovered by Boissier and Pagny[342]. Tested in cats by Domenjoz's method[74], doses of 10 mg/kg i.v. inhibited cough completely for 25 minutes to 3 hours, while codeine had about the same effects in doses of 1–6 mg/kg i.v. No synergism between the drug and codeine was detected. In guinea-pigs the drug had an $ED_{50}$ of about 20 mg/kg i.p. against cough produced by an aerosol of N/2 sulphuric acid, while codeine was found to have the same effects at about 40 mg/kg i.p. Doses of 40 mg/kg i.p. of methaqualone caused no drowsiness in the animals. No depressant effects upon respiration, and no cardiovascular effects were found, and the drug was stated to possess slight spasmolytic activity. The authors recommended it for clinical trials as an antitussive drug. Kohli, Gupta and Bhargava[141] studied the antitussive action of the drug by Domenjoz's method[74] and found it to be ineffective at doses of 1–2 mg/kg, but effective at 5 mg/kg. No clinical studies of the antitussive efficacy of the drug have appeared in print to date.

*Dextromethorphan (Romilar, d-3-methoxy-N-methylmorphinan, XXXVIII)*— Dextromorphan may be regarded as being structurally derived from

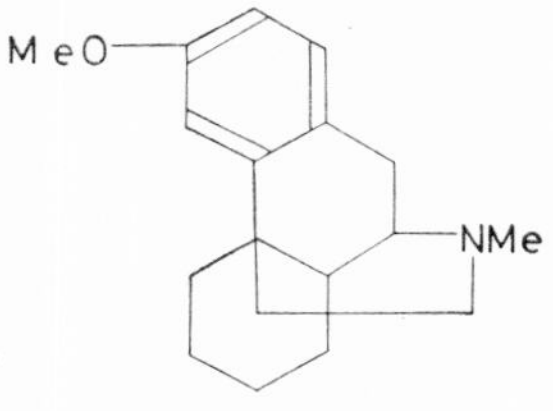

(XXXVIII)

codeine (see formula *II*), by elimination of the oxygen bridge $C^4$—$C^5$, the oxygen function on $C^6$, and the double bond $C^7$—$C^8$. Its preparation was first described by Schnider and Grüssner[343].

It may also be regarded as being the dextrorotatory methyl ether of race-morphan, the narcotic and addictive properties of which are well known (*c.f.* reference 32). However, Isbell and Fraser[181] showed that it was free from addiction liabilities while its laevorotatory enantiomer was highly addictive. In this series of compounds the *d*-enantiomers have no analgetic, sedative, or general morphine-like effects[180]. Derivatives of dextromethorphan, in which particularly the *N*-methyl and the *O*-methyl groups had been replaced by other substituents, were recently stated to possess antitussive properties[344,345], but no pharmacological or clinical data on those latter compounds seem to have been published so far.

The first thorough pharmacological study of dextromethorphan was carried out by Pellmont and Bächtold[346]. Using four different methods for determining antitussive activity, they found the drug to be equal in potency to codeine in two of them[54,74], active at 2 mg/kg i.v. in another[85], and superior to codeine in a procedure using ammonia to induce cough. It had practically no analgetic activity, no sedative action, and caused no inhibition of respiration; no constipating or antidiuretic effects were noted. Reichle and Friebel[78] thought that the drug was representative of a new class of antitussives with little analgetic effects. Van Dongen[160] found that doses of 2 mg/kg s.c. inhibited cough for 6 hours, 4 mg/kg s.c. for 8 hours, and that 5–10 mg/kg s.c. prevented cough in the cat when tested by the method of Ernst[34]. Dextromethorphan is relatively more effective in humans than in rats or guinea-pigs[129]. It is centrally active in doses of 0·25–2·0 mg/kg i.v., and it inhibits cough more than respiration[62]. It was reported to act more rapidly and more powerfully than codeine in guinea-pigs with cough induced by ammonia[347], but it was found less active than codeine in the same species with cough elicited by acrolein[132].

Cough induced experimentally in healthy human subjects was apparently not influenced by dextromethorphan, as no significant differences were detected between 10 mg doses of dextromethorphan, 10 mg or 15 mg codeine, or placebo[107,134]. On the other hand, in a double blind study, it was found to be significantly better than placebo, with 10 mg doses being equal to 15 mg codeine[144].

Clinical studies of the use of dextromethorphan in the treatment of cough of various origins show that it is effective in doses which vary between 4 and 30 mg[242,348–353]. It has been successfully used in infants and children[354,355], in patients suffering from pulmonary tuberculosis[356,357], and as an adjunct in surgical procedures associated with pulmonary diseases[358].

To summarize, dextromethorphan appears to be a useful and effective antitussive drug, with an optimal dose of 10 mg given three to four times per day, and a maximal single dose of 30 mg. Doses of 10 mg seem to be about as effective as 15 mg of codeine. The incidence of side-effects is much lower than that encountered with codeine, and the drug has no sedative, analgetic, habit-forming, nor addictive properties.

*Normethadone (desmethylmethadone, HOE 10582, XXXIX, 6-dimethylamino-4,4-diphenylhexan-3-one)*—The compound differs from methadone by the absence of a methyl group attached to position 6. It was synthesized by Bockmühl and Ehrhardt[359] as one of a series of closely related compounds with analgetic activity in which numerous variations were made in the basic group, in branching of the chain, and in the nature of the group replacing carbon atoms 1 and 2. The structure of normethadone corresponds to the formula (*XXXIX*) and it is used as the antitussive principle in the German preparation Ticarda, which contains 7·5 mg normethadone hydrochloride and 10 mg Suprifen (1-(4-hydroxyphenyl)-2-methylaminopropanol) in tablets, or 1 per cent normethadone and 2 per cent Suprifen in liquid form.

$$Me_2N \cdot CH_2 \cdot CH_2 \cdot CPh_2 \cdot CO \cdot CH_2 \cdot CH_3$$
$$(XXXIX)$$

The early pharmacological and clinical results with the drug have been reviewed[32]. The drug has mainly analgetic and less important antitussive properties in guinea-pigs[83,87], and this was confirmed[78] in rats. Friebel and Reichle[129] found the drug to be relatively more potent as an antitussive in rats than in guinea-pigs or in humans. Van Dongen[160], using Ernst's method[34] in cats, reported antitussive activity lasting for 6–7 hours with doses of 2 mg/kg s.c. which, however, inhibited ciliary movement. Doses of 5 mg/kg were stated to cause excitation. Using Domenjoz's method[74] the drug was shown to have an $ED_{50}$ of 0·3 mg/kg i.v., five times as active as codeine, and with a duration of effect of about 70 per cent of that of codeine[141]. In rats with cough produced by 0·02 per cent sulphur dioxide, an $ED_{50}$ of 14 mg/kg i.p. was found[360], almost twice the potency of codeine.

In clinical practice, reports[145,150] indicate that the drug is inferior to some other antitussive drugs, but it is efficacious in cases of irritative cough[361]. Conflicting views exist on whether the drug is addictive[32,360].

*R-522*—A molecular complex or possibly a salt of normethadone with 2,6-di-(-butyl)naphthalenedisulphonic acid, it was first described by Hengen and Kasparek[79]. They found it had about the same therapeutic index in rats as codeine, and a considerably better index than methadone. Schmidt[199] evaluated the compound in a clinical trial on 55 patients treated with 35–45 mg of the preparation per day for 4–6 weeks, and reported 30 good, 20 satisfactory, and 5 poor results. The compound was stated to have no influence upon blood pressure, haemogram, urine analysis, blood sugar levels in diabetics, or appetite, and no allergic manifestations, constipation, or development of tolerance were observed.

*1-Cyclopentyl-1-(β-N-morpholinoethyl)cyclopentane-2-one* (*Melipan, Ciba 10611, XL*)—It may be regarded as somewhat related to normethadone (*XXXIX*).

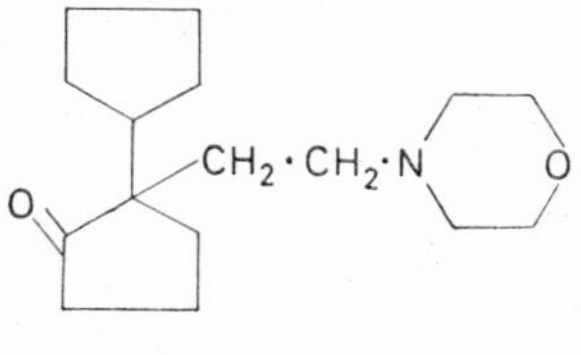

*(XL)*

No details of the synthesis of the compound or its analogues, nor of its pharmacological properties, have been found in the literature to date. The only published report concerns a trial[146] for antitussive activity in 28 volunteers who coughed regularly when exposed to a citric acid aerosol[109] and in whom cough reflex was suppressed by 30 mg of codeine. In a blind test using 25 and 50 mg doses of the drug and 30 mg of codeine, careful statistical evaluation showed that the drug was almost as effective as codeine, and that its antitussive activity was not increased when the dose was raised from 25 mg to 50 mg.

*Phenothiazine derivatives*

*Dimethoxanate*—Synthesized by von Seeman[363], dimethoxanate (Cothera, 2′-dimethylaminoethoxyethyl phenothiazine-10-carbōxylate, *XLI, R = H*,

$R' = R^2 = Me$) was one of a series of compounds in which the phenothiazine nucleus remained unsubstituted ($R = H$), while $R^1$ and $R^2$ were
varied to include ethyl and isopropyl radicals.

Chappel, Stegen and Grant[142] studied the pharmacological properties of
these compounds and found them to be powerful antitussives when tested
by Domenjoz's method[74], with the antitussive activity increasing as the size
of $R^1$ and $R^2$ increased. The dimethyl compound was found to be slightly
less active than codeine, and the compound with $R^1 = R^2 = Pr^i$ twice as
active as codeine. However, oral toxicity, antispasmodic activity, local
anaesthetic action, and inhibition of gastric emptying rate increased also

$$O:C \cdot O \cdot CH_2 \cdot CH_2 \cdot O \cdot CH_2 \cdot CH_2 \cdot N \overset{R^1}{\underset{R^2}{\big<}}$$

(XLI)

as the size of $R^1$ and $R^2$ increased, and for those reasons the title compound
($R^1 = R^2 = Me$) was chosen for further detailed study. It was found to
have neither anticholinergic nor antihistaminic activity, and it had no effect
upon gastric secretion in the Shay rat. The drug had no influence upon
spontaneous activity of the rat, and did not potentiate the hypnotic action
of pentobarbital in the mouse. Doses of 2 mg/kg i.v. had no influence upon
blood pressure or respiratory rate in the dog, and higher doses up to 8 mg/kg
produced only a transient fall in blood pressure accompanied by slight
tachycardia and tachypnoea, all of which returned to normal within
5–15 minutes. The compound in doses of 25 mg/kg s.c. had no analgetic
effects in the mouse. The acute oral toxicity was found to be about the same
as that of codeine in the mouse, but only 40 per cent that of codeine in the
rat. Chronic toxicity tests in rats receiving 0·1, 0·06, and 0·04 per cent of the
drug in their diet over a period of 32 weeks, equivalent to daily intakes of
the drug of 45–75, 25–40, and 15–30 mg/kg respectively, showed normal
growth curves in animals of both sexes. Dogs given daily oral doses of
50 mg/kg for one year gained weight and remained in good health. Chen,
Biller and Montgomery[91] compared the drug for duration of antitussive
effects with codeine and a number of other antitussives. Challenging dogs
with sulphuric acid aerosol[96] and administering the drugs orally either in
doses of 1 mg/kg, or in therapeutically equivalent doses (e.g. 0·8 mg/kg
dimethoxanate equivalent to 0·5 mg/kg codeine or to 0·2 mg/kg hydrocodone), they found dimethoxanate in both series of experiments superior
to all other drugs except chlophedianol: dimethoxanate reduced cough by
75 per cent for about 3·5 hours, chlophedianol for 7–9 hours, and codeine
for about one half-hour, while benzonatate, dextromethorphan, and noscapine
failed to reach the level of 75 per cent inhibition of cough with the doses
employed. Boissier and Pagny[364] used both guinea-pigs challenged with N/2

sulphuric acid aerosol[83] and cats[74] in their evaluations of the antitussive activities of a number of phenothiazine derivatives, mainly of the antihistamine or tranquillizer type, but also including dimethoxanate. They found the drug to be somewhat more active than codeine in the guinea-pig, and slightly less potent than codeine in the cat. The authors concluded that neuroleptic agents possess non-specific antitussive activities, not related to antihistaminic activity and not connected with the presence of the phenothiazine nucleus in the molecule of the drug.

Clinical studies with dimethoxanate were carried out by Klein[365], who evaluated the drug as a routine antitussive medication in 50 patients, and in 15 particularly severe cases of chronic cough, with doses of about 18 mg twice per day. Reactions of the 15 patients in the second group were evaluated with particular care. The onset of action of the drug was found to be rapid, usually within 5–10 minutes, with an average duration of effect of four hours. Severity and frequency of cough were both reduced, with complete suppression of cough after a single dose in 12 cases. No influence of the drug upon the excretion of sputum was noted, and no incompatibility with a large number of other drugs. No side-effects were seen, and the drug seemed to have no cardiovascular effects. The drug was superior to placebo, and was rated superior to the previously used hydrocodone by 12 patients and equally effective by two others. Parish[366] conducted a double-blind study of the drug compared with placebo in 139 patients, the majority of whom suffered from coryza or allergic rhinitis. Ninety-three of the 95 patients treated with the drug reported excellent relief following treatment with doses of 25 mg every four hours in adult cases, and 8–18 mg for children. Of 44 cases treated with placebo, 41 reported slight transient relief, possibly due to the demulcent action of the preparation, and 3 obtained excellent relief. Thirteen cases of side-effects were seen in the series, usually slight drowsiness or nausea, but one patient known to be drug-sensitive developed an allergic reaction which cleared after cessation of medication.

Following the initial work cited above[363], the series of phenothiazine derivatives was extended by Myers and Davis[367] to include compounds of the general structure (XLI) with R = H in which the ether linkage in the side chain had been replaced by a thioether $CH_2 \cdot CH_2 \cdot S \cdot CH_2 \cdot CH_2 \cdot NR^1R^2$, with $R^1$ and $R^2$ representing Me, Et, or $Pr^1$. Further extensions of the series were carried out by Davis[368], who prepared a group of compounds of structure (XLI) in which $R^1$ and $R^2$ were varied or in which $NR^1R^2$ represented a nitrogen-containing heterocycle, a second group in which both the length of the side chain and the nature of the basic group were varied, a third group containing variations in the nature of the ester linkage, and a fourth group in which R represented a variety of substituents in the 2- or 3-positions of the phenothiazine nucleus, with the ester linkage and the nature of the side chain as in formula (XLI) but with variations in the basic group. Some forty compounds were prepared in this manner, and most of them were found to possess important antitussive activities in laboratory animals[369].

*Derivatives of azaphenothiazine*

*Pipazethate*—Variously named as Selvigon, D-254, 2'-(2-piperidinoethoxy)-ethyl 1-azaphenothiazine-10-carboxylate; also (German nomenclature)

4-azaphenothiazine-10-carboxylate, or 10-thia-1,9-diaza-anthracene-9-carboxylate, or (*Chem. Abstr.* nomenclature) 10*H*-pyrido[3,2b][1,4]benzo-thiazine-10-carboxylate; this compound corresponds to formula (*XLII*). The compound is closely related to dimethoxanate (*XLI*, R = H, R¹ = R² =Me), from which it differs in the nature of the nucleus and of the basic group in the side chain. The synthesis of pipazethate has so far not been reported, but a series of closely related basically substituted lower alkyl

$$O:C \cdot O \cdot CH_2 \cdot CH_2 O \cdot CH_2 \cdot CH_2 N$$

(*XLII*)

esters of 1-aza- (or, according to German nomenclature, 4-aza-)pheno-thiazine-10-carboxylic acid was prepared by Schuler and Klebe[370] and described as spasmolytics.

The pharmacology of pipazethate was studied by Gulden[371]. The median lethal dose in the mouse was reported as 97 mg/kg i.p. and 214 mg/kg p.o.; the corresponding values in the rat were 70 and 560 mg/kg. The compound was reported to have hypnotic properties in mice with an $ED_{50}$ of 106 mg/kg. No cataleptic, anti-allergic, antihistaminic, or antiserotonin properties were observed. As a spasmolytic, the compound was found to have 5 per cent of the activity of atropine against acetylcholine, and to be 1·6 times as active as papaverine against barium-chloride-induced spasm. Its local anaesthetic activity was reported to be 40 per cent that of lignocaine. The drug was stated to be an effective antitussive both by s.c. or oral routes, but neither the experimental method used nor the results obtained were given. Libal[372], on the other hand, reported that the drug had only slight local anaesthetic activity, and that no sedative effects could be observed in mice.

The pharmacology of pipazethate as an antitussive in human subjects was first studied by Haslreiter[373]. The method of Tiffeneau[112] was first applied to 35 healthy subjects and 160 patients; the authors found that the former group did not react to the challenging agent (acetylcholine). Of the 160 patients with chronic inflammatory conditions of the respiratory tract, 70 reacted by cough after challenge with an aerosol of 0·1 per cent acetyl-choline, 49 reacted to 0·25 per cent, 5 to 0·5 per cent, and 7 to 1·0 per cent concentration. Bronchospasms occurred in a number of patients, but they were readily controlled by inhalations of hexamethonium aerosol. In a subsequent double-blind experiment, 120 patients were challenged with aerosols of the same range of concentration of acetylcholine as above, 30 minutes after receiving either 30 mg of codeine, 20 mg of pipazethate, or placebo. Cough was completely inhibited in 6 per cent of the patients treated with placebo, in 53 per cent of those treated with codeine, and in 41 per cent of those given pipazethate. Inhibition of cough was particularly marked in cases of chronic bronchitis, while the drugs seemed to be ineffective in cases of thoracoplasty, lobectomy, or silicosis. Prime[374], using a similar technique, confirmed that it was not applicable to healthy volunteers who were non-smokers. When repeating the test in another group of volunteers who were moderate smokers and admitted to having occasional slight cough, all of the subjects coughed after the challenge. A double-blind trial was then carried out with the latter group of 12 subjects, using doses of 20 mg pipazethate, 16 mg of codeine phosphate, or placebo, all of them given 20 minutes before challenge with acetylcholine aerosol. Cough rates before and after medication were determined individually and submitted to an analysis of covariance. The adjusted mean cough rates following administration of pipazethate, codeine, or placebo were found to be respectively 4·6, 7·9 and 14·0, with no variation in the cough rate before and after taking placebo. The author concluded that pipazethate was a potent antitussive drug. He stated furthermore, that oral doses of 20–40 mg appeared to be sufficient for most purposes; that the drug may be given in doses up to 160 mg per 24 hours without side-effects; and that it appeared to be useful in endoscopic or bronchospirometric procedures.

In clinical trials, pipazethate appears to be about as good as codeine in suppressing cough in patients suffering from pulmonary tuberculosis[371,372] and various respiratory disorders[373]. Side-effects were negligible or non-existent and no signs of habituation or addiction were observed.

In summing up the above pharmacological and clinical evidence, pipazethate appears to be a useful antitussive drug, somewhat less potent than codeine, and with an unusually low incidence of side-effects. Obviously further clinical studies are needed for a more complete evaluation of the drug.

*Oxolamine*—This compound (Perebron, 3-phenyl-5-(2-diethylaminoethyl)-1,2,4-oxadiazole, *XLIII*, X = H, $n = 2$, R = NEt$_2$) was first described by Silvestrini and Pozzatti[117] in a series of six substituted oxadiazoles of the general formula (*XLIII*) in which X represented hydrogen or chlorine, $n$ was varied from 1 to 3, and R represented dimethylamino, diethylamino, pyrrolidino, or piperidino groups.

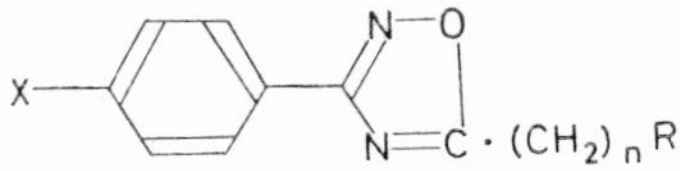

*(XLIII)*

The pharmacology of the above compounds was studied by the same authors[117], who reported that the acute i.p. toxicity was generally low. Some of the compounds showed local anaesthetic activity considerably greater than that of procaine, while others were much less potent. Only one had marked antispasmodic activity, being about twice as active as papaverine, while the others were as active as or less active than papaverine. Most of the compounds caused no significant cardiovascular effects in the cat in doses of 5 mg/kg i.v., while higher doses produced transient hypotension. Some evidence of respiratory stimulation was reported. The compounds were found to be inactive as analgesics in rats in the hot plate[375] and in the phenylquinone[376] tests, but three of them were found to have analgetic activities similar to or greater than that of acetylsalicylic acid when tested by the method of Randall and Selitto[377]. One of the compounds showed an anti-inflammatory activity[378] comparable to that of phenylbutazone, the others were less active. When tested for antitussive activity by the method of Domenjoz[74], all compounds were found to be less active than codeine; however, in the acrolein aerosol test on guinea-pigs[132], two compounds were found to be considerably superior, and one about equal to codeine.

No discernible relationship between structure and biological activities of compounds of this series was detected; however, all those compounds which had antitussive activity also had analgetic activity on inflamed tissue. The title compound showed the most interesting profile in the above tests: low toxicity ($LD_{50}$ 208 mg/kg mouse, i.p.), weak local anaesthetic activity, and a high degree of antitussive action, were combined with good anti-inflammatory and good analgetic activities upon inflamed tissue. Silvestrini[379] studied the compound in detail and found it to be twice as potent as codeine in guinea-pigs by means of the ammonia vapour test[84], but it showed only about one-third to one-fifth of the activity of codeine when tested by Domenjoz's method[74]. The drug did not inhibit nervous conduction, was found to be inactive at the neuromuscular junction, and did not potentiate the hypnotic action of barbiturates. The anti-inflammatory activity of oxolamine was compared with that of phenylbutazone and of acetylsalicylic acid[378], and equipotent doses were reported to be 50, 20 and 100 mg/kg rat, s.c., respectively. The drug was also found to have anti-inflammatory action in the rat oedema test[380], in which phenylbutazone and acetylsalicylic acid were both found to be inactive. On the other hand, it did not retard the development of connective tissue following the subcutaneous implantation of a cotton pellet[381]. Its lack of analgetic activity in the hot plate[375] and the phenylquinone[376] tests was confirmed[117]. The marked analgetic activity of oxolamine upon inflamed tissue[377] was found to be equal to that of phenylbutazone or of acetylsalicylic acid, but inferior to that of codeine or of morphine. The antipyretic activity of the drug was reported to be equal to that of phenylbutazone and about one-half that of acetylsalicylic acid. As a spasmolytic, oxolamine was stated to be about as active as papaverine, and its local anaesthetic activity equalled that of procaine. The drug had no cardiovascular effects in doses of 20 mg/kg rat i.p.; higher doses caused transient hypotension. Oxolamine did not inhibit intestinal peristalsis, and had no effects upon diuresis, conditioned reflexes, or monoamine oxidase activity; neither did it have any influence upon convulsions induced by electroshock, leptazole (pentylenetetrazol), or strychnine. Toxicity was relatively low. The author concluded that the mode of action of oxolamine was different from that of morphine or codeine. The possibility of explaining the antitussive action of oxolamine as a synergism between its peripheral anti-inflammatory and decongestant activities and its central effects was also discussed: as the peripheral stimuli originating in the respiratory tract are diminished, the centrally mediated effects of the drug may be relatively increased. An additional pharmacological study of oxolamine is in preparation[382].

Clinical investigations of the drug were carried out using the double-blind method with a positive (codeine) and a negative (placebo) control. Oxolamine was given as the citrate salt, usually in a syrup, in doses of 100 mg salt (=56 mg base) 4–5 times per day, and codeine was administered in the same manner in 30 mg doses, equivalent to 22 mg base. A high proportion of patients with tracheobronchitis were improved by oxolamine[383] and almost one-half of a group of elderly hospitalized patients improved[384]. Oxolamine also benefited nearly a half of patients with pulmonary tuberculosis[385]. Controlled clinical investigations in patients suffering from chronic respiratory conditions, in both adults[386] and children[387], and in bronchitis cases[388] gave moderately good results. A re-appraisal of these results showed that 100 mg of oxolamine citrate was equivalent to 30 mg codeine phosphate[389].

Summarizing the above results, oxolamine appears to be a potentially useful drug, characterized by low toxicity, antitussive activity in man somewhat less than one-half of codeine, with analgetic activity in the range of that of acetylsalicylic acid, antipyretic activity about one-half that of the latter, and anti-inflammatory activity about 40 per cent that of phenylbutazone. The unique combination of these activities in one single compound may prove to be of value, but undoubtedly additional clinical studies are needed for a more complete evaluation of the drug.

*Piperazine derivatives*—Compounds having the general structure (*XLIV*) in which R represented a mono- or polyhydroxylated alkyl group or an

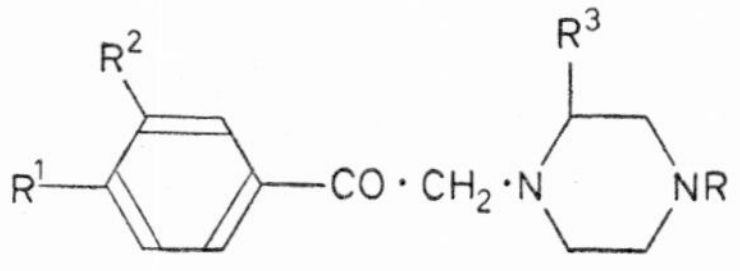

(*XLIV*)

alkoxyalkyl group, with $R^1$ and $R^2$ representing hydrogen or hydroxyl, and $R^3$ hydrogen or methyl, were synthesized by Morren[390–393]. The compounds were stated to have antitussive properties, and one of them (*XLIV*, R = $CH_2 \cdot CH_2 \cdot OH$, $R^1 = R^2 = OH$, $R^3 = H$) was claimed to have 150 per

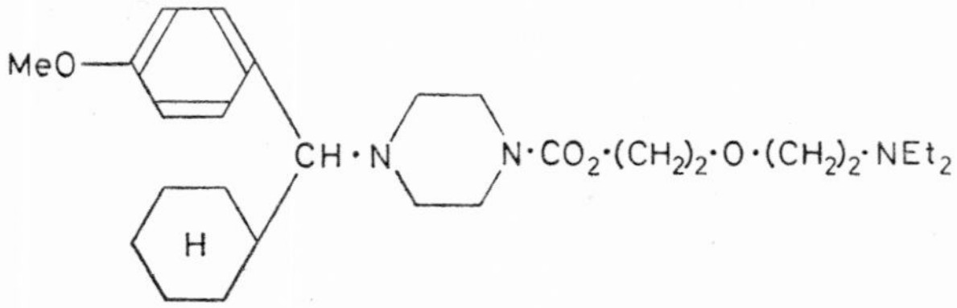

(*XLV*)

cent of the activity of codeine. Morren[246] also prepared a compound of the structure (*XLV*) which was claimed to have antitussive activity.

132

*Piperidine derivatives*—Compounds of the general formula (*XLVI*) were also claimed to have antitussive properties. Stern and Watt[394] described compounds with X = Ph, Y = OH or O-acyl, R = $(CH_2)_n R^1$ in which $n$ = 2–6 and $R^1$ represented an alkoxy, aryloxy, aralkoxy, or cycloalkoxy group. The compounds were stated to have analgetic and cough centre depressant activities. Another series of compounds[395] in which X represented

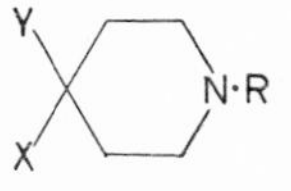

( *XLVI* )

the 2'-propyne-1'-yl group, $CH_2 \cdot C \equiv CH$, Y was a propionyloxy group, OCOEt, and R a phenethyl group, was stated to have antitussive, analgetic, and local anaesthetic activities.

No pharmacological or clinical studies of the piperazine or piperidine derivatives mentioned above have been published to date.

1-*Hydroxycyclopentanecarboxylic acid derivatives*—A study of over a hundred derivatives of this acid and of 1-aminocyclopentanecarboxylic acid showed that some of these compounds possessed antitussive activity equal to one half that of codeine when tested in the cat against chemical irritation[65a]. The compounds tested included those with one or two tertiary amino or quaternary ammonium groups. In contrast to the findings of some workers, Ellis, Golberg, King and Sheard[65a] found that activity present in a tertiary amine was usually retained on quaternizing this group.

*Other Pharmacologically Active Agents Investigated for Use in Cough Therapy*

Some sympathomimetics (isoprenaline, isoproterenol)[396–400], methamphetamine[401–404], Homarylamine[30,145,405,406]) have been used successfully, mostly in combined preparations. A few smooth muscle spasmolytics (atropine[120,132], adiphenine[70,132,407], papaverine[76,132]) have low activity. Certain antihistamines (mepyramine[132,364,408], promethazine[132,364,409,410], Thiazinamium[364], antazoline[410,414], tripelennamine[70,417], trimeprazine[17,364], [418,419], triprolidine[364,420]) are only weakly active, but others (diphenhydramine[104–106,411–413], chlorcyclizine[413,415,416]) are clinically effective. Some tranquillizers (chlorpromazine[141,364,421–427], thioridazine[364,428], reserpine[141], [429–432]) have weak antitussive activity, but others (azacyclonol, benactyzine, meprobamate[130,141]) are ineffective. The ganglion blocking agents hexamethonium[56] and pentamethonium[46,433] are effective only against experimental cough induced by lobeline. Certain local anaesthetics (lignocaine, procaine[70]) are weak antitussives, but amethocaine (tetracaine) is highly active[132]. Amongst the hypnotics and sedatives, pentobarbitone[119,132] and phenobarbitone[360] are inactive, but thiopentone has some antitussive activity[62].

### RETROSPECT AND PROSPECTS

When considering the progress in a given field it is almost inevitable that a number of strong impressions will be gained. This has been particularly true for this review of the medicinal chemistry of antitussives. Judging by the number of new antitussive compounds which have been synthesized, studied pharmacologically, and in many cases introduced into clinical use, there would appear to have been much progress in the field. Indeed, in many respects this is certainly the case: quite a number of the new compounds are effective antitussives, free from addictive liability and most of the side-effects associated with the older opium alkaloids. However, codeine remains the most widely utilized drug for antitussive therapy, and only one of the newer drugs, dextromethorphan, exceeds codeine in potency in terms of the clinical dose. It would seem that we are still far from having an ideal antitussive drug.

In so far as the chemistry of existing antitussive drugs is concerned, the common characteristic of the opium alkaloids and their close derivatives with antitussive activity, as well as of the synthetic antitussive drugs, is the presence of a tertiary amino group. The nitrogen atom of this group may be contained in an open chain or in a cyclic structure, and little, if any, difference in antitussive activity seems to result from this variation.

The morphine alkaloids and their close derivatives seem to belong to a particular class of compounds with antitussive action, with the basic nitrogen atom contained in a ring system of very special character. The analgetic activities of most of these compounds may account for a large part of their antitussive activity, with the exception of dextromethorphan, in which analgetic activity is largely absent. However, it has been said that the antitussive action of codeine may be due to the subjective 'sense of well-being' which it seems to impart to the patients.

The synthetic antitussives, most of which have been prepared in order to obtain compounds free from the noxious side-effects of the morphine alkaloids, including the danger of addiction, seem to have one feature in common. On one end of the molecule we find usually an accumulation of large bulky groups, such as aryl, aralkyl, cycloalkyl, or heterocyclic groups. These groups might possibly perform a shielding action after the molecule has become attached to the receptor site. The basic nitrogen is usually found near the other end of the molecule. The linkages between the 'bulky end of the molecule' and the basic nitrogen may be effected by various means, but two main types of structures appear to be closely discernible: first, those with a superficial resemblance to antispasmodic drugs, and second, compounds with an equally superficial resemblance to synthetic analgesics related to methadone.

An example from the first group of compounds may, perhaps, show the relationship. The dialkylaminoalkyl esters of phenothiazine-10-carboxylic acid were found to have important antispasmodic activity of a neurotropic, atropine-like character[434,435]. The same compounds were also synthesized independently and at about the same time by von Seemann and Grant, who subjected them later on to a number of structural modifications. They noted, *inter alia*, that anticholinergic activity was reduced by insertion of one or more carbon atoms between the nitrogen of the phenothiazine ring and the carboxylic acid group, and was not influenced by substitution in the phenothiazine nucleus[436]. This observation seemed to confirm Pfeiffer's[437] earlier thoughts about the structural requirements for anticholinergic activity.

134

Pfeiffer had theorized that certain substances with anticholinergic activity had structures in which the interatomic distances between the centres of each one of the two oxygen atoms in, for example, an ester group and the centre of the methyl group on the nitrogen resembled closely those found in acetylcholine itself. This should theoretically enable such compounds to become attached to the same receptor sites as acetylcholine. Calculations of the bond distances gave values of 5·3 Å and 7·0 Å for acetylcholine, and a number of acetylcholine antagonists showed indeed approximately the same values for the distances between each one of the two oxygen atoms and the methyl group on the nitrogen.

Pfeiffer's theory being perfectly applicable to the above dialkylaminoalkyl esters of phenothiazine-10-carboxylic acid, von Seemann speculated that a radical change in the structure might conceivably reduce anticholinergic action. The results vindicated this speculation: lengthening of the side chain by one ethoxy group gave basically substituted alkoxyalkyl esters such as, *e.g.* dimethoxanate, in which anticholinergic action had virtually disappeared, while direct smooth muscle relaxant activity was greatly enhanced. Moreover, those compounds were distinguished by pronounced antitussive activity, which was later found to be totally absent in the corresponding dialkyl-aminoalkyl esters[438].

Parallel differences in the nature of biological activities were also found between the basically substituted alkyl esters and the corresponding alkoxy-alkyl esters of 1-azaphenothiazine-10-carboxylic acid[370–372].

Another example in this class of compounds may be equally illustrative. Adiphenine is known to possess very weak antitussive properties, while the closely related caramiphen has moderate antitussive activity, conceivably brought about by the comparatively simple change in the nature of one of the two phenyl groups of adiphenine. Lengthening of the side chain of caramiphen gave carbetapentane, which possesses very marked antitussive activity. In this series, too, the increase in antitussive activity obtained by lengthening of the side chain seemed to be accompanied by a decrease in anticholinergic effect. Incorporation of an ethoxy group into a basically substituted alkyl side chain to obtain enhanced antitussive activity was also successful in the case of oxeladin.

At this juncture it should also be remembered that the basically substituted alkoxyalkyl side chain often imparts antitussive activity[14], and that dodecyl polyethylene oxide ether inhibited pulmonary stretch receptors[203],[204]. It would appear that the ether linkage in the side chain of antitussive drugs performs a very useful function.

In contrast to the above group of compounds, in which the basic group is attached to the bulky or shielding part of the molecule through a side chain carrying an ester linkage, the second group of compounds does not possess such an ester group.

The compounds in this class have a superficial resemblance to methadone: they are characterized by the presence of a quaternary carbon atom which carries at least one and usually two bulky substituents, and to which the alkylene side chain carrying the basic nitrogen atom is attached directly. The fourth valency on the quaternary carbon atom may be occupied by a polar radical, such as a nitrile group as in isoaminile or a hydroxyl group as in

Hoe 10682, or in KAT-256; or one of the alkyl groups attached to the basic nitrogen atom might be linked back to the quaternary carbon atom as, *e.g.* in pipendyl methane. A number of other variants in the nature of this group have been tried, with some measure of success, and its character would seem to be not too critical. The linkage between the basic nitrogen atom at one end of the molecule, and the bulky substituent at the other, is apparently not limited to an alkylene chain. In compounds such as methaqualone or oxolamine the link appears to be effected by a —C(R)=N– group.

It is not surprising, especially in view of the complex nature of cough, that certain compounds with antitussive properties do not belong to the two classes mentioned above: benzonatate, sodium dibunate, and TR-310 are among the most notable exceptions. Furthermore, it has been shown on a number of occasions that quaternization of a tertiary amino group reduced or destroyed antitussive activity: nevertheless, certain quaternary salts have been shown to be effective antitussives[65a], and some of them have even found clinical acceptance (Monadyl, Lysobex).

On the basis of the foregoing summary it would seem that the field of synthetic antitussive drugs is capable of wide expansion in the future, not too much limited by theoretical considerations: numerous varieties of compounds with spasmolytic actions of a musculotropic character, or with analgetic activities of the morphine type, might conceivably be transformed by comparatively simple modifications into useful antitussive drugs. We should, however, like to sound a note of warning at this point: it seems rather pointless to increase the number of antitussive drugs available to the physician in the absence of a reasonable expectation that such new drugs would be more effective than codeine. In clinical practice very few of the drugs discussed in this review have proved to be successful in doses smaller than equally effective doses of codeine. Although a number of the new drugs do not show the objectionable side-effects of codeine, detailed clinical studies have brought to light a number of other side-effects which might become statistically more important as those drugs gain wider acceptance. It is our belief that any new antitussive drugs synthesized according to the modes outlined above may ultimately suffer from similar disadvantages.

There seems to be no doubt that the physiological and pathological phenomena involved in the problem of cough will have to be made the subject of truly fundamental studies before any major progress may be expected. Only after a thorough elucidation of those phenomena will it be possible for the pharmacologist to develop investigative methods by which the influence of drugs upon the reflexogenic areas, upon afferent and efferent pathways, and above all upon the central regulatory mechanisms, may be measured specifically and with some degree of accuracy. And only after such methods have become established will it be possible to guide the chemist towards the synthesis of antitussive drugs with specific and well-defined activities.

## REFERENCES

1. GORDONOFF *Fortschr. Ther.* 1931, **7,** 549
2. DRILL *Pharmacology in Medicine* 2nd Edn.: McGraw-Hill, New York, 1958, p. 685
3. BOYD and LAPP *J. Pharmacol.* 1946, **87,** 24

4. BOYD, PALMER and PEARSON *Canad. med. Ass. J.* 1946, **54**, 216
5. UNVERRICHT *Dtsch. med. Wschr.* 1938, **64**, 1733
6. RIPPERGER *Med. Welt.* 1940, **14**, 61, 88
7. DAS *Antiseptic* 1942, **39**, 133
8. ZAHORSKY *Arch. Pediat.* 1943, **60**, 88
9. VINSON *Virginia med. (Semi-)Mon.* 1943, **70**, 579
10. NACHSHEN *Practitioner* 1959, **183**, 634
11. EICHLER *Ther. d. Gegenw.* 1957, **96**, 146
12. HOBBY *Dis. Chest* 1952, **22**, 196
13. HUNTER *Practioner* 1948, **161**, 449
14. ROTH *Sem. Hôp. Paris* 1956, **32**, 2032
15. GORDON *Practitioner*, 1957, **179**, 671
16. OSWALD *Brit. med. J.* 1959, **i**, 292
17. VASSELIN *France méd.* 1960, **23**, 151
18. BANYAI *Minn. Med.* 1959, **42**, 1279
19. SASLAVSKY *Sem. méd., B. Aires* 1958, **113**, 778
20. HOBBY *Nav. med. Bull., Wash.* 1949, **49**, 86
21. BROCKBANK *Clin. J.* 1949, **78**, 138
22. DOUGLASS *Med. Clin. N. Amer.* 1954, **38**, 949
23. BOISSIER *Prod. pharm.* 1956, **11**, 867
24. BOISSIER *Prod. pharm.* 1957, **12**, 33
25. BOISSIER *Vie méd.* 1957, **38**, (special No.) 125
26. CELICE *Rev. Praticien* 1959, **9**, 3577
27. GRAHAM *Practitioner* 1959, **183**, 344
28. GAARENSTROM *Ned. Tijdscht. Geneesk.* 1959, **103**, 1149
29. FRIEBEL *Klin. Wschr.* 1960, **38**, 621
30. BANDELIN *J. Amer. Pharm. Ass. NS* 1961, **1**, 240
31. CIESLAK *Nervenarzt* 1955, **26**, 30
32. EDDY, HALBACH, and BRAENDEN *Bull. World Hlth. Org.* 1957, **17**, 569, 857
33. MALLER and CONSTANTINESCU *Psychiat. Neurol. med. Psychol. (Lpz.)* 1958, **10**, 53
34. ERNST *Arch. int. Pharmacodyn.* 1938, **58**, 363
35. BUCHER *Pharmacol. Rev.* 1958, **10**, 43
36. BUCHER and JACOT *Helv. physiol. acta* 1951, **9**, 454
37. MÜLLER *Helv. physiol. acta* 1954, **12**, 137
38. WIDDICOMBE *J. Physiol.* 1954, **123**, 71
39. WIDDICOMBE *J. Physiol.* 1954, **123**, 105
40. ROSS *Fed. Proc.* 1955, **14**, 125
41. ROSS, GRAMIAK and RAHN *J. appl. Physiol.* 1955-56, **8**, 264
42. BORISON *Amer. J. Physiol.* 1948, **154**, 55
43. WARREN, McINTOSH and ESTES *Fed. proc.* 1955, **14**, 515
44. HEAD *J. Physiol.* 1889, **10**, 1
45. LARSELL and BURGET *Amer. J. Physiol.* 1924, **70**, 311
46. TOMORI, KORPÁŠ and IVANČO *Csl. Fysiol.* 1957, **6**, 175
47. CECIL and LOEB *A Textbook of Medicine* 10th Edn.: W. B. Saunders Company, Philadelphia, 1959
48. MEIER, BEIN and HELMICH *Experientia* 1949, **5**, 484
49. LARSELL *J. comp. Neurol.* 1922, **35**, 97
50. LARSELL *J. comp. Neurol.* 1921, **33**, 105
51. ELFTMAN *Amer. J. Anat.* 1943, **72**, 1
52. LARRABEE and KNOWLTON *Amer. J. Physiol.* 1946, **147**, 90
53. GROSS, LIARAS and LAMBERT *C.R. Soc. Biol., Paris* 1956, **150**, 1936
54. KROEPFLI *Helv. physiol. acta* 1950, **8**, 33
55. SCHOTL *Jahreskurse ärztl. Fortbild.* 1930, **21**, 29
56. HILLIS and KELLY *Glasg. med. J.* 1951, **32**, 71

57. HEYMANS, BOUCKAERT and DAUTREBANDE *Arch. int. Pharmacodyn.* 1931, **40,** 54
58. ADRIEN *J. Physiol.* 1933, **79,** 332
59. TEITELBAUM and REIS *Amer. J. Physiol.* 1935, **112,** 684
60. BANISTER, FEGLER and HEBB *Quart. J. exp. Physiol.* 1949, **35,** 233
61. WIDDICOMBE *J. Physiol.* 1954, **123,** 55
62. CHAKRAVARTY, MATALLANA, JENSEN and BORISON *J. Pharmacol.* 1956, **117,** 127
63. BUCHER *Pharmacol. Rev.* 1958, **10,** 43
64. MULINOS *Proc. Soc. pharm. exp. Therap.* 1960, **2a,** 98
65. MULINOS *Toxic. & appl. Pharmacol.* 1960, **2,** 635
65a. ELLIS, GOLBERG, KING and SHEARD *J. med. Chem.* 1963, in the press
66. BUCHER *Schweiz. med. Wschr.* 1954, **86,** 94
67. HERZOG *Schweiz. med. Wschr.* 1956, **86,** 96
68. MEIRE and BEIN *Arch. exp. Path. Pharmak.* 1952, **215,** 119
69. LANZ *Helv. physiol. acta* 1952, **10,** 62
70. BEIN and BUCHER *Helv. physiol. acta* 1957, **15,** 55
71. TIFFENEAU *Thérapie* 1956, **11,** 263
72. TIFFENEAU *Pr. méd.* 1955, **63,** 227
73. KLOSSEN and MOSTON *Surgery* 1951, **29,** 483
74. DOMENJOZ *Arch. exp. Path. Pharmak.* 1952, **215,** 19
75. BOBB and ELLIS *Amer. J. Physiol.* 1951, **167,** 768
76. ENDERS and SCHMIDT *Arch. int. Pharmacodyn.* 1958, **114,** 446
77. MAYER, MAGNE and PLANTEFOL *C.R. Acad. Sci., Paris* 1920, **170,** 1347
78. REICHLE and FRIEBEL *Arch. exp. Path. Pharmak.* 1955, **226,** 558
79. HENGEN and KASPAREK *Arzneimitt. Forsch.* 1958, **8,** 620
80. MATALLANA and BORISON *Fed. Proc.* 1955, **14,** 367
81. MAY and WIDDICOMBE *J. Pharm., Lond.* 1954, **9,** 335
82. KASÉ *Jap. J. Pharmacol.* 1952, **2,** 7
83. EICHLER and SMIATEK *Arch. exp. Path. Pharmak.* 1940, **194,** 621
84. WINTER and FLATAKER *J. Pharmacol.* 1954, **112,** 99
85. GREEN and WARD *Brit. J. Pharmacol.* 1955, **10,** 418
86. FRIEBEL and REICHLE *Arch. exp. Path. Pharmak.* 1955, **225,** 85
87. FRIEBEL, REICHLE and VON GRAEVENITZ *Arch. exp. Path. Pharmak.* 1955, **224,** 384
88. TAKAGI, FUKUDA and YANO *J. Pharm. Soc. Japan* 1960, **80,** 1497
89. CHAPPEL and STEGEN—Personal Communication
90. WINTER and FLATAKER *J. Pharmacol.* 1955, **113,** 55
91. CHEN, BILLER and MONTGOMERY *J. Pharmacol.* 1960. **128,** 384
92. CRAIGIE *Amer. J. Physiol.* 1922, **59,** 346
93. ROSIERE, WINDER and WAX *J. Pharmacol.* 1956, **116,** 296
94. WINTER and ROSIERE *J. Pharmacol.* 1955, **113,** 55
95. WINTER and ROSIERE *J. Pharmacol.* 1955, **113,** 46
96. WINTER and FLATAKER *Proc. Soc. exp. Biol. N.Y.* 1952, **81,** 463
97. KASÉ *Jap. J. Pharmacol.* 1955, **4,** 130
98. TEDESCHI, TEDESCHI, HITCHENS, COOK, MATTIS and FELLOWS *J. Pharmacol.* 1959, **126,** 338
99. GROSS, LEBON and RAMBERT *C.R. Soc. Biol., Paris* 1958, **152,** 495
100. STEFKO and BENSON *J. Pharmacol.* 1953, **108,** 217
101. SCHROEDER *Arch. exp. Path. Pharmak.* 1950/51, **212,** 433
102. PLISNIER *Thérapie* 1954, **9,** 737
103. TONER and MACKO *J. Pharmacol.* 1952, **106,** 246
104. HÖGLUND and MICHAELSSON *Acta physiol. scand.* 1950, **21,** 168
105. HAHN and WILBRAND *Arch. int. Pharmacodyn.* 1952, **91,** 144
106. TRENDELENBURG *Acta physiol. scand.* 1950, **21,** 174
107. GRAVENSTEIN, DEVLOO and BEECHER *J. appl. Physiol.* 1954, **7,** 119
108. BICKERMAN, COHEN and GERMAN *Amer. J. med. Sci.* 1956, **232,** 57

## C. I. CHAPPEL AND C. VON SEEMANN

109. BICKERMAN, BARACH, ITKIN and DRIMMER *Amer. J. med. Sci.* 1954, **228,** 156
110. SHANE, KRZYSKI and COPP *Canad. med. Ass. J.* 1957, **77,** 600
111. CHABRIER, GIUDICELLI and THUILLIER *Ann. pharm. franc.* 1950, **8,** 261
112. TIFFENEAU *Dis. Chest* 1957, **31,** 404
113. VLEESCHHOUWER *Arch. int. Pharmacodyn* 1954, **97,** 34
114. KONZETT and ROTHLIN *Experentia* 1954, **10,** 472
115. GUTH and GOLDENBERG *Fed. Proc.* 1960, **19,** 375
116. SALLÉ and BRUNAUD *Arch. int. Pharmacodyn.* 1960, **126,** 120
117. SILVESTRINI and POZZATTI *Arch. int. Pharmacodyn.* 1960, **129,** 249
118. JACKSON, *J. Amer. med. Ass.* 1922, **79,** 1399
119. HILLIS *Lancet* 1952, **1,** 1230
120. TIFFENEAU *Thérapie* 1954, **9,** 471
121. GONFAS *Ann. Oto-laryng.* 1946, **13,** 158
122. BOYD and MACLACHLAN *Canad. med. Ass. J.* 1944, **50,** 338
123. HUBER *Schweiz med. Wschr.* 1942, **72,** 936
124. KONAR and DASGUPTA *J. Indian med. Ass.* 1959, **32,** 189
125. HOLMES *The Alkaloids: Chemistry and Physiology,* Vol. II: Academic Press, London—New York, 1952, p. 1
126. HOLMES and STORK *The Alkaloids: Chemistry and Physiology,* Vol. II: Academic Press, London—New York, 1952, p. 161
127. STORK *The Alkaloids: Chemistry and Physiology,* Vol. VI: Academic Press, London—New York, 1960, p. 219
128. ERNST *Arch. int. Pharmacodyn.* 1939, **61,** 73
129. FRIEBEL and REICHLE *Arch. exp. Pathol. Pharmak.* 1956, **229,** 400
130. HUET *Arch. Inst. Farmacol. Exp., Madrid* 1958, **10,** 34
131. GROSS and LEBON *Thérapie* 1959, **14,** 275
132. SILVESTRINI and MAFFII *Farmaco Ed. Sci.* 1959, **14,** 440
133. TAKAGI, FUKUDA, WATANABE and SATO *J. pharm. Soc. Japan* 1960, **80,** 1506
134. GRAVENSTEIN and BEECHER *Arzneimitt. Forsch.* 1955, **5,** 364
135. WILSON *J. Mich. med. Soc.* 1943, **42,** 267
136. TAKAGI and FUKUDA *J. pharm. Soc. Japan* 1960, **80,** 1501
137. SEGAL, GOLDSTEIN and ATTINGER *Dis. Chest* 1957, **32,** 305
138. DONELSON *J. Mich. med. Soc.* 1951, **50,** 61
139. GROSS *C.R. Soc. Biol., Paris* 1957, **151,** 704
140. GRANIER-DOYEUX, HORANDE and KUCHARSKI *Arch. int. Pharmacodyn.* 1959, **121,** 287
141. KOHLI, GUPTA and BHARGAVA *Indian J. med. Res.* 1960, **48,** 193
142. CHAPPEL, STEGEN and GRANT *Canad. J. Biochem.* 1958, **36,** 475
143. LEVIS, PREAT and MOYERSOONS *Arch. int. Pharmacodyn.* 1955, **103,** 200
144. BICKERMAN, GERMAN, COHEN and ITKIN *Amer. J. med. Sci.* 1957, **234,** 191
145. BICKERMAN and ITKIN *Clin. pharmacol. Ther. (St. Louis),* 1960, **1,** 180
146. ARCHIBALD, SLIPP and SHANE *Canad. med. Ass. J.* 1959, **80,** 734
147. GUSEVA *Farmakol. i. Toksikol.* 1956, **19,** (5), 17
148. PROSINGER *Medizinische* 1956, 1099
149. PASTERKAMP and KAMPE *Ther. d. Gegenw.* 1959, **98,** 554
150. VOICULESCU and NEUMAN *Med. Klinik.* 1959, **54,** 2305
151. CHAN and HAYS *Amer. J. med. Sci.* 1957, **234,** 207
152. TOWNSEND, *New. Engl. J. Med.* 1958, **258,** 63
153. BECKMAN, *Wis. med. J.* 1959, **58,** 323
154. CASS and FREDERIK *Ann. intern. Med.* 1958, **49,** 151
155. HUSEN *Med. Welt* 1960, **No. 13,** 689
156. PLISNIER *C.R. Soc. Biol., Paris* 1960, **154,** 451
157. SNELL and ARMITAGE *Lancet* 1957, **1,** (6974), 860
158. RYDE *Svenska Läkartidn.* 1960, **57,** 797

159. MARSHALL, PYMAN and ROBINSON *J. chem. Soc.* 1934, 1315
160. VAN DONGEN *Acta physiol. pharmacol. néerl.* 1956, **4**, 500
161. ERVENIUS *Svensk. farm. Tidskr.* 1957, **61**, 773
162. LA BARRE and PLISNIER *Arch. int. Pharmacodyn* 1959, **119**, 205
163. *U.S. Patent* 2,167,351 (1939); *Chem. Abstr.* 1939, **33**, 8923
164. EISLEB and SCHAUMANN *Dtsch. med. Wschr.* 1939, **65**, 967
165. SCHAUMANN *Arch. exp. Pathol. Pharmak.* 1940, **196**, 109
166. BUSCHKEM *Ned. Tijdschr. Geneesk* 1953, **97**, 331
167. *German Patent Application* 70,217 (1941)
168. ANON *P. B. Reports* 248: 981 and *B.I.O.S. Report* 116
169. BOYD and BUELL *Canad. med. Ass. J.* 1950, **63**, 588
170. DEL CASTILLO JAQUOLOT *Med. Clin.* 1953, **20**, 247
171. RASCH *Nord. med.* 1957, **57**, 629
172. EASTON, GARDNER, EVANICK and STEVENS *J. Amer. chem. Soc.* 1948, **70**, 76
173. OFNER and WALTON *J. chem. Soc.* 1950, 2158
174. KLENK, SUTER and ARCHER *J. Amer. chem. Soc.* 1948, **70**, 3846
175. TULLAR, WETTERAU and ARCHER *J. Amer. chem. Soc.* 1948, **70**, 3959
176. LUDUEÑA and ANANENKO *Arch. int. Pharmacodyn.* 1950, **81**, 259
177. KASÉ, YUIZONO, SERIKAWA, YAMAMOTO, YAMASAKI, FUSHIMIZU, KATAYAMA, MORIYA and NOZUHARA *Chem. pharm. Bull.* (*Tokyo*) 1958, **6**, 109
178. GREWE *Naturwissenschaften* 1946, **33**, 333
179. GREWE *Angew. Chem.* 1947, **A59**, 194
180. BENSON, STEFKO and RANDALL *Fed. Proc.* 1952, **11**, 322
181. ISBELL and FRASER *J. Pharmacol.* 1952, **106**, 397
182. ISBELL and FRASER *J. Pharmacol.* 1953, **107**, 524
183. POHLAND and SULLIVAN *J. Amer. chem. Soc.* 1953, **75**, 4458
184. *German Patent* 637,875 (1936); *Chem. Abstr.*, 1937, **31**, 5381
185. HOTTINGER *Schweiz. med. Wschr.* 1940, **70**, 214
186. JACOBS *Med. Times N.Y.* 1948, **76**, 445
187. ROHRMANN and SHONLE *J. Amer. chem. Soc.* 1944, **66**, 1516
188. ORNSTON *Med. Times, N.Y.* 1947, **75**, 370
189. SILCOX *Arch. Otolaryng., Chicago* 1948, **47**, 822
190. CHRISTOPHE *Med. Rec., N.Y.* 1948, **161**, 417
191. *U.S. Patent* 2,404,913; *Chem. Abstr.* 1946, **40**, 6275
191a. MENARD, MITCHELL, KOMLOSSY, WRIGLEY and CHUBB *Canad. J. Chem.* 1961, **39**, 729
192. SALERNO *Arch. ital. Laring.* 1955, **63**, 359
193. ZAMBONI, MARCATO, and MARCUCCI *Arch. ital. Sci. farmacol.* 1957, **7**, 310
194. GRIGNON and AUBERTIN *Sem. Hôp. Paris* 1953, **29**, 2999
195. GRASSI *Minerva med., Torino* 1955, *46/II*, 1922
196. BORRI *Arch. ital. Otol.* 1957, **68**, 302
197. SIMON *Ohio St. med. J.* 1957, **53**, 1426
198. CREMONCINI *Riv. Clin. pediat.* 1956, **58**, 341
199. SCHMIDT *Med. Welt* 1960, *No. 9*, 505
199a. McCOLL and LEE *Canad. pharm. J.* (*Scientific Section*) 1961, **94**, 596
200. *U.S. Patents* 2,714,608–10 (1955); *Chem. Abstr.* 1956, **50**, 7137
201. *U.S. Patents* 2,857,417–9 (1958); *Chem. Abstr.* 1959, **53**, 10131–2
202. *U.S. Patent* 2,980,737 (1961); *Swiss Patent* 347175 (1960); *Chem. Abstr.* 1961, **55**, 15354
203. ZIPF and KREPPEL *Arch. exp. Path. Pharmak.* 1955, **226**, 340
204. ZIPF and REICHERTZ *Arch. exp. Path. Pharmak.* 1957, **231**, 96
205. SELL, LINDNER and JAHN *Arch. exp. Path. Pharmak.* 1958, **234**, 164
206. MARX *Arzneimitt. Forsch.* 1957, **7**, 663
207. GREGOIRE, THIBAUDEAU and COMEAU *Canad. med. Ass. J.* 1958, **79**, 180

## C. I. CHAPPEL and C. von SEEMANN

208. GIULIANO and ROSSA *Minerva med.*, *Torino* 1955, *46/II*, 1502
209. NAEGELI *Praxis* 1956, **45,** 56
210. TOJA *Minerva med.*, *Torino* 1956, **47,** 1998
211. CAVALCA, *Gazz. int. med. chir.* 1956, **61,** 1653
212. BASABE, GENTILE and CROCIONI *Sem. med.*, *B. Aires* 1957, **110,** 766
213. KAUCHTSCHISCHWILI *Gazz. med. ital.* 1957, **116,** 149
214. JULIANI and PAGNOTTA *G. Clin. med.* 1957, **38,** 589
215. FIOR *Arch. ital. Otol.* 1957, **68,** 1011
216. BALDINI *Gazz. med. ital.* 1958, **117,** 152
217. WILSON, FARBER and MANDEL *Antibiot. Med.* 1958, **5,** 567
218. VALENTI and DE PALMA *Gazz. med. ital.* 1958, **117,** 194
219. HANKE *Praxis* 1958, **47,** 610
220. VERGANI, PAGANI and LUPACCHINI *Gazz. med. ital.* 1956, **115,** 200
221. HUSEN *Tuberk Arzt* 1958, **12,** 248
222. NEUMANN *Rev. méd. Suisse rom.* 1956, **76,** 738
223. MASI *Riv. Clin. pediat.* 1957, **59,** 87
224. CARUGHI *Prensa. méd. argent.* 1957, **44,** 3621
225. GOTTI and GEROCARNI *Clin. pediat.*, *Bologna* 1957, **39,** 831
226. KOIKY *Wien. med. Wschr.* 1958, **108,** 493
227. FRANCESCHETTI *Gazz. med. ital.* 1958, **117,** 213
228. ALETTI and PALATRESI *Gazz. int. med. Chir.* 1956, **61,** 1660
229. CATTANEO *Minerva anest.*, *Torino* 1959, **25,** 373
230. SURIANI *Oto-rino-laring. ital.* 1958, **26,** 377
231. DIAMANT *Pract. oto-rhino-laryng.* 1957, **19,** 339
232. SIMON *Ann. Allergy* 1957, **15,** 521
233. SIMON *J. Amer. geriat. Soc.* 1960, **8,** 107
234. ANON (Council Report) *J. Amer. med. Ass.* 1959. **170,** 1927
235. *Swiss Patent* 234,452 (1945); *Chem. Abstr.* 1949, **43,** 6229
236. *Swiss Patent* 246,199 (1947); *Chem. Abstr.* 1949, **43,** 6229
237. *Swiss Patents* 249,036–249,043 (1948); *Chem. Abstr.* 1949, **43,** 6229
238. *Swiss Patent* 272,708 (1951); *Chem. Abstr.* 1952, **46,** 4563
239. ROTH *Sem. Hôp. Paris* 1956, **32,** 325
240. LIECHTI *Schweiz. med. Wschr.* 1950, **80,** 484
241. ABELMANN, GAENSLER and BADGER *Dis. Chest* 1954, **25,** 532
242. CASS and FREDERIK *J. Lab. clin. Med.* 1956, **48,** 879
243. HUDSON *Lancet* 1952, *I,* 1310
244. SNYDER *Laryngoscope, St. Louis* 1953, **63,** 1008
245. SEGAL, DULFANO and HERSCHFUS *Transactions of the 48th Annual Meeting of the National Tuberculosis Assn.*, *Boston* 1952, p. 374
246. *Belg. Patent* 520,988 (1953); *Chem. Abstr.* 1959, **53,** 8174; *Brit. Patent* 753,779 (1956); *Chem. Abstr.* 1957, **51,** 7443
247. DEPOORTER *Brux.-méd.* 1954, **34,** 422
248. PARISH *Med. Times, N.Y.* 1955, **83,** 870
249. SIRONI *Minerva anest.*, *Torino* 1956, **22,** 413
250. BARRANCO and COTTONE *Acta anaesth.*, *Padova* 1958, **9,** 171
251. TARTARO *Gazz. med. ital.* 1959, **11,** 36
252. CARTER and MALEY *Amer. J. med. Sci.* 1957, **233,** 77
253. HALPERN *Arch. int. Pharmacodyn.* 1938, **59,** 149
254. ENGELHARDT *Arzneimitt. Forsch.* 1957, **11,** *I,* 217
255. HOOK *Ther. d. Gegenw.* 1957, **96,** 384
256. NAJER, GIUDICELLI and CHABRIER *Bull. Soc. chim. Fr.* 1959, 1895
257. *U.S. Patent* 2,963,485 (1960); *Chem. Abstr.* 1961, **55,** 14484
258. NAJER, CHABRIER and GIUDICELLI *Bull. Soc. chim. Fr.* 1958, 355
259. CHEYMOL, GIUDICELLI, CHABRIER and NAJER *Arch. int. Pharmacodyn.* 1960, **125,** 121

260. *U.S. Patent* 2,952,685 (1960); *Chem. Abstr.* 1961, **55,** 11441
261. POLEZHAEVA *Farmakol. i. Toksikol.* 1957, **20,** 6, 56
262. PETROW, STEPHENSON and WILD *J. Pharm., Lond.* 1958, **10,** 40
263. DAVID, LEITH-ROSS and VALLANCE *J. Pharm., Lond.* 1957, **9,** 446
264. ROBERTS *Practitioner* 1957, **178,** 353
265. *British Patent* 765,510 (1957); *Chem. Abstr.* 1957, **51,** 14810
266. *German Patent* 960,462 (1957); *Chem. Abstr.* 1959, **53,** 16077
267. *German Patent* 964,499 (1957); *Chem. Abstr.* 1959, **53,** 16077
268. *German Patent* 964,500 (1957); *Chem. Abstr.* 1959, **53,** 17060
269. *U.S. Patent* 2,854,472 (1958); *Chem. Abstr.* 1959, **53,** 11317
270. MOFFETT and ASPERGREN *J. Amer. chem. Soc.* 1957, **79,** 4451
271. LANDS, ANANENKO, JONES, HOPPE and BECKER *J. Pharmacol.* 1949, **96,** 1
272. KRAUSE *Arzneimitt. Forsch.* 1958, **8,** 553
273. CHAPPEL, STEGEN and RONA—Personal communication
274. BOISSIER and PAGNY *Thérapie* 1960, **15,** 93
275. CHRISTOFFEL and KOLBERG *Med. Klinik.* 1958, **53,** 1507
276. ZEHBE *Medizinische* 1958, *No. 36,* 1401
277. BRENNER-GÖDDERZ *Med. Klin.* 1959, **54,** 2004
278. EIDMANN *Münch. med. Wschr.* 1959, **101,** 676
279. SCHMIEDEL *Ther. d. Gegenw.* 1959, **98,** 239
280. SCHUMACHER *Ther. d. Gegenw.* 1959, **98,** 581
281. FESER *Hippokrates, Stuttgart* 1960, **31,** 28
282. PETERSEN *Dtsch. med. J.* 1960, **11,** 235
283. JANSSEN, JAGENEAU and HUYGENS *J. med. pharm. Chem.* 1959, **1,** 299
284. MORRIS and SHANE *Canad. med. Ass. J.* 1960, **83,** 1093
285. *German Patent* 1,051, 281 (1959); *Chem. Abstr.* 1960, **54,** 24556; *British Patent* 811,659 (1959); *Chem. Abstr.* 1960, **54,** 424
286. *British Patent* 815,217 (1959); *Chem. Abstr.* 1960, **54,** 1453
287. GÖSSWALD *Arzneimitt. Forsch.* 1958, **8,** 550
288. ZUR LINDEN *Medizinische* 1958, **22,** 959
289. BOYD and BOYD *Canad. med. Ass. J.* 1960, **83,** 1298
290. DRAF *Ther. d. Gegenw.* 1958, **97,** 477
291. LORDICK and PÖPPELMANN *Med. Klin.* 1958, **53,** 2157
292. PALM *Dtsch. med. J.* 1959, **10,** 64
293. TACCANI *Minerva med., Torino* 1959, **50,** 4396
294. SISCHKA *Wien. med. Wschr.* 1959, **109,** 926
295. KLEY *Dtsch. med. J.* 1959, **10,** 580
296. KUKOWSKI *Ther. d. Gegenw.* 1960, **99,** 36
297. PRÜSSING *Dtsch. med. J.* 1960, **11,** 95
298. SCHRÖER *H.N.O. (Berl.)* 1960, **8,** 183
299. *U.S. Patent* 2,827,460 (1958); *Chem. Abstr.* 1959, **53,** 415
300. LINDNER and STEIN *Arzneimitt. Forsch.* 1959, **9,** 94
301. BRANDSCHWEDE *Med. Klin.* 1959, **54,** 2185
302. DANNENBERG *Medizinische* 1959, 1878
303. *Belgian Patent* 588,825 (1960) and *French Patent* M–160 (1960)
304. ENGELHORN *Arzneimitt. Forsch.* 1960, **10,** 785
305. RIEBEL *Arzneimitt. Forsch.* 1960, **10,** 794
306. ADAMSON *J. chem. Soc.* 1950, 885
307. ADAMSON and GREEN *Nature, Lond.* 1950, **165,** 122
308. GREEN *Brit. J. Pharmacol.* 1953, **8,** 2
309. KIMURA, YABUUCHI and TAMURA *Pharm. Bull., Tokyo* 1958, **6,** 159
310. ISBELL and FRASER *J. Pharmacol.* 1953, **109,** 417
311. ANON. *United Nations Documents* E/NS., 1955, *summaries 1 and 5,* and E/NS., 1956, *summaries 1, 3 and 5*

312. Kasé, Kaku, Yamamoto, Tanaka, Takasaki and Nagao *Pharm. Bull., Tokyo* 1955, **3,** 394
313. Kimura and Yabuuchi *Chem. pharm. Bull., Tokyo* 1959, **7,** 171
314. Kimura, Ogawa and Yabuuchi *Chem. Pharm. Bull., Tokyo* 1959, **7,** 175
315. *U.S. Patent* 2,739,968 (1956); *Chem. Abstr.* 1960, **54,** 15596
316. Nair and Haar *N.Y. St. J. Med.* 1956, **56,** 1773
317. Kasé, Yuizono, Yamasaki, Yamada, Io, Tamiya and Kondo *Chem. Pharm. Bull., Tokyo* 1959, **7,** 372
318. Sugimoto, Kowa, Higaki, Nakamura and Yasaka *Chem. Pharm. Bull., Tokyo* 1960, **8,** 745
319. Kasé and Yuizono *Chem. Pharm. Bull., Tokyo* 1959, **7,** 378
320. *U.S. Patent* 2,913,459 (1959); *Chem. Abstr.* 1960, **54,** 3203
321. Plisnier *C.R. Soc. Biol., Paris* 1958, **152,** 1267
322. Charlier and Vandersmissen *Arch. int. Physiol.* 1954, **62,** 433
323. Ghidini *G. Clin. med.* 1956, **37,** 1666
324. Fior *Arch. ital. Otol.* 1957, **68,** 660
325. Scalais *Scalpel, Brux.* 1959, **112,** 220
326. Janssen *J. Amer. chem. Soc.* 1956, **78,** 3862
327. Deligné and Gilles *Anésth. Analg.* 1957, **14,** 51
328. Serembe and Visentini *Gazz. med. ital.* 1959, **118,** 113
329. Malen and Boissier *Bull. Soc. chim. Fr.* 1956, 923
330. Maugé, Malen and Boissier *Bull. Soc. chim. Fr.* 1956, 926
331. Boissier, Malen and Dumont *C.R. Acad. Sci., Paris* 1956, **242,** 1086
332. Boissier, Dumont and Malen *Thérapie* 1956, **11,** 745
333. Boissier, Dumont and Malen *Anésth. Analg.* 1956, **13,** 569
334. Boissier, Dumont, Malen and Maugé *Thérapie* 1957, **12,** 223
335. Boissier, Dumont and Malen *Thérapie* 1957, **12,** 551
336. Kacker and Zaheer *J. Indian chem. Soc.* 1951, **28,** 344
337. Grimmel, Guenther and Morgan *J. Amer. chem. Soc.* 1946, **68,** 542
338. Gujral, Saxena and Tiwari *Indian J. med. Res.* 1955, **43,** 637
339. Boissier, Dumont and Malen *Thérapie* 1958, **13,** 30
340. Ravina *Pr. méd.* 1959, **67,** 891
341. Parsons and Thomson *Brit. med. J.* 1961, **I,** 171
342. Boissier and Pagny *Medicina Experimentalis, Basel* 1959, **1,** 368
343. *U.S. Patent* 2,676,177 (1954); *Chem. Abstr.* 1955, **49,** 6325
344. *British Patent* 843,752 (1960); *Chem. Abstr.* 1961, **55,** 4544
345. *British Patent* 837,512 (1960); *Chem. Abstr.* 1960, **54,** 24817
346. Pellmont and Bächtold *Schweiz. med. Wschr.* 1954, **84,** 1368
347. Marcato and Marcucci *Arch. ital. Otol.* 1957, **68,** 404
348. Cass and Frederik *New Engl. J. Med.* 1953, **249,** 132
349. Cass, Frederik and Andosca *Amer. J. med. Sci.* 1954, **227,** 291
350. Maurer *Dtsch. med. Wschr.* 1955, **80,** 351
351. Tünnerhof and Schwabe, *Klin. Wschr.* 1955, **33,** 576
352. Kummer *Praxis* 1955, **44,** 132
353. Skursky *Wien. med. Wschr.* 1959. **109,** 507
354. Hottinger *Schweiz. med. Wschr.* 1954, **84,** 1372
355. Huperz *Medizinische* 1958, **27-28,** 1105
356. Ralph *Amer. J. med. Sci.* 1954, **227,** 297
357. Capello and Di Pasquale *Schweiz. Z. Tuberk.* 1955, **12,** 80
358. Grafe *Medizinische* 1958, **43,** 1741
359. Bockmühl and Ehrhardt *Liebigs Ann.* 1948, **561,** 52
360. Wiedemeijer, Kramer and De Jongh *Acta Physiol. Pharmacol. Neerl* 1960, **9,** 501
361. de Beule *Belg. Tijdschr. Geneesk.* 1952, **8,** 220

362. NERRETER *Medizinische* 1957, 389
363. *U.S. Patent* 2,778,824 (1957); *Chem. Abstr.* 1957, **51,** 10591
364. BOISSIER and PAGNY *Thérapie* 1960, **15,** 97
365. KLEIN *Antibiot. Med.* 1958, **5,** 462
366. PARISH *Med. Times, N.Y.* 1959, **87,** 1488
367. *U.S. Patent* 2,951,077 (1960); *Chem. Abstr.* 1961, **55,** 1667
368. DAVIS—In preparation
369. STEGEN—Personal communication
370. *German Patent* 1,102,919 (1957); *Chem. Abstr.* 1959, **53,** 18067
371. GULDEN *Ther. d. Gegenw.* 1960, **99,** 133
372. LIBAL *Med. Welt.* 1960, 383
373. HASLREITER *Arzneimitt. Forsch.* 1959, **9,** 769
374. PRIME *Brit. med. J.* 1961, *I,* 1149
375. WOOLFE and MACDONALD *J. Pharmacol.* 1944, **80,** 300
376. SIEGMUND, CADMUS and LU *Proc. Soc. exp. Biol., N.Y.* 1957, **95,** 729
377. RANDALL and SELITTO *Arch. int. Pharmacodyn.* 1957, **111,** 409
378. RANDALL, SELITTO and VALDES *Arch. int. Pharmacodyn.* 1957, **113,** 233
379. SILVESTRINI *Minerva med., Torino* 1960, **51,** 4091
380. PARRAT and WEST *Brit. J. Pharmacol.* 1958, **13,** 65
381. MEIR, SCHULER and DESAULLES *Experientia* 1950, **6,** 469
382. SILVESTRINI and POZZATTI In Preparation
383. DEIDDA *Minerva med., Torino* 1960, **51,** 4059
384. REPACI *Minerva med., Torino* 1960, **51,** 4072
385. CORBELLA *Minerva med., Torino* 1960, **51,** 4077
386. CRESCI, FRANCO and FANCIULLACCI *Minerva med., Torino* 1960, **51,** 4080
387. TESTAFERRATA and FRANCALANCIA *Minerva med. Torino,* 1960, **51,** 4064
388. MACCAFERRI and TROCCOLI *Minerva med., Torino* 1960, **51,** 4069
389. DE GREGORIO *Minerva med., Torino* 1960, **51,** 4086
390. *Belgian Patent* 556,239 (1957); *Chem. Abstr.* 1959, **53,** 22027
391. *Belgian Patent* 570,393 (1958); *Chem. Abstr.* 1959, **53,** 18966
392. *British Patent* 853,783 (1960); *Chem. Abstr.* 1961, **55,** 13455
393. *U.S. Patent* 2,981,735 (1961); *Chem. Abstr.* 1961, **55,** 22346
394. *U.S. Patent* 2,960,507 (1960); *Chem. Abstr.* 1961, **55,** 18779
395. *Belgian Patent* 595,018 (1961); *Chem. Abstr.* 1961, **55,** 17659
396. ROMAGNOLI and BIRD *Canad. med. Ass. J.* 1956, **75,** 210
397. ETTER, RAYMER and JACKSON *Ann. Allergy* 1960, **18,** 667
398. KNOLL *Praxis* 1960, **49,** 357
399. FROHMAN *Med. Times, N.Y.* 1960, **88,** 924
400. BLATT *Ohio St. med. J.* 1957, **53,** 1028
401. CASS and FREDERIK *Amer. Practit.* 1951, **2,** 844
402. BLANCHARD and FORD *J-Lancet* 1954, **74,** 443
403. HAYES and JACOBS *Dis. Chest* 1956, **30,** 441
404. SCHWARTZ, LEVIN, LEIBOWITZ and McGINN *Amer. Practit.* 1956, **7,** 585
405. *U.S. Patent* 1,073,966 (1913) *Chem. Abstr.* 1913, **7,** 3819
406. *U.S. Patent* 2,820,739 (1958); *Chem. Abstr.* 1958, **52,** 6728
407. *Swiss Patent* 219,301 (1942); *Chem. Abstr.* 1948, **42,** 7329
408. BOVET, HORCLOIS and WALTHERT *C.R. Soc. Biol., Paris* 1944, **138,** 99
409. CHARPENTIER *C.R. Acad. Sci., Paris* 1947, **225,** 306
410. GROSS *J. Physiol. Path. gén.* 1959, **51,** 473
411. *U.S. Patent* 2,421,714 (1947); *Chem. Abstr.* 1947, **41,** 5550
412. BOYD *Canad. med. Ass. J.* 1952, **67,** 289
413. KÄLLQVIST and MELANDER *Arzneimitt. Forsch.* 1957, **7,** 301
414. *U.S. Patent* 2,449,241 (1948); *Chem. Abstr.* 1949, **43,** 692
415. BALTZLY, DuBREUIL, IDE and LORZ *J. org. Chem.* 1949, **14,** 775

416. KÄLLQVIST *Svenska Läkartidn.* 1956, **53**, 3177
417. HUTTRER, DJERASSI, BEEARS, MAYER and SCHOLZ *J. Amer. chem. Soc.* 1946, **68**, 1999
418. *U.S. Patent* 2,837,518 (1958); *Chem. Abstr.* 1958, **52**, 16382
419. POOLE *N.C. med. J.* 1960, **21**, 226
420. *British Patent* 719,276 (1954); *Chem. Abstr.* 1956, **50**, 1090
421. CHARPENTIER, GAILLIOT, JACOB, GAUDECHON and BUISSON *C.R. Acad. Sci., Paris* 1952, **235**, 59
422. COURVOISIER, FOURNEL, DUCROT, KOLSKY and KOETSCHET *Arch. int. Pharmacodyn.* 1953, **92**, 305
423. GROSS, MALMÉJAC and LIARAS *J. Physiol. Path. gén.* 1957, **49**, 183
424. POLEZHAEVA *Farmacol. i. Toksikol.* 1957, **20**, 3, 55
425. VIDAL, TER SCHIPHORST and CAVALIER *Montpellier méd.* 1955, **47**, 579
426. MORINI *Rif. med.* 1956, **70**, 1015
427. TOMORI, KNOTZ, TOMORIOVA and KLIMA *Anaesthesist* 1960, **9**, 169
428. BOURQUIN, SCHWARB, GAMBONI, FISCHER, RUESCH, GULDIMANN, THEUS, SCHENKER and RENZ *Helv. chim. acta* 1958, **41**, 1072
429. MUELLER, SCHLITTLER and BEIN *Experientia* 1952, **8**, 338
430. DORFMAN, FURLENMEIER, HUEBNER, LUCAS, MACPHILLAMY, MUELLER, SCHLITTLER, SCHWYZER and ST. ANDRÉ *Helv. chim. acta* 1954, **37**, 59
431. WOODWARD, BADER, BICKEL, FREY and KIERSTEAD *J. Amer. chem. Soc.* 1956, **78**, 2023
432. REHDER *Klin. Wschr.* 1957, **35**, 642
433. KORPÁŠ, TOMORI and IVANČO *Čsl. Fysiol.* 1957, **6**, 83
434. *U.S. Patent* 2,650,919 (1953); *Chem. Abstr.* 1954, **48**, 10783
435. *Swedish Patent* 140,298 (1953); *Chem. Abstr.* 1954, **48**, 8271
436. *Canadian Patents* 515,178 and 515,179 (1955)
437. PFEIFFER *Science* 1948, **107**, 94
438. *German Patent* 1,036,259 (1959); *Chem. Abstr.* 1960, **54**, 18562

# 4

# THE CHEMISTRY AND PHARMACOLOGY OF THE RAUWOLFIA ALKALOIDS

## R. A. LUCAS

## INTRODUCTION

SINCE the first report in 1952 by Mueller, Schlittler and Bein[1] of a new alkaloid, reserpine, from *Rauwolfia serpentina* Benth. ex Kurz there has been a tremendous resurgence of interest in alkaloid chemistry, and in the search for new pharmacologically interesting substances of plant origin. Reserpine, the most important of the *Rauwolfia* alkaloids, showed the typical pharmacological properties attributed to *Rauwolfia* root and the crude extracts used in India for many centuries. The natives of the Himalayan foothills had used the root of *Rauwolfia* for healing afflictions ranging from snake bite to insanity. This ancient remedy became known in Europe in the 16th century and was supposed to control epilepsy, insomnia, fevers, cholera, dizziness and head-aches. Commonly called 'insanity root' because of its alleged power to calm mentally deranged persons, it was not seriously considered by the medical profession of the Western world until studies in the period 1930–1940 clearly indicated the presence of physiologically interesting constituents. These researches culminated in the discovery of reserpine, which is now widely used in the treatment of hypertension and as a tranquillizing agent. Since 1952 several thousand articles have been published on the isolation, chemistry, pharmacology and clinical aspects of reserpine and other *Rauwolfia* alkaloids. Excellent reviews of *Rauwolfia* alkaloids have appeared in recent years covering early work in this field[2–9a], and this survey summarizes progress in the chemistry and pharmacology during the past five to seven years.

## RAUWOLFIA SPECIES AND ALKALOIDS ISOLATED

*Rauwolfia* is a genus of the family *Apocynaceae* (dogbane family), sub-family *Plumeroideae*, and occurs in nearly all habitable tropical and some sub-tropical regions. Of the more than 100 recorded species of *Rauwolfia*, nearly 50 have been investigated (*Table 4.1*)[10] and have yielded more than 50 alkaloids of which most of those listed in *Table 4.2* have been characterized. A check list of *Rauwolfia* alkaloid synonyms is included as *Table 4.3*.

*Table 4.1. Rauwolfia species*

| NAME | CODE | NAME | CODE |
|---|---|---|---|
| *affinis* Muell. Arg. | af | *cumminsii* Stapf. | cu |
| *amsoniaefolia* (Miq.) A. DC. | a | *decurva* Hook. f. | dc |
| *bahiensis* A. DC. | bh | *degeneri* Sherff | de |
| *beddomei* Hook. f. | b | *densiflora* Benth. et Hook | d |
| *boliviana* Mfg. (= *schuelii*) | bo | *fruticosa* Burck. | f |
| *caffra* Sand. | cf | *grandiflora* Mart. ex A. DC. | g |
| *cambodiana* Pierre ex Pitard | ca | *heterophylla* Willd. ex Roem. et Schult | |
| *canescens* L. (= *tetraphylla*) | c | (= *tetraphylla*) | h |
| *cubana* A. DC. | cb | *hirsuta* Jacq. (= *tetraphylla*) | ht |

146

Table 4.1. *Rauwolfia* species (contd.)

| NAME | CODE | NAME | CODE |
|------|------|------|------|
| *indecora* R. E. Woodson (= *ligustrina*) | i | *perakensis* King et Gamble | p |
| *inebrians* K. Schum | ie | *rosea* K. Schum. | r |
| *lamarckii* A. DC. (= *viridis*) | l | *salicifolia* Griseb. | sl |
| *ligustrina* Roem. et Schult. | lg | *sandwicensis* A. DC. | sd |
| *littoralis* Rusby | lt | *sarapiquensis* R. E. Woodson | sa |
| *macrophylla* Staph. | mp | *schueli* Speg. | sc |
| *mannii* Staph. | mn | *sellowii* Muell. -Arg. | sw |
| *mauiensis* Sherff | ma | *semperflorens* (Muell. -Arg.) Schltr. | sf |
| *micrantha* Hook. f. | m | *serpentina* (L.) Benth. ex Kurz | s |
| *mombasiana* Stapf. | mo | *sprucei* Muell. -Arg. | sp |
| *nana* E. A. Bruce | na | *sumatrana* (Mig.) Jack | su |
| *natalensis* Sond. (= *caffra*) | n | *ternifolia* HBK. (= *ligustrina*) | tr |
| *nitida* Jacq. | ni | *tetraphylla* L. | t |
| *obscura* K. Schum. | o | *verticillata* (Lour.) Baill. | ve |
| *paraensis* Ducke | pa | *viridis* (Muell. -Arg.) Guillaumin | vi |
| *pentaphylla* Ducke | pe | *vomitoria* Afzel. | v |

Table 4.2. Alkaloids of *Rauwolfia* species

| | Formula | m.p. | Rotation* | Source† |
|---|---------|------|-----------|---------|
| Ajmalicine | $C_{21}H_{24}N_2O_3$ | 253–254° | −62° | f, lg, r, s, su |
| Ajmalidine | $C_{20}H_{24}N_2O_2$ | 241–242 | | sw |
| Ajmaline | $C_{20}H_{26}N_2O_2$ | 158–160 | +141 | bo, c, cf, d, de, f, h, i, lg, n, p, s, sc, su, sw, v (Base-$H_2O$) |
| Ajmalinine | $C_{20}H_{26}N_2O_3$ | 180–181 | −97 | s, sw |
| Alstonine | $C_{21}H_{20}N_2O_3$ | >300 | | v, o, ht |
| Aricine | $C_{22}H_{26}N_2O_4$ | 190 | −59 (E) | a, c, h, lg, sc, su, sw |
| Amsoniaefoline | $C_{25}H_{32}N_2O_5$ | 220–223 | | a |
| Canembine | $C_{22}H_{28}N_2O_3$ | 228–229 | +57 (E) | c |
| Chalcupine B | $C_{15}H_{24}N_6O_{11}$ | | | h |
| Chandrine | $C_{25}H_{30}N_2O_8$ | 230–231 | | s |
| Corynanthine | $C_{21}H_{26}N_2O_3$ | 231–232 | −85 (P) | s |
| Deserpidine | $C_{32}H_{38}N_2O_8$ | 228–232 | −137 | a, af, c, lg, pe, r, sl, sp, tr |
| 3-Epi-α-yohimbine | $C_{21}H_{26}N_2O_3$ | 125–128 181–183 222–223 | −93 | s |
| Isoajmaline | $C_{20}H_{26}N_2O_2$ | 264–266 | +73 (E) | s |
| Isoraunescine | $C_{31}H_{36}N_2O_8$ | 241–242 | −70 | c |
| Isoreserpiline | $C_{23}H_{28}N_2O_5$ | 211–212 | −82 (P) | bo, c, ca, de, lg, p. sc, v |
| Isoreserpine | $C_{33}H_{40}N_2O_9$ | 152–156 | −164 | lg |
| Isoreserpinine | $C_{22}H_{26}N_2O_4$ | 225–226 | −18 | c, lg |
| Mauiensine | $C_{20}H_{26}N_2O$ | 240–242 | +184 (M) | ma |
| Mitoridine | $C_{20}H_{22}N_2O_2$ | 321 | +175 (P) | v |
| Neosarpagine | $C_{19}H_{22}N_2O$ | 390 | — | m |
| Obscuridine | | 228 | | o |
| Obscurine | | 255 | +250 | o |
| Pelirine | $C_{21}H_{28}N_2O_4$ | 130–131 | −121 (E) | p |
| Perakine | $C_{21}H_{22}N_2O_3$ | 183 | +112 | p, v |
| Pseudoreserpine | $C_{32}H_{38}N_2O_9$ | 257–258 | −65 | c, lg |
| Raugalline | $C_{21}H_{28}N_2O_3$ | 185 | +133 | s |
| Raugustine | $C_{32}H_{38}N_2O_9$ | 160–170 | −50 | lg |
| Raujemidine | $C_{33}H_{40}N_2O_9$ | 144–150 | −88 | c |
| Raumitorine | $C_{22}H_{26}N_2O_4$ | 138 | +60 | v |
| Raunescine | $C_{31}H_{36}N_2O_8$ | 160–170 | −74 | c |
| Raunamine | $C_{23}H_{30}N_2O_4$ | 206–207 | +60 | m |
| Rauniticine | $C_{21}H_{24}N_2O_3$ | 233–235 | −38 | ni |
| Raunitidine | $C_{22}H_{26}N_2O_4$ | 276–278 | −70 | ni |
| Rauvanine | $C_{23}H_{28}N_2O_9$ | 129–135 | +32 | v |
| Rauvomitine | $C_{30}H_{34}N_2O_5$ | 115–117 | −173 | v |
| Rauwolfinine | $C_{20}H_{26}N_2O_2$ | 235–236 | −35 (E) | p, s |
| Renoxidine | $C_{33}H_{40}N_2O_{10}$ | 238–241 | −100 | v |
| Rescidine | $C_{34}H_{40}N_2O_9$ | 183–186 | −63 | v |

*Table 4.2.* Alkaloids of *Rauwolfia* (*contd.*)

| | Formula | m.p. | Rotation* | Source† |
|---|---|---|---|---|
| Rescinnamine | $C_{35}H_{42}N_2O_9$ | 237–238 | −97 | a, cf, ie, ni, pe, s, sl, sp, su, tr, v |
| Reserpiline | $C_{23}H_{28}N_2O_5$ | — | −40 (E) | af, bh, bo, c, de, ie, lg, m, n, pa, pe, r, s, sc, sl, sp, su, tr, v |
| Reserpine | $C_{33}H_{40}N_2O_9$ | 264–265 | −117 | ‡ |
| Reserpinine | $C_{22}H_{26}N_2O_4$ | 243–244 | −131 | af, c, d, s |
| Sandwicensine | $C_{20}H_{26}N_2O_2$ | 260–262 | +56 (M) | sd |
| Sandwicine | $C_{20}H_{26}N_2O_2$ | 210–213 | +129 (M) | sd (Base · 2HCl) |
| Sarpagine | $C_{19}H_{22}N_2O_2$ | 310 | +53 (P) | b, c, d, dc, h, ht, i, lg, p, s, v |
| Semperflorine | $C_{21}H_{26}N_2O$ | 295 | — | se |
| Seredamine | $C_{22}H_{26}N_2O_2$ | 297 | +60 | v |
| Seredine | $C_{23}H_{30}N_2O_5$ | 291 | −1 | v |
| Serpentine | $C_{21}H_{20}N_2O_3$ | 158 | +292 (M) | c, f, h, lg, m, s, su, sw |
| Serpentinine | $C_{42}H_{44}N_2O_6$ | 265–266 | +75 (E) | de, lg, s, t |
| Tetrahydroalstonine | $C_{21}H_{24}N_2O_3$ | 228–230 | — | su |
| Tetraphyllicine | $C_{20}H_{24}N_2O$ | 320–322 | +61 | de, sw, t |
| Tetraphylline | $C_{22}H_{26}N_2O_4$ | 220–223 | −73 | de, t, v |
| Vomalidine | $C_{21}H_{26}N_2O_3$ | 242–243 | +318 | v |
| Vomilenine | $C_{21}H_{22}N_2O_3$ | 207 | −72 (P) | v |
| Yohimbine | $C_{21}H_{26}N_2O_3$ | 241–243 | +101 (P) | a, c, h, s, su, v |
| α-Yohimbine | $C_{21}H_{26}N_2O_3$ | 231–232 | −40 (E) | c, h, ht, lg, su, v |
| β-Yohimbine | $C_{21}H_{26}N_2O_3$ | 246–249 | −54 (P) | c |
| ψ-Yohimbine | $C_{21}H_{26}N_2O_3$ | 293 | +27 (P) | c |

* Rotations listed are for chloroform solution except as noted: E, ethanol; M, methanol; P, pyridine.
† See Ref. 10, 11, 12, 12a, for literature relating to most of the alkaloid isolations and physical data.
‡ Isolated from all *Rauwolfia* species listed except b, de, f, ma, sf, ve. In addition, it has been identified in *Alstonia constricta* F. Muell., *Tonduzia longifolia* (A. DC.) Markgraf, *Vallesia dichotoma* Ruiz and Pav., *Vinca* (*Lochnera*) *rosea* L. and *Excavatia coccinea* (Tejsmann and Binnendijk) MGF and *Ochrosia Power* Bailey 12b.

*Table 4.3.* Check list of *Rauwolfia* Alkaloid synonyms

| Synonym | Name |
|---|---|
| Alkaloid A | Reserpinine |
| Alkaloid C | Reserpinine |
| Alkaloid C | Ajmalinine |
| Alkaloid F | Ajmalicine |
| Alkaloid F-2 | Vomilenine |
| Alkaloid 3078 | 3-Epi-α-yohimbine |
| Amsonine | β-Yohimbine |
| Canescine | Deserpidine |
| Chalchupine A | α-Yohimbine |
| 11-Desmethoxyreserpine | Deserpidine |
| 3-Epirauwolscine | 3-Epi-α-yohimbine |
| Heterophylline | Aricine |
| Isorauhimbine | 3-Epi-α-yohimbine |
| Micranthine | Reserpiline or 10,11-Dimethoxyajmalicine |
| Neoajmaline | Ajmaline |
| Perakenine | Rauwolfinine |
| Raubasine | Ajmalicine |
| Raubasinine | Reserpinine |
| Rauhimbine | Corynanthine |
| Raupine | Sarpagine |
| Rauwolfine | Ajmaline |
| Rauwolscine | α-Yohimbine |
| Recanescine | Deserpidine |
| Renoxydine | Renoxidine |
| Reserpoxidine | Renoxidine |
| Serpentidine | Serpentinine |
| Serpine | α-Yohimbine + Yohimbine |
| Serpinine | Tetraphyllicine |
| Substance I (Alkaloid I) | Reserpinine |
| Substance II (Alkaloid II) | Ajmalicine |
| py-Tetrahydroserpentine | Ajmalicine |
| γ-Yohimbine | β-Yohimbine + Yohimbine |
| δ-Yohimbine | Ajmalicine |

The indole and dihydroindole bases listed in *Table 4.2* may be divided into three groups according to their structural types:

(a) Alkaloids with the yohimbine skeleton (*I*), including diesters of the reserpine type.

(b) Ajmalicine-like indoles (*II*), whose distinguishing feature is the oxygen-heterocyclic E ring.

(c) Dihydroindoles of the ajmaline type (*III*) and biogenetically related indoles and indolenines.

Numbering of the rings of yohimbine follows the convention proposed by Barger and Scholz[13]. The numbers assigned to the atoms of the other *Rauwolfia* alkaloids correspond to those of their supposed equivalents in yohimbine. One stereochemical feature, the configuration at $C_{15}$, is common to all. For convenience, the rings are designated as A, B, C, D and E as shown. The indole nitrogen and the tertiary nitrogen are called $N_a$ and $N_b$ respectively.

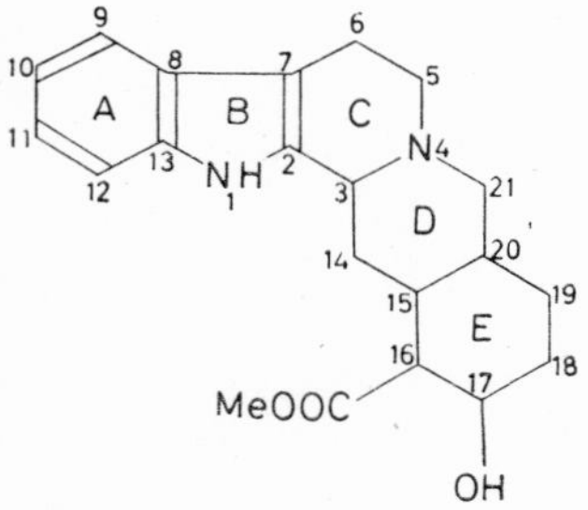

(*I*) Yohimbine

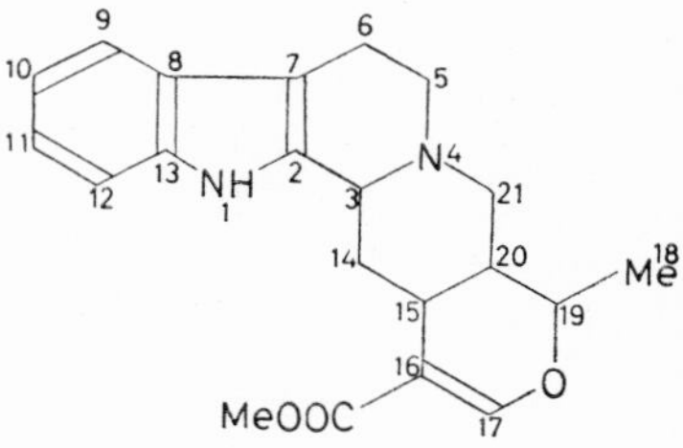

(*II*) Ajmalicine

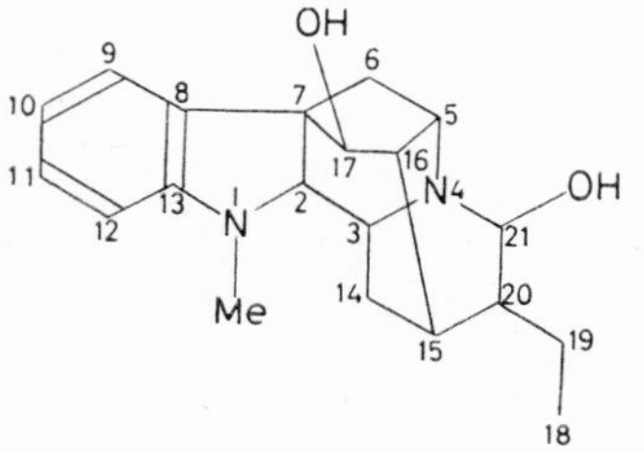

(*III*) Ajmaline

## ALKALOIDS WITH THE YOHIMBINE SKELETON

### Chemistry of the Yohimbines

While less interesting biologically than reserpine, the yohimbine alkaloids provided the basis for studying the more complex reserpine-type heterocycles isolated from *Rauwolfia*. Of 32 possible stereoisomers, yohimbine and five others which have been isolated from various *Rauwolfia* species are listed in *Table 4.4*.

149

The nature of the pentacyclic nucleus of yohimbine was first elucidated by Barger and Scholz[13]. Since then the many studies on yohimbine and its relatives have culiminated in the total synthesis of yohimbine[15]. Systematization of yohimbine nomenclature and transformational relations of yohimbine

Table 4.4. Configuration of yohimbine stereoisomers[14]

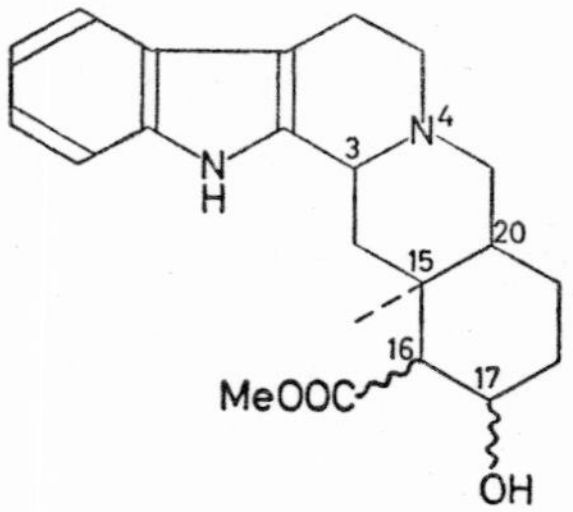

|  | $C_3(H)$ | $C_{20}(H)$ | $C_{16}(COOMe)$ | $C_{17}(OH)$ |
|---|---|---|---|---|
| Yohimbine | $\alpha$ | $\beta$ | $\alpha$ (e) | $\alpha$ (a) |
| Corynanthine | $\alpha$ | $\beta$ | $\beta$ (a) | $\alpha$ (a) |
| $\beta$-Yohimbine | $\alpha$ | $\beta$ | $\alpha$ (e) | $\beta$ (e) |
| $\psi$-Yohimbine | $\beta$ | $\beta$ | $\alpha$ (e) | $\alpha$ (a) |
| $\alpha$-Yohimbine | $\alpha$ | $\alpha$ | $\beta$ (e) | $\alpha$ (e) |
| 3-Epi-$\alpha$-yohimbine | $\beta$ | $\alpha$ | $\beta$ (e) | $\alpha$ (e) |

stereoisomers have recently been described[16]. The name yohimbane is retained for the D/E trans pentacyclic system (*IV*) (with the $\alpha$-hydrogen at $C_{15}$ common to all known *Rauwolfia* alkaloids) and isomers are named by appropriate indication of epimerization. Thus, for example, 3-epi-$\alpha$-yohimbine becomes 16$\beta$-methoxycarbonyl-17$\alpha$-hydroxy-3$\beta$,20$\alpha$-yohimbane.

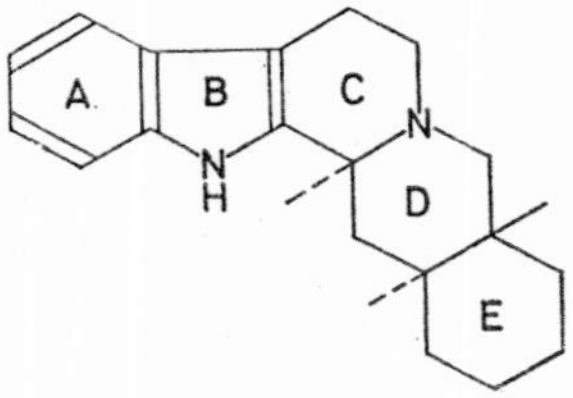

(IV) Yohimbane

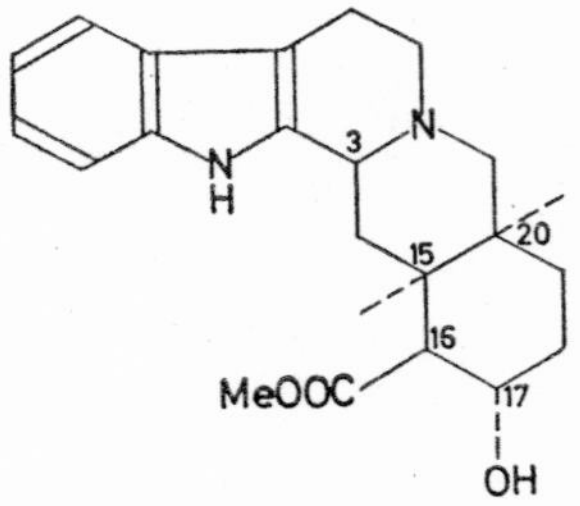

(V) 3-Epi-$\alpha$-yohimbine

Only one analogue, seredine (10,11-dimethoxy-$\alpha$-yohimbine)[17] has been discovered in nature. Canembine[17a] has been reported to be 19-methyl-$\alpha$-yohimbine. It should be noted here that ajmalinine $(C_{20}H_{26}N_2O_3)$[18] bears a striking similarity to 3-epi-$\alpha$-yohimbine (*V*) in melting point, rotation and melting point of its hydrochloride and methiodide, although the reported ultraviolet absorption is slightly different.

Increased understanding of the chemistry of the pentacyclic yohimbine system and its isomers has led to a number of synthetically useful reactions. Some are reactions which require little comment; thus, acylation of the

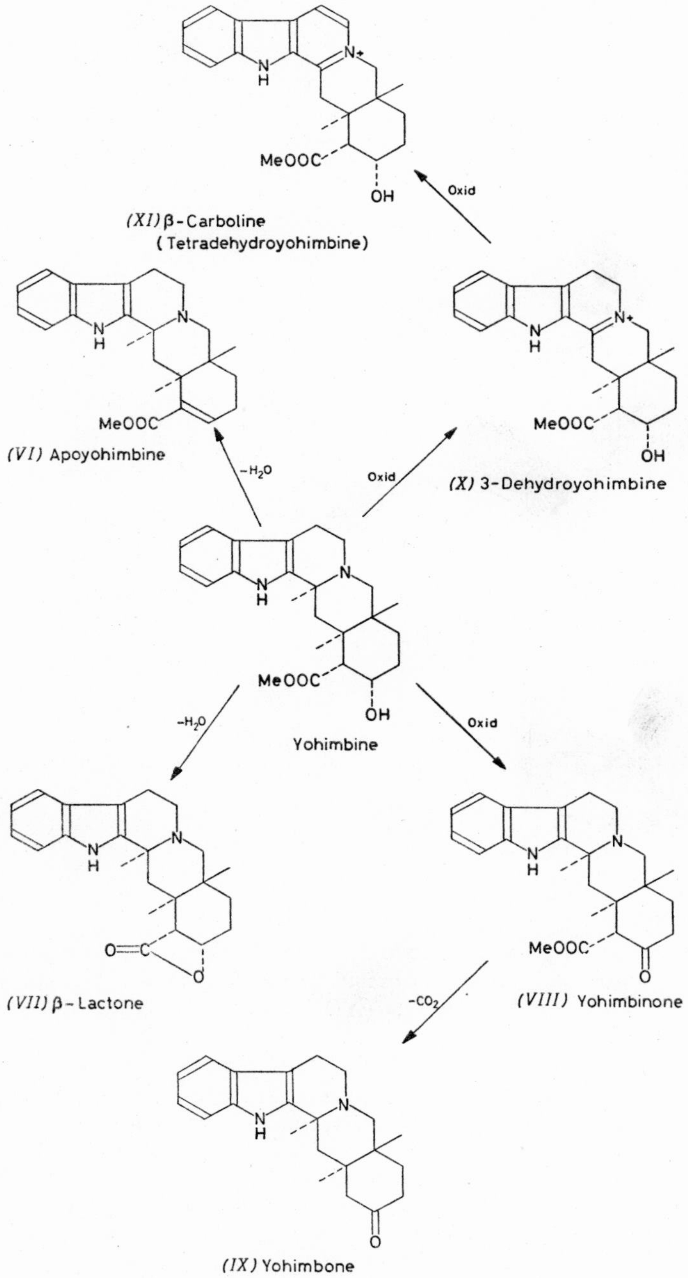

(XI) β-Carboline
(Tetradehydroyohimbine)

(VI) Apoyohimbine

(X) 3-Dehydroyohimbine

Yohimbine

(VII) β-Lactone

(VIII) Yohimbinone

(IX) Yohimbone

17-hydroxyl, ester exchange at C-16, or substitution on the indole nitrogen lead to the corresponding derivatives. Dehydration of yohimbine may give either apoyohimbine[19] (*VI*) or a $\beta$-lactone[20] (*VII*), Oppenauer oxidation of the 17-hydroxyl yields either the 16-methoxycarbonyl-17-ketoyohimbane

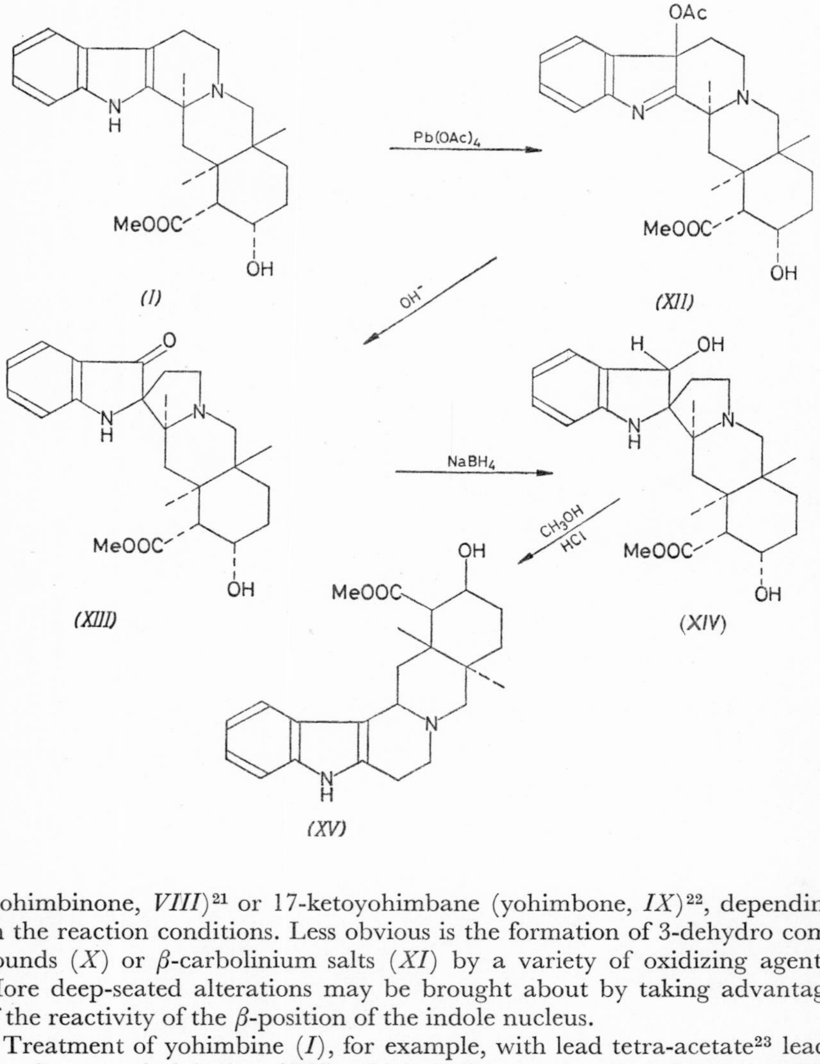

(yohimbinone, *VIII*)[21] or 17-ketoyohimbane (yohimbone, *IX*)[22], depending on the reaction conditions. Less obvious is the formation of 3-dehydro compounds (*X*) or $\beta$-carbolinium salts (*XI*) by a variety of oxidizing agents. More deep-seated alterations may be brought about by taking advantage of the reactivity of the $\beta$-position of the indole nucleus.

Treatment of yohimbine (*I*), for example, with lead tetra-acetate[23] leads to a 7-acetoxyindolenine (*XII*) which undergoes an elimination in acidic media to give 3-dehydroyohimbine, but rearranges in base to furnish the pseudoindoxyl (*XIII*) and a trace of oxindole. Reduction of the pseudoindoxyl with sodium borohydride gives an intermediate hydroxy compound (*XIV*) which on treatment with methanolic hydrogen chloride produces rings A and B inverted yohimbine (*XV*), (a tetrahydro $\gamma$-carboline)[23].

A better yield of the oxindole[23] is obtained by way of 7-chloroyohimbine (*XVI*)[24] formed by reaction of yohimbine with t-butylhypochlorite. The intermediate chloroyohimbine, although yielding dehydroyohimbine with mineral acid, gives a rearranged amido ether (*XVII*) in methanolic alkali. On subsequent acid treatment, this is converted to the oxindole (*XVIII*).

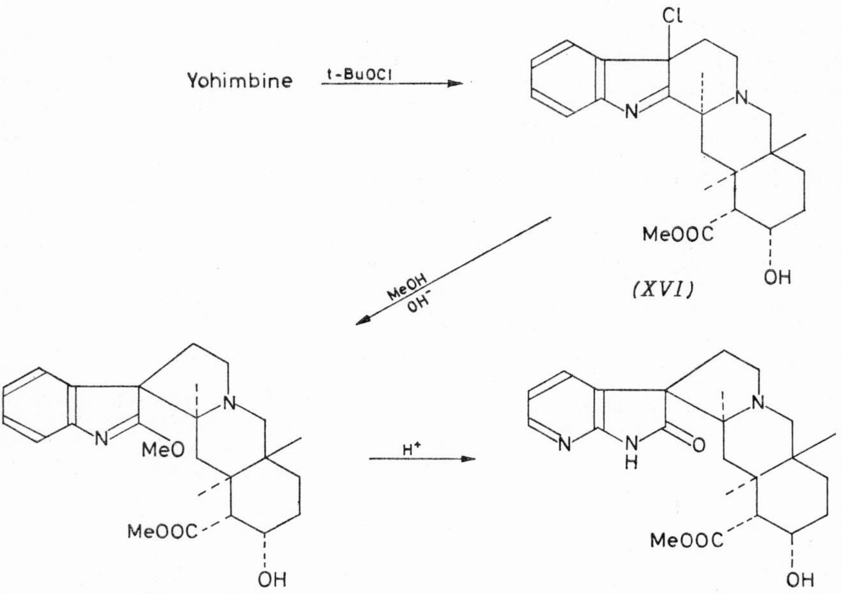

Yohimbine    <u>t-BuOCl</u>   ⟶

(*XVI*)

(*XVII*)

(*XVIII*)

Application of the same reaction sequence to various yohimbine isomers indicates that with *trans* D/E ring configuration about 40–50 per cent of the oxindole is obtained, while in the case of *cis* D/E only 5–10 per cent of the oxindole may be isolated.

## Pharmacology of the Yohimbines

Biologically, yohimbine is a sympathicolytic agent formerly used as an aphrodisiac with somewhat questionable rationale. Study of the pharmacology of yohimbine and some of its esters has demonstrated definite adrenolytic activity[25]. So far, however, practical applications have not been realized. Both yohimbine and 3-epi-α-yohimbine are reported to be able to block reserpine-induced pigeon emesis[26]. Enhanced sympathicolytic activity has been claimed for the O,N-dipropionyl, dibutyryl and di-isobutyryl derivatives of corynanthine[27]. Yohimbine exerts some inhibition of respiration of rat brain homogenate[28]. α-Yohimbine produces short-acting reversible adrenergic blockade[29,30] and has general non-specific spasmolytic activity[31,31a]. It is reported to show slight stimulation followed by marked depression in mice, rats, guinea-pigs and rabbits[32]. For the most part the various modifications of the yohimbines have yielded pharmacologically

153

uninteresting compounds. A notable exception is the 'invert' compound which is a powerful analeptic agent with concomitant blood pressure-elevating properties[33].

## THE RESERPINE-TYPE ALKALOIDS

### Chemistry of Reserpine and its Isomers

The first isolation of crystalline reserpine and its subsequent characterization as a diester indole alkaloid $(C_{33}H_{40}N_2O_9)$[34] led to intensive structural work and finally to an elegant synthesis[2-7,35-37]. Both degradation and synthesis provided independent proofs of the stereochemistry[38] of reserpine (methyl 18-O-(3,4,5-trimethoxybenzoyl)reserpate or 11,17α-dimethoxy-16β-methoxy-carbonyl-18β-3′,4′,5′-trimethoxybenzoyloxy-3β,20α-yohimbane, $XIX$[16].

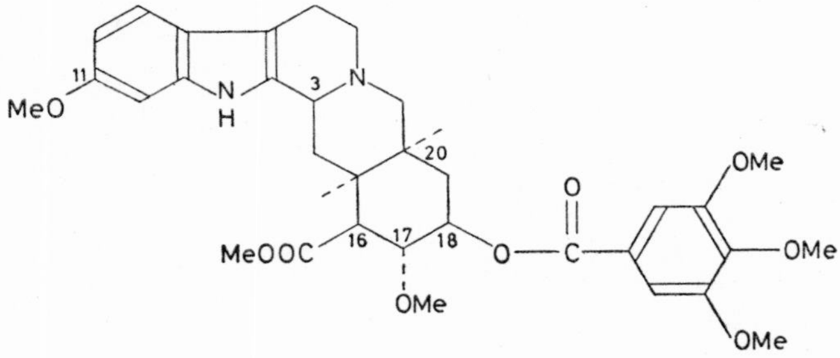

(XIX) Reserpine

The interpretation of the stereochemistry of reserpine and its congeneric alkaloids was a most involved problem since reserpine contains six asymmetric carbon atoms thus allowing for 64 stereoisomers. Reserpine occurs in nature as the laevorotatory substance, whilst the d-antipode has been prepared by synthesis[37]. A new proof of the absolute stereochemistry has been provided via the Prelog asymmetric synthesis[39].

The following isomers of reserpine, prepared by chemical manipulation,

Table 4.5. Isomers of reserpine

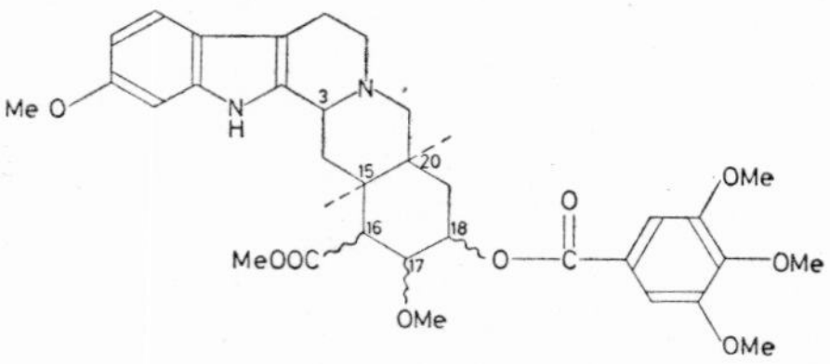

|  | 3H | 16-COOMe | 17-OMe | 18-O-TMB |
|---|---|---|---|---|
| 3-Isoreserpine[40] | α | β | α | β |
| 16-Epi-17-epireserpine[41] | β | α | β | β |
| 18-Epireserpine[42] | β | β | α | α |
| 18-Epi-3-isoreserpine[42] | α | β | α | α |

154

All the above retain the *cis* $C_{15}$-$C_{20}$ ring juncture. So far no example of a reserpine with *trans*-fused D/E ring system has been recognized.

In addition to the compounds above, a naturally occurring isomer of reserpine, raujemidine, has been isolated from *R. canescens*[43]. Although it has not been completely characterized, spectral and degradational evidence indicate that it may possess a *pseudo* configuration ($\beta$-H at $C_3$ and $C_{20}$)[43a].

## Chemistry of Natural Alkaloids Related to Reserpine

A number of alkaloids closely related to reserpine have been isolated from *Rauwolfia* species. In addition to renoxidine, the *N*-oxide of reserpine[44,45], the following have been identified:

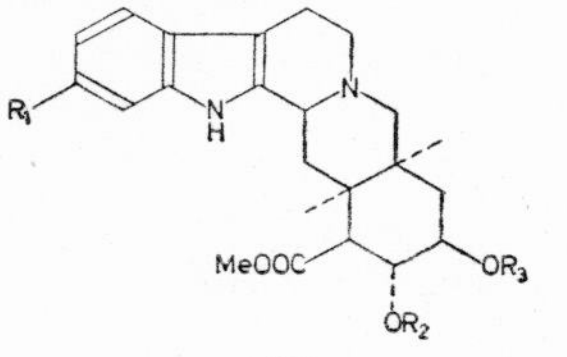

(XX)

Deserpidine[46] XXa, $R_1$ = H; $R_2$ = Me; $R_3$ =

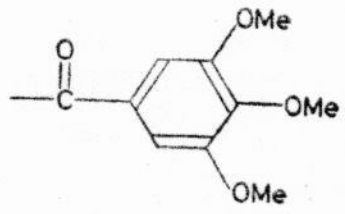

Raunescine[47] XXb, $R_1$ = $R_2$ = H; $R_3$ =

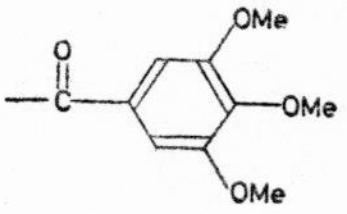

Isoraunescine[47] XXc, $R_1$ = $R_3$ = H; $R_2$ =

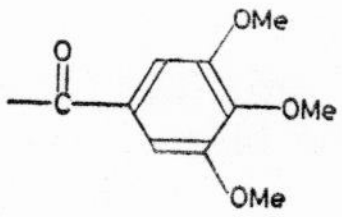

Rescinnamine[48] XXd, $R_1$ = MeO; $R_2$ = Me; $R_3$ =

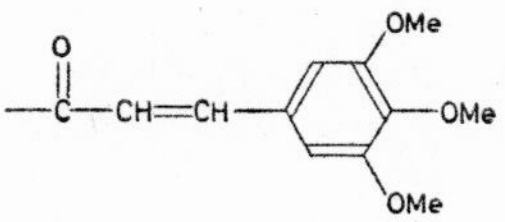

Pseudoreserpine[49] XXe, $R_1$ = MeO; $R_2$ = H; $R_3$ =

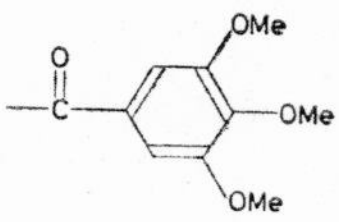

Raugustine[50] XXf, $R_1$ = MeO; $R_2$ = 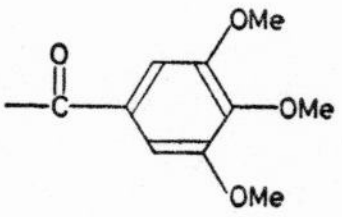 ; $R_3$ = H

Rescidine XXg, $R_1$ = MeO; $R_2$ = H; $R_3$ =

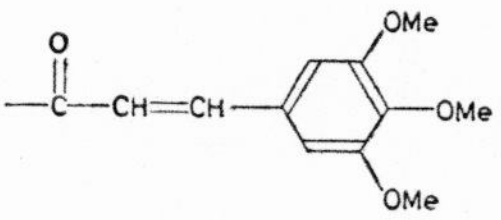

The structure of rescidine, originally uncertain as to the position of the trimethoxycinnamate moiety[51], has now been established. Methylation of dihydrorescidine with aluminium propoxide and diazomethane yields dihydrorescinnamine[51a].

## Pharmacology of Reserpine

### Hypotensive and associated effects

Although the pharmacology of crude reserpine mixtures had been investigated earlier, it was Bein[52] who first demonstrated the hypotensive action of the pure drug. Subsequent work on the pharmacology of reserpine has been reviewed[6] and brought up to date with particular reference to the hypotensive properties[53]. Wien has also reviewed the hypotensive action of reserpine, and laboratory methods for its measurement[54].

It is generally agreed that the hypotensive effects of *Rauwolfia* derivatives are related to the diminution in sympathetic arteriolar vasoconstrictor tone and the resultant vascular relaxation which these alkaloids produce. Detailed studies of the effects of reserpine on the vasoconstrictor amines show that the action of these amines is inhibited, and in some cases transformed into vasodilation[55]. This suppressant action on the sympathetic nervous system is due to the removal of noradrenaline (norepinephrine), its neuromediator, from the regions of the post-ganglionic sympathetic nerves, from the sympathetic centres of the hypothalamus, and from the heart and blood vessels[56-58]. Such an alteration may be styled a 'chemical sympathectomy', serving to reduce the arterial resistance, to slow the heart, and to lower the blood pressure. Significantly, noradrenaline produces an exaggerated pressor effect in a reserpinized animal[59], probably related to the increased sensitivity of the blood vessels. The primary alteration responsible for the hypotensive action of reserpine is probably the depletion of the catechol amine neuro-effector substance from the brain and peripheral sympathetic nerves, alterations in the reactivity of the blood vessels to catechol amines being secondary to this depletion.

Reserpine acts directly on the cells of the adrenal medulla of the rat, and the catechol amines do not accumulate in the cytoplasmic sap[60]. The effect has also been noted in sheep[61] and fowl[62]. It has also been shown that reserpine produces depletion of catechol amines in isolated nerve tissue[63]. Monamine oxidase inhibitors, like iproniazid, antagonize the reserpine action[64,65] by blocking the oxidation of the liberated catechol amines, and when administered prior to reserpine they may even produce hypertension and hyperactivity[66]. Reserpine increases the rate of metabolism of tritium-labelled adrenaline (epinephrine) in mice[67], and reduces the urinary catechol amine excretion in man[68]. The absence of a hypertensive response in electro-shocked reserpinized rabbits[69] and the inhibiting effect of reserpine on the spreading of dye by hyaluronidase[70] are attributed to a lack of peripheral catechol amines.

Although reserpine depletes catechol amines in the brain stem of the rabbit[71], it probably does not interfere with the decarboxylating and $\beta$-hydroxylating steps in amine synthesis[72], and does not prevent the uptake of newly synthesized amines by mitochondria[73]. The principal effect of reserpine on tissue 3-hydroxytyramine, adrenaline and 5-hydroxytryptamine (serotonin) is claimed to be due to an action on the active transport of the amines into the storage sites[74]. Reserpine does not release histamine from rabbit tissues, with the exception of the platelets[75]. Experiments with dogs indicate that some areas of the brain are markedly inhibited by reserpine, but the respiratory centre is stimulated[76]. The peripheral dilator action of reserpine in man has been demonstrated by infusing reserpine into the brachial artery, and obtaining a marked and prolonged vasodilation confined to the skin of the limb[77]. An interesting action of reserpine, related to a circulatory effect, is the inhibition of experimentally-provoked thrombus formation in rats[78].

*Sedative action*

The sedative or tranquillizing activity of reserpine and laboratory methods for its determination have been described by Parkes[79]. In addition, ptosis or active eyelid closure in mice and rats has been used to evaluate the degree of sedation induced by reserpine[80]. A recently described 'chimney test'[81] determines the sedative activity of drugs in mice by utilizing a glass tube 30 cm long by 22–28 mm in diameter; with the tube in horizontal position the mouse is inserted head first and allowed to reach the other end, whereupon the tube is raised to a vertical position: the test depends on whether the mouse, climbing backwards up the tube, reaches the 20 cm mark within 30 seconds; untreated mice invariably climb the tube within this interval. Betta fighting fish have also been suggested for the evaluation of psycholeptics[82].

There is still some difference of opinion regarding the mechanism of the sedative action of reserpine. In one theory, the sedative activity has been attributed to changes in the level of serotonin in the brain[83–86]. The observation of Pletscher, Shore and Brodie[87] that reserpine releases serotonin from binding sites in the brain, pointed to the importance of this effect for the pharmacologic action of reserpine on the central nervous system. In this mechanism, the highly active free serotonin is said to stimulate the reception sites of the trophotropic division of the nervous sytem, the function of which is to integrate parasympathetic function with somato-motor activity. Therefore, the primary relation of reserpine to sedation is one of parasympathetic overactivity, rather than diminished sympathetic central activity.

The opposing view implicates noradrenaline as the mediator for the sedative effect of reserpine. Carlsson and co-workers[88] have shown that catechol amines disappear from the heart, brain and adrenal in the cat after reserpine administration, and have provided evidence that the sympathetic dampening produced by reserpine is related to a shortage of sympathetic transmitter substance both centrally and peripherally. For example, it is claimed that the central nervous system action of reserpine is not dependent on the presence of serotonin in the rat brain, since reserpine action occurs even in rats whose brain serotonin has been pre-lowered by feeding a tryptophan-free diet[89]. Carlsson[90] found that the tranquillizing effect of reserpine was antagonized by 3,4-dihydroxyphenylalanine, a precursor of the catechol amines, while 5-hydroxytryptophan, a precursor of serotonin, was ineffective in this respect. These findings suggest that the effect of reserpine on catechol amine metabolism may be as important for the central as for the peripheral actions. Interestingly, administration of a mixture of the two precursors in equal parts produced a more complete and prolonged antagonism of reserpine than when the catechol amine precursor was given alone.

Recently, investigations on the mechanism of the reserpine effect on the hypophysis favour serotonin as the mediator of the sedative action of reserpine[91]. Injection of reserpine (1 mg/kg) into the rat produces a significant increase of corticosterone level in the plasma, a depletion of ascorbic acid in the suprarenals, an increase of free fatty acids in the plasma, and an increase of the tryptophan peroxidase in the liver. These actions are thus related to a stimulation of the hypophysis-suprarenal systems (ACTH-excretion) since they are completely hindered by hypophysectomy or adrenalectomy. With a single large dose of reserpine (5 mg/kg) or a number of smaller doses (0·5 mg/kg) for several days, the ACTH content of the hypophysis may be reduced as much as 60 per cent. Only reserpine analogues which produce sedation (like raunescine and rescinnamine) and which liberate biogenic amines, stimulate ACTH secretion. It is also known that reserpine produces in frogs a skin-darkening effect which lasts several weeks and may be related to intensified endogenous melanophore-stimulating hormone secretion[92]. It was furthermore shown[91] that the stimulating effect of reserpine on ACTH secretion is not tied to the peripherally liberated catechol amines, since selective depletion of noradrenaline in the periphery, through syrosingopine (a reserpine derivative described later), or operative removal of the suprarenal medulla, does not modify the reserpine action. A significant and long lasting increase of the ACTH secretion was observed when the serotonin and noradrenaline content of the brain were reduced by at least 50 per cent. However, α-methyl-m-tyrosine, which selectively depletes noradrenaline without changing the serotonin content, is non-sedative and exerts no influence on the ACTH secretion of the hypophysis. Thus, ACTH secretion stimulated by reserpine is connected with depletion of biogenic amines in the brain, and this implies that the depletion of brain serotonin alone is the significant factor in sedation.

Studies in rats have indicated that sedative doses of reserpine are associated with stress as a result of the release of large amounts of ACTH by the pituitary[93]. This effect eventually disappears if reserpine treatment is continued and may be prevented by monoamine oxidase inhibitors. It has also been noted that a moderate increase of free serotonin is correlated with tranquillization while a greater increase is associated with excitation, as manifested for example by temporary aggravation of the psychosis in psychiatric patients[94]. Quantitative studies in conditioned rats and mice[95] assessed tranquillizing effects of reserpine as influenced by cold stress, monoamine oxidase inhibitors or stimulants. Results suggested that the mechanism of action involves two components: one is short central stimulation brought about by liberation of serotonin and noradrenaline, and the other is a long lasting central depressing effect which is a consequence of a direct molecular action of reserpine. It has also been observed that nicotinamide potentiates the degree of sedation produced by reserpine in mice[96].

*Other nervous system effects of reserpine*

The lowered seizure threshold to electroshock in rats[97] and mice is said to be related to the depletion of brain $\gamma$-aminobutyric acid. Mice given 5 mg/kg of reserpine showed this effect, which was inhibited by iproniazid[98]. The content of the polypeptide, substance P, in the brain of rats is increased by reserpine independently of its effect on serotonin[99]. Syrosingopine, however, which has a hypotensive and only slightly sedative effect, had no influence on the brain substance P content. Substance P has been described as a 'physiologic tranquillizer'[100]. Reserpine has no analgesic activity and antagonizes rather than potentiates that of morphine[101]; it shortens the latent period of conditioned and unconditioned reflexes to aural stimulus[102], and decreases avoidance conditioning[103]; sweating of the rat paw is inhibited[104]. A depletion of the secretory granules of the rat hypophysis occurs after daily injections of reserpine[105].

*Gastric effects*

Increase in gastric acidity[106] and decreased blood flow[107] may be responsible for gastric ulceration observed in rats, mice[108] and cats[109] after large doses of reserpine. Protection against the diarrhoea and gastrointestinal haemorrhage produced in adrenalectomized rats by reserpine has been shown with desoxycorticosterone[110]. Increase in circulating serotonin is not believed to be responsible for the gastric effects of reserpine in mice, since iproniazid protects against these effects even when large supplementary doses of serotonin are given[111].

*Growth effects*

The antileukemic activity of reserpine[112] is apparent only in doses which produce marked depression and it may be related to release of adrenal steroids, while the increased metabolic rate may be attributed to the release of adrenaline[113]. This may also be connected with decreased oxygen utilization in the brain[114–116] and the liver[117]. The observed anti-tumor effect of reserpine[118] and reduced thyroid secretion rate[119] depend on reduced caloric intake[120,121]. However, reserpine relieves stress factors in some farm animals so that better growth is attained with less feed[122].

Reserpine inhibits thyroid function in the rat[123], apparently through suppression of thyrotropin secretion[124]. When rats are given reserpine and thyroid extracts, growth is retarded and the heart nucleotide levels are depressed[125].

*Effects on some endocrine systems*

Reserpine may affect anterior pituitary function in several ways. For example, it prolongs the menstrual cycle[126] and inhibits the estrous cycle[127], with involvement of the hypothalamus[128,129] resulting in an indirect action on the ovary[130]. This inhibitory effect on some gonadotrophins is not carried over to the lactogenic hormone of the pituitary, the release of which is not inhibited by reserpine[131]; instead, the release in some species and under some conditions may even be stimulated to the extent that lactation is induced[132, 133]. Daily intramuscular injections of reserpine induce milk formation and ovulation in rabbits with well-developed ovaries but have no effect in those with small inactive ovaries[134]. Reserpine in small doses modifies the sexual behaviour of male rats by lowering the threshold of nervous sensitivity and by facilitating genital reflexes, but in larger doses it rapidly inhibits sexual activity[135,136]. A reversible stoppage of ovulation is produced in insects[137] and an inhibition of sperm release in the toad is effected by reserpine[138].

### Pharmacology of Reserpine Isomers and Related Alkaloids

Most of the natural or synthetic reserpine analogues, with the exception, for example, of deserpidine[139] and rescinnamine[140], are pharmacologically less interesting than reserpine. Both these analogues approach the biological potency of reserpine while renoxidine[44], pseudoreserpine and raunescine are considerably less potent[141]. Raugustine, like isoraunescine, lacks appreciable reserpine-like activity[50]. Of the stereoisomers of reserpine, only raujemidine has the typical hypotensive-sedative activity. Deserpidine in addition to its typical hypotensive and sedative activity shows some inhibition of endocrine function of the gonads of the rat. In the female rat it suppresses vaginal keratinization and induces a permanent œstrus[142,143]. Raunescine, isoraunescine, deserpidine and rescinnamine lower the noradrenaline content of rat hearts without affecting the adrenaline level[144]. Raunescine also releases serotonin from blood platelets of the rat[145]. Isoraunescine is only one-tenth as potent as raunescine in behavioural studies using pigeons[146]. Many of these reserpine-type alkaloids effect a transient cardio-acceleration and facilitation of atrio-ventricular transmission by release from the heart tissue of sym-pathomimetic amines, especially noradrenaline[147]. Depressant action is thus concealed until the release of these amines is no longer sufficient to counteract it. The retarding action of these *Rauwolfia* alkaloids on atrio-ventricular transmission distinguishes their action from that of veratramine which also decreases heart rate, but in equivalent depressant doses has no effect on atrio-ventricular transmission.

### Structure-activity Relationships of Reserpine Analogues

The attempted modification and alteration of the biological action of reserpine by chemical methods has led to many interesting observations. The configurational changes in reserpine (natural and synthetic isomers) responsible for decrease of sedative and hypotensive activity have been noted above. In addition, the substituent groups bear a most important relationship to pharmacological activity.

Primary modifications of reserpine are represented by exchange of ester groups at $C_{16}$ and $C_{18}$, substitution of the indole nitrogen, substitution in the aromatic ring A and hetero ring C, and functionalization of the tertiary nitrogen. More subtle stereochemical modifications encompass the 3-dehydro-derivatives, the fully aromatic ring C ($\beta$-carbolinium compounds) and various manipulations of the substituents in ring E, such as inversion of $C_{16}$, $C_{17}$ substituents (already mentioned under isomers of reserpine), removal of $C_{17}$ methoxyl, and inversion at $C_{18}$. Much less obvious modifications are those involving changes in ring structure, such as enlargement of ring C, synthesis of heterocyclic analogues of ring A, the formation of indolenines and oxindoles, and the preparation of pseudoindoxyls and so-called 'invert' structures. The following paragraphs summarize many of the efforts to modify reserpine in the search for enhancement of its valuable biological properties or recognition of new and useful ones. It has become apparent that there exists no simple relationship between structure and biological activity.

Some generalizations concerning reserpine-like activity are first made from the available data[148,149]. The 11-methoxy group is not essential since deserpidine and reserpine are nearly equal in activity. Both positions 16 and 18 must be esterified since methyl reserpate and trimethoxybenzoyl reserpic acid are inactive. The presence of an etherified hydroxyl at $C_{17}$ is not essential since pseudoreserpine and raunescine with a free hydroxyl group are active, albeit considerably weaker than reserpine. Furthermore, dl-17-desmethoxydeserpidine obtained by synthesis[150] shows a typical although reduced reserpine-like response. Alkylation of reserpine on the indole nitrogen[151] to make N-methyl- or N-allylreserpine, changes the typical activity to that of reserpine antagonism. Recently, the N-diethylaminoethyl derivative of reserpine[152] has been claimed to have hypotensive activity with low sedative effect[153]. This is the first example of an N-alkylated reserpine with significant hypotensive activity. Quaternization of the tertiary nitrogen appears to reduce activity. N-Oxide formation lessens but does not eliminate it. Some members of a group of N-oxide esters of reserpic acid[154] show sedative activity but none are as active as reserpine. While epimerization at $C_3$ and $C_{16}$ eliminate reserpine-like biological properties, epimerization at $C_{18}$ of methyl reserpate produces varying effects, depending on the nature of the substituent. 18-Epireserpine lacks reserpine-like activity while ethers of methyl 18-epireserpate (described on p. 163) are quite interesting.

The nature of both the 16- and 18-substituents in diesters of reserpic acid is most important for biological activity. It is significant that while many derivatives have been synthesized which approach reserpine in activity, none has proved to be superior. One of the practical results of variation of the 18-substituent, entailing the preparation of many diverse esters of reserpic acid[155,156], was the separation of the hypotensive from the sedative activity as exemplified by syrosingopine (Singoserp, XXI), in which the latter effect has been virtually lost[157]. Another ester, Su-5171* (methyl 18-O-(3-dimethyl-aminobenzoyl)reserpate, XXII) exhibited good sedative but low hypotensive activity in the laboratory test animal, but was not interesting enough to become a marketable product.

Syrosingopine is less sedative than reserpine by virtue of its reduced central amine liberating action, since it has been found[158] that effective hypotensive doses produce a marked reduction of cardiac noradrenaline levels with little effect on either the noradrenaline or the serotonin content of the brain. Thus, its activity is probably due to a predominantly peripheral action. It is less active in releasing intestinal serotonin than reserpine[159] and causes less gastro-intestinal effects[160]. Syrosingopine lacks antioedema properties in rats treated with dextran[161], in contrast with Su-5171 which inhibits oedema and is a stronger serotonin releaser. Although reserpine and Su-5171 injected intraperitoneally in rats increase the blood glucose level, syrosingopine has no hyperglycemic effect[162]. Syrosingopine is without

---

* Su-numbers designate compounds isolated or prepared in the Summit, N.J., laboratories of CIBA Pharmaceutical Company.

adverse behavioural effects in man[163] and has only very weak effects on the endocrine system[164]. After pre-treatment of cats and dogs with a small dose of ephedrine, syrosingopine produces marked hypertension[165] due to peripheral liberation of catechol amines, principally noradrenaline.

The *dl*- and *l*-forms of the 10-methoxy positional isomer of syrosingopine[166,167] have been prepared, but biological evidence indicating practical

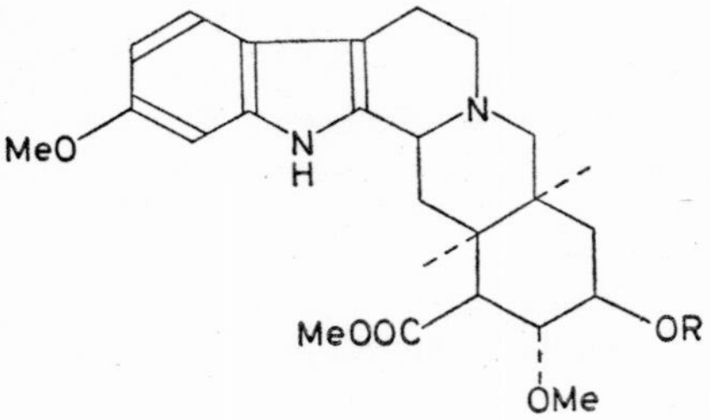

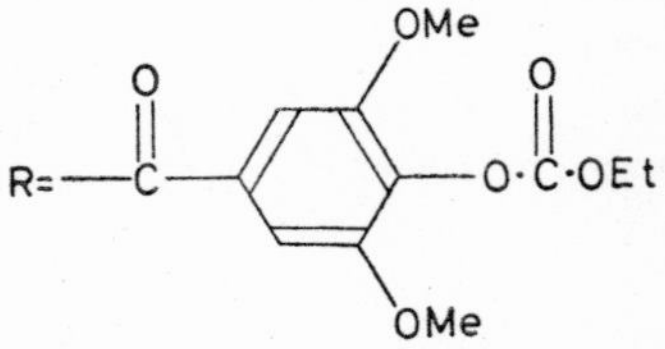

(*XXI*) Syrosingopine

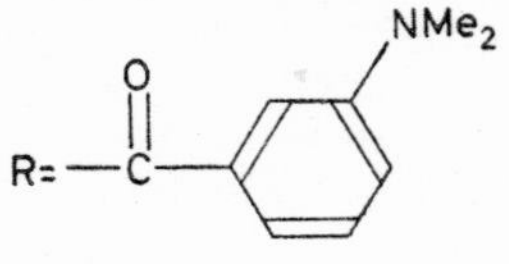

(*XXII*) Su-5171

utility is unavailable. Variation of the 16-ester substituent may reverse the effect of the 18-acyl group: for example, 2-methoxyethyl 18-*O*-ethoxy-carbonylsyringoyl)reserpate, in contrast to syrosingopine, shows pronounced sedative activity.

The reaction of reserpine with chloramine yields a hydrazine-like compound (*XXIII*), claimed to have hypotensive activity[168], but concerning which there are, so far, no reports of practical application.

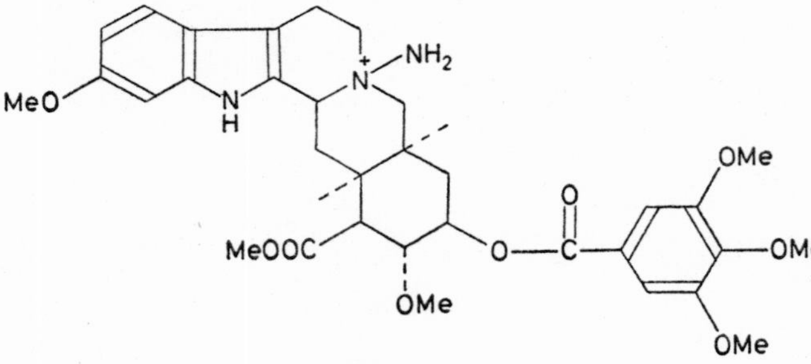

(*XXIII*)

Efforts to synthesize 18-ethers as new derivatives of methyl reserpate yielded compounds with potent biological properties. The first compounds prepared were the cyclic acetals (*XXIV*) obtained by reaction of methyl reserpate and its analogues with dihydropyran[42].

When R = methyl (Su-7064), the compound exhibited good sedative with low hypotensive activity in the dog[169] but was found to be clinically lacking in potency. Interestingly its sedative activity is converted to stimulant activity when administered at the peak of action of monoamine oxidase inhibitors, suggesting that it liberates amines more rapidly than reserpine, and that the stimulant properties of the amines are enhanced by inhibition of monoamine oxidase[170]. Su-7064 also shows specific activity in the rat in

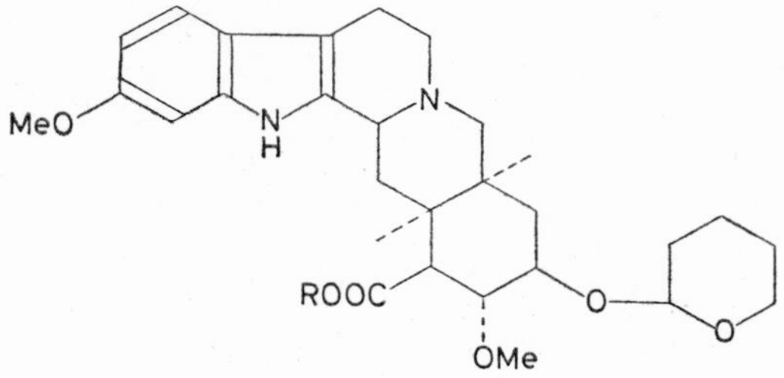

*(XXIV)*

suppressing oestrus and fertility, in stimulating ACTH release and in altering kidney function[171]. It is unique in showing its endocrine actions in doses which are without adverse effects on the growth rate. Where R = n-propyl (Su-7192), the situation is reversed. The compound now has strong hypotensive with some sedative activity and the specific endocrine actions are greatly weakened. Hopes that 18-glycosides of methyl reserpate might have potent activity proved false for they were, surprisingly, almost devoid of either sedative or hypotensive activity.

Synthesis of alkyl ethers of methyl reserpate, accomplished first by the fluoboric acid catalyzed reaction of diazoalkanes[172] with methyl reserpate, proved much more fruitful. The 18$\beta$-ethers *(XXV)* thus obtained were

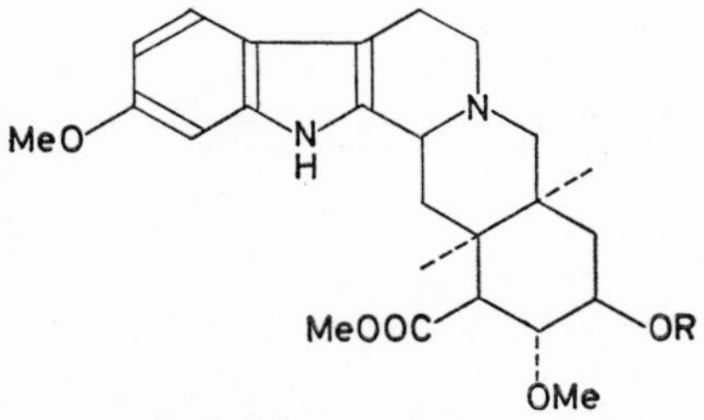

*(XXV)* 18–$\beta$–ethers

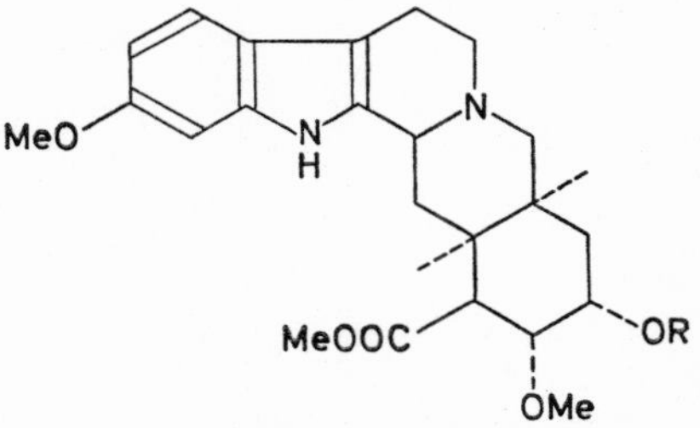

*(XXVI)* 18–$\alpha$–ethers

supplemented by the much more easily and safely prepared isomeric 18$\alpha$-ethers *(XXVI)*[173] resulting from the alcoholysis of methyl reserpate 18-O-p-bromobenzenesulphonate.

The 18-ethers of methyl reserpate and their analogues are interesting compounds. Not only do the 18$\alpha$- and $\beta$-methyl, 18$\alpha$- and $\beta$-ethyl and 18$\alpha$-n-propyl ethers of methyl reserpate exhibit potent, fast-acting, sedative activity with minimal hypotensive effect, but they also protect the cat heart against aconitine-induced fibrillations[174]. In contrast to reserpine and its congeners, the ethers offer the advantage of forming readily soluble salts whose rapid onset of activity appears to be related to a more rapid rate of absorption, since the difference in time of appearance of drug action following oral and parenteral administration is brief. Thus, the 18α-methyl ether of methyl reserpate at 2·5 mg/kg given orally or intravenously lowers rabbit brain serotonin by 50 per cent, produces sedation, increases central parasympathetic output and enhances light reflex and blepharospasm with a peak effect after two to four hours and return to initial level in ten hours[175]. The effects last only while the drug is present in the brain. In comparison with reserpine, the methyl ether produces non-cumulative, reproducible and brief tranquillization and less marked maximal effects with almost equal central effects from single oral or intravenous doses. In addition to its sedative action, the 18β-methyl ether has local anaesthetic activity at one per cent concentration when applied to the eye of the rabbit.

In common with the 18-tetrahydropyranyl derivatives of methyl reserpate, substitution of the 16-methoxycarbonyl by 16-propoxycarbonyl results in the reappearance of strong hypotensive activity along with sedative activity[174]. Furthermore, the sedative activity is practically eliminated in 2-methoxyethyl 18-epireserpate 2-methoxyethyl ether which has once again strong hypotensive activity. Epimerization of this compound at $C_3$ yields 2-methoxyethyl 18-epi-3-isoreserpate 2-methoxyethyl ether which now has lost both hypotensive and sedative properties and exhibits stimulant action. The corresponding N-methyl compound (XXVII) was

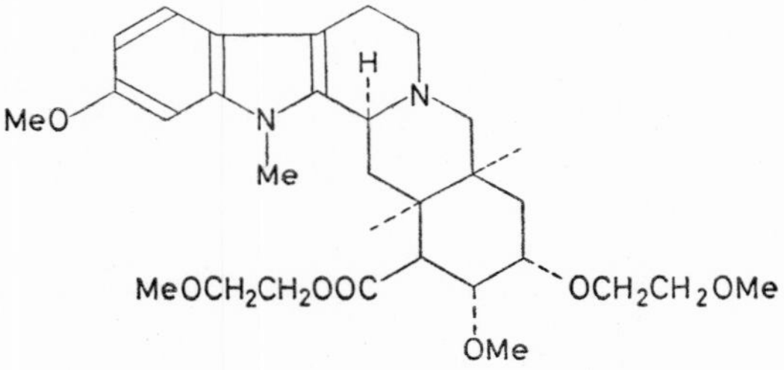

(XXVII)

found to be practically inactive, demonstrating that the antagonistic or stimulant-like activity observed in N-methylreserpine was not to be added to the stimulant activity of the 3-iso compound.

Quite recently the synthesis of methyl 18-ketoreserpate (XXVIII) has been accomplished[175a]:

Methyl reserpate ⟶ methyl reserpate brosylate $\xrightarrow{\text{Dimethyl sulphoxide}}$

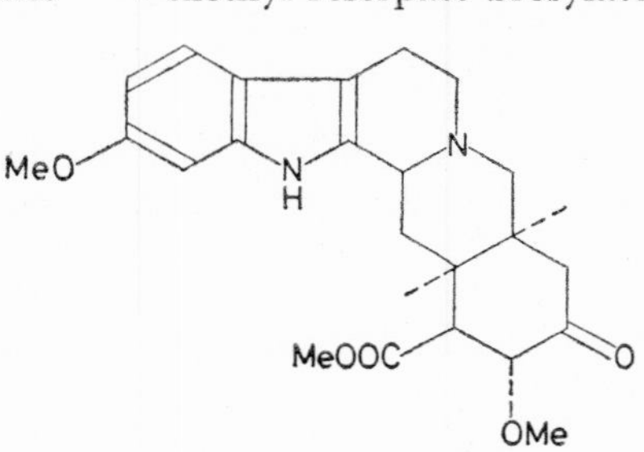

(XXVIII)

164

Although the ketone was only a moderate sedative agent, its availability suggested many new synthetic possibilities. Among others, reductive aminations yielded the expected 18α- and 18β-amino derivatives (*XXIX*) along with the unexpected 17-desmethoxy analogues (*XXX*):

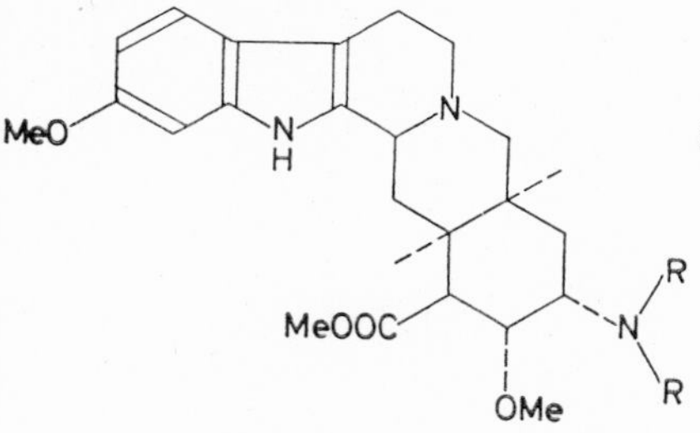

(*XXIXa*)

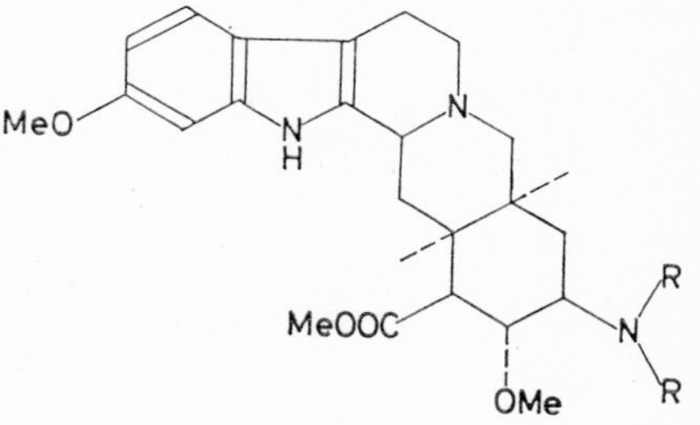

(*XXIXb*)

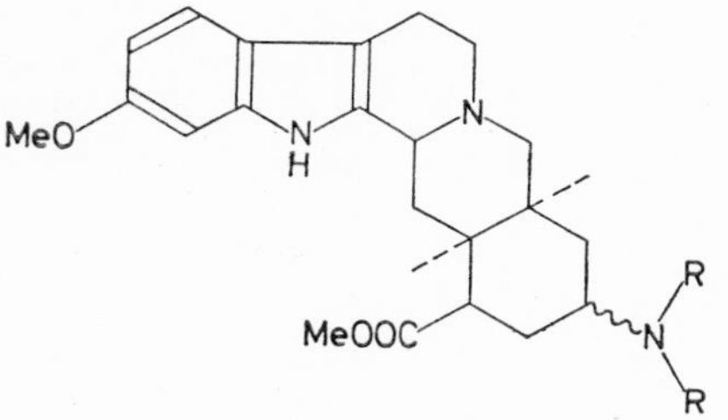

(*XXX*)

The latter compounds exhibited curare-like activity, which is unusual for a tertiary base and the first case in this group of alkaloids[174]. Upon oral administration in dogs there is a delayed action, the effect appearing only after one day, and lasting four to five days. The most active compound was methyl 17-desmethoxy-18-desoxy-18-piperidinoreserpate.

Application of a modified Wittig reaction to methyl 18-ketoreserpate led to the preparation of an 18-ethoxycarbonylmethylene derivative (*XXXI*), which had no useful biological activity:

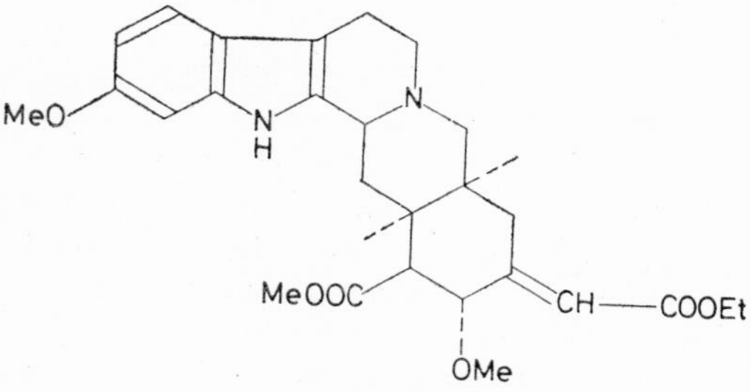

(*XXXI*)

Extension to reserpine derivatives of the indole to oxindole rearrangement previously discussed under yohimbine chemistry (p. 153) led to several new

165

compounds (*XXXII–XXXIV*)[23], none of which showed any significant biological activity:

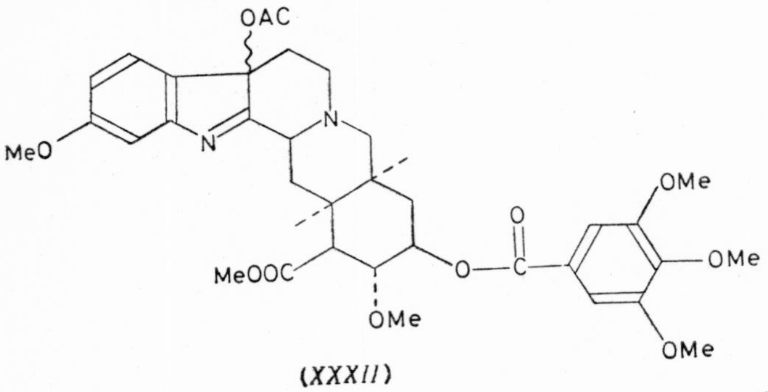

(*XXXII*)

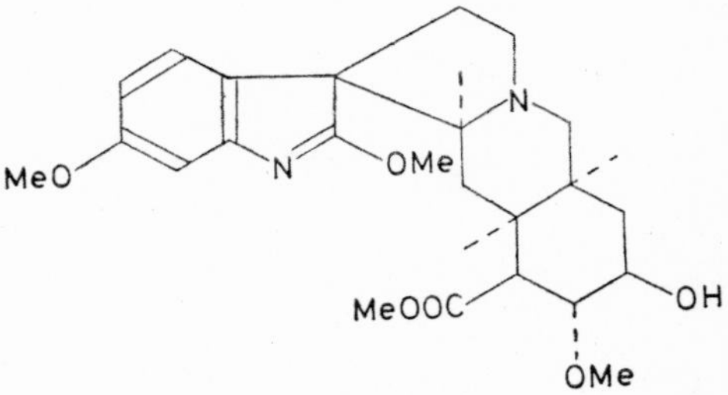

(*XXXIII*)

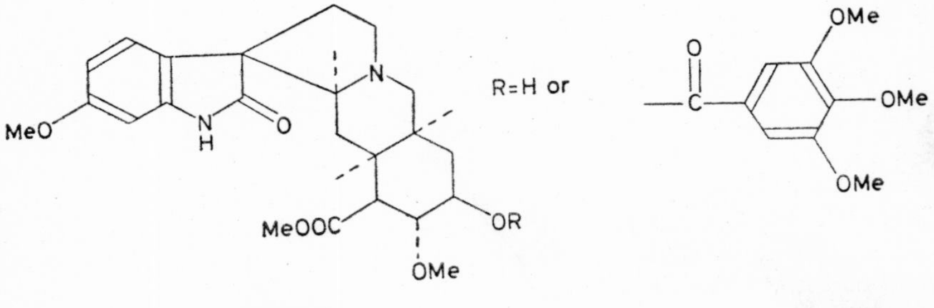

(*XXXIV*)

## Synthetic Reserpine Analogues

Preparation of synthetic modifications of reserpine was first undertaken by French chemists[176] who developed a commercial process from the Woodward reserpine synthesis[37]. Velluz and his associates in France, and later Protiva and co-workers in Czechoslovakia, and Sandoz chemists in Switzerland have reported more than fifty compounds (*Table 4.6*) with various substituents in the A, C, and E rings of reserpine.

So far only one of these compounds, methoserpidine (10-methoxydeserpidine, Decaserpyl) has been introduced as a drug for the control of hypertension. Like syrosingopine it exhibits low sedative with greater hypotensive activity[191], but appears much less potent than syrosingopine and reserpine[153], [192,193]. Pharmacological comparison in the dog[194] indicates that equal

Table 4.6. Reserpine analogues

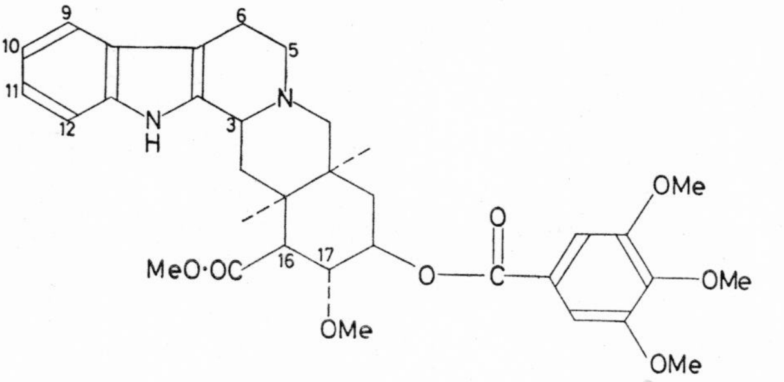

(XIX)

| Ring A substituted deserpidines* | m.p. | $\alpha_D$† | Reference |
|---|---|---|---|
| 10-Acetyl-11-methoxy‡ | 274–278° | −141 | 177 |
| 12-Acetyl-11-methoxy‡ | 254–256 | − 47 | 177 |
| 12-Aza | 290 | −157 | 166 |
| 9,10-Benzo | 248 | −172 | 176 |
| 10-Benzyloxy | 150–152 | −152 (P) | 178 |
| 11-Benzyloxy | 170 | −100 | 179 |
| 10-Bromo‡ | 262–264 | | 180 |
| 10-Bromo-11-methoxy‡ | 285–286 | | 180 |
| 10-Butoxy | 210 | −132 | 179 |
| 11-Butoxy | 206 | − 96 | 179 |
| 12-Butoxy | 209 | −120 | 179 |
| 10-Chloro | 160–170 | −147 | 176 |
| 11-Chloro | 280 | −125 (E) | 176 |
| 12-Chloro | 179 | −116 | 176 |
| 9-Chloro-12-methoxy | — | −132 | 176 |
| 10-Chloro-11-methoxy | 300 | −120 | 176 |
| 11-Chloro-12-methoxy | 183 | −129 | 176 |
| 12-Chloro-11-methoxy | 240 | −106 | 181 |
| 9,12-Dichloro | 172 | −119 | 182 |
| 11,12-Dichloro | 222 | − 97 | 183 |
| 10,11-Dimethoxy | 264–266 | −157 (P) | 178 |
| 11-Dimethylamino | 150–160 | | 166 |
| dl-10-Ethoxy | | | 184 |
| 11-Ethoxy | 282–283 | −158 (P) | 178 |
| 11-Ethylmercapto | 250–252 | −160 (P) | 178 |
| dl-10-Fluoro | 230 | — | 185 |
| 11-Fluoro | 261 | −123 | 186 |
| 11-Hydroxy | 166–168 | −165 (P) | 178 |
| 11-Isopropoxy | 270 | −125 | 179 |
| 9-Methoxy | 203–205 | −133 (P) | 178 |
| 10-Methoxy | 171 | −142 | 176 |
| 12-Methoxy | 200 | −120 | 176 |
| 9-Methyl | 175–180 | −137 (P) | 178 |
| dl-10-Methyl (hemihydrate) | 224–226 | — | 187 |
| 11-Methyl | 275 | −132 | 176 |
| 12-Methyl | 231 | −124 | 176 |
| 12-Methyl-11-methoxy | | | 188 |
| 10,11-Methylenedioxy | 251–253 | −164 (P) | 178 |
| d-10,11-Methylenedioxy | 252–254 | +158 (P) | 178 |

* Compounds listed are the l-enantiomers, corresponding to the naturally occurring l-reserpine, except as noted.
† Rotations are given for chloroform solution except where noted: P = pyridine; E = ethanol.
‡ Compound partially synthetic.

*Table 4.6.* Reserpine analogues (*contd.*)

| | m.p. | $\alpha_D$† | Reference |
|---|---|---|---|
| *Ring A substituted deserpidines** (contd). | | | |
| dl-10-Methylmercapto (hemihydrate) | 206 | — | 187 |
| 11-Methylmercapto | 270–272 | −164 (P) | 178 |
| 11-Propoxy | 215–217 | −160 (P) | 178 |
| 9,10,11-Trimethoxy | 171–173 | −111 | 176 |
| *Ring C substituted deserpidines* | | | |
| 3-Cyano-11-methoxy | 205 | −136 | 166 |
| 6-β-Ethyl-10-chloro | 265 | − 80 | 166 |
| 6-α-Ethyl-10-methoxy | 268 | −129 | 166 |
| 6-β-Ethyl-10-methoxy | 225 | −105 | 166 |
| 6-Ethyl-11-methoxy | 130 | − 82 | 189 |
| C-Homo-11-methoxy | 170, 220, 242 | −125 (P) | 190 |
| 5-α-Methyl-11-methoxy | 254 | −165 (P) | 178 |
| 5-β-Methyl-11-methoxy | 190–191 | −141 (P) | 178 |
| 6-α-Methyl-11-methoxy | 150, 223 | − 87 | 182 |
| 6-β-Methyl-11-methoxy | 220 | −134 | 182 |
| *Ring E modified deserpidines* | | | |
| dl-17-Desmethoxy | 247–248 | — | 150 |
| 17-Desmethoxy-17-α-cyano-11-methoxy | 297 | −110 | 166 |
| 17-Desmethoxy-17-α-(N-acetyl-N-methylamino-11-methoxy) | 300 | −127 | 166 |
| 17-Desmethoxy-17-ethoxy-11-methoxy | 240–242 | −149 (P) | 178 |
| 17-Desmethoxy-17-isopropoxy-11-methoxy | 248–250 | −125 (P) | 178 |
| 17-Desmethoxy-17-n-propoxy-11-methoxy | 215–217 | −157 (P) | 178 |

* Compounds listed are the *l*-enantiomers, corresponding to the naturally occurring *l*-reserpine, except as noted.
† Rotations are given for chloroform solution except where noted: P = pyridine; E = ethanol.

hypotensive activity is produced by 0·2 mg of reserpine, 3·0 mg of syrosingopine and 30 mg of methoserpidine. The latter does not inhibit convulsions produced experimentally in the rabbit although they are controlled by reserpine[195]. It has been reported that methoserpidine produces a fall in the blood pressure of the anaesthetized cat only when the initial pressure is high[196]. In mice it effects no changes in the catechol amine levels of the brain or heart even at doses of 25 mg/kg intraperitoneally. In contrast, syrosingopine at 5 mg/kg diminishes noradrenaline in the heart, but does not affect the brain level[197]. In rats, methoserpidine has been shown to have a potent hypotensive action without depressing the central nervous system, and to exert a favourable pharmacological action in hypertensive patients[198–200].

Pharmacological data have been reported for some of the other synthetic modifications of reserpine. 10-Chloro- or 6-methylreserpine exert weight depressive action on the genital tract of the male rat and produce pseudo-pregnancy or lactation in the female which is correlated with neuro-depression[201]. 10-Chlorodeserpidine has been studied in psychomotor agitation of the aged[202]. Doses as high as 15 mg daily gave some reduction of agitation and insomnia. dl-10-Fluorodeserpidine is hypotensive in dogs, but in mice exerts only ten per cent of the sedative effect of reserpine[203]. 6-α-Methyl-reserpine is claimed to be more active and 6-ethylreserpine to have longer lasting effect than reserpine itself[189]. It is claimed that separation of the depressive effect from tranquillization has been achieved in 10-chloro-deserpidine[182].

## RING E OXYGEN HETEROCYCLES

### Chemistry

Alkaloids placed in this group include the anhydronium bases, such as alstonine (*XXXV*) and serpentine (*XXXVI*) and their tetrahydroderivatives,

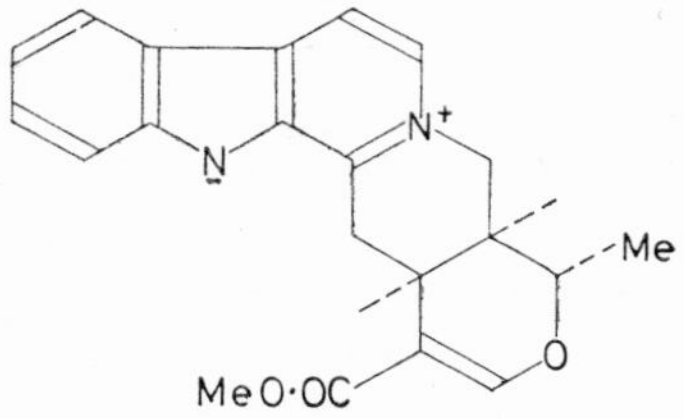

(*XXXV*)    Alstonine

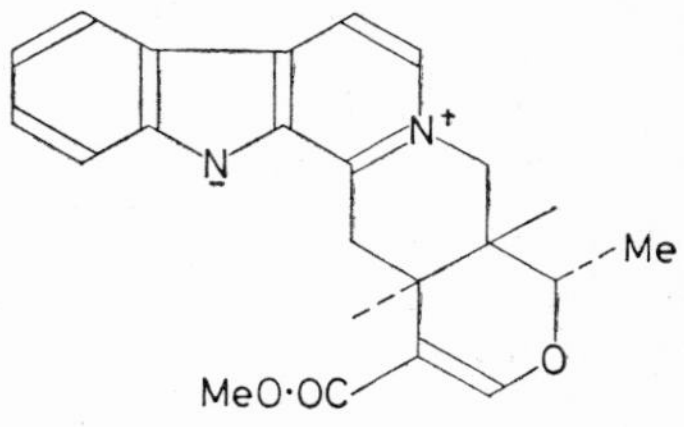

(*XXXVI*)    Serpentine

for example, tetrahydroserpentine or ajmalicine. Early assignments[204,205] of stereoconfiguration of these alkaloids have recently been revised[206], the principal new finding being the allotment of a *trans* D/E ring juncture to the ajmalicine group and a *cis* one to the alstonine compounds. At the same time the $C_{19}$ methyl was shown to have an α-configuration. Chemical evidence was afforded by the following degradation of ajmalicine:

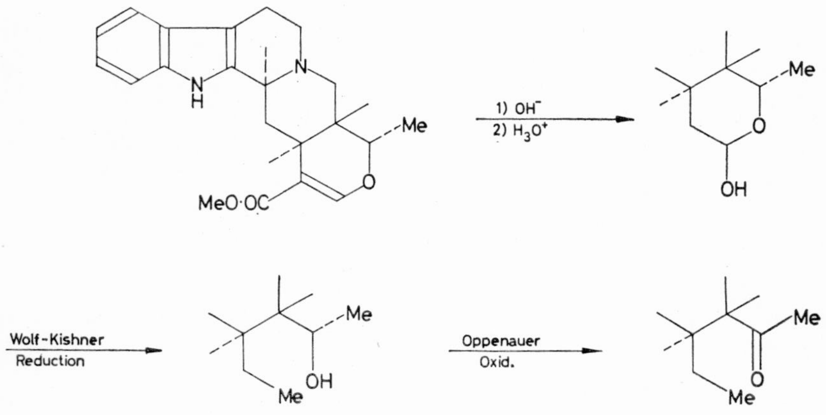

(*XXXVII*)    *trans* – ketone

The stability of the ketone compared with that of the base indicated the *trans* fusion of the D/E rings. Wolf–Kishner reduction of the ketone yielded the *trans*-diethyl derivative of known structure (synthesis) which was also obtainable by treatment of the alcohol with hydrogen bromide followed by catalytic debromination:

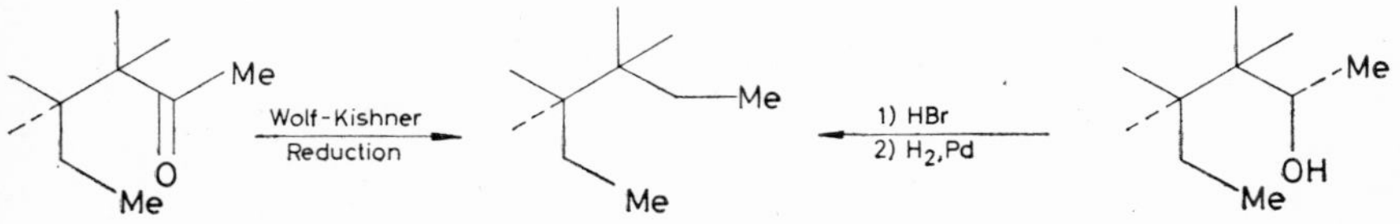

169

Similarly, tetrahydroalstonine yielded the *cis*-diethyl derivative. The intermediate *cis*-ketone derived from tetrahydroalstonine underwent methoxide catalyzed isomerization to yield the same *trans*-ketone (*XXXVII*) as that obtained from ajmalicine. Independent confirmation of the revised structure of ajmalicine has also been afforded by a synthesis of *dl*-ajmalicine[207] which would be expected to yield *trans*-fused D/E rings.

One of the many observations which support these conclusions was based on studies of the rate of formation of alkaloid methiodides[208]. The yohimbine-oxindole conversion supplies additional evidence. As noted previously[23], 7-chloroyohimbine (D/E *trans*) gives 5–10 times as much oxindole as the 7-chloro derivative of methyl reserpate or methyl 3-isoreserpate (both D/E *cis*). 7-Chlorotetrahydroalstonine gives a relatively low yield of oxindole and thus must belong to the D/E *cis* series. Ajmalicine is correctly assigned D/E *trans* since a good yield of oxindole is obtained from its 7-chloro-intermediate. This reaction is also the means to a novel conversion of ajmalicine to mitraphylline (*XXXVIII*)[209].

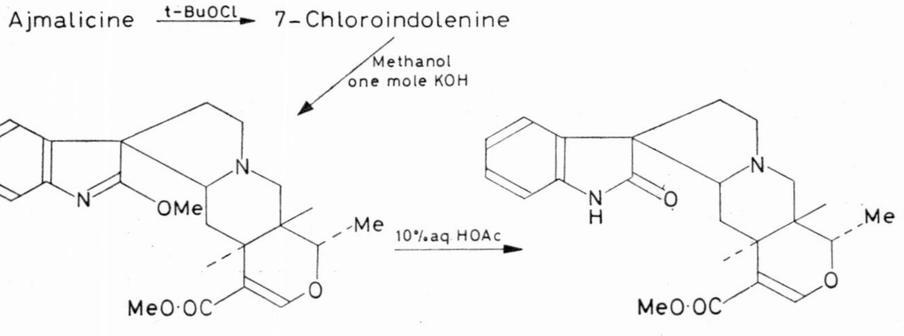

Ajmalicine $\xrightarrow{\text{t-BuOCl}}$ 7-Chloroindolenine

(*XXXVIII*) Mitraphylline

By application of the reaction sequence described for yohimbine on p. 152 (pseudo-indoxyl formation, reduction and treatment with acid) ajmalicine may be converted to an 'invert' derivative (*XXXIX*)[23].

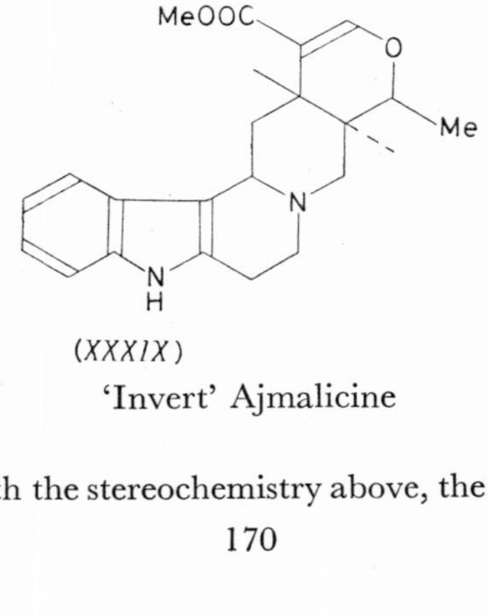

(*XXXIX*)

'Invert' Ajmalicine

In conformance with the stereochemistry above, the other related alkaloids of *Rauwolfia* should be revised as shown below, since these have already been correlated[205] with tetrahydroalstonine[210] and tetrahydroserpentine:

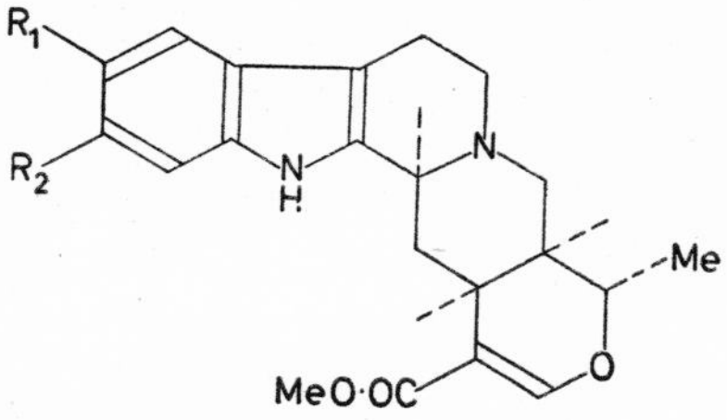

*(XL)*

| Tetrahydroalstonine | $R_1 = R_2 = H$ |
|---|---|
| Aricine | $R_1 = MeO; R_2 = H$ |
| Reserpinine | $R_1 = H; R_2 = MeO$ |
| Isoreserpiline | $R_1 = R_2 = MeO$ |

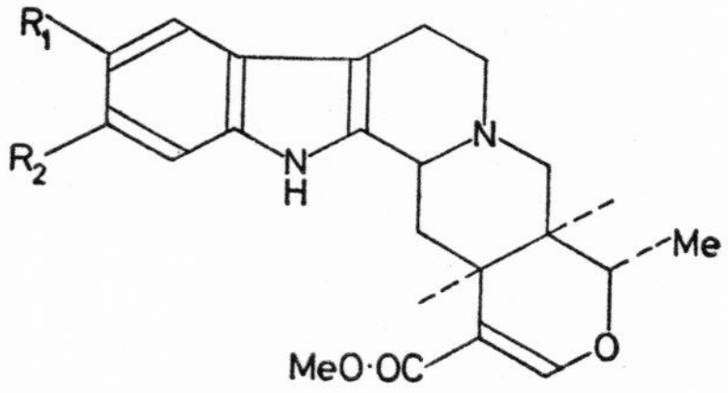

*(XLI)* 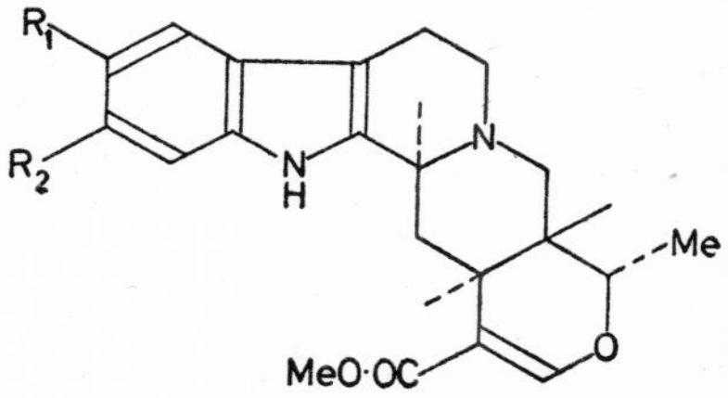      *(XLII)*

| *(XLI)* Isoreserpinine | $R_1 = H; R_2 = MeO$ |
|---|---|
| *(XLI)* Reserpiline | $R_1 = R_2 = MeO$ |
| *(XLII)* Ajmalicine (tetrahydroserpentine) | $R_1 = R_2 = H$ |
| *(XLII)* Raumitorine† | $R_1 = MeO; R_2 = H$ |
| *(XLII)* Tetraphylline | $R_1 = H; R_2 = MeO$ |
| *(XLII)* Rauvanine | $R_1 = R_2 = MeO$ |

Rauvanine is a recently reported alkaloid isolated from *R. vomitoria* and correctly reported as 10,11-dimethoxyajmalicine[211].

Two new *Rauwolfia* alkaloids belonging to this group are raunitidine ($C_{22}H_{26}N_2O_4$) and rauniticine ($C_{21}H_{24}N_2O_3$)[212]* which are isomeric and exhibit ultraviolet absorption identical with reserpinine and ajmalicine respectively. The available data do not permit further definition of the structure of either base. It is interesting that raunitidine undergoes isomerization in refluxing acetic anhydride to yield a new isomer, with strong positive rotation, $[\alpha]_D + 131°$ (pyridine), but with an unchanged ultraviolet spectrum and infrared absorption bands characteristic of the 3α-configuration. However, N.M.R. studies indicate that rauniticine and raunitidine possess 3α-configuration while isoraunitidine is 3β, and all three bear C-19 methyl in the β-configuration[210a].

---

* Raunitidine has been independently isolated from *R. nitida* in the CIBA Laboratories by Dr. P. R. Ulshafer[213].

† Recent studies indicate that the C-19 methyl is in the β-configuration[210a].

The constitution of serpentinine has remained unsettled for a long time. Spectral data and the existence of two $pK_a$ values pointed to the presence of either a double molecule or an unseparated mixture, in spite of homogeneity indicated by paper chromatography or countercurrent distribution. The proposal to represent its structure as 3-hydroxyserpentine[214] cannot be taken seriously. Kaneko[215] has advanced a reasonable bimolecular

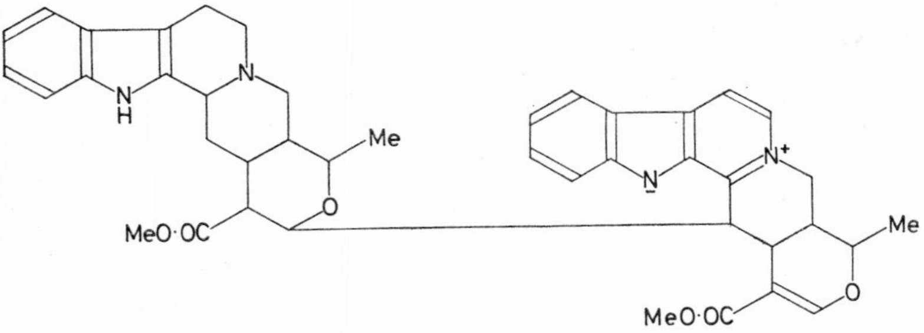

(XLIII)

structure (*XLIII*) for serpentinine, which is supported by both chemical degradation and nuclear magnetic resonance studies.

## Pharmacology

Serpentine has been investigated pharmacologically for a period of years and at one time was thought to be the active principle responsible for the typical activity of *Rauwolfia serpentina*. However, serpentine has been shown to have no hypotensive effect in normal or in hypertensive humans[216]. It exhibits some antifibrillatory action in experimental animals[217,218] but no successful clinical trials have been reported. It is claimed to be five times as active as reserpine in inhibiting cholinesterase in the nervous system and in serum[219]. Serpentine potentiates histamine responses of guinea-pig ileum, uterus, and tracheal chain[220]. It inhibits histaminase *in vitro*.

Alkaline hydrolysis of serpentine to serpentinic acid and re-esterification with various alcohols yielded homologues of serpentine with greater hypotensive activity in animals than serpentine. The isobutyl homologue is the most potent of those prepared. It has relatively low toxicity, and, like serpentine, lacks any sedative activity[153,221].

Little pharmacological information is available concerning the other ring-E heterocyclic indole alkaloids of *Rauwolfia*. 3-Dehydroreserpinine chloride, obtained by oxidation of reserpinine with potassium dichromate in acetic acid, exhibits some antifibrillatory activity against aconitine in the isolated cat heart[222]. Ajmalicine reverses the effect of adrenaline and noradrenaline on the arterial blood pressure of the cat[223]; it reduces the spontaneous activity of mice. In dogs and cats ajmalicine produces loss of certain reflexes arising from the cerebral cortex; hypnotic and anaesthetic effects of barbiturates are potentiated[224]. Ajmalicine has adrenergic blocking effects highly specific for the rabbit uterus and guinea-pig seminal vesicles[225]. Recently ajmalicine (raubasine) in combination with a vitamin preparation has been introduced in Germany[226] under the name Mitavin. It is claimed that the preparation tends to slow the psychic breakdown conditions of middle and old age. Reserpiline reportedly is hypotensive without causing sedation in dogs[227]. Raumitorine produces hypotension in cats and dogs[228], and it is claimed in dogs and rats to have a tranquillizing effect qualitatively like reserpine[229].

## THE AJMALINE GROUP

### Chemistry

Ajmaline (*III*) is the most important representative of the dihydroindole alkaloids and its structure has been known for some time[230]. Much of the structural elucidation was performed by the Robinson group, and the problem of the remaining rings and position of the hydroxy group was solved by Woodward and Schenker[231]. Recently, the deduction of the absolute stereochemistry and a new simple proof of structure led to the detailed picture below[232,233], wherein the numbering system follows the related yohimbine convention:

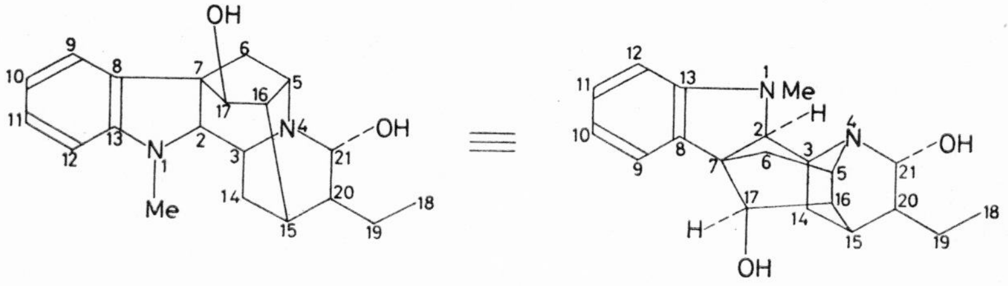

Structures of the type shown on the right above depict with greater clarity the quinuclidine moiety.

The key step in the proof of structure is based on an elimination reaction involving a carbon-carbon bond fission. Deoxyajmaline (*XLIV*) is first oxidized to the indole aldehyde (a sarpagine-like compound, *XLV*) and reduced to deoxyajmalol (*XLVI*). Treatment of its *O*-tosyl derivative (*XLVII*) in refluxing collidine yields a β-carboline (*XLVIII*) which on catalytic hydrogenation gives a *cis*-diethyl derivative (*XLIX*) as the perchlorate, identical in all respects with $N_a$-methyl tetradehydrocorynantheidane perchlorate[234].

By the same series of reactions isoajmaline was converted to a *trans*-diethyl derivative (*L*) identical with the known compound prepared from dihydrocorynantheane.

This degradation established the stereochemistry of all centres except $C_2$, $C_{17}$ and $C_{21}$. The $C_{21}$ hydroxyl would be expected to assume the more stable position (possibly *trans* with respect to the $C_{20}$ ethyl) since the carbinolamine is known to exist at least in part in the open chain amino aldehyde form. The $C_{17}$ hydroxyl in ajmaline is shown in a β-configuration on the basis of the reduction of deoxyajmalone (*LI*) either catalytically or with borohydride to an epimer of deoxyajmaline (*LII*).

The degree of hindrance to rearward attack must be quite severe since

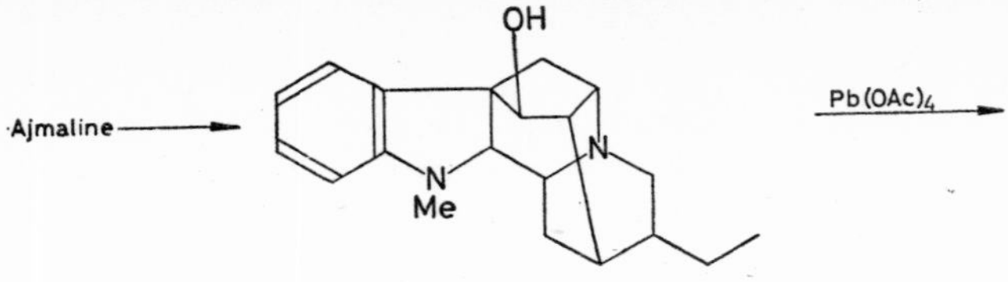

Ajmaline ⟶ $\xrightarrow{\text{Pb(OAc)}_4}$

(XLIV) Deoxyajmaline

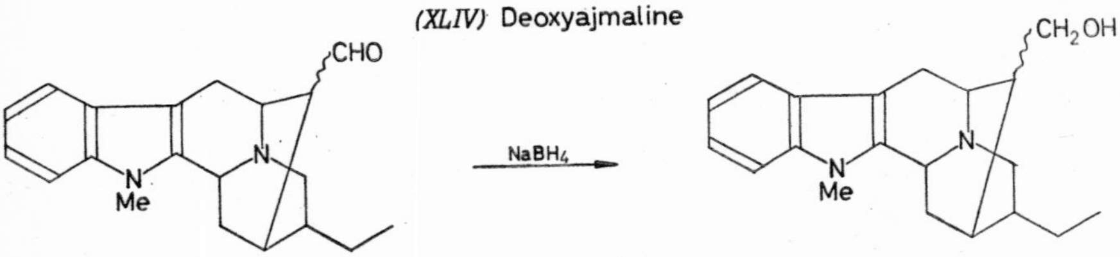

$\xrightarrow{\text{NaBH}_4}$

(XLV)  (XLVI) Deoxyajmalol

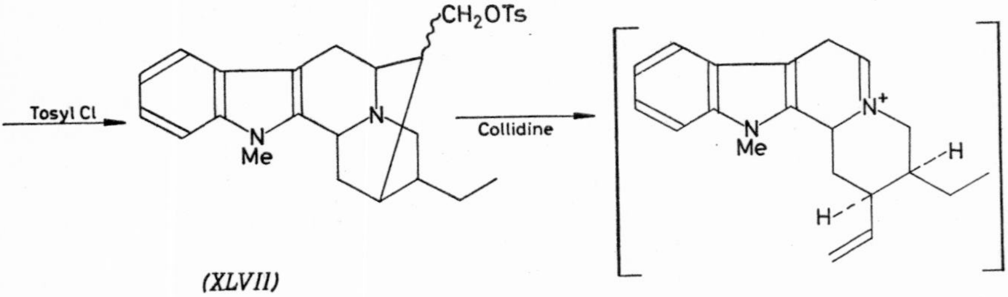

$\xrightarrow{\text{Tosyl Cl}}$ $\xrightarrow{\text{Collidine}}$

(XLVII)

$\xrightarrow{\text{[O]}}$ $\xrightarrow{\text{[H]}}$ $ClO_4^-$

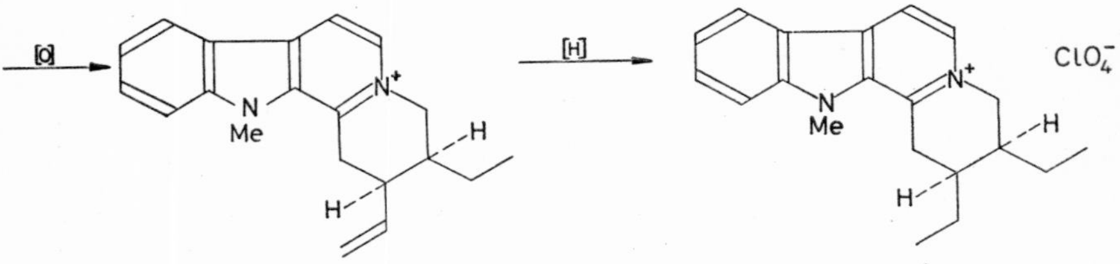

(XLVIII)  (XLIX)  cis – diethyl  derivative

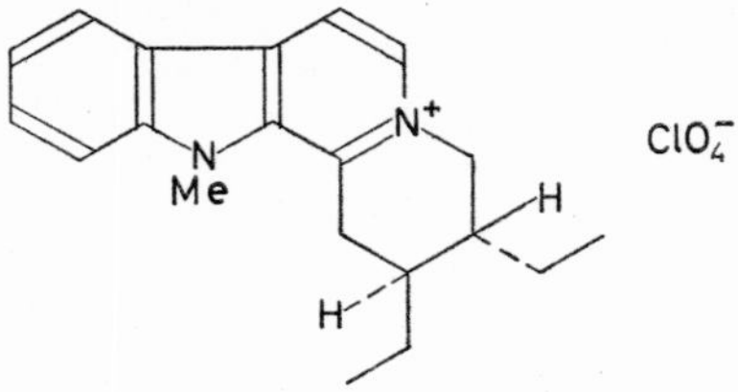

$ClO_4^-$

(L)

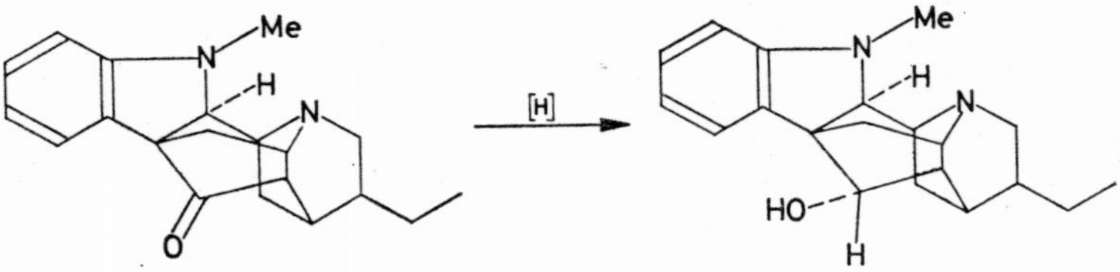

$\xrightarrow{\text{[H]}}$

(LI)  (LII) Epideoxyajmaline

the epimeric alcohol is the only product isolated. Support for this configuration was also afforded by nuclear magnetic resonance spectra of ajmaline derivatives.

That the orientation at $C_2$ is as depicted was proved by oxidation of the acetate ester (*LIII*) of deoxyajmaline with chromic acid[232] or lead tetra-acetate[235] directly to an indolenine (*LIV*) which on catalytic reduction and hydrolysis yielded a hydroxyindoline (*LV*) epimeric with $N_a$-demethyldeoxyajmaline (*LVI*). Methylation with methyl iodide yielded a base (*LVII*) also epimeric with deoxyajmaline:

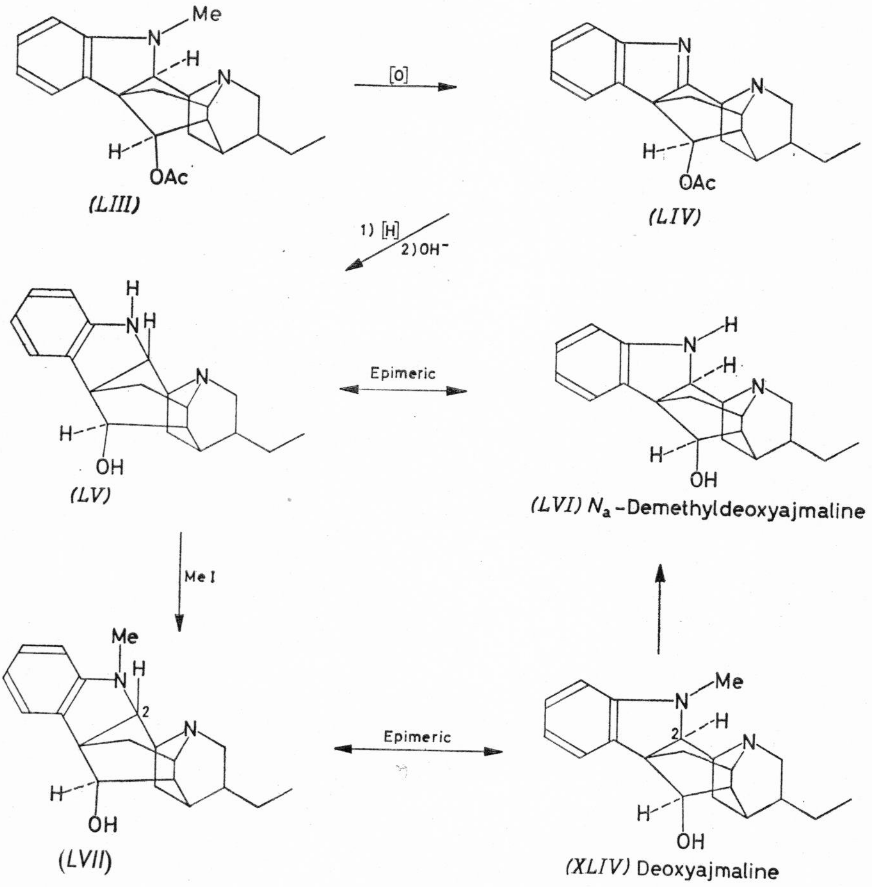

The *O*-acetate of the $N_a$-methylated product above and deoxyajmaline *O*-acetate exhibited rotatory dispersion curves having a mirror image relationship to each other, illustrating graphically the stereochemical change adjacent to the chromophoric moiety. Since hydrogenation of the indolenine to the epimeric indoline should take place 'topside' giving a $\beta$-hydrogen at $C_2$, ajmaline is correctly pictured with an $\alpha$-hydrogen at $C_2$. These conclusions are proved by a comparison of the dissociation constants of deoxyajamaline and its $C_3$ epimer. The proton in the conjugate acid of the former which is bonded to $N_a$ is a stronger base (pK$_a$' 8·44) then the latter (pK$_a$' 7·80).

Isoajmaline (*LVIII*) is a $C_{20}$ epimer of ajmaline. It would also have been

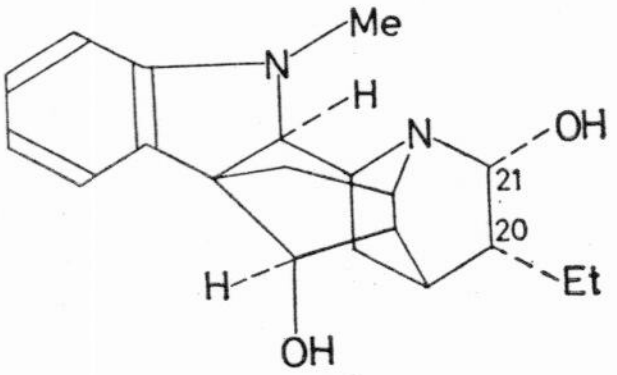

(*LVIII*)

expected here that the neighbouring $C_{21}$ hydroxyl would be *trans* with reference to the $C_{20}$ ethyl, since the alternative structure should result in increase in the steric strain due to an additional 1:2 diaxial interaction. However, nuclear magnetic resonance study of a number of derivatives of ajmaline and isoajmaline indicates that they may be isomeric only at $C_{20}$. Failure of the $C_{21}$ hydroxyl to invert is probably connected with the conformation of the quinuclidine moiety[236]. Recognition that isoajmaline is epimeric at $C_{20}$ with ajmaline may support the possibility that neoajmaline[236a], thought to be an anhydrous form of ajmaline, is actually a $C_{21}$ epimer of ajmaline[236].

It is now possible to write the detailed structures of the known ajmaline congeners. Rauvomitine[237] on hydrolysis gives tetraphyllicine[238] which has been converted to deoxyajmaline[239]. Their stereo structures are shown below:

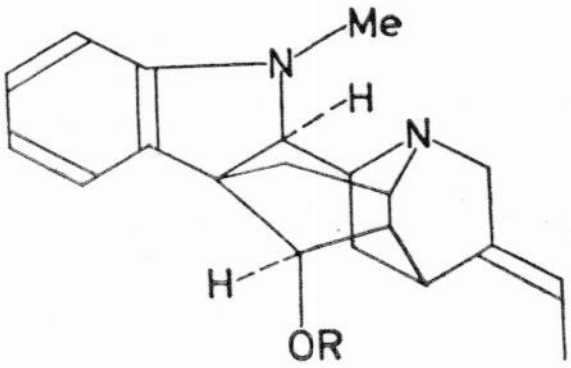

(*LIX*)

Tetraphyllicine   R = H

Rauvomitine   R = —CO— [with trimethoxyphenyl group: OMe, OMe, OMe]

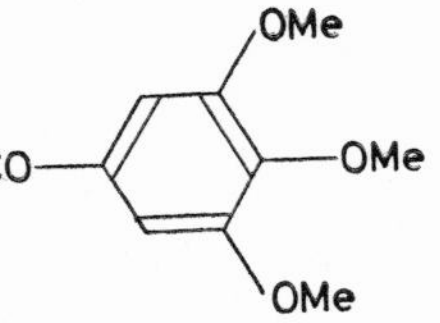

Although no direct comparison has been made, there is little doubt that serpinine[240] is identical with tetraphyllicine. Since ajmalidine[241], vomalidine (11-methoxyajmalidine)[242] and sandwicine have previously been related[243] with ajmaline the detailed structures are:

176

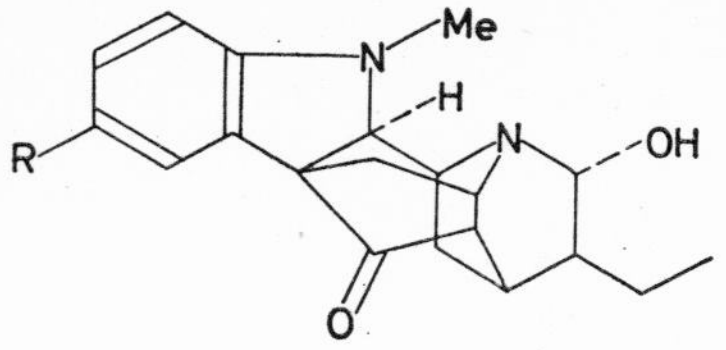

(LX)

Ajmalidine  R = H
Vomalidine  R = Me

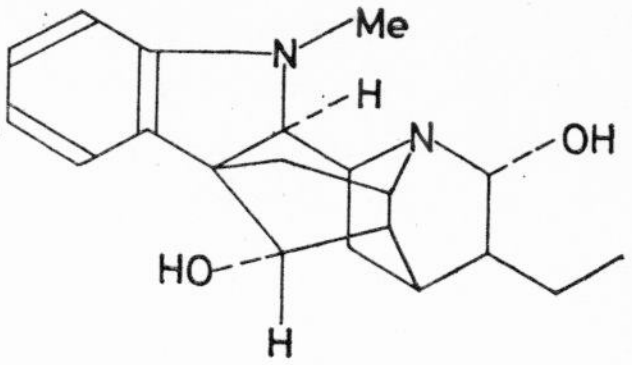

(LXI)

Sandwicine

Mitoridine ($C_{20}H_{22}N_2O_2$) has recently been partially characterized as a tetraphyllicine-like substance[239a].

Mauiensine ($C_{20}H_{26}N_2O$) and sandwicensine ($C_{20}H_{26}N_2O_2$) although not characterized are probably of the ajmaline type[243]. Semperflorine C($C_{21}H_{26}N_2O$), an indoline alkaloid isolated from *Rauwolfia semperflorens*[244] has an infrared spectrum almost identical with tetraphyllicine; however, further data are not available. Seredamine ($C_{22}H_{26}N_2O_2$) is an uncharacterized dihydroindole alkaloid[239a].

Closely related biogenetically to ajmaline is a hydroxyindole alkaloid, sarpagine (*LXII*)[245,246], whose stereochemistry has been determined by chemical degradations linking it to ajmaline[233,247]:

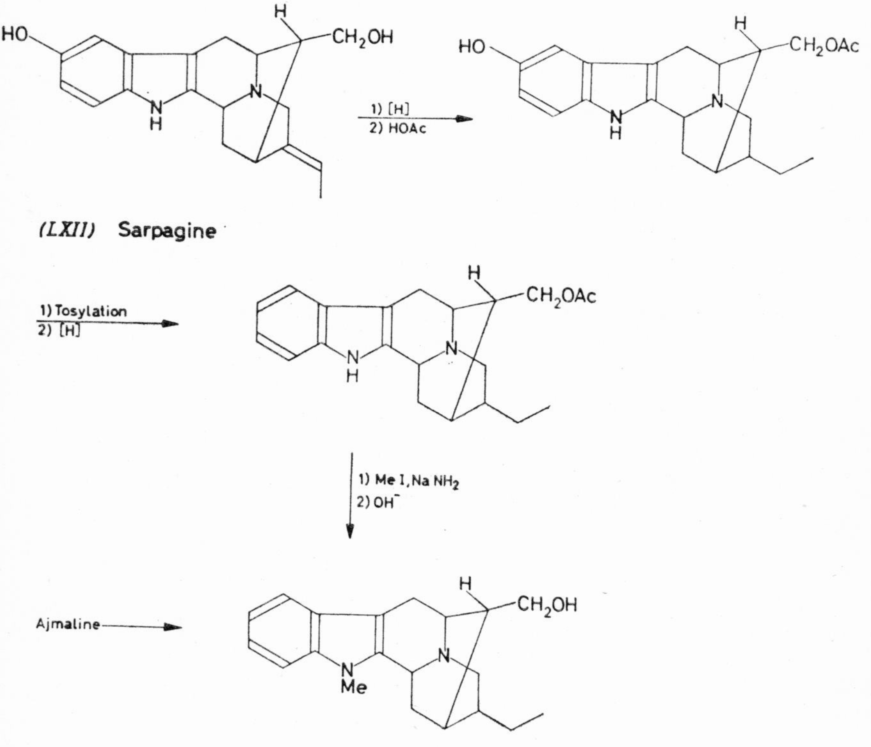

(LXII)  Sarpagine

1) Tosylation
2) [H]

1) Me I, Na NH$_2$
2) OH$^-$

Ajmaline ⟶

Deoxyajmalol B

177

Identity of the degradation product with deoxyajmalol B, establishes the stereochemistry of sarpagine with the exception of the geometry of the ethylidene group which has been solved by X-ray[248]. Recently the carbon skeleton of sarpagine has been determined by mass spectrometry[249] and is in agreement with the chemical degradations.

Neosarpagine ($C_{19}H_{22}N_2O$) is believed to have a desoxysarpagine-like structure[250]. It has been suggested from infrared spectral evidence that it has a vinyl group at $C_{20}$:

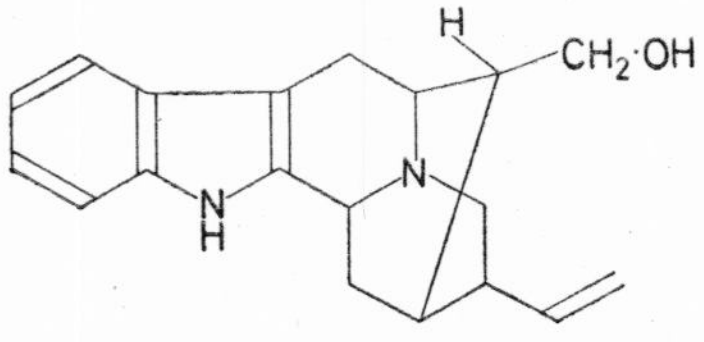

*(LXIII)*

Determination of the structure[251] of perakine[252] represents the first recognition of an indolenine alkaloid from any species of *Rauwolfia*:

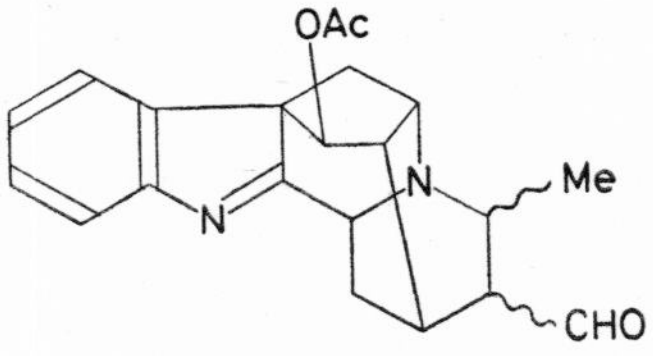

*(LXIV)*

The structure evolved from chemical and spectral data, supported by nuclear magnetic resonance observations. It is interesting that an isomeric indolenine, vomilenine *(LXV)* was isolated from the same species, *Rauwolfia vomitoria*[253], and may be readily converted to perakine by boiling for 10 minutes in 10 per cent acetic acid[254]:

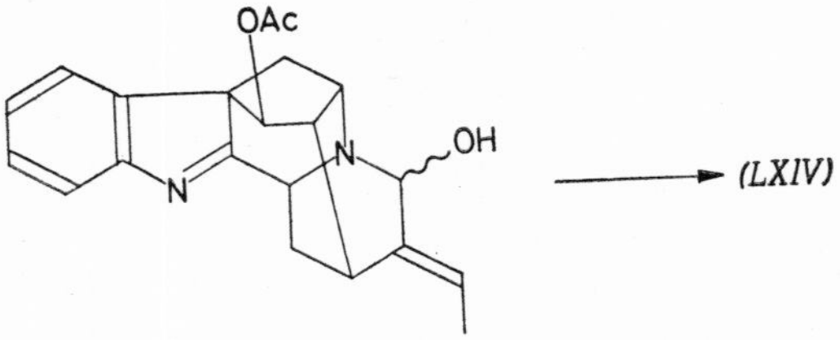

*(LXV)* Vomilenine

Because of this facile conversion, the possibility of formation of perakine as an artifact during extraction and separation of the alkaloids from the plant material cannot be discounted, especially since perakine was obtained from manufacturing mother liquors. None the less, vomilenine and perakine represent the heretofore missing biosynthetic link between indole alkaloids of the corynantheine and sarpagine types, and indoline bases of the ajmaline structure.

Rauwolfinine ($LXVI$, $C_{20}H_{26}N_2O_2$)[255] has been formulated[256] as an unusual cyclic hemiacetal, whose structure has been confirmed by nuclear magnetic resonance studies[257]:

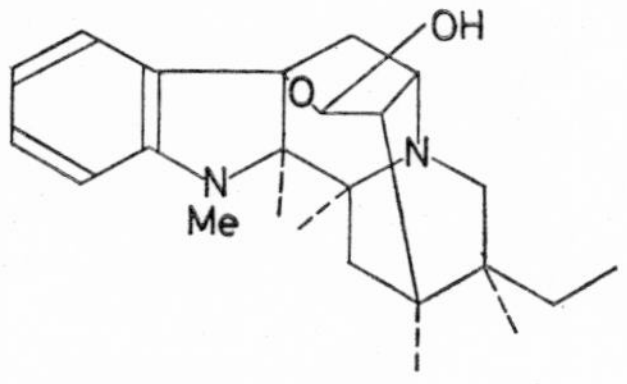

*(LXVI)*   Rauwolfinine

Perlirine $(C_{21}H_{28}N_2O_4)$[252], obscuridine and obscurine[258], although not characterized, probably belong to the group of dihydroindole alkaloids. Raugalline ($C_{21}H_{28}N_2O_3$)[259] is a methanol solvate of ajmaline[259a].

*Pharmacology*

There have been differences of opinion regarding the pharmacology of ajmaline, perhaps partly due to the use of mixtures of ajmaline with other alkaloids in many early biological investigations. There is, however, general agreement that ajmaline does not produce sedation or tranquillization in unanaesthetized animals[6]. Antifibrillatory activity has been attributed to ajmaline[260] and its mode of action has been found to be qualitatively and quantitatively like that of quinidine[261]; comparison of ajmaline and cinchonamine showed slight differences[262]. Recently, isoajmaline has been studied and appears to have greater antifibrillatory activity than ajmaline, at least in the experimental animal[263]. Ajmaline weakens the toxic effect of strophanthin[264] and reduces the hypertensive action of adrenaline and noradrenaline, but not the bradycardial and hypotensive action of acetylcholine[265]. Tetraphyllicine, more recently isolated from *R. vomitoria*, has been shown to have antifibrillatory activity comparable to isoajmaline[266].

There is little available pharmacological information concerning other members of the ajmaline group. One may presume this indicates that they are lacking in practical biological utility. Rauvomitine has no adrenergic blocking, analgetic, or sedative effects[267]. Raugalline is reported to have mild ganglionic, parasympathicolytic and sympathicolytic properties[268].

### UNIDENTIFIED ALKALOIDS

Amsoniaefoline $(C_{25}H_{32}N_2O_5)$[269], raunamine $(C_{23}H_{30}N_2O_4)$[250], chandrine $(C_{25}H_{30}N_2O_8)$[270], and chalchupine B $(C_{15}H_{24}N_6O_{11})$[271] remain as undefined substances obtained from various *Rauwolfia* species. Chandrine is claimed to show marked hypotensive activity without tranquillizing action[272].

*The author wishes to acknowledge with sincere appreciation the many helpful suggestions made by colleagues at CIBA, especially Drs. MacPhillamy, Schlittler and*

179

*Taylor for their help with the chemical section and Dr. Plummer for his assistance with the biological information.*

## REFERENCES

1. MÜLLER, SCHLITTLER and BEIN *Experientia* 1952, **8,** 338
2. MANSKE *The Alkaloids* Vol. VII: Academic Press, New York, 1960
3. SAXTON *Quart. Rev. chem. Soc., Lond.* 1956, **10,** 128
4. HOFMANN *Planta med.* 1957, **5/6,** 145
5. CHATTERJEE, PAKRASHI and WERNER *Fortschritte Der Chemie Organischer Naturstoffe*, Vol. 10: Springer-Verlag, Vienna, 1956
6. WOODSON, YOUNGKEN, SCHLITTLER and SCHNEIDER *Rauwolfia: Botany, Pharmacognosy, Chemistry and Pharmacology* Little, Brown, Boston, 1957
7. "Rauwolfia Alkaloids," in *Research Today* (Ed. Eli Lilly and Co.) Indianapolis, 1958
8. SCHLITTLER, DRUEY and MARXER *Progress in Drug Research* (Ed. Jucker) Vol. 4: Birkhäuser, Basel, in press
9. PAKRASHI *J. Indian chem. Soc.* 1961, **38,** 587
9a. BOIT *Ergebnisse der Alkaloid-chemie Bis 1960*, Akademie-Verlag, Berlin, 1961
10. *Alkaloid-Bearing Plants and Their Contained Alkaloids* Tech. Bull. No. 1234, Agricultural Research Service, U.S. Dept. of Agriculture, Washington, D.C., 1961
11. *Physical Data of Indole and Dihydroindole Alkaloids:* Lilly Research Laboratories, Eli Lilly and Co., Indianapolis, Indiana, Fourth Revised Ed., 1960
12. MATTHIEU and JANOT *Selected Constants* IV. *Optical Rotatory Power of Alkaloids:* Pergamon Press, London, 1961
12a. BHATTACHARJI, DHAR and DHAR *J. sci. industr. Res.* 1962, **21B,** 454
12b. DOY and MOORE *Aust. J. Chem.* 1962, **15,** 548
13. BARGER and SCHOLZ *J. chem. Soc.* 1933, 614
14. PAKRASHI *Ann. Biochem.* 1960, **20,** 77
15. VAN TAMELEN, SHAMMA, BURGSTAHLER, WOLINSKY, TAMM and ALDRICH *J. Amer. chem. Soc.* 1958, **80,** 5006
16. JANOT, GOUTAREL, WARNHOFF and LE HIR *Bull. Soc. chim. Fr.* 1961, 637
17. POISSON, NEUSS, GOUTAREL and JANOT *Bull. Soc. chim. Fr.* 1958, 1195
17a. BHATTACHARJI, DHAR and DHAR *J. sci. industr. Res.* 1956, **15B,** 506; 1957, **16B,** 97
18. RAYMOND-HAMET *C.R. Acad. Sci., Paris* 1953, **237,** 1435
19. BARGER and FIELD *J. chem. Soc.* 1923, 1038
20. DIASSI and DYLION *J. Amer. chem. Soc.* 1958, **80,** 3746
21. KIMOTO, OKAMOTO and KONDO *Chem. pharm. Bull., Tokyo* 1959, **7,** 650
22. WITKOP *Liebigs Ann.* 1943, **554,** 83
23. TAYLOR and FINCH *J. Amer. chem. Soc.* 1962, **84,** 1318, 3871
24. GODTFREDSON and VANGEDAL *Acta chem. scand.* 1956. **10,** 1414
25. CHASE, YONKMAN and YOUNG *Proc. Soc. exp. Biol., N.Y.* 1939, **40,** 308; YONKMAN, STILWELL and JEREMIAS *J. Pharmacol.* 1943, **81,** 111; YONKMAN *J. Lab. clin. Med.* 1944, **29,** 1222
26. GUPTA and DHAWAN *Arch. int. Pharmacodyn.* 1960, **128,** 481
27. *U.S. Patent* 2,975,183; *German Patent* 1,080,562; *Chem. Abstr.* 1961, **55,** 22357
28. SHATZKO and SIM *J. Amer. pharm. Ass.* 1959, **48,** 332
29. KOHLI, BALWANI, RAY and DE *Arch. int. Pharmacodyn.* 1957, **111,** 108
30. LEVY and KOELLE *J. Pharmacol.* 1958, **123,** 278
31. KOHLI, BALWANI and DE *Arch. int. Pharmacodyn.* 1958, **115,** 32
31a. KOHLI, VOHRA, DAS and DE *Arch. int. Pharmacodyn.* 1962, **138,** 105
32. KOHLI, VOHRA and DE *Arch. int. Pharmacodyn.* 1961, **84,** 447
33. PLUMMER—Personal communication

34. FURLENMEIER, LUCAS, MACPHILLAMY, MÜLLER and SCHLITTLER *Experientia* 1953, **9,** 331

35. BURGER *Medicinal Chemistry:* Interscience Publishers, New York, Second Ed. 1960

36. SCHLITTLER and TAYLOR *Experientia* 1960, **16,** 244

37. WOODWARD *J. Amer. chem. Soc.* 1956, **78,** 2023, 2657; WOODWARD, BADER, BICKEL, FREY and KIERSTEAD *Tetrahedron* 1958, **2,** 1

38. ALDRICH *et al. J. Amer. chem. Soc.* 1959, **81,** 2481

39. BAN and YONEMITSU *Chem. & Ind.* 1961, 948

40. MACPHILLAMY, HUEBNER, SCHLITTLER, ST. ANDRÉ and ULSHAFER *J. Amer. chem. Soc.* 1955, **77,** 4335

41. ROSEN and O'CONNER *J. org. Chem.* 1961, **26,** 3051; ROSEN and SHEPPARD *J. Amer. chem. Soc.* 1961, **83,** 4240; ROSEN and SHOOLERY *J. Amer. chem. Soc.* 1961, **83,** 4816

42. ROBISON, LUCAS, MACPHILLAMY, DZIEMIAN, HSU, KIESEL and MORRIS *Abstr. 139th Meeting Amer. chem. Soc.:* March, 1961, p. 3N

43. ULSHAFER, PANDOW and NUGENT *J. org. Chem.* 1956, **21,** 923

43a. SHAMMA and WALKER *Chem. & Ind.* 1962, 1866

44. ULSHAFER, TAYLOR and NUGENT *C.R. Acad. Sci., Paris* 1957, **244,** 2989

45. *British Patent* 824,311; *Chem. Abstr.* 1960, **54,** 6786

46. SCHLITTLER, ULSHAFER, PANDOW, HUNT and DORFMAN *Experientia* 1955, **11,** 64

47. HUEBNER and SCHLITTLER *J. Amer. chem. Soc.* 1957, **79,** 250

48. KLOHS, DRAPER and KELLER *J. Amer. chem. Soc.* 1955, **77,** 2241

49. KLOHS, KELLER, WILLIAMS and KUSSEROW *Chem. & Ind.* 1956, 187

50. MÜLLER *Experientia* 1957, **13,** 479

51. POPELAK, HAACK, LETTENBAUER and SPINGLER *Naturwissenschaften* 1961, **48,** 73

51a. HAACK and POPELAK—Personal communication

52. BEIN *Pharmacol. Rev.* 1956, **8,** 435; BEIN *Experientia* 1953, **9,** 107

53. PLUMMER *Hypertension, Recent Advances*, The Second Hahnemann Symposium on Hypertensive Disease (Ed. Brest and Moyer): Lea and Febriger, Philadelphia, 1961, p. 399; PLUMMER and YONKMAN *Amer. J. Cardiology* 1960, **5,** 642

54. WIEN *Progress in Medicinal Chemistry* (Ed Ellis and West), Volume 1: Butterworths, London, 1961, p. 34

55. SABELLI *Nature, Lond.* 1960, **187,** 784

56. DE SCHAEPDRYVER and PREZIOSI *Arch. int. Pharmacodyn.* 1959, **121,** 177; DE SCHAEPDRYVER *Arch. int. Pharmacodyn.* 1960, **124,** 42

57. VON EULER and LISHAJKO *Science* 1960, **132,** 351

58. MALECKI *Acta physiol. polon.* 1959, **10,** 729

59. TORÜ *Nippon Yakurigaku Zasshi* 1959, **55,** 1227

60. HILLARP *Nature, Lond.* 1960, **187,** 1032

61. HILLARP *Acta physiol. scand.* 1960, **49,** 376

62. BURACK, WEINER and HAGEN *J. Pharmacol.* 1960, **130,** 245

63. VON EULER and LISHAJKO *Science* 1960, **132,** 351

64. CAMANNI, LASANA, MOLINATTA and OLIVETTI *Arch. int. Pharmacodyn.* 1960, **123,** 430

65. CHEN and BOHNER *J. Pharmacol.* 1961, **131,** 179

66. GARATTINI, FRESIA, MORTARI and PALMA *Med. exp.* 1960, **2,** 252

67. AXELROD and TOMCHICK *Nature, Lond.* 1959, **184,** 2027

68. CUSEVA *Terap. Arkh.* 1961, **33,** 16

69. DE SCHAEPARYVER and PIETTE, *Arch. int. Pharmacodyn.* 1961, **130,** 225

70. MATHIES *Med. exp.* 1961, **4,** 12

71. WEIL-MALHERBE and BONE *J. Neurochem.* 1959, **4,** 251

72. BERTLER, HILLARP and ROSENGREN *Acta physiol. scand.* 1961, **52,** 44

73. WEIL-MALHERBE *Proc. Intern. Congr. Biochem. 4th Congr., Vienna*, 1958, **3,** 190 (pub. 1959)

74. BERTLER *Acta physiol. scand.* 1961, **51,** 75

75. BURKHALTER, COHN and CHORE *Biochem. Pharmacol.* 1960, **3,** 328
76. HAVLÍČEK *Activitas Nervosa Superior,* 1960, **2,** 381
77. DE LA LANDE, PARKS, SANDISON, SKINNER and WHELAN *Aust. J. exp. Biol. med. Sci.* 1960, **38,** 313
78. ASHWIN and JACQUES *Thromb. et Diath. Haemorrhag.* 1961, **5,** 543
79. PARKES *Progress in Medicinal Chemistry* (Ed. Ellis and West), Volume 1: Butterworths, London, 1961, p. 72
80. COSTA and PSCHEIDT *Proc. Soc. exp. Biol., N.Y.* 1961, **106,** 693
81. BOISSIER, TARDY and DIVERRES *Med. exp.* 1960, **3,** 81
82. BOISSIER and PAGNY *Thérapie* 1959, **14,** 324
83. BRODIE, SINGER, ORLANS, QUINN and SULSER *J. Pharmacol.* 1960, **129,** 250; SHORE, CARLSSON, BRODIE *Fed. Proc.* 1956, **15,** 483
84. GARATTINI *Schweiz. Arch. Neurol. Psychiat.* 1959, **84,** 269
85. BRODIE *Dis. nerv. Syst.* 1960, **21,** 107; SULSER and BRODIE *Science* 1960, **131,** 1440
86. ORLANS and BRODIE *Nature, Lond.* 1960, **187,** 1034
87. PLETSCHER, SHORE and BRODIE *Science* 1955, **122,** 374
88. CARLSSON, ROSENGREN, BERTLER and NILSSON *Psychotropic Drugs:* Elsevier, Amsterdam, 1957, p. 363
89. GAL, DREWES and BARRACLOUGH *Abstr. Papers, First Int. Pharmacol. Meet.* Stockholm *Biochem. Pharmacol.* 1961, **8,** 32
90. CARLSSON, LINDQUIST and MAGNUSON *Nature, Lond.* 1957, **180,** 1200
91. WESTERMANN, MAICKEL and BRODIE *Arch. exp. Path. Pharmak.* 1961, **241,** 189
92. KHAZAN and SULMAN *Proc. Soc. exp. Biol., N.Y.* 1961, **107,** 282
93. Editorial *Med. Trib.* 1962, **3,** 25
94. BRUNE and HIMWICH *Science* 1961, **133,** 190
95. KNOLL and KNOLL *Arch. int. Pharmacodyn.* 1961, **133,** 310
96. BURTON, SALVADOR, GOLDIN and HUMPHREYS *Arch. int. Pharmacodyn.* 1960, **128,** 253
97. KNOLL *Arch. exp. Path. Pharmak.* 1960, **238,** 114
98. BALZER, HOLTZ and PALM *Experientia* 1961, **17,** 38
99. STERN and MITROVIC-KOCIC *Arch. exp. Path. Pharmak.* 1960, **238,** 57
100. STERN and LEKOVIC *Acta pharm., jugosl.* 1961, **11,** 11
101. SCHNEIDER *Proc. Soc. exp. Biol., N.Y.* 1954, **87,** 614; SIGG, CAPRIO and SCHNEIDER *Proc. Soc. exp. Biol., N.Y.* 1958, **97,** 97; WITKIN, MAGGIO and BARRETT *Proc. Soc. exp. Biol., N.Y.* 1959, **101,** 377
102. KIT and KULCHITSKAYA *Farmakol. i. Toksikol.* 1960, **23,** 475
103. ITO *Folia pharm. jap.* 1960, **56,** 377
104. BLOZOVSKI and SIVADJIAN *Arch. int. Pharmacodyn.* 1959, **123,** 58
105. GABE, TUCHMANN-DUPLESSIS and MERCIER-PAROT *C.R. Acad. Sci., Paris* 1961, **252,** 1857
106. GAITONDE, SATOSKAR and MANDREKAR *Arch. int. Pharmacodyn.* 1960, **127,** 118
107. NICOLOFF, STONE, LEONARD, DOBERNECK and WANGENSTEEN *Proc. Soc. exp. Biol., N.Y.* 1961, **106,** 877
108. LEUSEN and LACROIX *Arch. int. Pharmacodyn.* 1959, **121,** 114
109. LEONARD, GRIFFIN and WANGENSTEEN *Proc. Soc. exp. Biol., N.Y.* 1960, **103,** 190
110. ASHWIN *Proc. Soc. exp. Biol., N.Y.* 1960, **104,** 188
111. BLACKMAN, CAMPION and FASTIER *Proc. Univ. Ottago med. Sch.* 1958, **36,** 1
112. KRUGER, ROBISON and SCHUELER *Arch. int. Pharmacodyn.* 1960, **129,** 125; DRUGER, STANDEFFER and SCHUELER *Arch. int. Pharmacodyn.* 1960, **129,** 395
113. JOHNSON and SELLERS *Canad. J. Biochem. and Physiol.* 1961, **39,** 279
114. SCHWEMMLE and HEIM *Med. exp.* 1959, **1,** 351
115. MIETKIEWSKI and JANKOWSKA *Wien. klin. Wschr.* 1960, **72,** 642
116. BOSE and VIJAYVARGIRJA *Arch. int. Pharmacodyn.* 1960, **127,** 27
117. KIRPEKAR and LEWIS *Anaesthesia* 1960, **15,** 175

118. West, Baird, Steward and Pradhan *J. Pharmacol.* 1961, **131**, 171
119. Premachandra and Turner *Proc. Soc. exp. Biol., N.Y.* 1960, **104**, 306
120. Soulairac and Soulairac *C.R. Soc. Biol., Paris* 1960, **154**, 510
121. Salvador, Humphreys, Burton and Goldin *Nature, Lond.* 1961, **190**, 723
122. Schneeberger and Schürch *Mitt. Lebensm. Hyg., Bern* 1959, **50**, 523
123. Romano, Romano and Biggi *Arch. E. Maragliano* 1960, **16**, 745
124. Moon and Turner *Proc. Soc. exp. Biol., N.Y.* 1959, **102**, 134
125. Mascitelli-Coriandoli *Experientia* 1960, **16**, 546
126. Erikson, Reynolds and De Feo *Endocrinology* 1960, **66**, 824
127. Dischler *Naturwissenschaften* 1960, **47**, 401
128. Khazan, Sulman and Winnik *Proc. Soc. exp. Biol., N.Y.* 1960, **105**, 201
129. Khazan *Harokeach Haivri* 1961, **8**, 312
130. Mayer, Meunier and Thevenot-Duluc *Ann. endocr., Paris* 1960, **21**, 1
131. Gaunt, Renzi, Antonchak, Miller and Gilman *Ann. N.Y. Acad. Sci.* 1954, **59**, 22
132. Sawyer *Anat. Rec.* 1957, **127**, 362; Meites *Proc. Soc. exp. Biol., N.Y.* 1957, **96**, 728
133. Benson *Proc. Soc. exp. Biol., N.Y.* 1960, **103**, 132
134. Czyba, Becache and Arnaud *C.R. Soc. Biol., Paris* 1960, **154**, 2312
135. Soulairac and Soulairac *Pr. méd.* 1961, **69**, 1560
136. Soulairac and Soulairac *C.R. Soc. Biol., Paris* 1961, **155**, 1010
137. Hunt, Carrivault and Bourbeau *Arch. int. physiol. et biochem.* 1960, **68**, 577
138. Zieleniewski *Endokrynol., Polska* 1959, **10**, 43
139. Schneider, Plummer, Earl, Barrett, Rinehart and Dibble *J. Pharmacol.* 1955, **114**, 10
140. Cronheim and Toekes *J. Pharmacol.* 1955, **113**, 13; 1957, **119**, 357
141. Rothman, Toekes, Cawthorne and Bitterman *Proc. Soc. exp. Biol., N.Y.* 1957, **95**, 789
142. Tuchmann-Duplessis and Mercier-Parot *C.R. Soc. Biol., Paris* 1958, **152**, 29
143. Tuchmann-Duplessis and Mercier-Parot *Ann. endocr., Paris* 1959, **19**, 1143
144. Paasonen and Krayer *Experientia* 1959, **15**, 75
145. Kärki and Paasonen *Nature, Lond.* 1960, **185**, 109
146. Paasonen and Dews *Brit. J. Pharmacol.* 1958, **13**, 84
147. Innes, Krayer and Waud *J. Pharmacol.* 1958, **124**, 324
148. Pakrashi *Ann. Vol. Physiol. and Exptl. Med. Sc. India* 1958-59, **2**, 97
149. Pakrashi *Ann. Biochem.* 1960, **20**, 77
150. Weisenborn *J. Amer. chem. Soc.* 1957, **79**, 4819
151. Huebner *J. Amer. chem. Soc.* 1954, **76**, 5792
152. Buzas and Regnier *C.R. Acad. Sci., Paris* 1960, **250**, 1340
153. Garattini, Lamesta, Mortari and Valzelli *J. Pharm., Lond.* 1961, **13**, 548
154. *Swiss Patent* 346,552; *Chem. Abstr.* 1961, **55**, 602
155. Lucas, Kiesel and Ceglowski *J. Amer. chem. Soc.* 1960, **82**, 493
156. Lucas, Kuehne, Ceglowski, Dziemian and MacPhillamy *J. Amer. chem. Soc.* 1959, **81**, 1928
157. Barbour, Irwin, Yamahiro, Frasher and Maronde *Amer. J. Cardiol.* 1959, **3**, 220
158. Brodie, Spector and Shore *Pharmacol. Rev.* 1959, **11**, 548; Orlans, Finger and Brodie *J. Pharmacol.* 1960, **128**, 131
159. Garattini, Kato and Valzelli *Experientia* 1960, **16**, 120
160. Blackman, Campion and Fastier *Brit. J. Pharmacol.* 1959, **14**, 112
161. Jori and Leonardi *Atti Soc. lombarda Sci. med. biol.* 1959, **14**, 274
162. Lamesta, Valsecchi and Valzelli *Boll. Soc. ital. Biol. sper.* 1960, **36**, 683
163. Miller and Uhr *Toxicol. Appl. Pharmacol.* 1959, **1**, 534
164. Tuchmann-Duplessis and Mercier-Parot *C.R. Acad. Sci., Paris* 1960, **251**, 800
165. Schmitt and Schmitt *C.R. Soc. Biol., Paris* 1960, **154**, 55

166. MULLER and ALLAIS *Naturwissenschaften* 1960, **47,** 82
167. ERNEST and PROTIVA *Naturwissenschaften* 1960, **47,** 156
168. *U.S. Patent* 2,933,500; *Chem. Abstr.* 1960, **54,** 18577
169. BARRETT, RUTLEDGE and PLUMMER *The Pharmacologist* 1960, **2,** 2
170. FURNESS and PLUMMER *Fed. Proc.* 1961, **20,** 394
171. GAUNT, RENZI and CHART *Endocrinology* 1962, **71,** 527
172. NEEMAN, CASERIO, ROBERTS and JOHNSON *Tetrahedron* 1959, **6,** 36
173. ROBISON, LUCAS, MACPHILLAMY, DZIEMIAN, HSU and KIESEL *J. Amer. chem. Soc.* 1961, **83,** 2694
174. BARRETT and PLUMMER—Personal communication
175. CUENCA, COSTA, KUNTZMAN and BRODIE *Med. exp.* 1961, **5,** 20
175a. ROBISON, PIERSON, LUCAS, HSU and DZIEMIAN—In the press
176. VELLUZ, MULLER, JOLY, NOMINÉ, MATHIEU, ALLAIS, WARNANT, VALLS, BUCOURT and JOLLY *Bull. Soc. chim. Fr.* 1958, 673
177. ULSHAFER, NUGENT and DORFMAN *Chem & Ind.* 1962, 1863
178. *Union of South Africa Patent* 1248/58
179. *French Patent* 1,238,756; *Chem. Abstr.* 1961, **55,** 24807
180. *U.S. Patent* 2,912,436; *Chem. Abstr.* 1960, **54,** 4652
181. *French Patent* 1,214,119; *Chem. Abstr.* 1961, **55,** 10489
182. VELLUZ *Ann. pharmacol. franç.* 1959, **17,** 15
183. *French Patent* 1,202,121; *Chem. Abstr.* 1961, **55,** 9451
184. PROTIVA, RAJSNER and JILEK *Mh. Chem.* 1960, **91,** 703
185. NOVÁK and PROTIVA *Naturwissenschaften* 1959, **46,** 579
186. *French Patent* 1,194,842; *Chem. Abstr.* 1962, **56,** 1491
187. *Czechoslovak Patent* 98,829; *Chem. Abstr.* 1962, **56,** 514
188. *French Patent* 1,214,122; *Chem. Abstr.* 1961, **55,** 9452
189. VELLUZ, MÜLLER and ALLAIS *C.R. Acad. Sci., Paris* 1958, **247,** 1746
190. *French Patent* 1,238,738; *Chem. Abstr.* 1961, **55,** 23575
191. PETERFALVI and JEQUIER *Arch. int. Pharmacodyn.* 1960, **124,** 237
192. VELLUZ, PETERFALVI and JEQUIER *C.R. Acad. Sci., Paris* 1958, **247,** 1905
193. READ *Med. J. Australia* 1961, **1,** 245
194. PLUMMER—Personal communication
195. REUSE and LA BARRE *C.R. Acad. Sci., Paris* 1960, **154,** 471
196. MIR and LEWIS *J. Pharm., Lond.* 1960, **12,** 677
197. LEROY and DE SCHAEPDRYVER *Arch. int. Pharmacodyn* 1961, **130,** 231
198. HOLT *Brit. med. J.* 1961, **2,** 415
199. CARP *Brit. med. J.* 1961, **2,** 584
200. MIGNAULT *Un méd. Can.* 1961, **90,** 598
201. FEYEL-CABANES *C.R Acad. Sci., Paris* 1961, **252,** 1860
202. CUNY, GEURCI and PETITIER *Pr. méd.* 1961, **69,** 1096
203. NOVÁK and PROTIVA, *Coll. Trav. chim. Tchécosl.* 1961, **26,** 681
204. WENKERT and ROYCHAUDHURI *J. Amer. chem. Soc.* 1957, **79,** 1519
205. NEUSS and BOAZ *J. org. Chem.* 1957, **22,** 1001
206. WENKERT, WICKBERG and LEICHT *J. Amer. chem. Soc.* 1961, **83,** 5037
207. VAN TAMELEN and PLACEWAY *J. Amer. chem. Soc.* 1961, **83,** 2594
208. SHAMMA and MOSS *J. Amer. chem. Soc.* 1961, **83,** 5038
209. FINCH and TAYLOR *J. Amer. chem. Soc.* 1962, **84,** 3871
210. PAKRASHI, DJERASSI, WASICKY and NEUSS *J. Amer. chem. Soc.* 1955, **77,** 6687
210a. SHAMMA and MOSS *J. Amer. chem. Soc.* 1962, **84,** 1739
211. GOUTAREL, GUT and PARELLO *C.R. Acad. Sci., Paris* 1961, **253,** 2589
212. SALKIN, HOSANSKY and JARET *J. pharm. Sci.* 1961, **50,** 1038
213. ULSHAFER—Personal communication
214. CHATTERJEE and BOSE *Sci. & Cult.* 1959, **25,** 84
215. KANEKO *J. pharm. Soc. Japan* 1960, **80,** 1357; *Chem. Abstr.* 1961, **55,** 6511

216. BACHMANN *Arzneimittel Forsch.* 1960, **10,** 813
217. DEININGER *Pakistan J. sci. Industr. Research* 1959, **2,** 114
218. MADAN and SHARMA *Arch. int. Pharmacodyn.* 1959, **122,** 323
219. VINCENT, SEGONZAC and MATHA *C.R. Acad. Sci., Paris* 1956, **150,** 1462; VINCENT and SEGONZAC *Pathol. et biol. Semaine hôp* 1958, **6,** 59
220. SACHDEV, AIMAN and RAJAPURKAR *Brit. J. Pharmacol.* 1961, **16,** 146
221. PROOSDIJ-HARTZEMA, AKKERMAN and DE JONGH *Arch. int. Pharmacodyn.* 1959, **123,** 168
222. PLUMMER—Personal communication
223. SCHMITT and GONARD *Thérapie* 1957, **12,** 274
224. SCHMITT and SCHMITT *Thérapie* 1958, **13,** 246
225. KRONEBERG *Arch. exp. Path. Pharmak.* 1958, **233,** 72
226. BETZIEN *Medica Boehringer* Overseas Edn., Feb., 1961
227. LA BARRE and GILLO *C.R. Acad. Sci., Paris* 1958, **533,** 530
228. LA BARRE and HANS *C.R. Soc. Biol., Paris* 1958, **152,** 1269
229. LA BARRE and DESMAREZ *C.R. Soc. Biol., Paris* 1958, **152,** 1272
230. ROBINSON *Angew. Chem.* 1957, **69,** 40
231. WOODWARD and SCHENKER *Angew. Chem.* 1956, **68,** 131
232. BARTLETT, SCHLITTLER, SKLAR, TAYLOR, AMAI and WENKERT *J. Amer. chem. Soc.* 1960, **82,** 3792
233. BARTLETT, SKLAR, TAYLOR, SCHLITTLER, AMAI, BEAK, BRINGI and WENKERT *J. Amer. chem. Soc.* 1962, **84,** 622
234. VAN TAMELEN, ALDRICH and KATZ *J. Amer. chem. Soc.* 1957, **79,** 6426
235. BARTLETT, SKLAR and TAYLOR (To be published).
236. BARTLETT and TAYLOR—Personal communication
236a. SIDDIQUI *J. Indian chem. Soc.* 1939, **16,** 421
237. HAAK, POPELAK and SPINGLER *Naturwissenschaften* 1955, **42,** 627; POISSON, GOUTAREL and JANOT *C.R. Acad. Sci., Paris* 1955, **241,** 1840
238. DJERASSI and FISHMAN *Chem. & Ind.* 1955, 627; DJERASSI, GORMAN, PAKRASHI and WOODWARD *J. Amer. chem. Soc.* 1956, **78,** 1259
239. DJERASSI, FISHMAN, GORMAN, KUTNEY and PAKRASHI *J. Amer. chem. Soc.* 1957, **79,** 1217
239a. POISSON *Thesis*, School of Pharmacy, Paris, 1959
240. BOSE *J. Indian chem. Soc.* 1956, **33,** 374
241. PAKRASHI, DJERASSI, WASICKY and NEUSS *J. Amer. chem. Soc.* 1955, **77,** 6687
242. HOFMANN and FREY *Helv. chim. acta* 1957, **40,** 1866
243. GORMAN, NEUSS, DJERASSI, KUTNEY and SCHEUER *Tetrahedron* 1957, **1,** 328
244. SCHLITTLER and FURLENMEIER *Helv. chim. acta* 1953, **36,** 996
245. STAUFFACHER, HOFMANN and SEEBECK *Helv. chim. acta* 1957, **40,** 508
246. TALAPATRA and CHATTERJEE *Sci. & Cult.* 1957, **22,** 692
247. BARTLETT, SKLAR and TAYLOR *J. Amer. chem. Soc.* 1960, **82,** 3790
248. SILVERS and TULINSKY *Tetrahedron Letters* 1962
249. BIEMANN *Tetrahedron Letters* 1960, 9; BIEMANN *J. Amer. chem. Soc.* 1961, **83,** 4801
250. PILLAY, RAO and RAO *J. sci. industr. Res.* 1960, **19B,** 135
251. ULSHAFER, BARTLETT, DORFMAN, GILLEN, SCHLITTLER and WENKERT *Tetrahedron Letters* 1961, 363
252. KIANG and WAN *J. chem. Soc.* 1960, 1394
253. HOFMANN and FREY *Helv. chim. acta* 1957, **40,** 1866
254. TAYLOR, FREY and HOFMANN *Helv. chim. acta* 1962, **45,** 611
255. CHATTERJEE and BOSE *Sci. & Cult.* 1951, **17,** 139
256. BOSE *J. Indian chem. Soc.* 1958, **35,** 72
257. CHATTERJEE and BOSE *J. Indian chem. Soc.* 1961, **38,** 403
258. ROLAND *J. Pharm. Belg.* 1959, **14,** 347
259. LE GALL *Ann. pharm. franç.* 1960, **18,** 817

259a. Taylor—Personal communication
260. Göing and Kempe *Arch. int. Pharmacodyn.* 1956, **107**, 255
261. Kuschinsky and Reuter *Arch. exp. Path. Pharmak.* 1961, **242**, 17; Reuter *Arch. Path. Pharmak.* 1961, **241**, 530
262. Dick and McCawley *Clinical Research* 1962, **10**, 100
263. Barrett and Plummer—Personal communication
264. Gendenštejn and Chadžaj *Farmakol. i toksikol.*, Moscow 1961, **24**, 49
265. Schmitt and Schmitt *Arch. int. Pharmacodyn.* 1960, **127**, 163
266. Dickel, Barrett and Plummer—Personal communication
267. Kroneberg *Naturwissenschaften* 1955, **42**, 627
268. Quevauviller, Blanpin and Garot-Pottier *Pr. méd.* 1961, **69**, 2161; *Ann. pharm. franç.* 1962, **20**, 19
269. Gomez *J. Philipp. pharm. Ass.* 1957, **44**, 101
270. Rakshit *Indian Pharm.* 1954, **9**, 226; 1954, **10**, 84
271. Deger *Arch. Pharm., Berl.* 1935, **275**, 496
272. Reynolds, Presutti and MacLeod *Can. J. Biochem. & Physiol.* 1960, **38**, 889

# 5

# STATISTICS AS APPLIED TO PHARMACOLOGICAL AND TOXICOLOGICAL SCREENING

G. A. Stewart and P. A. Young

## INTRODUCTION

THE day seems far off when the actions and interactions of chemical compounds on biological systems may be predicted from their chemical structures. Although there are instances where closely related members of a chemical series exhibit a similar action, in general such examples are rare. Thus, although ganglion blocking activity was found in methonium compounds with the general formula:

$$Me_3\overset{+}{N}\cdot(CH_2)_n\cdot\overset{+}{N}Me_3$$

reaching a peak in hexamethonium (n = 6)[1], similar ganglion blockade was subsequently obtained with mecamylamine[2], a compound whose structure

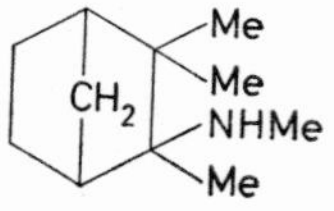

has little in common with the methonium series. Frequently even when an active series has been developed some members may possess markedly different types of action from others. Thus while hexamethonium has an important ganglion blocking action, the higher members of the series, particularly decamethonium, show principally a neuromuscular blocking action. Therefore it is necessary to resort to direct experimentation to determine whether or not each chemical compound possesses a particular activity. Since it is rare for drugs to display only one type of action, the testing procedure must ensure that any compounds selected with the desirable effect, do not possess to a greater degree other less desirable properties. At its simplest, the problem is to ensure that the action sought is elicited by doses below those producing death in the experimental species. On the assumption that the desired effect is most likely to be detected following the administration of the maximum tolerated dose (not necessarily true in all cases), Schneiderman[3] described a combined toxicity-therapeutic trial regime for the screening of compounds for some anti-tumour actions. Treatment with a compound of groups of 6 tumour-infected mice is commenced at a dose level of 500 mg/kg, regarded as about the maximum dose that may be given (*i.e.* 10 mg to a 20 g mouse). If more than two animals in the group are killed by the compound, a new experiment is started at a dose level proportionately lower than the previous one according to the schedule:

If 3/6 die, give 0·7 times previous dose
„ 4/6 „ „ 0·6 „ „ „
„ 5/6 „ „ 0·5 „ „ „
„ 6/6 „ slowly, give 0·25 times previous dose
„ 6/6 „ rapidly, give 0·20 times „ „

While the choice of appropriate dose levels confronts all experimenters, the combined toxicity-therapeutic trial is only appropriate in limited circumstances. In most screening programmes the toxicity test is a single item in a battery of pharmacological testing procedures. The problem remains of deciding whether an apparent response to drug treatment constitutes evidence of a desirable effect due to the drug, or whether it is within the expected limits of error of the response measurement. Since screening tests are usually carried out in uniform sized groups of animals, or in uniform *in vitro* preparations, Mantel (*cit* Schneiderman[3]) proposed an approach on the lines of a quality control chart (*Figure 5.1*). If in the test situation the biological

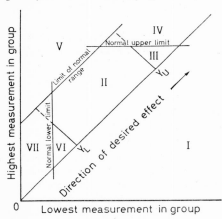

*Figure 5.1.* Control chart for use in the screening of substances for pharmacological activity (after Schneiderman[3]). For explanation of areas I–VII see text.

variable is measured so that the desired effect is an increase in such a measurement, then the chart is entered by plotting a point having as its co-ordinates the highest and lowest measurements within the treatment group under consideration. The area in which this point is located determines the interpretation to be placed on the result. The chart is formed from the following lines:

(*a*) the diagonal through the origin
(*b*) a line parallel to the diagonal at a distance from it corresponding to the limit of the normal range
(*c*) lines at right angles to the diagonal through $Y_L$ and $Y_U$, indicating the lower and upper expected mean values for the highest and lowest measurements within groups

(*d*) the vertical line at the abscissal value for the lower limits of the normal range

(*e*) the horizontal line at the ordinate value for the upper limit of the normal range.

With these definitions the significance by areas is as follows:

    I. error of plotting
    II. point within normal bounds
    III. possibility of positive effect as upper mean is exceeded, investigate further
    IV. more likely positive effect as both values exceed normal limit, investigate further
    V. normal range exceeded, experimental conditions possibly at fault, investigate
VI and VII. possible negative effect, or failure in technique, investigate.

This scheme essentially requires that the nature of the 'normal' distribution is known or defined. In practice the variation from one experiment to another may often be excessive compared with the variation within each experiment. The test is made more sensitive by setting up treated and control groups on each occasion. It is then necessary to establish criteria by which the contrast between measurements from treated and control animals may be judged, and the course of any further action determined. In this type of test there is the risk that if too great a contrast is sought between treated and control groups, a proportion of potentially valuable compounds will be dismissed as 'inactive,' whereas if too small a contrast is required, the number of truly inactive compounds coming up for retest might be prohibitive. The situation is aggravated by the probability of any one compound possessing the appropriate activity being generally accepted as being about 1/1000 or less (in the absence of a chemical 'lead').

Various authors have reviewed the problem of setting up efficient procedures for minimizing these two risks. Davies[4], Armitage and Schneiderman[5], and Dunnett[6] favour a form of sequential screening, and generally agree that three stages of testing may be adequate. A compound may be rejected as inactive at any stage, but is only passed for more extensive investigation if it is found to be active at the final stage. The design of the tests must be tailored to the specific pharmacological situation, while the criteria on which acceptance and rejection are based must be adjusted to ensure that any compounds considered to be of clinical value pass through. Much of this work has been developed in the cancer chemotherapy programme described by Schneiderman[3]. The special circumstances of that programme require that an accurate balance be struck between efficiency and cost of testing. While no undertaking can afford to ignore these two aspects of screening, compounds are likely to be tested in general for more than one possible type of action, and are very often examined as possible alternatives to an existing form of therapy. Such factors influence the design of the tests employed. In particular, when substituting a new compound for an established drug, proper experimental design becomes essential. Although rarely claiming to meet all the criteria of an analytical biological assay, in which the substances compared differ only quantitatively with respect to the responses measured, a screening test comparison between the established drug and the unknown must be capable of interpretation as an assay of relative potency, once the unknown is shown to possess the desired pharmacological action. While the general layout of testing may be in the form:

control *v.* unknown treatment(s) *v.* reference drug(s)

it is often possible to omit the control group. Evidence of specific activity of the unknown compound may be deduced from the nature of the relationship between responses at various dose levels. A significant regression of response on dose is positive evidence of activity. A lack of significance may be due to (*1*) insufficient data, (*2*) maximal responses being elicited, or (*3*) no response. (*1*) Should not apply if the test is adequately designed; the choice between (*2*) and (*3*) is made by comparison with the responses to the reference drug.

Although the tests considered so far relate as closely as possible to the type of action being sought either in human or veterinary medicine, they are of necessity primary screening methods. Compounds accepted by them are usually passed on to a secondary system of testing employing a range of techniques and a variety of species. This not only eliminates doubtful starters, but also indicates any species variation in the activity spectra of the unknown compounds, particularly necessary when man is the intended recipient of the new compound. In an unpublished communication to the Leiden symposium (1960), Pelikan showed that when the doses eliciting a defined effect in a number of species were plotted on a logarithmic scale against the respective mean body weights of the various species, also on a log scale, a straight line often fitted the data. Marked species differences showed up as deviations from such lines, the slopes of which appeared to be otherwise well-defined. It is therefore possible to employ this method to predict suitable dose levels in species as yet untested, with greater precision than is the case if body-weight effects are not taken into account. He also showed that similar relationships held within species, so that although dosage is commonly expressed as log (mg drug/kg body weight), in the more general case it should be log [mg drug/(kg body weight)$^b$] where $b$ is obtained experimentally.

Even when a compound has succeeded in passing through the secondary screening test, it is customary before administration to human subjects to complete its testing by giving repeated doses to animals. Any chronic toxic effects which develop provide a safeguard against possible untoward reactions in man. Using (*1*) doses which on a body weight basis are well in excess of those intended for clinical use, (*2*) actively growing animals, and (*3*) prolonged course of treatment in several species (usually including dogs and monkeys), the likely pathological effects of the drug in man should be exaggerated.

The factors determining the choice of design for a screening test vary considerably. An efficient screening method may only be constructed against an adequate background knowledge of the particular technique of measurement. Suitable experimentation to determine possible sources of error, the reproducibility of responses, the sensitivity of the technique to any compounds known to be active, as well as to demonstrate any lack of specificity in the

190

method, should precede any attempt to define the form of routine test to be adopted.

The types of measurement available fall into four main categories.

(1) 'Direct assays'—the measurement of the dose required to elicit a specific response in individual animals or *in vitro* preparations.

(2) Indirect estimation of the dose required to elicit a specific response, by consideration of the proportions of animals (or preparations) showing such a response in groups given various doses—so called 'quantal' or 'all or none' responses.

(3) Direct 'quantitative' measurement of the responses elicited in individual animals (or preparations) by doses of varying size.

(4) 'Non-parametric' observations of response for which no working hypothesis exists about the distribution or absolute numerical relationships of different degrees of response. The adoption of arbitrary scoring routines sometimes converts these systems into empirical quantitative methods.

In the sections which follow, the principal methods by which response systems of these various kinds may be analysed are described, with examples to illustrate both the appropriate design and the arithmetic procedures. As far as possible the symbols used follow those listed by Gaddum[7].

### SCREENING TEST DESIGNS

Although a primary screening test is carried out to determine whether a compound produces a particular pharmacological effect, it is often advantageous to design the test so that information may also be obtained about the relationship between dose and response. This determines not only whether the compound is active, but also whether it is likely to act in a manner similar to some known drug, and if so to obtain an approximate estimate of potency in terms of the known drug. The two examples which follow are typical of such screening procedures.

### *Test for Substances Acting on the Myocardium*

The guinea-pig myocardium is sensitive to cardioactive agents known to be effective in man, and is therefore a suitable preparation for screening potential cardioactive substances. The isolated right ventricle of the guinea-pig is stimulated electrically, and the amplitude of the isotonic contraction recorded on a kymograph. A substance is added to the bath in a series of doses starting with 1 $\mu$g, such that with the addition of each dose, the summated dose is twice that of the previous summated dose. Doses are added at 20-minute intervals without washing between doses. If the substance produces an increase in the amplitude of contraction (positive inotropic effect), the summated dose producing the first increase is noted, and also the summated dose reducing the amplitude to zero. These are the non-toxic (therapeutic) and toxic doses respectively. Substances are screened on two separate ventricle preparations to obtain confirmation of results. With digitalis-like substances, the increase in amplitude is linearly related to the logarithm of the summated dose. Although no statistical analyses are performed on the data, this initial test is so designed that such analyses may be carried out if necessary to obtain a preliminary assessment of the comparative potency of one substance in terms of another. The data may be plotted and the potency deduced from a graph. A more detailed assessment is made using (2 + 2) or (3 + 3) assay procedures, where only one dose is allowed to act on each ventricle, with doses replicated on different ventricles.

### Test for Potential Oral Hypoglycaemic Agents

In setting up a test for potential oral hypoglycaemic agents, a species of animal is selected which shows a marked lowering of blood sugar when the sulphonylureas, known to produce hypoglycaemia in man, are administered orally. The guinea-pig is suitable since after fasting overnight its blood sugar remains fairly constant throughout a continued fast of some 8 hours during which the compounds are examined. Male guinea-pigs, weighing 300–400 g are divided into 3 groups each of 3 animals. An initial sample of blood is taken from the heart for sugar estimation. The compound is then given orally in doses of 2·0, 1·0 and 0·5 g/kg to the 3 groups respectively. Blood samples are obtained at the 1st, 2nd, 4th, 6th and 8th hours after administration. The blood sugar concentrations are expressed as a percentage of the corresponding initial concentration for each animal. Since the blood sugar level of untreated guinea-pigs may sometimes fall to about 80 per cent of the initial level during the 8-hour test period, only values which are less than 80 per cent are used as evidence of a hypoglycaemic response. An example of this test is shown in *Table 5.1*.

*Table 5.1.* Maximum hypoglycaemic responses in fasted guinea-pigs to a compound given orally

| Oral dose (g/kg) | Maximum response detected in 8 hours in each guinea-pig (as % of initial blood sugar) | | | Mean response |
|---|---|---|---|---|
| *First test* | | | | |
| 2·0 | 23, | 44, | 32 | 33 |
| 1·0 | 29, | 32, | 29 | 30 |
| 0·5 | 33, | 39, | 29 | 34 |
| *Second test* | | | | |
| 0·5 | 34, | 37, | 36 | 36 |
| 0·25 | 22, | 29, | 16 | 22 |
| 0·125 | 30, | 30, | 45 | 35 |
| *Third test* | | | | |
| 0·125 | 40, | 41, | 37 | 39 |
| 0·0625 | 37, | 45, | 60 | 47 |
| 0·0313 | 80, | 56, | 67 | 68 |
| *Fourth test* | | | | |
| 0·0313 | 64, | 71, | 65 | 67 |
| 0·0156 | 84, | 80, | 72 | 79 |
| 0·0078 | 84, | 80, | 76 | 80 |

Since in the first test all animals showed a profound hypoglycaemic response, the screening procedure was repeated using lower doses in the same dose ratio as that used previously, the highest dose being the smallest dose of the first test.

Activity was again found at all 3 dose levels and the responses to the common dose in the first and second tests were similar. The compound was screened on two further occasions in a similar manner until it became evident that the limiting dose for hypoglycaemic activity was being approached. With a dose of 0·0039 g/kg no responses were obtained.

Although in the initial test no statistical analyses are carried out, the design permits such analyses to be made if required. *Figure 5.2* shows that

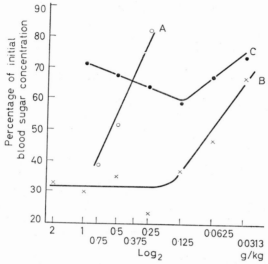

*Figure 5.2.* Relationship between dose and maximum hypoglycaemic response of three compounds screened for oral hypoglycaemic activity in the guinea-pig.

for compound B there is a linear relationship between the mean maximum hypoglycaemic response and log dose (between 0·125 and 0·0313 g/kg). It is therefore possible to use such data to calculate comparative hypoglycaemic potencies of compounds which possess parallel log dose–response lines. Compound A is chemically similar to compound B and produces a linear log dose–response curve which, within the limits of experimental error, is parallel to that of compound B. Although A is less potent than B, the parallel log dose–response curves suggest a similar mode of action. Compound C, of different chemical structure, produces a different log dose–response curve, its shape suggesting that it exerts at least two different actions on blood sugar which are dependent on the range of doses used.

This screening procedure therefore allows a comparison of the activities of compounds which may act similarly and also shows possible differences in mode of action.

## DIRECT ASSAYS

In a direct assay the smallest dose required to produce a specific effect in an animal, or *in vitro* preparation, is determined. The compound is administered by slow continuous infusion, or in small equal doses given at constant intervals, until the sharply-defined end-point is reached. The relative potencies of compounds are obtained from the ratios of the means of their threshold doses.

## Rabbit Head-drop Method for the Assay of Curare-like Substances

The assay of curare by the rabbit head-drop method[8,9] is based on the slow infusion of the drug into the ear-vein of a rabbit until its neck muscles become paralysed, so that it is unable to hold up its head. Knowing the concentration and rate of infusion of the solution, the amount of drug to

*Table 5.2.* Assay of d-tubocurarine chloride by the rabbit head-drop method[9]

| Group | Rabbit No. | Body weight (kg) | Standard ($\mu$g) | Standard (log$_{10}$ $\mu$g)* | Day | Unknown ($\mu$g) | Unknown (log$_{10}$ $\mu$g)* | Day | Sum (log$_{10}$ $\mu$g) |
|---|---|---|---|---|---|---|---|---|---|
| A | 1 | 2·0 | 287 | 2·458 | 1 | 276 | 2·441 | 2 | 4·899 |
|  | 2 | 1·8 | 285 | 2·455 |  | 303 | 2·481 |  | 4·936 |
|  | 3 | 2·0 | 286 | 2·456 |  | 314 | 2·497 |  | 4·953 |
|  | 4 | 1·7 | 341 | 2·533 |  | 378 | 2·578 |  | 5·111 |
| Sum |  |  |  | 9·902 |  |  | 9·997 |  | 19·899 |
| B | 5 | 1·7 | 294 | 2·468 | 2 | 312 | 2·494 | 1 | 4·962 |
|  | 6 | 1·8 | 311 | 2·493 |  | 320 | 2·505 |  | 4·998 |
|  | 7 | 1·9 | 391 | 2·592 |  | 315 | 2·498 |  | 5·090 |
|  | 8 | 1·8 | 443 | 2·646 |  | 401 | 2·603 |  | 5·249 |
| Sum |  |  |  | 10·199 |  |  | 10·100 |  | 20·299 |
| Sum of A+B |  |  |  | 20·101 |  |  | 20·097 |  | 40·198 |

\* The log transformation of the curarizing dose is used since within each treatment group the logarithms of the doses are expected to be normally distributed[70,97].

produce this effect may be calculated. The potency of one preparation in terms of another is determined in two groups of rabbits. To reduce the error due to variation between animals the assay is carried out as a two-day test employing a cross-over design, where one group of animals receives one drug on the first day and the other on the second, and vice versa.

The threshold dose is influenced by rate of infusion[8,9]; if the infusion time is less than 7 minutes or greater than 12, the dose required to produce head-drop is increased. Therefore concentrations of the standard and unknown solutions are chosen to produce end-points within 7–12 minutes. The mean infusion times for each group of animals should lie close to each other. After receiving tubocurarine, the sensitivity of the rabbit to the drug usually increases and remains reasonably constant, if it is used frequently.

If the body weights of the two groups are similar and the range kept small, it is unnecessary to adjust the curarizing dose for body weight. An assay of d-tubocurarine chloride designed to allow for these factors is shown in *Table 5.2*[9]. Each preparation (standard and unknown) was infused as an 0·01 per cent solution in 0·9 per cent saline, at a rate of 0·4 ml per minute.

An analysis of variance then carried out so that errors due to differences between days, standard and unknown, and rabbits are removed from the total error (see *Table 5.3*).

Table 5.3. Analysis of variance of data in *Table 5.2*.

| Source of variation | Sum of squares | Degrees of freedom | Mean square | Variance ratio F | Probability P |
|---|---|---|---|---|---|
| Days | 0·002353 | 1 | 0·002353 | 2·46 | >0·20 |
| Standard v. Unknown | 0·000001 | 1 | 0·000001 | 0·00 | >0·20 |
| Rabbits | 0·047738 | 7 | 0·006820 | 7·13 | 0·05 |
| Residual error | 0·005734 | 6 | 0·000956 | | |
| Total | 0·055826 | 15 | | | |

The sums of squares of deviations shown in *Table 5.3* are calculated from the data in *Table 5.2*:

$$\text{Days} \quad \frac{(9 \cdot 902 + 10 \cdot 100)^2 + (9 \cdot 997 + 10 \cdot 199)^2}{8} - \frac{(40 \cdot 198)^2}{16} = 0 \cdot 002353$$

$$\text{Standard v. Unknown} \quad \frac{(20 \cdot 101)^2 + (20 \cdot 097)^2}{8} - \frac{(40 \cdot 198)^2}{16} = 0 \cdot 000001$$

$$\text{Rabbits} \quad \frac{(4 \cdot 899)^2 + (4 \cdot 936)^2 + \ldots + (5 \cdot 090)^2 + (5 \cdot 249)^2}{2} - \frac{(40 \cdot 198)^2}{16}$$
$$= 0 \cdot 047738$$

$$\text{Total sum of squares} \quad (2 \cdot 458)^2 + (2 \cdot 455)^2 + \ldots +$$
$$(2 \cdot 498)^2 + (2 \cdot 603)^2 - \frac{(40 \cdot 198)^2}{16}$$
$$= 0 \cdot 55826$$

*Residual error*   Total sum of squares minus sums of squares attributable to days, standard v unknown, and rabbits

$$= 0 \cdot 055826 - 0 \cdot 002353 - 0 \cdot 000001 - 0 \cdot 047738$$
$$= 0 \cdot 005734.$$

Each source of variation has associated with it a number of 'degrees of freedom', (d.f.) representing the number of independent comparisons which may be made between observations. Between both days there is 1 d.f., between standard and unknown, 1 d.f., and among the 8 rabbits, 7 d.f. The total number of d.f. $= 16 - 1$ since 16 curarizing doses were obtained. The d.f. associated with the residual error is therefore $15 - 1 - 1 - 7 = 6$. The mean squares are obtained by dividing the sums of squares by their respective degrees of freedom. The variance ratios, $F$, are calculated by dividing the mean square of the residual error into the mean squares of the

3 unknown sources of variation. These values are compared with the tabulated probability values for the distribution of the variance ratio given in Fisher and Yates Tables[10], entering the table where $n_1$ and $n_2$ correspond to the degrees of freedom associated with the particular source of variation and with the residual error respectively. In *Table 5.3* the probability value, $P$, for days, and for standard $v$. unknown is $>0.20$. This means that the variation is not greater than would be expected by chance in more than 20 out of 100 assays. With rabbits the error mean square is significant, the variation being equal to that expected by chance in only 5 out of 100 assays.

The log potency ratio, $M = \bar{x}_S - \bar{x}_U$, where $\bar{x}_S$ and $\bar{x}_U$ are the mean of the log curarizing doses for the standard and unknown respectively, *i.e.*

$$M = \frac{20 \cdot 101 - 20 \cdot 097}{8} = 0 \cdot 0005$$

Therefore the ratio of the potency of Unknown to that of Standard = Antilog $0 \cdot 0005 = 1 \cdot 001$.

The residual error mean square, $s^2$, is used to calculate the limits of error on this estimate.

$V_M$, the variance of the log potency ratio, is given by

$$V_M = \left( \frac{1}{n_S} + \frac{1}{n_U} \right) s^2$$

where $n_S = n_U = 8$, the number of observations on standard and unknown respectively, therefore

$$V_M = (\tfrac{1}{8} + \tfrac{1}{8})0 \cdot 000956 = 0 \cdot 000239$$

The standard error of $M$,

$$s_M = \sqrt{V_M} = \pm \, 0 \cdot 01546$$

Since this standard error is obtained from an estimate of variance based on the data, use is made of Student's $t$ values to calculate the fiducial limits of the mean. These limits are the bounds within which the true value of the mean lies with a given probability. Tables of $t$ exist for different levels of probability and degrees of freedom[10]. The value of $t$ for $P = 0.95$ and 6 degrees of freedom (the number on which the error variance is based) is 2·447, from which

$$ts_M = \pm \, 2 \cdot 447(0 \cdot 01546) = \pm \, 0 \cdot 0378$$

Log limits of error $(P = 0.95)$ are $0 \cdot 0005 \pm 0 \cdot 0378 = \bar{1} \cdot 9627$ and $0 \cdot 0383$. Limits of error $(P = 0.95)$ of the estimate of unknown in terms of standard are from $0 \cdot 918$ to $1 \cdot 092$.

### *Assay of Cardiac Glycosides by Slow Intravenous Infusion Method in Guinea-pigs*

In this assay, a guinea-pig under urethane anaesthesia is given artificial respiration and infused intravenously at a constant rate with a solution of a cardiac glycoside, until cardiac arrest occurs. The dose required to reach this end-point is calculated. Guinea-pigs of the same sex are divided into groups with similar body weight. One group is allocated to each glycoside. The lethal dose of the glycoside is determined for each animal. If possible the experiment is completed within one day, otherwise the assay must be designed so that equal numbers of animals are used on each glycoside each day. To reduce errors which may arise if the individual lethal doses for one glycoside are determined before proceeding to the next, the times of day at which the individual lethal doses for each glycoside are determined must be comparable.

In the following example, the potency of ouabain in terms of digoxin was determined in male guinea-pigs weighing 275 to 707 g. The analysis shows the need for correcting the lethal dose for body weight since a significant regression of log lethal dose on log body weight was found. Each group contained animals of comparable weight. Digoxin, 1/18 mg/ml, and ouabain 1/35 mg/ml were infused at 0·400 ml/min.

Table 5.4. Assay of ouabain in terms of digoxin by slow intravenous infusion in guinea-pigs

| | Digoxin | | | Ouabain | | |
|---|---|---|---|---|---|---|
| Body weight (g) | Log body weight (g) $x_1$ | Log lethal dose (mg 10) $x$ | Body weight (g) | Log body weight (g) $x_1$ | Log lethal dose (mg 10) $x$ | |
| 492 | 2·692 | 0·660 | 485 | 2·686 | 0·190 | |
| 565 | 2·752 | 0·728 | 598 | 2·777 | 0·224 | |
| 445 | 2·648 | 0·726 | 447 | 2·650 | 0·100 | |
| 649 | 2·812 | 0·910 | 615 | 2·789 | 0·281 | |
| 275 | 2·439 | 0·690 | 302 | 2·480 | 0·190 | |
| 442 | 2·645 | 0·763 | 437 | 2·641 | 0·242 | |
| 707 | 2·849 | 1·003 | 666 | 2·824 | 0·418 | |
| 388 | 2·589 | 0·857 | 367 | 2·565 | 0·201 | |
| Sum | 21·426 | 6·337 | | 21·412 | 1·846 | |
| Mean | 2·6783 | 0·7921 | | 2·6765 | 0·2308 | |

Total for $x_1$ = 42·838.   Grand Mean for $x_1 = \bar{\bar{x}}_1$ = 2·6774
Total for $x$ = 8·183.   Grand Mean for $x = \bar{\bar{x}}$ = 0·5114

Table 5.5. Analysis of variance of data in Table 5.4.

| Source of variance | Degrees of freedom | $S_{x_1x_1}$ | $S_{x_1x}$ | $S_{xx}$ | Corrected $S_{xx}$ | Mean square | Variance ratio F | Probability P |
|---|---|---|---|---|---|---|---|---|
| Drugs | 1 | 0·000013 | 0·003929 | 1·260568 | 1·256473 | 1·256473 | 163·84 | <0·001 |
| Residual error | 14 | 0·217509 | 0·113436 | 0·158852 | 0·099692 | 0·007669 | (7·71 | 0·05) |
| Total | 15 | 0·217522 | | | | | | |

197

The sums of squares and products, $S_{x_1x_1}$, $S_{x_1x}$, and $S_{xx}$ are derived as follows:

$$S_{x_1x_1} = Sx_1^2 - \frac{(Sx_1)^2}{N}$$

where $Sx_1^2$ and $Sx_1$ are respectively the sums of the squares of the $x_1$ values and the sum of the $x_1$ values as listed in *Table 5.4*. Similarly

$$S_{x_1x} = Sx_1x - \frac{(Sx_1Sx)}{N} \text{ and } S_{xx} = Sx^2 - \frac{(Sx)^2}{N}$$

where $N$ is total number of observations, 16. The sum of squares attributable to the regression of log lethal dose on body weight is $(S_{x_1x})^2/S_{x_1x_1}$, obtained from the sum of squares for residual error in *Table 5.5*.

$$\frac{(0 \cdot 113436)^2}{0 \cdot 217509} = 0 \cdot 059160$$

0·059160 is subtracted from the $S_{xx}$ for residual error to give the corrected value of $S_{xx}$, 0·158852 — 0·059160 = 0·099692.

Since 1 d.f. is used in making the covariance analysis, the d.f. associated with corrected $S_{xx}$ is $14 - 1 = 13$. The mean square $= \dfrac{0 \cdot 099692}{13} =$ 0·007669. The significance of the sum of squares due to this regression is determined by a variance ratio test using the corrected residual error mean square as divisor,

$$F = \frac{0 \cdot 059160}{0 \cdot 007669} = 7 \cdot 71$$

which for 13 and 1 d.f. is significant at the 5 per cent level. Therefore there is a significant regression of log lethal dose on log body weight,

$$\text{the slope } b_1 = \left(\frac{S_{x_1x}}{S_{x_1x_1}}\right) = \frac{0 \cdot 113436}{0 \cdot 217509} = 0 \cdot 521523$$

The formula for corrected $S_{xx}$ for drugs is

$$S_{xx} - 2b_1 S_{x_1x} + b_1^2 S_{x_1x_1} = 1 \cdot 260568 - 2(0 \cdot 521523)(0 \cdot 003929)$$
$$+ (0 \cdot 521523)^2 (0 \cdot 000013)^2 = 1 \cdot 256473$$

The corrected values of $\bar{x}$ are given by the expression $\bar{x} - b(\bar{x}_1 - \bar{\bar{x}}_1)$, which for digoxin is 0·7916, and for ouabain is 0·2313.

Log potency ratio, $M = 0 \cdot 7916 - 0 \cdot 2313 = 0 \cdot 5603$.

The variance of $M$,

$$V_M = \left(\frac{1}{n_D} + \frac{1}{n_O}\right)s^2$$

where $s^2 =$ corrected residual error mean square and $n_D$, $n_O = 8$, the number of animals per group.

$$V_M = (\tfrac{1}{8} + \tfrac{1}{8})0 \cdot 007669 = 0 \cdot 00191725 \ s_M = \sqrt{V_M} = \pm 0 \cdot 04379$$

$Log_{10}$ limits of error $(P = 0.95)$ are $0.5603 \pm 0.04379(2.160) = 0.4657$ and $0.6549$, where $2.160$ is $t$ for 13 d.f. $(P = 0.95)$.

$$\text{The potency ratio} = \text{Antilog } 0.5603 = 3.63$$

Limits of error $(P = 0.95) = \text{Antilog } 0.4657$ and $\text{Antilog } 0.6549 = 2.92$ to $4.52$.

In this example, the lethal dose is approximately proportional to the square root of the body weight. Finney[11] analysed an experiment in which 12

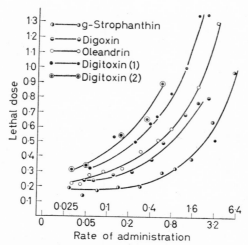

*Figure 5.3.* Intact anaesthetized cats. Relationship of rate of administration of g-strophanthin, digoxin, oleandrin and digitoxin to the lethal dose of these glycosides[13].

cardioactive substances were screened for cardiotoxic potency in anaesthetized cats. He found after covariance analysis that lethal dose was approximately proportional to (heart weight)$^{2/3}$. Further, Jacobsen and Larsen[12] found that the lethal dose of digitalis in guinea-pigs was proportional to (body weight)$^{2/3}$.

*Figure 5.3* shows the relationship between lethal dose and the rate of administration of 4 cardiac glycosides in anaesthetized cats[13]. For each glycoside there is a rate of administration below which the lethal dose tends to become constant. The highest rate at which the smallest mean lethal dose of a glycoside is still obtained is defined as the optimal rate for that glycoside. The potency of one glycoside relative to another is determined by using the lethal doses obtained at the optimal rate of administration for each glycoside.

These aspects of the relationship between dose, response, body weight and rate of administration underline the necessity for standardizing the conditions under which an experiment is conducted if results are to be repeatable, and errors reduced to a minimum.

## QUANTAL ASSAYS

The previous section dealt with the direct measurement of the threshold dose required to elicit a specific effect in each animal or each tissue preparation. Situations in which this technique is applied are comparatively few. More often the parameters of the distribution of threshold dose (mean and standard deviation) have to be indirectly assessed by observing the proportionate occurrences of the desired effect in groups of animals or test preparations where each group receives a fixed dose. Such experiments follow Trevan's method[14], in that they endeavour to estimate the median lethal dose (LD50) or the median effective dose (ED50). The ED50 is the dose which, when administered to a group of animals, elicits the pharmacological effect in 50 per cent of the animals. It only corresponds exactly to the mean threshold dose if the latter is derived from a symmetrical distribution. For practical purposes it is usually assumed that the logarithms of individual threshold doses are normally distributed. Various authors have demonstrated that the sigmoid curve relating the proportion of animals showing an effect to the logarithms of the corresponding doses, is equivalent to a plot of the integral of the normal curve at successive dose levels[15,16].

Methods for interpreting quantal response experiments are numerous, and their computational requirements vary considerably. In spite of the simplicity in this respect of the Spearman-Kärber method[17] and of Thompson's moving average method[18], pharmacologists have tended to adopt the more complex techniques of the maximum likelihood approach. This may be because more elaborate methods of analysis may be applied to sets of results irrespective of their pattern, whereas the simpler methods of computation have fairly specific requirements for the percentage response range covered. The Spearman-Kärber method, for example, requires that doses range from one giving 0 per cent response to one giving 100 per cent response. For maximum efficiency, and to facilitate the estimation of error variance, it further requires equal numbers of animals to have been tested at a succession of doses with a constant log dose-interval. Thompson's moving average method, in common with the Reed-Muench and Dragstedt-Behrens[20] techniques, does not require complete coverage of the response range, but the ED50 estimate is affected by asymmetry in the distribution of responses. Detailed comparisons of the various methods available have been published by various authors and no attempt is made to reproduce them here. Consideration is given to the design requirements for the application of the 'short cut' procedures, and to the overall validity of the numerous transformations which periodically have been put forward. With the latter it is generally agreed that the scope of screening tests is normally so limited by the numbers of subjects tested at each dose level, that there can be little to choose between any of the transformations. The method selected therefore may well be based on personal preference and computational considerations.

The examples which follow illustrate their respective calculation requirements with some comment on the extensions of their use. Each method is used to estimate the LD50 and its limits of error from the results of a toxicity study of cocaine injected intravenously into groups of 20 mice. The proportions of animals dying within 24 hours at each of 5 dose levels are shown in *Table 5.6.*

*Table 5.6.* Mortality data in mice
injected with cocaine

| Dose (mg/kg) | Deaths |
|:---:|:---:|
| 16·0 | 2/20 |
| 20·0 | 2/20 |
| 25·0 | 11/20 |
| 31·3 | 15/20 |
| 39·8 | 20/20 |

### The Spearman-Kärber Method

This method is used to estimate the mean threshold dose from the experimental data, treating the proportions dying as if they were cumulative frequencies in a grouped distribution of individual thresholds. The interval

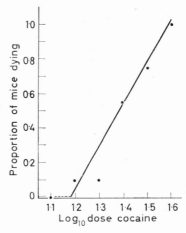

*Figure 5.4.* Relationship between $\log_{10}$ dose of cocaine (I.V.) and proportion of mice dying (Spearman-Kärber method).

boundaries correspond to the values of log dose employed, and the differences in the proportions responding at successive dose levels are equivalent to the frequency with which individual thresholds fall within the respective boundaries. When the experimental results fail to reach either 0 or 100 per cent, it is necessary to be satisfied that these limits would have been reached at the next lower or next higher dose level in the series. A line fitted by eye to the proportions dying, plotted against log dose (*Figure 5.4*), shows that with the cocaine data this requirement is met; a fictitious log dose level of 1·1 may be inserted with an expected death rate of zero. The line is also used to obtain smoothed estimates of $P_i$, the expected proportion dying at each log dose level, $x_i$, for the estimation of the error variance[21]. *Table 5.7* gives the dose levels and their logarithms $(x_i)$, the numbers dying at each level $(r_i)$ the numbers tested $(n_i)$, $p_i = r_i/n_i$, and the means of successive pairs of $p_i$ against the successive differences of log dose $(I)$. The constancy of $n_i$ and of $I$ in this example permits some reduction in this tabulation, which is retained to illustrate the technique required for irregular sizes of groupings. The final columns give $P_i$, read from the graph, and $Q_i = 1 - P_i$.

The logarithm of the LD50,

$$m = x_k - S\left[\frac{(p_i + p_{i+1})I}{2}\right]$$

where $x_k$ is the log dose at which all the animals died, and

$$S\left[\frac{(p_i + p_{i+1})I}{2}\right]$$

indicates the sum of the values within the brackets.

From *Table 5.7*, $m = 1\cdot60 - 0\cdot20 = 1\cdot40$, the antilogarithm of which

*Table 5.7.* Cocaine toxicity data analysed by Spearman-Kärber method

| Dose (mg/kg) | log dose ($x_i$) | $r_i$ | $n_i$ | $p_i$ | $\frac{p_i + p_{i+1}}{2}$ | $I$ | $P_i$ | $Q_i$ |
|---|---|---|---|---|---|---|---|---|
| — | 1·1 | — | — | 0 | | | 0 | 1·00 |
| | | | | | 0·050 | 0·10 | | |
| 16·0 | 1·2 | 2 | 20 | 0·10 | | | 0·05 | 0·95 |
| | | | | | 0·100 | 0·10 | | |
| 20·0 | 1·3 | 2 | 20 | 0·10 | | | 0·30 | 0·70 |
| | | | | | 0·325 | 0·10 | | |
| 25·0 | 1·4 | 11 | 20 | 0·55 | | | 0·54 | 0·46 |
| | | | | | 0·650 | 0·10 | | |
| 31·3 | 1·5 | 15 | 20 | 0·75 | | | 0·78 | 0·22 |
| | | | | | 0·875 | 0·10 | | |
| 39·8 | 1·6 | 20 | 20 | 1·00 | | | 1·00 | 0 |

gives the LD50 as 25·1 mg/kg. From Irwin and Cheeseman[21] the variance of $m$,

$$V_m = I^2 \cdot S\left(\frac{P_i Q_i}{n_i}\right) = (0\cdot1)^2(0\cdot033875) = 0\cdot00033875$$

From which, $S.E._m = \pm 0\cdot0184$.

Assuming the applicability of the normal distribution, approximate 95 per cent fiducial limits will be given by the range, $\pm 1\cdot96(0\cdot0184)$ about the mean, or $1\cdot40 \pm 0\cdot0361$. These correspond to the range 23·1 to 27·3 mg/kg.

### The Thompson Moving Average Method[18]

From the observed values of $p_i$, the proportion dying at log dose levels $x_i$, moving averages of $p$ are calculated with a span $K$. These are associated with similar moving averages of the $x_i$ values. The value of $m$, the log LD50, is then estimated by direct interpolation between the successive $p'$, $p''$ values falling respectively below and above 0·5. As has already been stated the method is only free from bias if the response distribution is symmetrical. It operates most satisfactorily if equal numbers of animals are tested at equal log increments of dose. It is customary to employ $K = 3$, taking moving averages over a span of 3 successive doses. Four or more dose levels must therefore be employed. If under these conditions, $r_1$, $r_2$, $r_3$, and $r_4$ are the observed numbers responding in successive groups of $n$ animals tested at dosages $x_1$, $x_1 + I$, $x_1 + 2I$ and $x_1 + 3I$ respectively such that,

$$p' = \frac{r_1 + r_2 + r_3}{3n} \leqslant 0 \cdot 5, \quad p'' = \frac{r_2 + r_3 + r_4}{3n} \geqslant 0 \cdot 5$$

and $p' \neq p''$, then the log LD50, $m = x_1 + I + If$ where,

$$f = \left(\frac{3n}{2} - r_1 - r_2 - r_3\right) / (r_4 - r_1)$$

The variance of $m$ may be estimated as:

$$V_m = I^2 \cdot \frac{(1 - f)^2 r_1 s_1 + r_2 s_2 + r_3 s_3 + f^2 r_4 s_4}{(n - 1)(r_4 - r_1)^2} \text{ where } s_i = n - r_i$$

*Table 5.8.* Cocaine toxicity data analysed by Thompson's moving average method

| Dose (mg/kg) | $x_i$ | $r_i$ | $n_i$ | $s_i$ | $p_i = r_i/n_i$ | Moving average, $p$ $K = 3$ | | |
|---|---|---|---|---|---|---|---|---|
| 16·0 | 1·2 | 2 | 20 | 18 | 0·10 | | | |
| 20·0 | 1·3 | 2 | 20 | 18 | 0·10 | 0·25 | | |
| 25·0 | 1·4 | 11 | 20 | 9 | 0·55 | | 0·47 = $p'$ | |
| 31·3 | 1·5 | 15 | 20 | 5 | 0·75 | | | 0·77 = $p''$ |
| 39·8 | 1·6 | 20 | 20 | 0 | 1·00 | | | |

In this example $p'$ and $p''$ are derived from the central 3 doses and top 3 doses respectively in order to straddle the $p = 0 \cdot 50$ value (*Table 5.8*). Since

$$f = \frac{1 \cdot 5(20) - 2 - 11 - 15}{20 - 2} = 0 \cdot 111$$

$m = 1 \cdot 3 + 0 \cdot 1 + 0 \cdot 1(0 \cdot 111) = 1 \cdot 4111$, the antilogarithm of which gives the LD50 as 25·8 mg/kg.

$$V_m = (0 \cdot 1)^2 \left[ \frac{(1 - 1/9)^2 (2)(18) + (11)(9) + (15)(5) + (1/9)^2 (20)(0)}{19(20 - 2)^2} \right]$$

$$= 0 \cdot 0003289$$

The standard error of $m$ is therefore $\pm 0 \cdot 01813$, and the approximate $P = 0 \cdot 95$ limits will be $1 \cdot 4111 \pm 1 \cdot 96 (0 \cdot 01813)$ or $1 \cdot 3756$ to $1 \cdot 4466$. These are equivalent to 23·7 and 28·0 mg/kg.

The ease with which generalized solutions for all possible combinations of results are computed by the moving average method has commended it to many workers. Thus Weil[22] has published tables of $f$ and $\sigma f$ for groups of $n = 2, 3, 4, 5, 6$ and 10 for $K = 3$. These values may readily be inserted in the equations $m = x_i + I(1 + f)$ and standard error$_m = \pm I\sigma_f$ to obtain the LD50 and its limits.

In this form the log dose interval may be varied to suit the specific characteristics of the substance tested, but must remain constant for each test. When even further limitations in design are accepted, the LD50 and its limits are obtained from the Tables of Horn[23], where values corresponding to the observed series of responses are shown. These values require simple multiplication to convert into the experimental scale. As with Weil's tables, Horn uses $K = 3$, but limits $n$ to values of 4 or 5. The log dose intervals he allows for are 0·5 and 0·3333. Since the biological errors of work of this nature are usually large compared with errors of volumetric measurement, the corresponding dose ratios of approximately 3·16 and 2·15 should have wide applicability.

## The Probit Method

This method is founded on the assumption that the logarithms of individual threshold doses, or 'tolerances,' may be normally distributed. The observations of proportions responding at the various dosages are subjected to a maximum likelihood technique for the estimation of the parameters of the distribution. A detailed exposition of probit analysis has been given by Finney[16]. What follows merely enumerates the step by step procedure in obtaining the LD50 and its variance.

Table 5.9. Cocaine toxicity data. First cycle of probit calculations

| Dose (mg/kg) | $x$ | $r$ | $n$ | % | Empirical probit | $Y$ | $nw$ | $y$ | $nwx$ | $nwy$ |
|---|---|---|---|---|---|---|---|---|---|---|
| 16·0 | 1·20 | 2 | 20 | 10 | 3·72 | 3·3 | 4·2 | 3·89 | 5·04 | 16·338 |
| 20·0 | 1·30 | 2 | 20 | 10 | 3·72 | 4·2 | 10·1 | 3·81 | 13·13 | 38·481 |
| 25·0 | 1·40 | 11 | 20 | 55 | 5·13 | 5·1 | 12·7 | 5·13 | 17·78 | 65·151 |
| 31·3 | 1·50 | 15 | 20 | 75 | 5·67 | 6·0 | 8·8 | 5·62 | 13·20 | 49·456 |
| 39·8 | 1·60 | 20 | 20 | 100 | | 6·9 | 3·1 | 7·34 | 4·96 | 22·754 |
| | | | | | | | 38·9 | | 54·11 | 192·180 |

In Table 5.9, $x = $ log dose, $r = $ numbers dying (or responding) in each group, $n = $ numbers tested $(100\ r/n) = $ percentage kill (or response), (these values may be given to the nearest whole number). At this stage it may be necessary to adjust the percentages to allow for 'natural mortality' or spontaneous responses in control animals. Although not applicable to the cocaine experiment, circumstances are frequently met where the techniques employed involve an appreciable risk to the life of the animals. Alternatively some responses, such as mice dropping off an inverted grid or off a rotating rod, may well occur spontaneously in the absence of drug treatment. Correction[24] is then made using the relationship

$$\text{corrected percentage} = \left( \frac{\text{observed percentage} - \text{control percentage}}{100 - \text{control percentage}} \right) 100$$

Empirical probit values corresponding to the percentage of responses, corrected where necessary for natural responses, are obtained from tables of probits. These and the other functions to be employed are found in several works[10,11a,16,25].

The empirical probits are plotted against their respective $x$ values and a straight line fitted to the points by eye (*Figure 5.5*). At each $x$ value the ordinates are read off from this line and listed as expected probits, $Y$, to one place of decimals.

The values of the weighting coefficient, $w$, corresponding to each value of $Y$ are then obtained from the appropriate tables, allowing for the control response rate (zero in the example). The products $nw$ are listed and totalled.

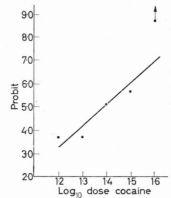

*Figure* 5.5. Relationship between $\log_{10}$ dose of cocaine (I.V.) and probit of response in mice.

The working probits, $y$, obtained from tables, take into account the observed percentage of responders (corrected where necessary) and the expected probit values, $Y$. The final columns list the products $nwx$ and $nwy$ and their sums, $Snwx$, $Snwy$.

The sum of squares for deviations of $x$ from the weighted mean, $S_{xx}$, is

$$Snwx^2 - (Snwx)^2/Snw = 75 \cdot 745 - 75 \cdot 267 = 0 \cdot 478$$

Similarly, the sum of products, $S_{xy}$, adjusted for the means of $x$ and $y$ is

$$Snwxy - (Snwx)(Snwy)/Snw = 271 \cdot 4327 - 267 \cdot 3229 = 4 \cdot 1098$$

Similarly

$$S_{yy} = Snwy^2 - (Snwy)^2/Snw = 989 \cdot 3491 - 949 \cdot 4384 = 39 \cdot 9107$$

An estimate for $\chi^2$ for the heterogeneity of the observed and expected responses may then be obtained by subtracting from $S_{yy}$ the square of $S_{xy}$ divided by $S_{xx}$.

Thus, $$(S_{xy})^2/S_{xx} = 35 \cdot 3357$$

hence $$\chi^2 = 39 \cdot 9107 - 35 \cdot 3357 = 4 \cdot 5750$$

This is associated with 3 degrees of freedom, 2 less than the number of doses employed. Reference to the tables of $\chi^2$ show that the probability of the observed value being equalled or exceeded by chance is greater than $0 \cdot 20$. There is therefore no evidence of significant heterogeneity. Had heterogeneity been indicated it would have been necessary to allow for this in the subsequent estimation of variances.

It is now possible to obtain the equation to the provisional probit regression line in the form:

$$Y_1 = \bar{y} + b(x - \bar{x})$$

where

$$\bar{y} = Snwy/Snw = 4\cdot940$$
$$\bar{x} = Snwx/Snw = 1\cdot391$$
$$b = S_{xy}/S_{xx} = 8\cdot598$$

Hence

$$Y_1 = 8\cdot598x - 7\cdot019$$

Substituting in this equation the values of $x$ employed in the test, the $Y_1$ estimates are compared with the expected probits, $Y$ (*Table 5.10*). Since these do not agree within the first place of decimals, the provisional line must be regarded as inadequate. A second cycle of computations is therefore carried out in which the $Y_1$ values replace the previous estimates of expected probits, $Y$.

*Table 5.10.* Cocaine toxicity data. Second cycle of probit calculations

| $x$ | $r$ | $n$ | % | $Y$ | $Y_1$ | $nw$ | $y$ | $nwx$ | $nwy$ |
|---|---|---|---|---|---|---|---|---|---|
| 1·20 | 2 | 20 | 10 | 3·3 | 3·3 | 4·2 | 3·89 | 5·04 | 16·338 |
| 1·30 | 2 | 20 | 10 | 4·2 | 4·2 | 10·1 | 3·81 | 13·13 | 38·481 |
| 1·40 | 11 | 20 | 55 | 5·1 | 5·0 | 12·7 | 5·13 | 17·78 | 65·151 |
| 1·50 | 15 | 20 | 75 | 6·0 | 5·9 | 9·4 | 5·65 | 14·10 | 53·110 |
| 1·60 | 20 | 20 | 100 | 6·9 | 6·7 | 4·2 | 7·17 | 6·72 | 30·114 |
| | | | | | | 40·6 | | 56·77 | 203·194 |

$$S_{xx} = 79\cdot911 - 79\cdot380 = 0\cdot531$$
$$S_{xy} = 288\cdot6897 - 284\cdot1213 = 4\cdot5684$$
$$S_{yy} = 1060\cdot38094 - 1016\cdot94093 = 43\cdot44001$$
$$\chi^2 = 43\cdot44001 - 39\cdot30373 = 4\cdot14 \text{ (to 2 places)}$$

$$\bar{x} = 1\cdot3983$$
$$\bar{y} = 5\cdot0048$$
$$b = 8\cdot603$$

The new estimate of the provisional line is therefore:

$$Y_2 = 5\cdot0048 + 8\cdot603(x - 1\cdot3983)$$
$$= 8\cdot603x - 7\cdot025$$

Substitution in this equation gives values of $Y_2$ which do not differ from the previous estimates of $Y_1$ when taken to one decimal place. This degree of agreement is considered adequate for the present purpose, but a more stringent requirement might be imposed. In the event of successive estimates of $Y_j$ and $Y_{j+1}$ not agreeing, additional cycles of calculation should be made, each commencing with the provisional probits calculated from the previous cycle, until satisfactory agreement is reached.

From the final equation to the regression line the logarithm of the LD50 is computed as the value of $x$ for which $Y = 5\cdot00$. Hence

$$m = \frac{5\cdot00 + 7\cdot025}{8\cdot6034} = 1\cdot3977$$

and the LD50 is therefore 25·0 mg/kg.

The fiducial limits of $m$ are given by

$$m + \frac{g}{1-g}(m - \bar{x}) \pm \frac{t}{b(1-g)}\left[\frac{1-g}{Snw} + \frac{(m-\bar{x})^2}{S_{xx}}\right]^{\frac{1}{2}}$$

where $g = t^2/b^2 S_{xx}$. The variance of $b$, $V_b = 1/S_{xx}$. For the 95 per cent fiducial limits, $t = 1·96$ and

$$g = \frac{(1·96)^2}{(8·603)^2(0·531)} = 0·0977$$

The limits are therefore:

$$1·3977 + \frac{0·0977}{0·9023}(0·0006) \pm \frac{1·96}{(8·6034)(0·9023)}\left[\frac{0·9023}{40·6} + \frac{(0·0006)^2}{0·531}\right]^{\frac{1}{2}}$$

which reduces to $1·3978 \pm 0·0376$ or $1·3602$ to $1·4354$. These correspond to limits of 22·9 to 27·3 mg/kg.

When the value of $g$ is small enough to be ignored, a simplified expression for the limits can be used:

$$m \pm \frac{t}{b}\left[\frac{1}{Snw} + \frac{(m-\bar{x})^2}{S_{xx}}\right]^{\frac{1}{2}}$$

This formula leads to estimates of 1·3620 to 1·4334, or 23·0 to 27·1 mg/kg. For practical purposes it would be reasonable to employ the simpler expression when $g < 0·10$. In the example the results were sufficiently balanced around the LD50 for $(m - \bar{x})^2$ to be negligible in the variance estimation.

Many attempts have been made to develop techniques to simplify the computation of results when the maximum likelihood procedure is used. The simplest is a graphical method using 'probability' graph paper. Available commercially, this paper has horizontal (ordinate) rulings marked off in percentages, with spacings in proportion to empirical probit values. The abscissal scales are either in arithmetic or logarithmic rulings covering one or more cycles of logarithms. A normal sigmoid response line is rectified on such a grid, and a straight line, fitted by eye, can be used to interpolate the ED50 value.

Some experience is needed in drawing such lines, to allow for the greater weight attached to values around the 50 per cent point. Since the percentage scale cannot be plotted to the zero and 100 per cent limits ($\pm \infty$ probits), Bartlett[26] suggested that in groups of $n$ animals showing 0 or 100 per cent response, values of $100(0·25/n)$ and $100[(n - 0·25)/n]$ should be plotted. Miller and Tainter[27] described a method for obtaining the ED50 and its error from plots of this sort. De Beer[28] published details of a set of nomographs and a protractor for the estimation of slopes; means and errors are readily estimated with the minimum of calculation. A more complex system was subsequently devised by Litchfield and Wilcoxon[29], which included a test for heterogeneity of the data. Keeping the arithmetic required to a minimum, it attempted to approximate the results of formal analysis. Because of the claims made for it, the Litchfield-Wilcoxon system was subjected to careful scrutiny by others. Eisenberg[30] used it in parallel with the full computational method to analyse 52 quantal response experiments and concluded that while the ED50 estimates were in fair agreement, the nomographic method tended to overestimate the fiducial range. From the data of an insulin assay published by Hemmingsen[31], Finney[32] showed that estimates of relative potency of test and standard preparations fluctuated widely when obtained by the technique of Litchfield and Wilcoxon from lines fitted to the data by inexperienced workers. The original authors[33] demonstrated however that this fluctuation was largely due to Finney's requirement that his volunteers should fit the data with lines parallel for standard and test results. Without this restriction, the range of values was very much reduced. While the evidence convincingly demonstrated that a single cycle of probit calculation overcame the subjective errors of poorly fitting provisional lines, it was equally apparent that the nomographic technique gave good approximations to the calculated values when individual lines were fitted, although errors were in general likely to be overestimated.

### The Angle Transformation Method

In the method of analysis of quantal response data proposed by Knudsen and Curtis[34], the proportion, $p$, of animals responding is transformed according to the relationship

$$p = \sin^2 Y$$

Although the fit afforded by this metameter to the normal integral is empirical, and breaks down at the extremes of response, it is a sufficiently close approximation for the differences to be insignificant in all studies, except those using very large numbers of animals. In this transformation

Table 5.11. Cocaine toxicity data. First cycle of angle calculations

| Dose (mg/kg) | $x$ | $r$ | $n$ | $p$ | Empirical angle° | $Y$ | $y$ | $Y_1$ |
|---|---|---|---|---|---|---|---|---|
| 16·0 | 1·2 | 2 | 20 | 0·10 | 18 | 13 | 19·6 | 12·5 |
| 20·0 | 1·3 | 2 | 20 | 0·10 | 18 | 30 | 20·1 | 29·4 |
| 25·0 | 1·4 | 11 | 20 | 0·55 | 48 | 46 | 47·9 | 46·4 |
| 31·3 | 1·5 | 15 | 20 | 0·75 | 60 | 63 | 59·9 | 63·4 |
| 39·8 | 1·6 | 20 | 20 | 1·00 | — | 79 | 84·6 | 80·4 |
| | 7·0 | | | | | | 232·1 | |

the variance of the transformed response is independent of the response. Whereas in probit analysis the weighting coefficient, $w$, must be separately assessed against each value of expected probit ($Y$), in calculation with angles (measured in degrees) $w$ has the constant value

$$\frac{4\pi^2}{(180)^2} = 0.0012185 \text{ for all expected angles}$$

The computation of the LD50 for cocaine using angles, follows therefore on similar lines to the probit analysis, but with the elimination of separate $nw$ entries.

Data are listed as before up to the column, $p$ (the proportions dying within each dosage group). These values are converted from tables into empirical angles. A straight line is then fitted by eye to a plot of these angles against their respective $x$ values, and expected angles $Y$, read off from the graph (*Figure 5.6*).

Again from tables, the working angles $y$ are obtained by entering the table for each combination of expected angle and $p$ value in turn.

Calculations of sums of squares and products follow in a manner analogous to the probit analysis. In the example, advantage is taken of the fact that $n$ and $w$ are constant. The adjustment of these estimates by the factor $nw$ = 20(0·0012185) = 0·02437, is left to the end of each manipulation.

Thus
$$Sx^2 = 9·90$$
$$(Sx)^2/5 = 9·80$$
$$S_{xx} = (Sx^2 - (Sx)^2/5)(nw) = 0·002437$$
$$Sy^2 = 13827·75$$
$$(Sy)^2/5 = 10774·08$$
$$S_{yy} = (Sy^2 - (Sy)^2/5)(nw) = 74·4179$$
$$Sxy = 341·92$$
$$(Sx)(Sy)/5 = 324·94$$
$$S_{xy} = (Sxy - (Sx)(Sy)/5)(nw) = 0·4138026$$
$$\chi^2 \text{ 3 d.f.} = S_{yy} - (S_{xy})^2/S_{xx} = 74·4179 - 70·2637$$
$$= 4·1542 \text{ (indicating no significant heterogeneity)}$$

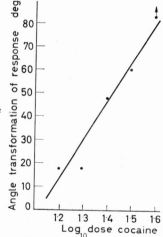

*Figure 5.6.* Relationship between $\log_{10}$ dose of cocaine (I.V.) and angle of response in mice.

For the equation to the regression line:
$$\bar{x} = 7·0/5 = 1·4$$
$$\bar{y} = 232·1/5 = 46·42$$
$$b = S_{xy}/S_{xx} = 169·8$$
hence:
$$Y_1 = \bar{y} + b(x - \bar{x}) = 169·8x - 191·30$$

Substitution in this equation of the $x$ values employed in the test, yields the $Y_1$ estimates listed in *Table 5.11*. These agree, within 2° (the limit suggested by Finney[11b], with the expected angles derived from the provisional line, and no further cycles are necessary. Had the agreement not been so close, the process would have been repeated using the $Y_1$ values as expected angles for the next cycle, and so on.

The estimate of $m$ is that value of $x$ for which $Y_1 = 45$ and therefore

$$m = \frac{45 + 191 \cdot 30}{169 \cdot 8} = 1 \cdot 3916$$

giving the LD50 as 24·6 mg/kg.

The expression for the fiducial limits of $m$, is identical with that used in probit analysis. In this instance,

$$g = \frac{t^2 V_b}{b^2} = \frac{(1 \cdot 96)^2}{(169 \cdot 8)^2 (0 \cdot 002437)} = 0 \cdot 0547$$

a value which may reasonably be ignored. The expression for the limits is therefore reduced to:

$$m \pm \frac{t}{b} \left[ \frac{1}{Snw} + \frac{(m - \bar{x})^2}{S_{xx}} \right]^{\frac{1}{2}}$$

Substituting the values obtained this becomes,

$$1 \cdot 3916 \pm \frac{1 \cdot 96}{169 \cdot 8} \left[ \frac{1}{5(0 \cdot 02437)} + \frac{(0 \cdot 0084)^2}{0 \cdot 002437} \right]^{\frac{1}{2}}$$

giving values of 1·3585 to 1·4247, the antilogarithms of which give 95 per cent limits of the LD50 of 22·8 to 26·6 mg/kg.

Table 5.12. The results on the cocaine toxicity experiment obtained by various methods, expressed as mg/kg

| Method | LD50 | Lower (P = 0·95) limit | Upper (P = 0·95) limit |
|---|---|---|---|
| Spearman-Kärber | 25·0 | 23·1 | 27·3 |
| Thompson moving average | 25·8 | 23·7 | 28·0 |
| Probit | 25·0 | 22·9 | 27·3 |
| Angle | 24·6 | 22·8 | 26·6 |

A comparison of the estimates derived from the various methods of calculation on the example quoted shows that there is little to choose between them (Table 5.12). To generalize on the basis of one example is fruitless, but for practical purposes the choice of method is safely determined by the nature of the experiment. Thus responses in groups of uniform number and at constant log dose-intervals are adequately analysed by one of the short-cut methods. Irregularities of design, particularly when the coverage of the overall response range is incomplete, necessitate the maximum likelihood approach. For experiments including factors in addition to the variation of dose levels, probit analysis becomes extremely complex, necessitating the estimation of 'probit planes' (see Finney[16a]). Claringbold and Emmens[35] suggested using a simple scoring procedure, allowing 0 for the survival and 1 for the death of each animal. Total scores may then be subjected to a normal analysis of variance. The types of experiment for which this approach appears appropriate are probably more applicable to general research than to screening procedures. Warner and Collier[36,37], however, have described a method for testing compounds displaying analgesic properties which is more directly applicable to screening procedures. In their method, five dose levels of morphine were given subcutaneously, each to a group of 5 guinea-pigs. One hour after injection each animal was tested for its responsiveness to pain by the application of a light artery clip to each of its 14 toes in turn. The control animal responds by squealing within 2–3 seconds of the clip being applied. Increasing doses of analgesic drug decrease the probability of obtaining such a response; with sufficiently high doses the response is abolished. The proportion of applications failing to elicit a squeal is estimated from the 14 single toe applications within each guinea pig; these estimates, $p_i$, are listed as individual scores for the 25 pigs (*Table 5.13*). The scores for each dosage group of 5 pigs are averaged to give $p$ values which are then subjected to the angle transformation. Two cycles of calculation in their experience gave good agreement between the $Y_1$ and $Y_2$ values.

Since at each dose level, $p$ was obtained from the $p_i$ values of individual animals, it was possible to estimate directly from the data a residual sum of squares for the error between animals. In normal analysis of transformed quantal responses, the residual error is assumed to be unity where significant heterogeneity exists when it takes the value of $\chi^2$ divided by its degrees of freedom. In the present case the sum of squares for error is:

$$\text{Sum, for all dose levels, of } \frac{S(p_i - p)^2}{P_2 Q_2}$$

where

$$P_2 = 1 - Q_2 = \sin^2 Y_2$$

Using the relationship,

$$P_1 Q_1 = \sin^2 Y_2 (1 - \sin^2 Y_2) = 1/4 \sin^2 2Y_2$$

the authors tabulate $\sin^2 2Y_2$ and obtain the residual sum of squares as

$$\frac{S(p_i - p)^2}{\frac{1}{4} \sin^2 2Y_2}$$

Table 5.13. Proportions, $p_i$, of applications of clip failing to elicit a squeal response

| Morphine dose (mg/kg) | $x$ | $p_i$ for each guinea-pig | | | | | Mean values $p$ |
|---|---|---|---|---|---|---|---|
| 2·825 | 0·45 | 0 | 0·36 | 0 | 0 | 0 | 0·07 |
| 4·0 | 0·60 | 0·57 | 0·14 | 0 | 0·43 | 0·14 | 0·26 |
| 5·65 | 0·75 | 0·43 | 0·07 | 1·00 | 0·71 | 0·43 | 0·53 |
| 8·0 | 0·90 | 0·86 | 0·29 | 0·57 | 0·64 | 1·00 | 0·67 |
| 11·3 | 1·05 | 1·00 | 1·00 | 1·00 | 1·00 | 1·00 | 1·00 |

Table 5.14. Analysis of data of Table 5.13.

| $x$ | $p$ | Empirical angle | Expected angle $Y_1$ | Working angle $y_2$ | Expected angle $Y_2$ | $\frac{1}{4}\sin^2 2Y_2$ | $S(p_i - p)^2$ |
|------|------|------|------|------|------|------|------|
| 0·45 | 0·07 | 15·3 | 13·8 | 15·4 | 13·9 | 0·054375 | 0·1020 |
| 0·60 | 0·26 | 30·7 | 30·2 | 30·7 | 30·1 | 0·188275 | 0·2204 |
| 0·75 | 0·53 | 47·5 | 46·6 | 46·7 | 46·4 | 0·249400 | 0·4857 |
| 0·90 | 0·67 | 64·9 | 63·0 | 54·2 | 62·6 | 0·166925 | 0·3020 |
| 1·05 | 1·00 | 82·2 | 79·4 | 84·8 | 78·8 | 0·036300 | 0 |

Omitting the 1st cycle of computations the fitting of the regression lines takes the following form:

$nw$ = animals per dosage group multiplied by constant weight for angle transformation.

$$= 5 \left(\frac{2\pi}{180}\right)^2 = 0·0060925$$

$$Sx^2 = 3·055527$$

$$(Sx)^2/5 = 2·829024$$

$$Sx^2 - (Sx)^2/5 = 0·226503$$

$$S_{xx} = nw(Sx^2 - (Sx)^2/5)$$

$$= (0·226503)(0·0060925) = 0·001380$$

$$Sxy_2 = 198·7822$$

$$(Sx)(Sy_2)/5 = 174·3600$$

$$Sxy_2 - (Sx)(Sy_2)/5 = 24·4222$$

$$S_{xy} = (24·4222)(0·0060925) = 0·1488$$

$$Sy_2^2 = 13489·22$$

$$(Sy_2)^2/5 = 10746·25$$

$$Sy_2^2 - (Sy_2)^2/5 = 2742·97$$

$$S_{yy} = (2742·97)(0·0060925) = 16·71$$

$$\chi^2_{3d.f.} = S_{yy} - (S_{xy})^2/S_{xx} = 0·67$$

$$\bar{x} = 0·7522, \qquad \bar{y}_2 = 46·36, \qquad b = \frac{S_{xy}}{S_{xx}} = 107·83$$

Hence,
$$Y_2 = y_2 + b(x - \bar{x}) = 107·83x - 34·75$$

from which the $Y_2$ estimates are obtained.

$$m = \frac{45 + 34·75}{107·83} = 0·7396$$

From which the ED50 = 5·49 mg/kg.

The analysis of variance is then built up by the authors as follows:

Table 5.15. Analysis of variance for guinea-pig data in Table 5.14.

| Source of variation | Sum of squares | d.f. | Mean square | F Ratio |
|---|---|---|---|---|
| Regression | $\dfrac{(S_{xy})^2}{S_{xx}} = 16 \cdot 048$ | 1 | 16·048 | 47·2 $(P < 0 \cdot 001)$ |
| Deviations about regression | $S_{yy} - \dfrac{(S_{xy})^2}{S_{xx}} = 0 \cdot 67$ | 3 | 0·223 | <1 (not significant) |
| Residual | $S\left[\dfrac{S(p_i - p)^2}{\frac{1}{4} \sin^2 2Y_2}\right] = 6 \cdot 803$ | 20 | 0·340 | |

The residual mean square, an estimate of error variance, $V_e$, is used as a multiplier for the estimates $V_b$ and $V_m$ just as $\chi^2/\text{d.f.}$ could be used in heterogeneous data.

Hence,
$$V_b = 0 \cdot 340 \left(\frac{1}{S_{xx}}\right) = 246 \cdot 4$$

$$g = \frac{t^2 V_b}{b^2} = \frac{(2 \cdot 086)^2 (246 \cdot 4)}{(107 \cdot 83)^2} = 0 \cdot 0922$$

using $t = 2 \cdot 086$ for $P = 0 \cdot 95$ and 20 degrees of freedom, the number with which the error variance was determined.

Ignoring the contribution of $g$ to the error of the estimate,

$$V_m = \frac{V_e}{b^2}\left[\frac{1}{Snw} + (m - \bar{x})^2 V_b\right]$$

$$= \frac{0 \cdot 340}{(107 \cdot 83)^2}\left[\frac{1}{5(0 \cdot 0060925)} + (0 \cdot 0126)^2 (246 \cdot 4)\right]$$

$$= 0 \cdot 0009611$$

The standard error of $m$ is therefore

$$\sqrt{V_m} = \pm 0 \cdot 031$$

and the $P$ 0·95 limits for $m$ are given by $m \pm t\sqrt{V_m}$, or

$$0 \cdot 7396 \pm 2 \cdot 086(0 \cdot 031) = 0 \cdot 6749 \text{ and } 0 \cdot 8042$$

the antilogarithms of which give 4·73 to 6·37 mg/kg.

The authors[36,37] also compute an information ratio, the reciprocal of the residual mean square, which indicates the proportionate gain of information effected by the multiple observations on each animal. Whether or not allowance should be made at the extremes of the dosage range for replicated $p_i$ values of 0 and 1, which tend to artificially depress the residual sum of squares, is arguable. It appears, however, that their method may be of use in handling multiple, correlated, quantal responses.

213

## The 'Up and Down' (Sequential) Method

The experimental approach required by this method is similar to that which many workers employ in establishing the effective dose range for new compounds with unknown pharmacological characteristics. Dixon and Mood[38] showed that by following a more rigid procedure than usual, the results yield a very efficient estimate of the ED50, and if certain requirements are met a short-cut method of evaluating the error is also possible.

Firstly a geometric series of doses is established at which testing may be carried out. As in the Spearman-Kärber method the increment of log dose should be small. Testing takes place in one animal at a time, the outcome in that animal determining the dose for the next, and so on. Thus in a toxicity test, if the first animal survives, the second receives the next higher dose in the series. If the first dies, the second is given the next lower in the series. Finney[16b] gives the technique for evaluating the ED50 and its error by the Dixon and Mood method, substituting equations for the diagrams of the original authors.

Modifications of the procedure have been introduced by Brownlee, Hodges and Rosenblatt[39]. Recognizing the difficulty of forecasting the range of dose levels which will yield useful information, the first modification requires the experimenter to decide on the number of animals $N$, to be examined in the region of the ED50. The 'count down' for $n$ is not commenced until the first contrary response is reached. Thus, if testing begins at too low a dose level, the early results are likely to take the form of a series of animals each surviving a dose level one interval above that given to the preceding animal. A sufficiently high dose level is reached when the animal receiving it dies. This is taken as the first of the series of $n$, those tested prior to it being disregarded since the starting level was inadequately selected. Because this initial lead-in run of like results is eliminated, the calculation of LD50 differs slightly from that of Dixon and Mood. It is not necessary to test the last of the $N$ animals, but merely to know that it would have been tested at a dose level one above or one below that given to the penultimate animal, according to whether survival or death had been observed. The log LD50 is computed as the sum of the logarithms of the doses used for the last $N$ animals (including the final fictitious dosage) divided by $N$. Using this procedure, Rümke[40] determined the toxicity of thialbarbitone injected intravenously into rats pre-treated with saline.

*Table 5.16.* Rümke's sequential toxicity test

| Dose (mg/kg) | $x_i$ | 1 | 2 | 3 | 4 | 5 | 6 | 7 | 8 | 9 | 10 | 11 | 12 | 13 | 14 | 15 | 16 | 17 | 18 | 19 | 20 | 21 | 22 | 23 | 24 | $n_i$ |
|---|---|---|---|---|---|---|---|---|---|---|---|---|---|---|---|---|---|---|---|---|---|---|---|---|---|---|
| | | | | | | | | | | | | | | | | | | | | | | | | | Animal Number | |
| 127 | 2·10 | | | | | | | | | | | | | | + | | + | | + | | + | | + | | + | 6 |
| 113 | 2·05 | | | | | + | | + | | | | + | | 0 | | 0 | | 0 | | 0 | | 0 | | 0 | | 9 |
| 101 | 2·00 | | | | 0 | | 0 | | + | | 0 | | 0 | | | | | | | | | | | | | 4 |
| 90 | 1·95 | | | 0 | | | | | | 0 | | | | | | | | | | | | | | | | 1 |
| 80 | 1·90 | | 0 | | | | | | | | | | | | | | | | | | | | | | | |
| 71 | 1·85 | 0 | | | | | | | | | | | | | | | | | | | | | | | | |

'0' indicates survival, '+', death of a rat

$N$ was fixed as 20 rats. *Table 5.16* shows that four animals survived in a preliminary run before the main run commenced with the death of the 5th rat. 'Rat 24' is the fictitious animal which would have completed the group of 20 and would have received a dose of 127 mg/kg. Using this design the log LD50, $m$, is obtained as the mean log dose administered to the main group of 20 animals, including the fictitious dosage.

$$m = \frac{Sn_i x_i}{Sn_i} = \frac{41 \cdot 00}{20} = 2 \cdot 05$$

(the logarithms are taken to 2 decimals for simplicity).

The second modification[39] involves running two or more experiments simultaneously. The selection of doses is made independently from the observations, animal by animal, within each series. From each experiment an estimate of $m$ is obtained, and the mean of these values derived as the final estimate of log LD50. Since the Dixon and Mood method for determining the fiducial limits of $m$ is inadequate for small numbers, Rümke supports Finney in suggesting that probit analysis may be used. In this event the 'fictitious' animals have no place in the probit calculations.

### Combination of Results from Quantal Data

Although the expression of LD50 or ED50 in absolute units is inevitable in the appraisal of pharmacological agents, any uncontrollable variation in the sensitivity of the test animals limits the value of such estimates. Attempts are made either to estimate the magnitude of the uncontrolled variation from one test to another, or to overcome this effect by using a reference drug to serve as a biological standard, so that the activity of a compound is related to that of the reference material.

If it is assumed that several estimates of the log ED50 have been obtained such that on each occasion the values of $(m - \bar{x})$ and of $g$ were small enough to be ignored, then for each estimate the simplest expression for the variance of $m$ may be employed. In probit analysis for example, $V_m = 1/b^2 Snw$. The

Table 5.17. ED50 estimates of the analgesic activity of amidone in rats[41]

| Experiment No. | $m$ | $V_m$ | $W = 1/V_m$ | $Wm$ |
|---|---|---|---|---|
| 1 | 0·040 | 0·003663 | 273 | 10·920 |
| 2 | 0·005 | 0·003846 | 260 | 1·300 |
| 3 | 0·186 | 0·003096 | 323 | 60·078 |
| 4 | 0·057 | 0·004608 | 217 | 12·369 |
| 5 | 0·197 | 0·005348 | 187 | 36·839 |
| 6 | 0·514 | 0·010640 | 94 | 48·316 |
| | | | 1354 | 169·822 |

reciprocals of these values may be used as weights $(W)$ in obtaining a weighted mean estimate, $\bar{m}$, the variance of which is $1/SW$ in the absence of heterogeneity, or proportionately greater if significant heterogeneity is demonstrated. Thus, *Table 5.17*, gives log ED50 estimates for the analgesic effect of amidone in rats, measured by the 'heat method' 30 minutes after subcutaneous injection on 6 independent groups of rats at various times[41].

The weighted mean,

$$\bar{m} = \frac{SWm}{SW} = \frac{169 \cdot 822}{1354} = 0 \cdot 1254$$

the antilogarithm of which gives the weighted mean estimate of the ED50 as 1·33 mg/kg.

Homogeneity of the estimates may be tested by

$$\chi^2 = SWm^2 - (SWm)^2/SW$$
$$= 44 \cdot 414548 - 21 \cdot 299492 = 23 \cdot 12 \text{ (to 2 decimal places)}$$

With 5 degrees of freedom, this value of $\chi^2$ indicates heterogeneity, since it would only be exceeded with a probability of $P < 0 \cdot 001$. The estimate of the variance of $\bar{m}$ $(1/SW)$, must therefore be corrected as

$$V_{\bar{m}} = \left(\frac{\chi^2}{\text{d.f.}}\right)\left(\frac{1}{SW}\right) = \left(\frac{23 \cdot 11}{5}\right)\left(\frac{1}{1354}\right) = 0 \cdot 003415$$

The 95 per cent fiducial limits for $\bar{m}$ are given by

$$\bar{m} \pm t\sqrt{V_{\bar{m}}} = 0 \cdot 1254 \pm (2 \cdot 571)(0 \cdot 0584) \text{ or } -0 \cdot 0247 \text{ to } +0 \cdot 2755$$
$$(t = 2 \cdot 571, \text{ obtained from the tables for } P = 0 \cdot 95 \text{ and 5 d.f.})$$

These values are equivalent to doses of 0·94 to 1·88 mg/kg.

A similar series of estimates of the ED50 for morphine also gives evidence of heterogeneity, and the weighted mean has been computed as 2·90 mg/kg with $P = 0 \cdot 95$ limits from 2·05 to 4·08 mg/kg. Since the two drugs were tested in parallel on each of the six occasions, the estimates of the relative activity of amidone to that of morphine may be made separately for each experiment. If $M = $ log of the relative potency:

$$M = \text{log ED50 (morphine)} - \text{log ED50 (amidone)}$$
or $m_m - m_a$
and $V_M = V_{m_m} + V_{m_a}$

A combined estimate, $\overline{M}$, and a test of homogeneity of the 6 observed values is made as shown for the ED50 values.

Table 5.18. ED50 estimates of amidone and morphine analgesic activity in rats[41]

| Experiment No. | Amidone | | Morphine | | Morphine/Amidone | | |
|---|---|---|---|---|---|---|---|
| | $m$ | $V_m$ | $m$ | $V_m$ | $M$ | $V_m$ | $W = 1/V_M$ |
| 1 | 0·040 | 0·003663 | 0·512 | 0·003234 | 0·472 | 0·006897 | 145 |
| 2 | 0·005 | 0·003846 | 0·313 | 0·003348 | 0·308 | 0·007194 | 139 |
| 3 | 0·186 | 0·003096 | 0·530 | 0·002684 | 0·344 | 0·005780 | 173 |
| 4 | 0·057 | 0·004608 | 0·427 | 0·003867 | 0·370 | 0·008475 | 118 |
| 5 | 0·197 | 0·005348 | 0·358 | 0·005069 | 0·161 | 0·010417 | 96 |
| 6 | 0·514 | 0·010640 | 0·883 | 0·012616 | 0·369 | 0·023256 | 43 |

$\overline{M} = SMW/SW = 245\cdot747/714 = 0\cdot3442$, indicating that the activity of amidone was antilog $0\cdot3442$, or $2\cdot21$ times that of morphine.

$$\chi^2 = SWM^2 - (SWM)^2/SW$$
$$= 90\cdot459 - 84\cdot582 = 5\cdot877$$

For 5 d.f., $0\cdot5 > P > 0\cdot3$. There is therefore no evidence of significant heterogeneity among the estimates of $M$. Hence, $V_M = 1/SW = 1/714 = 0\cdot001401$ for $P = 0\cdot95$, $t = 1\cdot96$ for the theoretical distribution of error, and the fiducial limits of $M$ are

$$0\cdot3442 \pm 1\cdot96 \sqrt{0\cdot001401} \text{ or } 0\cdot2709 \text{ to } 0\cdot4175$$

Taking antilogs of these values, the limits of error ($P = 0\cdot95$) of the potency ratio of amidone to morphine are $1\cdot87$ to $2\cdot62$.

Not only has the uncontrolled source of variation between the tests been overcome by using morphine as a reference substance, but the lack of heterogeneity in the ratio estimates enables the full precision of the method to be used in obtaining the limits of error of the mean.

While calculations of this nature are commonplace in screening procedures, it is important not to lose sight of the assumptions on which they are based. Analyses using the transformations provide graphical as well as computational checks on these assumptions. It is desirable that the potency estimate of one drug in terms of another should be independent of the dose levels at which the comparison is made. This usually requires that the lines relating response to log dose for each substance are parallel. A test for the significance of departure from parallelism and the fitting of a common mean slope are carried out as follows. Assuming that parallel provisional lines have been drawn from which the expected probits (or angles) may be read, values of $S_{xx}$, $S_{xy}$, and $S_{yy}$ are computed separately for each drug as in normal analysis.

The common slope, $b_c$, used in the formula for the regression lines is

$$b_c = \frac{(S_{xy})_1 + (S_{xy})_2 + (S_{xy})_3 + \cdots}{(S_{xx})_1 + (S_{xx})_2 + (S_{xx})_3 + \cdots} = \frac{S(S_{xy})}{S(S_{xx})}$$

the subscripts 1, 2, 3 . . . representing the values from individual drugs.

When sufficient cycles of computation have been carried through to give satisfactory agreement between successive estimates of $Y$, the total $\chi^2$ may be computed as

$$\chi^2_{total} = S(S_{yy}) - \frac{[S(S_{xy})]^2}{S(S_{xx})}$$

This $\chi^2$ may be split into two parts, one representing overall heterogeneity about the regression lines, and the other, by difference, a residual corresponding to a measure of departure from parallelism of the individual lines. The heterogeneity value is the sum of the $\chi^2$ separately assessed for each drug, thus:

$$\chi^2_{heterogeneity} = S\left[(S_{yy})_i - \frac{(S_{xy})_i^2}{(S_{xx})_i}\right]$$

For the test of parallelism:

$$\chi^2_{parallelism} = \chi^2_{total} - \chi^2_{heterogeneity}$$

217

The degrees of freedom associated with these values depend on the number of drugs tested, and the numbers of dose levels used.

If $n_1, n_2, n_3 \ldots n_j$ represent the numbers of dose levels for each drug 1, 2, 3 . . . $j$, the total degrees of freedom are:

$$n_{\text{total}} = (n_1 + n_2 + n_3 \ldots + n_j) - (j + 1)$$

For $\chi^2_{\text{heterogeneity}}$ the degrees of freedom are,

$$n_{\text{heterogeneity}} = (n_1 + n_2 + n_3 \ldots n_j) - (2j)$$

and for $\chi^2_{\text{parallelism}}$:

$$n_{\text{parallelism}} = j - 1$$

In applying the tests, the significance of the heterogeneity $\chi^2$ is first assessed. If it is not significant, the $\chi^2$ for parallelism may likewise be compared with expectation. If, however, significant heterogeneity is indicated, the $\chi^2$ values are treated as sums of squares. By dividing by their respective degrees of freedom, the mean square so obtained for parallelism is compared with the mean square for heterogeneity, by the variance ratio test. The latter mean square is used as the heterogeneity factor in the estimation of variances.

In the absence of heterogeneity the full expression for the fiducial limits of $M$, the logarithm of relative potency, is:

$$M + \frac{g}{(1 - g)} (M - \bar{x}_2 + \bar{x}_1) \pm \frac{t}{b_c(1 - g)}$$

$$\times \sqrt{\left\{ 1 - g \left[ \frac{1}{(Snw)_1} + \frac{1}{(Snw)_2} \right] + (M - \bar{x}_2 + \bar{x}_1)^2 \, V_{b_c} \right\}}$$

Since,

$$g = t^2 \frac{V_{b_c}}{b_c}$$

the precision with which the slope is determined is of considerable importance. In many screening tests the numbers of animals employed is kept to a minimum, and for individual regressions $g$ is often too large to be ignored. However, as $V_b = 1/S_{xx}$ for each regression, so for the common slope,

$$V_{b_c} = \frac{1}{S(S_{xx})}$$

Provided no evidence of non-parallelism is found, it follows that the variance of the combined slope is approximately inversely proportional to the number of drugs to be compared (*i.e.* assuming their $S_{xx}$ values to be about equal). This strengthening of the estimate of slope frequently results in $g$ being negligible.

The danger exists, however, that a genuine difference of slope may remain undetected, since individual slopes are so poorly determined. This risk is probably slight when compared with the greater risk of transferring the results from one test situation to another.

In the expression for the fiducial limits of $M$, the item

$$(M - \bar{x}_2 + \bar{x}_1) = (m_2 - \bar{x}_2) - (m_1 - \bar{x}_1)$$

disappears only when each drug is tested at levels symmetrical about the 50 per cent response, when $m_i = \bar{x}_i$, or when by accident or design the mean log doses are at a constant interval from the respective log ED50's when $m_2 - \bar{x}_2 = m_1 - \bar{x}_1$. These items demonstrate the necessity for testing the drugs at equiactive dose levels.

## QUANTITATIVE ASSAYS

### Regression

The analysis of quantitative data usually requires the fitting of a straight line to some function of the observed response against some function of dose, such that deviations about the line are at a minimum. The regression coefficient of this fitted line is the slope, '$b$'.

The following example outlines the calculation of the regression coefficient relating 'percentage paralysis' of the isolated rat diaphragm-phrenic nerve preparation to log dose of $d$-tubocurarine chloride. The four responses obtained to each of 4 doses of drug are shown in *Table 5.19*.

*Table 5.19.* Rat diaphragm-phrenic nerve preparation. 'Percentage paralysis' produced by $d$-tubocurarine chloride (based on data of Mogey, Trevan and Young[42])

| Dose in tenths of mg | 1·000 | 1·111 | 1·234 | 1·371 |
|---|---|---|---|---|
| Log$_{10}$ dose ($x$) | 0·000 | 0·0457 | 0·0913 | 0·1370 |
| Percentage inhibition ($y$) | 25<br>18<br>17<br>19 | 36<br>35<br>32<br>37 | 48<br>52<br>49<br>52 | 64<br>60<br>67<br>67 |
| Total | 79 | 140 | 201 | 258 |

Grand total, $Sy = 678$; Grand total, $Sx = 1·0960$.

The regression coefficient, $b = S_{xy}/S_{xx}$, where $S_{xy}$ is sum of products of deviations for $xy$ and $S_{xx}$, the sum of squares of deviations for $x$.

$$S_{xy} = 79(0·0000) + 140(0·0457) + 201(0·0913) + 258(0·1370)$$
$$- \frac{(1·0960)(678)}{16} = 13·6523$$

$$S_{xx} = 4(0·0000) + 4(0·0457)^2 + 4(0·0913)^2 + 4(0·1370)^2 - \frac{(1·0960)^2}{16}$$
$$= 0·0417$$

therefore
$$b = \frac{13·6523}{0·0417} = 327$$

An analysis of variance may be carried out to check for the significance of the regression, and also for any deviations from linearity.

Table 5.20. Analysis of variance of data in Table 5.19

| Source of variation | Sum of squares | Degrees of freedom | Mean square | Variance ratio F | Probability P |
|---|---|---|---|---|---|
| Linear regression | 4470 | 1 | 4470 | 545 | <0·001 |
| Deviations from linearity | 2 | 2 | 1·0 | 0·1 | >0·05 |
| Residual error | 98 | 12 | 8·2 | | |
| Total | 4570 | 15 | | | |

The sums of squares are obtained from *Table 5.19* as follows:

Linear regression: $\dfrac{(S_{xy})^2}{S_{xx}} = \dfrac{(13 \cdot 6523)^2}{0 \cdot 0417} = 4470$

Deviations from linearity: $S(y_p S y_p) - \dfrac{(S_y)^2}{N} - \dfrac{(S_{xy})^2}{S_{xx}}$

where $y_p$ = total of responses for each dose.

$$\frac{(79)^2 + (140)^2 + (201)^2 + (258)^2}{4} - \frac{(678)^2}{16} - 4470 = 2$$

Total: $Sy^2 = (25)^2 + (18)^2 + + + (67)^2 - \dfrac{(678)^2}{16} = 4570$

The sum of squares for residual error is obtained by difference. The remainder of the analysis of variance is carried out as previously described. The linear regression is highly significant and there are no significant deviations from linearity.

The variance of the slope:

$$V_b = \frac{s^2}{S_{xx}} = \frac{8 \cdot 17}{0 \cdot 0417} = 195 \cdot 9233$$

and its standard error:

$$S.E.(b) = \sqrt{\frac{V_b}{N - 2}}$$

where N = total number of observations $= \sqrt{\dfrac{195 \cdot 9233}{14}} = \pm 3 \cdot 7409$

As an alternative to the calculation of regression, a simple graphical procedure may, under certain conditions, be used to obtain the best-fitting straight line through a series of points[43]. Responses must be measured at equal log dose-intervals with the same number of observations (1 or more) at each dose. The mean responses are plotted against log dose. The scale of the latter should enable the constant log dose interval (I) to be visually divisible by 3 (*Figure 5.7*). Points A and B are joined by a straight line. At a log dose interval of $\frac{2}{3}I$ from dose A the point on AB is designated B′. The same procedure is applied to the line B′C, giving a point, C′, $\frac{2}{3}I$ along the log dose scale from B′, and so on. The final point is labelled T. The whole process is then carried out in the opposite direction and the final point labelled U. A line drawn through UT is the best fitting straight line through the points, with minimum sum of squares of deviations of the responses. In practice, it is not necessary to draw all the lines, but merely to mark off their intersections at appropriate intervals on the dosage scale. This has been indicated in the reverse sequence of the figure.

Although the examples of the quantitative assays which follow are based on the use of *in vitro* preparations, the statistical procedures outlined may be

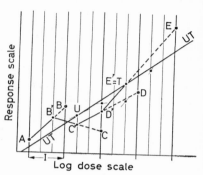

*Figure 5.7.* Graphical method of fitting regression line to response on log dose (after Askovitz[43]). For explanation see text.

adapted to *in vivo* assays. With the latter the design will usually be simpler, since a Latin Square arrangement applied to animals within cages or to order of dosing will only occasionally apply to screening tests. Response to a drug may be influenced by the health, strain, sex and body weight of the animal. Environmental conditions and the number of animals in a cage may also influence the response.

### Without Covariance

In an assay where doses are added repeatedly to a preparation and the response to each dose measured, the experimental design should permit the elimination of the effects of any trend in the sensitivity of the preparation, due either to changes in the preparation itself or to a carry-over effect of one dose to the next.

*Figure 5.8* is an example where such allowances have not been made[44]. Doses of the unknown are added in descending order of magnitude, followed by doses of the standard in the same way. The procedure is repeated on two further occasions. Ignoring dose level 2, there is progressive decrease in response with time, indicating a fall-off in sensitivity. The estimate of potency for the unknown is biased on the high side since unknown always precedes standard. Since doses are given in descending order of magnitude, it is not possible to eliminate bias due to a carry-over effect from one dose to the next.

The examples which follow incorporate designs which allow for known sources of variation.

Ergometrine produces a contraction of the isolated uterus of the stilbo-estrol-treated rat, the response being linearly related to log dose[45]. A synthetic compound related to ergometrine was assayed in terms of the latter using two dose levels of each of the substances $(2 + 2)$, the doses being injected every 4 minutes in the order determined by a $4 \times 4$ Latin square design. After the uterus had contracted to a dose, the solution was washed from the bath and fresh solution introduced, enabling the muscle to relax

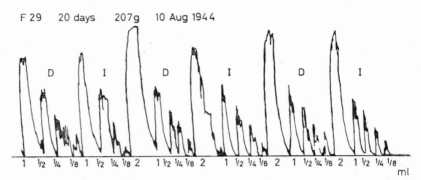

F 29    20 days    207g    10 Aug 1944

D    I    D    I    D    I

1  ½  ¼  ⅛ 1  ½  ¼  ⅛ 2    1 ½  ¼ ⅛  2    1  ½  ¼ ⅛  2    1  ½ ¼  ⅛ 2    1 ½  ¼ ⅛

ml

*Figure 5.8.* Response of isolated uterus of guinea-pig to posterior pituitary extract[44]. The experimental design does not allow for the carry-over effect from one dose to the next, or for tachyphylaxis.

before the introduction of the next dose. The height of the contraction to each dose was measured.

The doses were as follows:

$$A_H = 1 \cdot 6 \; \mu g \text{ of ergometrine acid maleate}$$
$$A_L = 1 \cdot 2 \; \mu g \text{ of ergometrine acid maleate}$$
$$B_H = 1 \cdot 6 \; \mu g \text{ of the synthetic 'ergometrine' acid maleate}$$
$$B_L = 1 \cdot 2 \; \mu g \text{ of the synthetic 'ergometrine' acid maleate}$$

The ratio between $A_H/A_L$ and $B_H/B_L$ is $1 \cdot 333$. The log of this ratio, $I = 0 \cdot 1249$.

The order of dosing was determined by the rows in sequence. The responses obtained are shown in *Table 5.21*.

$M$, the log of potency ratio $R$ (estimated potency of B in terms of A) is obtained from the equation

$$M = \bar{x}_A - \bar{x}_B - \frac{(\bar{y}_A - \bar{y}_B)}{b}$$

where $\bar{x}_A$, $\bar{x}_B$ are the mean log doses for A and B respectively, $\bar{y}_A$, $\bar{y}_B$ the corresponding mean responses, and $b$, the slope of the line connecting $y$ with $x$ (log dose). Since, in the present example, the same dose levels were used for both drugs, $\bar{x}_A = \bar{x}_B$, the expression for $M$ is reduced to $\frac{\bar{y}_B - \bar{y}_A}{b}$.

$$\bar{y}_A = \frac{169 + 109}{n} \text{ and } \bar{y}_B = \frac{184 + 99}{n}$$

therefore $\quad \bar{y}_B - \bar{y}_A = \frac{1}{n} \left[ (184 + 99) - (169 + 109) \right] = \frac{5}{n}$

where $n$ is the number of responses to each compound, 8.

*Table 5.21.* Uterine responses in assay of synthetic ergometrine acid maleate

| Column No. | 1 | 2 | 3 | 4 | Row totals |
|---|---|---|---|---|---|
| Row No. | | Responses ($y$) in mm | | | |
| 1 | $A_H$ 55 | $A_L$ 33 | $B_L$ 34 | $B_H$ 56 | 178 |
| 2 | $B_L$ 28 | $A_H$ 41 | $B_H$ 54 | $A_L$ 29 | 152 |
| 3 | $B_H$ 38 | $B_L$ 22 | $A_L$ 22 | $A_H$ 46 | 128 |
| 4 | $A_L$ 25 | $B_H$ 36 | $A_H$ 27 | $B_L$ 15 | 103 |
| Column totals | 146 | 132 | 137 | 146 | 561 Grand total = $Sy$ |
| Dose totals | $A_H$ 169 | $A_L$ 109 | $B_H$ 184 | $B_L$ 99 | |

$$b = \frac{\text{Sum of responses to high doses} - \text{sum of responses to low doses}}{n \,(\text{log high dose} - \text{log low dose})}$$

$$= \frac{(Sy_H - Sy_L)}{nI} = \frac{(169 + 184) - (109 + 99)}{8(0 \cdot 1249)} = 145$$

It is not necessary to calculate $b$ for the determination of $M$, but it is required for the calculation of the standard error of M at a later stage. $M = 5(0 \cdot 1249)/145 = 0 \cdot 0043$. $R =$ Potency ratio of B in terms of A $=$ Antilog $M = 1 \cdot 01$.

To determine the precision with which the estimate $R$ has been made, the standard error $(s_M)$ of $M$ is calculated. This is obtained from $s$, the standard deviation of a single observation $(y)$, deduced from an analysis of variance, where variation due to known causes can be separated from the inherent variation of the uterus. The Latin square design permits the removal of error due to alteration of the response of the preparation with time. The columns (*Table 5.21*) give a measure of the mean effect over the time taken for the application of single doses; the rows give the mean effect over the time taken for groups of 4 doses. The other known sources of variation are those due to doses, subdivided as differences between A and B, difference between high and low doses (slope) and difference between the slopes of the two regression lines (deviation from parallelism). The analysis of variance showing how these 5 sources of variation are removed from the total error is given in *Table 5.22*.

The sums of squares of deviations, $S_{yy}$ (*Table 5.22*) are calculated from *Table 5.21*.

223

Table 5.22. Analysis of variance of data in Table 5.21.

| Source of variation | Sum of squares $S_{yy}$ | Degrees of freedom | Mean square | Variance ratio $F$ | Probability $P$ |
|---|---|---|---|---|---|
| Rows | 775 | 3 | 258·3 | 7·95 | 0·05 > P > 0·01 |
| Columns | 36 | 3 | 12·0 | 0·37 | > 0·20 |
| Difference between A and B | 1·6 | 1 | 1·6 | 0·05 | > 0·20 |
| Difference between high and low doses | 1314·1 | 1 | 1314·1 | 40·43 | < 0·001 |
| Deviation from parallelism | 39·1 | 1 | 39·1 | 1·20 | > 0·20 |
| Residual Error | 195 | 6 | 32·5 | | |
| Total | 2361 | 15 | | | |

Rows: $\dfrac{(178)^2 + (152)^2 + (128)^2 + (103)^2}{4} - \dfrac{(561)^2}{16} = 775$

Columns: $\dfrac{(146)^2 + (132)^2 + (137)^2 + (146)^2}{4} - \dfrac{(561)^2}{16} = 36$

Difference between A and B: $\dfrac{(169 + 109 - 184 - 99)^2}{16} = 1\cdot6$

Difference between high and low doses: $\dfrac{(169 + 184 - 109 - 99)^2}{16}$
$$= 1314\cdot1$$

Deviations from parallelism: $\dfrac{(169 + 99 - 184 - 109)^2}{16} = 39\cdot1$

The sum of squares of deviations of all the observations from their grand mean is

$$Sy^2 - \frac{(561)^2}{16} = (55^2 + 33^2 + 34^2 + 56^2 + 28^2 + \text{etc.}) - \frac{(561)^2}{16} = 2361$$

The residual sum of squares is calculated by subtracting the sums of squares of the 5 known sources of error from the total sum of squares,

$$2361 - 775 - 36 - 1\cdot6 - 1314\cdot1 - 39\cdot1 = 195$$

The mean squares are derived as before. The variance ratios of the individual mean squares to that of the residual error are tested for significance.

The analysis of variance shows in this particular assay that, while there is a change in the sensitivity of the uterus over the 4 rows with time, there is no significant difference among columns, nor is there deviation from parallelism. The combined slope, the difference between high and low doses, has a significant $F$ ratio. The assay is therefore valid, and the residual error mean square may be used to calculate the variance of $M$.

The standard error of $M$ may be obtained from the formula:

$$s^2{}_M = \frac{4s^2}{Nb^2}\left(\frac{M^2}{I^2} + 1\right) = \frac{4(32\cdot5)}{16(21058\cdot68)}\left[\left(\frac{0\cdot0043}{0\cdot1249}\right)^2 + 1\right] = 0\cdot0003863$$

therefore
$$s_M = \sqrt{0\cdot0003863} = \pm\,0\cdot01965$$

The fiducial limits of $M$ are obtained by the addition and subtraction of $ts_M$ and $M$. $t$ is 2·447 for 6 d.f., $P = 0\cdot95$.

Therefore the fiducial limits of $M$ are:

$$0\cdot0043 \pm 0\cdot01965(2\cdot447) = \bar{1}\cdot9562 \text{ and } 0\cdot0524$$

The antilogarithms of these values are 0·90 and 1·13 respectively. Therefore, B the synthetic compound has a potency ratio of 1·01 in terms of ergometrine with limits of error ($P = 0\cdot95$) from 0·90 to 1·13.

Since in the analysis of variance (*Table 5.22*) the variance ratio of the difference between A and B was not significant, it could have been deduced that the fiducial limits of the potency ratio would have fallen on either side of unity. For screening purposes the calculation of limits of error may be deemed unnecessary.

Suxamethonium causes the rectus abdominis muscle of the frog to contract, the response being linearly related to log dose between about 25 per cent and 75 per cent of the maximal response[46]. In an assay, doses are chosen to give responses within this portion of the curve. Since the response to a given dose decreases linearly with time, an experimental design should be chosen to enable this source of error to be removed from the residual error. The results obtained from a 4 × 4 randomized block, a 4 × 4 Latin square and a 25-dose serially balanced design, based on (2 + 2) dose patterns, were compared (*Table 5.23*).

While the slopes obtained by all 3 designs are similar, the variance, $s^2$, is least with the Latin square design, and the precision of the assay is greatest. The 25-dose serially balanced design is the least efficient.

*Table 5.23.* Assay of a solution of suxamethonium using three different designs[46]

| Design of assay | Potency $\mu$g/ml | 95% Fiducial limits | | Slope (b) | Variance $s^2$ | Index of precision $\lambda = s/b$ |
| --- | --- | --- | --- | --- | --- | --- |
| | | $\mu$g/ml | % | | | |
| Latin Square | 92·81 | 91·23–94·39 | 98·3–101·7 | 26·00 | 1·50 | 0·047 |
| Randomized block | 92·41 | 87·60–97·40 | 94·8–105·4 | 21·38 | 11·40 | 0·158 |
| Serially balanced | 91·75 | 86·43–97·44 | 94·2–106·2 | 29·83 | 24·63 | 0·166 |

Anaphylatoxin, prepared by incubation of rat plasma with agar or starch, stimulates guinea-pig ileum. Repeated doses produce decreasing effects until the preparation becomes desensitized (tachyphylaxis). Each response is thus correlated with the response to the previous dose. Matching techniques and randomized blocks do not allow for the marked bias introduced by this tachyphylactic effect. A 4 × 4 Latin square design and (2 + 2) dose pattern is suitable[47].

It is possible to obtain responses to 4 doses of anaphylatoxin on a piece of ileum, so that for each column of the Latin square design a fresh piece of ileum from the same guinea-pig is used. Doses are added in the order determined by columns, and the height of contraction after each dose is measured.

In the analysis of variance, the sum of squares attributable to columns removes from the total error the error due to the four pieces of ileum, and the sum of squares attributed to rows removes the error (or bias) due to tachyphylaxis.

*Table 5.24* shows the analysis of variance of a typical assay.

If the variance of error is recalculated by including the sum of squares corresponding to rows (tachyphylactic effect) with 9 d.f., the corresponding variance will be 292·7 and the standard deviation of a single response 17·1 instead of 6·28, a 7–8 fold decrease in the amount of information given by the assay. This underlines the importance of using the Latin square design to eliminate bias due to tachyphylaxis.

*Table 5.24*. Analysis of variance of data from assay of anaphylatoxin[47]

| Source of variation | Sum of squares | Degrees of freedom | Mean square | Variance ratio F | Probability P |
|---|---|---|---|---|---|
| Between doses | 2779·69 | 3 | 926·56 | 23·5 | <0·01 |
| Between rows | 2397·69 | 3 | 799·23 | 20·3 | <0·01 |
| Between columns | 1260·69 | 3 | 420·23 | 10·7 | <0·01 |
| Residual error | 236·37 | 6 | 39·40 | | |
| Total | 6674·44 | 15 | — | | |

Use has been made of the $4 \times 4$ Latin square designs with a $(2 + 2)$ dose procedure for the comparative assay of depolarizing substances on the isolated semispinalis muscle of the chick[48].

### With Covariance

It is not always possible to eliminate concomitant sources of error by, for example, selecting animals from a narrow weight range. If the response is directly related to some other measurement, such as body weight or initial value, allowance is made for such relationships by the technique of covariance. The example which follows shows how this may be done in an *in vitro* test where the weight of tissue provides the source of variation to be eliminated.

The uptake of glucose by the epididymal fat pad of the rat is enhanced in the presence of insulin-like substances[49], a response which provides the basis of a method for their assay.

In this work the circular Warburg apparatus fitted with 16 flasks was used to assay a sample for insulin-like activity, employing a $(2 + 2)$ dose procedure in a $4 \times 4$ Latin square design[49a]. The two epididymal fat pads from each of six rats, 113 to 125 g in body weight, were each divided

226

into 8 pieces. As there is considerably greater variation in the response to insulin between rats than within rats, a piece of fat pad from each rat was included in each flask. To enable the variation within rats from left to right pad to be balanced overall, alternate left and right pieces of fat pad were placed in consecutive flasks around the Warburg. This alternation was reversed with each rat to achieve a balance. Two solutions of insulin, one

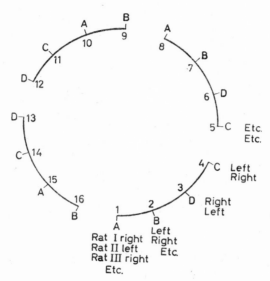

*Figure 5.9.* Plan of Warburg apparatus showing a 4 × 4 Latin square design applied to the 16 flasks, and the distribution of fat pad tissue to each flask.

of 'high' and one of 'low' concentration, and two dilutions of the insulin-like preparation diluted similarly were used. The ratio between 'high' and 'low' concentrations was constant (2:1).

The four solutions assigned at random to the letters ABCD, were added to the flasks in the order determined by the Latin square. After 3 hours incubation at 37° the glucose concentration and weight of fat pad within each flask were determined.

*Figure 5.9* shows the 4 × 4 Latin square design applied to the 16 flasks, and the distribution of tissue.

The data, arranged in *Table 5.25* facilitate calculation of the mean potency and the residual error mean square.

To find whether the response $y$ should be corrected for tissue weight, $x$, an analysis of covariance is carried out to determine whether there is a linear regression of $y$ on $x$ (*Table 5.26*).

$S_{xx}$, the sum of squares of deviations of $x$ are calculated from *Table 5.25*. Difference between standard and unknown:

$$\frac{[(357 + 342) - (357 + 341)]^2}{16} = \frac{1}{16} = 0$$

227

*Table 5.25.* Assay of a sample for insulin-like activity using the epididymal fat pad of the rat

| Row | A = $S_H$ | | B = $S_L$ | | C = $U_H$ | | D = $U_L$ | | Sum | |
|---|---|---|---|---|---|---|---|---|---|---|
| | $x$ | $y$ | $x$ | $y$ | $x$ | $y$ | $x$ | $y$ | $x$ | $y$ |
| 1 | 83 | 129·3 | 80 | 141·5 | 98 | 124·8 | 84 | 140·0 | 345 | 535·6 |
| 2 | 116 | 118·5 | 80 | 139·8 | 77 | 131·3 | 90 | 135·5 | 363 | 525·1 |
| 3 | 88 | 137·0 | 84 | 139·8 | 96 | 128·0 | 100 | 139·3 | 368 | 544·1 |
| 4 | 70 | 138·0 | 97 | 134·8 | 86 | 131·8 | 68 | 141·5 | 321 | 546·1 |
| Sum | 357 | 522·8 | 341 | 555·9 | 357 | 515·9 | 342 | 556·3 | 1397 | 2150·9 |
| Mean | 89·25 | 130·70 | 85·25 | 138·98 | 89·25 | 128·98 | 85·50 | 139·08 | 87·31 | 134·43 |

| Column totals | 1 | 2 | 3 | 4 |
|---|---|---|---|---|
| $x$ | 312 | 344 | 330 | 411 |
| $y$ | 541·9 | 545·8 | 545·8 | 517·4 |

$x$ = fat pad weight (mg). Assumed that $S_H = U_H = 48\ \mu u/ml$.
$y$ = glucose remaining in flask (mg%). $S_L = U_L = 24\ \mu u/ml$.
Dose ratio = 2:1.

*Table 5.26.* Analysis of variance of data in *Table 5.25.*

| Source of variation | $S_{xx}$ | $S_{xy}$ | $S_{yy}$ | Corrected $S_{yy}$ | Degrees of freedom | Mean square | Variance ratio $F$ | Probability $P$ |
|---|---|---|---|---|---|---|---|---|
| Standard v. Unknown | 0 | −0·4 | 2·64 | 2·25 | 1 | 2·25 | 0·81 | >0·2 |
| Regression | 60 | −142·2 | 337·64 | 212·41 | 1 | 212·41 | 75·86 | 0·001 |
| Deviations from parallelism | 0 | 0·5 | 3·33 | 3·82 | 1 | 3·82 | 1·36 | >0·2 |
| Rows | 339 | −70·4 | 68·67 | 81·14 | 3 | 27·05 | 9·66 | 0·05 |
| Columns | 1399 | −402·1 | 140·23 | 82·28 | 3 | 27·43 | 9·80 | 0·01 |
| Residual error | 405 | −198·6 | 111·38 | 13·99 | 6 | 2·80 | | |
| Total | 2203 | −813·2 | 663·89 | 395·89 | 15 | | | |

Regression (Difference between high and low doses):

$$\frac{[(357 + 357) - (342 + 341)]^2}{16} = \frac{(31)^2}{16} = 60$$

Deviations from parallelism:

$$\frac{[(342 + 357) - (341 + 357)]^2}{16} = \frac{1}{16} = 0$$

Rows:

$$\frac{(345)^2 + (363)^2 + (368)^2 + (321)^2}{4} - \frac{(1397)^2}{16} = 339$$

Columns:

$$\frac{(312)^2 + (344)^2 + (330)^2 + (411)^2}{4} - \frac{(1397)^2}{16} = 1399$$

Total:

$$(83)^2 + (116)^2 + (88)^2 + (70)^2 + + + (100)^2 + (68)^2 - \frac{(1397)^2}{16} = 2203$$

Therefore residual sum of squares $S_{xx}$ attributable to $x$ is 2203 minus all other sums of squares = *405*.

Sums of squares attributable to $y$ ($S_{yy}$) are calculated in the same way as those for $x$, but using the values for $y$. Similarly the sums of products for $xy$($S_{xy}$) are calculated from the products of $x$ and $y$.

The sums of squares attributable to the regression of response on tissue weight is $(S_{xy})^2/(S_{xx})$ which is obtained from the sum of squares for residual error in *Table 5.26*, i.e. $(-198\cdot6)^2/405 = 97\cdot39$. This value is subtracted from $S_{yy}$ to obtain corrected $S_{yy}$, $111\cdot38 - 97\cdot39 = 13\cdot99$, the residual sum of squares after removing error due to the regression of response on tissue weight. One d.f. is lost in making the covariance adjustment, so that the corrected residual sum of squares must be divided by $6 - 1$ d.f. to obtain the residual error mean square, $13\cdot99/5 = 2\cdot80$. The significance of the sum of squares due to regression of response on tissue weight is determined by a variance ratio test, using the corrected residual error mean square as divisor, $97\cdot39/2\cdot80 = 34\cdot78$. This has 5 and 1 d.f., and its level of significance, $P$, is $0\cdot01$.

The slope of this regression $b_1 = S_{xy}/S_{xx} = -198\cdot6/405 = -0\cdot49037$. The formula for corrected $S_{yy} = S_{yy} - 2b_1 S_{xy} + b^2_1 S_{xx}$. This is applied to each $S_{yy}$ in the analysis of variance to obtain the corrected value of $S_{yy}$. For example, corrected $S_{yy}$ for Standard v. Unknown is

$$2\cdot64 - [2(-0\cdot49037)](-0\cdot4) + (-0\cdot49037)^2 0^2 = 2\cdot25$$

The variance ratios and the level of their significance are calculated as described previously. *Table 5.26* shows that the assay is valid since there is a significant regression of corrected response on $\log_{10}$ dose, and no significant deviation from parallelism. The significant error mean squares for rows and columns indicate the importance of using a Latin 'square' design for increasing the precision of the assay.

### Calculation of Relative Potency

$\bar{y}'_U - \bar{y}'_S$, the difference of the means between standard and unknown after correcting for tissue weight is

$$\frac{(Sy_U - Sy_S) - b_1(Sx_U - Sx_S)}{N/2} = -\frac{6\cdot5 - (-0\cdot49037)(1)}{8} = -0\cdot751204$$

where $b_1$ is the regression coefficient of $y$ on tissue weight, $x$, and $N =$ total number of observations. $b$, regression of corrected responses, $y'$, on $\log\sqrt{2}$ dose is

$$\frac{(Sy_H - Sy_L) - b_1(Sx_H - Sx_L)}{N} = -\frac{73\cdot5 - (-0\cdot49037)(31)}{16} = -3\cdot6437$$

$$m = \log\sqrt{2} \text{ potency ratio} = \frac{\bar{y}'_U - \bar{y}'_S}{b} = \frac{-0\cdot751204}{-3\cdot6437} = 0\cdot2062$$

$M = \log_{10}$ potency ratio $= m \cdot \log_{10}\sqrt{2} = (0\cdot2062)(0\cdot1505) = 0\cdot0310$. Potency ratio $=$ Antilog $0\cdot0310 = 1\cdot07$ or equivalent to $1\cdot07(48)$ $\mu u/ml$ $= 51\cdot4$ $\mu u/ml$, since the assumed potency of the unknown was $48$ $\mu u/ml$.

The fiducial limits of this estimate are given by the expression

$$M \pm \frac{t}{b} \log_{10}\sqrt{2}[s^2(v_{11} - 2mv_{12} + m^2v_{22})]^{\frac{1}{2}}$$

where $M$ is log potency ratio; $t$, Student's value for 5 d.f. $(P = 0\cdot95)$, $b$ is the slope of the regression of corrected response on $\log\sqrt{2}$ dose, $s^2$ is corrected residual error mean square and the three remaining terms are given by the equations: $s^2v_{11}$, the variance of the difference between the corrected means for standard and unknown,

$$s^2\left[\frac{1}{n_s} + \frac{1}{n_u} + \frac{(Sx_U - Sx_S)^2}{n^2{}_S}\left(\frac{1}{S_{xx}}\right)\right]$$

$$= 2\cdot80\left[\frac{1}{8} + \frac{1}{8} + \left(\frac{1}{8}\right)^2 \cdot \left(\frac{1}{405}\right)\right] = 2\cdot80(0\cdot250039)$$

$s^2v_{22}$, the variance of the adjusted regression

$$= s^2\left[\frac{1}{N} + \frac{(Sx_H - Sx_L)^2}{N^2}\left(\frac{1}{S_{xx}}\right)\right]$$

$$= 2\cdot80\left[\frac{1}{16} + \left(\frac{31}{16}\right)^2 \cdot \left(\frac{1}{405}\right)\right] = 2\cdot80(0\cdot071769)$$

$s^2v_{12}$, the covariance of the corrected means and regression

$$= s^2\left[\left(\frac{Sx_U - Sx_S}{n_S}\right)\left(\frac{Sx_H - Sx_L}{N}\right)\right] \cdot \frac{1}{S_{xx}}$$

$$= 2\cdot80\left(\frac{1}{8}\right)\left(\frac{31}{16}\right)\left(\frac{1}{405}\right) = 2\cdot80(0\cdot000598)$$

The fiducial limits are:

$$0\cdot0310 \pm \left[\frac{2\cdot571}{-24\cdot2104}\right.$$

$$\left. \sqrt{\{2\cdot80(0\cdot250039) - 2(0\cdot2062)(0\cdot000598) + (0\cdot2062)^2 0\cdot071769\}}\right]$$

$$= 0\cdot0310 \pm 0\cdot0894$$

Fiducial limits $(P = 0\cdot95)$ are:

Antilog of $\bar{1}\cdot9416$ and $0\cdot1204 = 0\cdot87$ and $1\cdot32$, or $41\cdot8$ to $63\cdot4$ $\mu u/ml$.

These limits of error have been calculated without using the value $g$ (see page 207). When $g$ is taken into account the limits of error are 41·8 to 64·5 $\mu u/ml$, which are not very different from those obtained using the more simplified formulae. In screening procedures when $g$ is less than 0·1 it may be ignored.

### Slope Ratio Design

The response, or some function of the response, of a biological system to a drug is usually linearly related to log dose. In some microbiological systems, however, response is found to be linearly related to dose. While only a few pharmacological examples of such a relationship have so far been found, Gaddum[7] states that it may apply when the dose is near the threshold of response and the data include measurements on control animals which receive no drug at all.

Since the procedure for statistical analysis is the same whether a microbiological or macrobiological system is used, an example is given of the assay of riboflavine using a 'common-zero' five point design[50]. Twenty tubes containing nutrient medium devoid of riboflavine are divided into 5 equal groups. To one group is added 0·20 $\mu g$ of riboflavine, to another 0·10 $\mu g$; two further groups are treated similarly with 0·05 g and 0·025 g of malt respectively; the fifth group remains untreated. All are inoculated with *Lactobacillus helveticus*. The amount of lactic acid formed in each tube after incubation is determined by titration with sodium hydroxide solution. The doses of riboflavine (standard) and malt (unknown) are respectively equally spaced on an arithmetic scale. *Table 5.27* shows the data obtained.

*Table 5.27.* Data from the assay of riboflavine[50]

| Group | Individual responses (ml N/10 NaOH) | | | | Mean response |
|---|---|---|---|---|---|
| Zero dose | 1·90 | 2·25 | 2·00 | 2·20 | $Z = 2.088$ |
| ½ unit Std. Prep. | 4·85 | 5·00 | 5·25 | 4·90 | $S_1 = 5.000$ |
| 1 unit Std. Prep. | 8·35 | 8·20 | 7·95 | 7·80 | $S_2 = 8.075$ |
| ½ unit Test Prep. | 4·00 | 4·40 | 4·50 | 4·10 | $U_1 = 4.250$ |
| 1 unit Test Prep. | 6·05 | 6·20 | 6·10 | 6·10 | $U_2 = 6.113$ |

1 unit Std. Prep. = 0·20 $\mu g$ of riboflavine. 1 unit Unknown Prep. = 0·05 $\mu g$ of malt

$L_S$ and $L_U$ are corrections for the deviations of $S_1$ and $U_1$ from the lines joining the zero and high doses. Each is zero if each set of three points lies exactly on a straight line.

Calculate $L_S = Z + S_2 - 2S_1 = 2.088 + 8.075 - 2(5.000) = 0.163$
$$L_U = Z + U_2 - 2U_1 = 2.088 + 6.113 - 2(4.250)$$
$$= -0.299$$
$$a = Z - (L_S + L_U)/7 = 2.088 - (-0.136/7) = 2.107$$

$b_S$ and $b_U$ are the slopes of the two lines, obtained from the equations

$$b_S = (S_2 - Z) + (6L_U - L_S)/35 = 5.987 - (1.957/35) = 5.931$$
$$b_U = (U_2 - Z) + (6L_S - L_U)/35 = 4.025 + (1.277/35) = 4.061$$

The values 7 and 35 are divisors appropriate to the '5-point design'. Values applicable to other designs are given by Finney[11c].

The potency ratio, $R$, is the ratio of the slopes

$$b_U/b_S = \frac{4\cdot061}{5\cdot931} = 0\cdot6847$$

Correcting for the unknown amounts of substances added to the tubes, the potency of the sample of malt is $0\cdot6847(0\cdot2/0\cdot05) = 2\cdot74$ $\mu$g per g.

The residual error mean square is obtained from an analysis of variance.

Table 5.28. Analysis of variance of data in Table 5.27.

| Source of variance | Sum of squares | Degrees of freedom | Mean square |
|---|---|---|---|
| Doses | 78·7333 | 4 | |
| Residual error | 0·5412 | 15 | 0·03608 |
| Total | 79·2745 | 19 | |

$$s = \sqrt{0\cdot03608} = \pm\,0\cdot190$$

Standard error of $L_S$ and $L_U$,

$$s_L = \sqrt{\frac{30s^2}{N}} = 1\cdot225(0\cdot190) = 0\cdot23275$$

If $L_S$ and $L_U$ are each significantly less than twice $s_L$ the assay is valid. This is checked by determining the significance of the ratio $L_S/s_L$ in a 't-test' with the number of d.f. for residual error, i.e. 15.

The standard error of the potency is:

$$s_R = \frac{s}{b_S} \sqrt{\frac{8}{7N}} (8R^2 - 9R + 8) =$$

$$\frac{0\cdot190}{5\cdot931} \sqrt{\frac{8}{140}} [8(0\cdot6847)^2 - 9(0\cdot6847) + 8] = \pm\,0\cdot0181$$

Fiducial limits of $R = 0\cdot6847 \pm 2\cdot131(0\cdot0181)$, where $2\cdot131 = t$ for 15 d.f. $(P = 0\cdot95)$, therefore $R = 0\cdot6847 \pm 0\cdot0386$ or $0\cdot6461$ and $0\cdot7233$. These are equivalent to $2\cdot58$ to $2\cdot89$ $\mu$g/g.

While the statistical methods for the analysis of data showing a linear relationship between dose on an arithmetic scale and response have evolved from microbiological studies, there are nevertheless a number of macrobiological examples showing this relationship. A linear dose-response curve has been found between comb growth of caponized birds and dose of androsterone[51], degree of healing and dose of vitamin $D_2$ in rachitic rats[52], thyroid weight and dose of thyrotropic extract in chicks[53], adrenal weight and dose of adrenocarticotrophic hormone in chicks[54], and reciprocal of survival time and concentration of mustard or phosgene gas to which mice were exposed[55]. More recently a slope ratio design has been used in the assay of the antitetanus toxin activity of drugs[56] and in the chromatographic assay of insulin, where the spectrophotometrically determined mean extinction of the eluate was found to be linearly related to the dose of insulin applied to the paper[57].

## Assays Based on Time

In many experiments time is used as a measure of dose or response. In studies employing radiation from a constant source, for example, responses may be related to the duration of exposure.

The more common usage from which examples are given relates to the measurement of response in terms of latent period, duration of action or survival time.

### Survival time

In a quantal assay each animal contributes either a positive or negative reading. Since more information is usually yielded by quantitative than by quantal methods, the time elapsing from injection of a drug to the response obtained has been used as a continuous variate. In the determination of the toxicity of neoarsphenamine[58], doses were chosen such that all the mice died. The survival time of each animal was then recorded (*Table 5.29*).

*Table 5.29.* Assay of neoarsphenamine by survival time method[58]

| Percentage strength of solution | $5\frac{1}{2}$ | 6 | $6\frac{1}{2}$ | 7 | $7\frac{1}{2}$ | 8 | $8\frac{1}{2}$ |
|---|---|---|---|---|---|---|---|
| | Survival time in minutes | | | | | | |
| Experiment No. 1 | (1)<br>248<br>381<br>710<br>860<br>1039<br>1309 | (1)<br>57<br>107<br>209<br>294<br>390<br>499<br>639<br>704 | (2)<br>(10)†<br>164<br>290<br>290<br>290<br>322<br>321<br>521<br>564 | (3)<br>98<br>148<br>161<br>224<br>229<br>228<br>493<br>536<br>549 | (3)<br>87<br>89<br>103<br>103<br>238<br>293<br>354<br>404<br>476 | (4)<br>78<br>113<br>115<br>128<br>157<br>202<br>207<br>281 | (3)<br>27*<br>89<br>98<br>116<br>117<br>119<br>140<br>147<br>210 |

\* Animal died during the latent period, a most unusual occurrence. Mice weighed between 13–15 g. Injections intravenously.
† () discarded as non-specific deaths.

The data were plotted graphically using various functions of response and dose. Ignoring non-specific deaths, mean log survival time was linearly related to log dose.

The means of log survival time and their variances are shown in *Table 5.30*. There is no correlation between the variance and percentage strength of solution. This is confirmed by applying Bartlett's Test[59], which determines whether the variances of different groups are homogeneous. ($\chi^2$ between variances $= 6\cdot6175$, degrees of freedom $= 6$, $0\cdot50 > P > 0\cdot30$, which is not significant.) The data can therefore be subjected to analysis of variance.

In the assay of neoarsphenamine using $(2 + 2)$ dose procedures, the limits of error for graded response assays are roughly half as wide as those for quantal response assays when using the same number of animals. The ratio of the variances of the estimates of potency is $1:4$. The precision of the assay is four times as great, hence only one quarter of the number of animals is required if a graded response assay is used. This finding may not apply to all drugs.

The example quoted is dependent on the use of doses producing responses in all animals. However, it may happen that several animals fail to respond, and some workers assume that the response of the animals occurs at infinite time. If the reciprocal of time is used as metameter, then infinite time gives

Table 5.30. Means and variances of $\log_{10}$ survival time from data in Table 5.29.

| Percentage strength of solution | $5\frac{1}{2}$ | 6 | $6\frac{1}{2}$ | 7 | $7\frac{1}{2}$ | 8 | $8\frac{1}{2}$ |
|---|---|---|---|---|---|---|---|
| Mean $\log_{10}$ survival time (min) | 2·816 | 2·440 | 2·511 | 2·400 | 2·288 | 2·172 | 2·024 |
| Variance $= \sigma^2 \times$ 10,000 | 7577 | 14882 | 2784 | 7162 | 9357 | 3212 | 6110 |
| No. of animals per group | 6 | 8 | 8 | 9 | 9 | 8 | 9 |

a value of zero on the reciprocal time scale. In an analysis of variance, for each value of zero one degree of freedom is subtracted from the degrees of freedom attributable to residual error. In the example given in Table 5.29, the reciprocals of the survival times show marked heterogeneity of variances between groups ($\chi^2 = 38\cdot57$, $P < 0\cdot001$ for 6 d.f.), so that it is not possible to use such a metameter in analyses of variance. Comparisons however may still be made using the $t$ test.

Liljestrand[60] used log survival time as metameter for the assay of the curative activity of neoarsphenamine in mice infected with trypanosomes. Infected mice were injected with the drug, and the numbers surviving within approximately equal log intervals of time were recorded. Since the first infected mouse, untreated, died after 55 hours it was assumed that peak infection occurred between 48–52 hours. The probit for the percentage of mice dying within each time interval when plotted against the logarithm of (survival time in hours minus 48 and 52 respectively) produced a straight line relationship. $(2 + 2)$ assays were carried out based on this.

In studying the survival times of mice infected with doses of a fatal tumour, Schneiderman[3] observed that no deaths were expected within 5 days of infection and the logarithm of (survival time in days minus 5) appeared to be normally distributed.

*Latent period*

Ergometrine produces contraction of the isolated uterus of the oestrone-treated rabbit. The latent period, from the addition of the drug to the bath until the uterus contracts, is a function of the dose, a linear relationship existing between log latent period and log dose[61].

Various doses of the unknown are alternated with a constant dose of the standard, a $(1 + n)$ design. Doses of the unknown are chosen such that some produce a latent period longer and some shorter than those with the standard. Doses are selected to give latent periods of about 2–5 minutes.

As the latent period for a constant dose of standard varies throughout the assay, the latent period for each dose of the unknown is compared with the expected latent period for the standard at that time, by averaging the latent periods obtained with standard immediately preceding and following the dose of the unknown. Since log latent period is normally distributed, all latent periods must be converted to logarithms before calculations are made.

*Table 5.31.* Assay of ergometrine on isolated rabbit uterus[61]

| Dose No. | Dose (ml) | | Latent period | |
|---|---|---|---|---|
| | Standard | Unknown | Standard | Unknown |
| 1 | 1·0 | | 5 min 30 sec | |
| 2 | 1·0 | | 3 min 26 sec | |
| 3 | 0·8 | | 3 min 18 sec | |
| 4 | | 0·8 | | 2 min 31 sec |
| 5 | 0·8 | | 2 min 10 sec | |
| 6 | | 0·9 | | 1 min 57 sec |
| 7 | 0·8 | | 1 min 58 sec | |
| 8 | | 0·7 | | 2 min 43 sec |
| 9 | 0·8 | | 1 min 59 sec | |
| 10 | | 1·0 | | 2 min  3 sec |
| 11 | 0·8 | | 2 min 42 sec | |
| 12 | | 0·8 | | 3 min  1 sec |
| 13 | 0·8 | | 2 min 54 sec | |
| 14 | | 0·9 | | 3 min 32 sec |
| 15 | 0·8 | | 3 min 27 sec | |
| 16 | | 1·0 | | 2 min 40 sec |
| 17 | 0·8 | | 4 min 16 sec | |

*Table 5.31* is a protocol of an assay of one sample of ergometrine in terms of another, where the unknown and standard are assumed to be equipotent.

*Table 5.32* shows the conversion of the data in *Table 5.31* to $\log_{10}$. The interpolated response, $y_S$, is the average of the log latent periods of alternate responses to the constant dose of standard. Each value of the unknown is then subtracted from the corresponding value of the standard, giving $x$ for log-dose difference and $y$ for log-latent period difference.

The data in *Table 5.32* are used to fit a straight line to the regression of $y$ on $x$, finding the value of $x$ on this line corresponding to $y = 0$, and determining the standard error of this value of $x$. These calculations are given in *Table 5.33*.

Corrected $S_{yy}$ is obtained by subtracting the sum of squares attributable to regression from the total sum of squares. $s^2$ is the residual error mean square obtained by dividing corrected $S_{yy}$ by its corresponding degrees of freedom, *i.e.* total d.f., $n - 1$, minus 1 for regression $= n - 2$. In the formula for standard error of potency 2·303 is the 't' value for 5 d.f., $P = 0.95$.

The design allows for a change in sensitivity of the preparation with time, and does not require a constant log dose ratio; but it is assumed that the dose response lines for standard and unknown are parallel.

The design has been used for the assay of the oxytocic hormone of posterior pituitary in the chicken[62].

Table 5.32. Transformation of data shown in Table 5.31

| Dose No. | Log dose Standard $x_S$ | Log dose Unknown $x_U$ | Log latent period (min) Observed | Log latent period (min) Interpolated $y_S$ | Log latent period (min) Unknown $y_U$ | $x$ ($x_S - x_U$) | $y$ ($y_S - y_U$) |
|---|---|---|---|---|---|---|---|
| 3 | 0·903–10 | | 0·519 | | | | |
| 4 | | 9·903–10 | | 0·428 | 0·401 | 0·000 | 0·027 |
| 5 | 9·903–10 | | 0·336 | | | | |
| 6 | | 9·954–10 | | 0·315 | 0·290 | −0·051 | 0·025 |
| 7 | 9·903–10 | | 0·294 | | | | |
| 8 | | 9·845–10 | | 0·296 | 0·434 | 0·058 | −0·138 |
| 9 | 9·903–10 | | 0·297 | | | | |
| 10 | | 0·000 | | 0·364 | 0·312 | −0·097 | 0·052 |
| 11 | 9·903–10 | | 0·431 | | | | |
| 12 | | 9·903–10 | | 0·446 | 0·479 | 0·000 | −0·033 |
| 13 | 9·903–10 | | 0·462 | | | | |
| 14 | | 9·954–10 | | 0·500 | 0·548 | −0·051 | −0·048 |
| 15 | 9·903–10 | | 0·538 | | | | |
| 16 | | 0·000 | | 0·584 | 0·426 | −0·097 | 0·158 |
| 17 | 9·903–10 | | 0·630 | | | | |

The log latent period is the $\log_{10}$ time expressed as mins and fractions of a minute.

Table 5.33. Analysis of data shown in Table 5.32

| Parameter | Formula | Value |
|---|---|---|
| $n$ | Doses of unknown | 7 |
| $Sx$ | Sum of $x$ | −0·238 |
| $Sx^2$ | Sum of $x^2$ | 0·027384 |
| $Sy$ | Sum of $y$ | 0·043 |
| $Sy^2$ | Sum of $y^2$ | 0·051459 |
| $Sxy$ | Sum of $xy$ | −0·027201 |
| $\bar{x}$ | $\dfrac{Sx}{n}$ | −0·034 |
| $\bar{y}$ | $\dfrac{Sy}{n}$ | 0·00614 |
| $S_{xx}$ | $S(x^2) - \bar{x}S(x)$ | 0·019292 |
| $S_{yy}$ | $S(y^2) - \bar{y}S(y)$ | 0·0511950 |
| $S_{xy}$ | $S(xy) - \bar{x}S(y)$ | −0·025739 |
| $b$ | $\dfrac{S_{xy}}{S_{xx}}$ | −1·3342 |
| $M$ | $\bar{x} - \bar{y}/b$ | −0·0294 = 9·9706–10 |
| Potency in per cent | 100 (Antilog. $M$) | 93·5% |
| Corrected $S_{yy}$ | $S_{yy} - bS_{xy}$ | 0·016854 |
| $s^2$ | $\dfrac{\text{Corrected } S_{yy}}{n-2}$ | 0·0033708 |
| $V_M$ | $\dfrac{s^2}{b^2}\left\{\dfrac{\bar{y}^2}{b(S_{xy})} + \dfrac{1}{n}\right\}$ | 0·0002726 |
| $sM$ | $\sqrt{V_M}$ | ±0·01651 |
| Limits of error ($P = 0·95$) | 100 Antilog. $2\cdot303 s_M$ | 85·6 − 102·0% |

*Time to given effect*

The potency of ouabain and digitoxin in terms of digoxin may be determined on the isolated guinea-pig ventricle, using the logarithm of the time (in minutes) to maximum inotropic effect as response metameter[63], since it is normally distributed. The isolated ventricle is suspended in an organ bath containing a modified Ringer Locke solution. The preparation is stimulated electrically, and the amplitude of contraction recorded on a kymograph. After a settling-in period of 1 hour, a dose of glycoside is added to the bath and the time to maximum inotropic effect (maximum amplitude) recorded.

Doses of 20, 40 and 80 $\mu$g, Low, Medium and High doses respectively, of each glycoside were used[63]. Using two baths (Nos. 1 and 2), each dose of each glycoside was administered three times to both baths, but only one dose administered to any ventricle. There were 54 ventricles in all (*Table 5.34*).

*Table 5.34.* Assay of digitoxin and ouabain in terms of digoxin, based on the time to maximum inotropic effect in the isolated guinea-pig ventricle

| Dose ($\mu$g) | Digoxin | | | Digitoxin | | | Ouabain | | |
|---|---|---|---|---|---|---|---|---|---|
| | 20 | 40 | 80 | 20 | 40 | 80 | 20 | 40 | 80 |
| Bath No. 1 Responses log$_{10}$ min ($y$) | 2·756 2·362 2·538 | 2·332 1·903 2·497 | 1·763 1·431 1·771 | 2·176 2·204 2·371 | 1·813 1·740 1·740 | 1·301 1·491 1·447 | 2·430 2·568 1·954 | 1·740 1·820 1·602 | 1·477 1·301 1·580 |
| Dose totals = Bath total = 52·108 | 7·656 | 6·732 | 4·965 | 6·751 | 5·293 | 4·239 | 6·952 | 5·162 | 4·358 |
| Bath No. 2 Responses log$_{10}$ min ($y$) | 2·512 2·114 2·644 | 2·124 1·903 1·740 | 1·740 1·681 1·716 | 2·000 2·146 2·000 | 1·763 1·806 1·431 | 1·519 1·519 1·380 | 2·550 2·375 2·770 | 1·978 1·982 1·580 | 1·301 1·255 1·362 |
| Dose totals = Bath total = 50·891 | 7·270 | 5·767 | 5·137 | 6·146 | 5·000 | 4·418 | 7·695 | 5·540 | 3·918 |
| Totals for doses, both baths | 14·926 | 12·499 | 10·102 | 12·897 | 10·293 | 8·657 | 14·647 | 10·702 | 8·276 |
| Total for drugs | | 37·527 | | | 31·847 | | | 33·625 | |

Grand total of responses, $Sy = 102·999$
Number of responses, $N = 54$

An analysis of variance is carried out to check the validity of the assay and to obtain the residual error mean square after removing variance due to known sources.

In *Table 5.35* the $\alpha$'s are the sums of squares into which doses may be subdivided, and the $\beta$'s are part of the subdivisions of Doses × Baths. Drugs × Linear regression is the measure of non-parallelism between drugs.

The main sources of variation are between the 9 doses with $9 - 1 = 8$ d.f. and the 2 baths with $2 - 1 = 1$ d.f. Since two baths have been used, an additional source of variation is that of 'doses by baths' with $(18 - 1)$

$-(8 + 1) = 8$ d.f. The latter bracket is the d.f. removed for the main effects, 8 for doses and 1 for baths. The residual error therefore has associated with it the total number of d.f. minus those for all other sources, $53 - 8 - 1 - 8 = 36$. The sum of squares for doses may be subdivided into the

Table 5.35. Analysis of variance of data in Table 5.34

| Source of variation | | Sum of squares | Degrees of freedom (d.f.) | Mean square | Variance ratio F | Probability P |
|---|---|---|---|---|---|---|
| Doses | $\alpha$ | 7·847948 | 8 | 0·980994 | 29·7 | <0·001 |
| Baths | | 0·027428 | 1 | 0·027428 | 0·83 | >0·20 |
| Doses × Baths | $\beta$ | 0·386281 | 8 | 0·048285 | 1·46 | >0·20 |
| Residual error | | 1·188884 | 36 | 0·033025 | | |
| Total | | 9·450541 | 53 | | | |
| Drugs | $\alpha$ | −0·937950 | 2 | 0·468975 | 14·20 | <0·001 |
| Linear regression (R) | $\alpha$ | −6·617756 | 1 | 6·617756 | 200·39 | <0·001 |
| Drugs × Linear R | $\alpha$ | −0·202095 | 2 | 0·101048 | 3·06 | 0·10>P>0·05 |
| Baths × Linear R | $\beta$ | 0·000703 | 1 | 0·000703 | 0·02 | >0·20 |
| Quadratic R | $\alpha$ | −0·058660 | 1 | 0·058660 | 1·78 | 0·20>P>0·10 |
| Drugs × Quadratic R | $\alpha$ | −0·031487 | 2 | 0·015744 | 0·48 | >0·20 |
| Baths × Quadratic R | $\beta$ | 0·018749 | 1 | 0·018749 | 0·57 | >0·20 |

sources shown beneath total error in Table 5.35. The d.f. for each source is calculated in a similar manner.

The sums of squares for the upper part of Table 5.35 are calculated as follows:

Doses:

$$\left[\frac{(14\cdot926)^2 + (12\cdot499)^2 + (10\cdot102)^2 + (12\cdot897)^2 + + + + etc. + (8\cdot276)^2}{6}\right.$$

$$\left. - C\right] = 7\cdot847948, \text{ where } C = \frac{(Sy)^2}{N} = \frac{(102\cdot999)^2}{54} = 196\cdot459148$$

Baths:
$$\frac{(52\cdot108)^2 + (50\cdot891)^2}{27} - C = 0\cdot027428$$

Doses × Baths:
$$\frac{(7\cdot656)^2 + (6\cdot732)^2 + + (7\cdot270)^2 + + etc. (3\cdot918)^2}{3}$$

minus $C$ minus sum of squares attributable to doses minus sum of squares attributable to baths $= 0\cdot386281$.

Total: $$S(y^2) - C$$

$$= (2\cdot756)^2 + (2\cdot362)^2 + + + (1\cdot362)^2 - C = 205\cdot909689 - 196\cdot459148$$
$$= 9\cdot450541$$

therefore sum of squares (S.S.) due to residual error

= Total S.S. − S.S. doses − S.S. baths − S.S. doses by baths $= 1\cdot188884$

In *Table 5.35*, to assist in the calculation of the sum of squares for the sources of variation shown below that of total error, use is made of coefficients of orthogonal contrasts[11d].

For the 3 + 3 + 3 dose design of the present assay, where the doses are equally spaced on a $\log_2$ scale and there are an equal number of observations in each group, the coefficients of orthogonal contrasts are given in *Table 5.36*.

*Table 5.36*. Orthogonal coefficients for regression analysis of a (3 + 3 + 3) assay

|  | Digoxin | | | Digitoxin | | | Ouabain | | |
|---|---|---|---|---|---|---|---|---|---|
| Dose ($\mu$g) | 20 | 40 | 80 | 20 | 40 | 80 | 20 | 40 | 80 |
| Linearity | −1 | 0 | 1 | −1 | 0 | 1 | −1 | 0 | 1 |
| Quadratic | 1 | −2 | 1 | 1 | −2 | 1 | 1 | −2 | 1 |

*Table 5.37*. Calculation of divisors for drugs using the coefficients in *Table 5.36*

| Drugs | Response total | Linear | Divisor | Quadratic | Divisor |
|---|---|---|---|---|---|
| Digoxin | 37·527 | −4·824 | 12 | 0·030 | 36 |
| Digitoxin | 31·847 | −4·240 | 12 | 0·968 | 36 |
| Ouabain | 33·625 | −6·371 | 12 | 1·519 | 36 |
| Sum | 102·999 | −15·435 | 36 | 2·517 | 108 |

The response totals for each drug are those given in *Table 5.34*. The divisor for each drug for linearity is obtained from the coefficients for linearity in *Table 5.36* as follows: $6(-1)^2 + 6(0)^2 + 6(1)^2 = 12$, since there are 6 observations on each dose.

Over the three drugs, since there are 18 responses at each dose level, the divisor is $18(-1)^2 + 18(0)^2 + 18(1)^2 = 36$.

The divisors, like the total responses and linear components, are additive. The quadratic term is calculated from

$$\begin{bmatrix} \text{sum of responses} \\ \text{to high dose} \end{bmatrix} + \begin{bmatrix} \text{sum of responses} \\ \text{to low dose} \end{bmatrix} - 2 \begin{bmatrix} \text{sum of responses} \\ \text{to medium dose} \end{bmatrix}$$

*e.g.* for digoxin $= 14·926 + 10·102 - 2(12·499) = 0·030$.

From *Table 5.36* the divisor for each drug is:

$$6(1)^2 + 6(-2)^2 + 6(1)^2 = 36$$

The quadratic components and their divisors, like those of the linear components and their divisors, must be additive.

In a similar way to that described for *Table 5.37*, *Table 5.38* is constructed from the data shown in *Tables 5.34* and *5.36*.

239

Table 5.38. Calculation of divisors for baths using the coefficients
in Table 5.36

| Bath No. | Response Total | Linear | Divisor | Quadratic | Divisor |
|---|---|---|---|---|---|
| 1 | 52·108 | −7·797 | 18 | 0·547 | 54 |
| 2 | 50·891 | −7·638 | 18 | 1·970 | 54 |
| | 102·999 | −15·435 | 36 | 2·517 | 108 |

The sums of squares shown in Table 5.35 are now calculated:

Linear regression;

From Table 5.38,  $\dfrac{(-15\cdot435)^2}{36} = 6\cdot617756$

Drugs × Linear regression;

From Table 5.37,

$$\left[\frac{(-4\cdot824)^2 + (-4\cdot240)^2 + (-6\cdot371)^2}{12}\right] - 6\cdot617756 = 0\cdot202095$$

Baths × Linear regression;

From Table 5.38,

$$\left[\frac{(-7\cdot797)^2 + (-7\cdot638)^2}{18}\right] - 6\cdot617756 = 0\cdot000703$$

Quadratic regression;

From Table 5.37 or 5.38,  $\dfrac{(2\cdot517)^2}{108} = 0\cdot058660$

Drugs × Quadratic regression;

From Table 5.37,

$$\left[\frac{(0\cdot030)^2 + (0\cdot968)^2 + (1\cdot519)^2}{36}\right] - 0\cdot058660 = 0\cdot031487$$

Baths × Quadratic regression;

From Table 5.38,

$$\left[\frac{(0\cdot547)^2 + (1\cdot970)^2}{54}\right] - 0\cdot058660 = 0\cdot018749$$

The mean square, variance ratio, $F$, and its significance, $P$, are obtained as previously described. Only the sources of error due to doses and the linear component are significant. Since the assay is valid, the mean potency ratio of digitoxin and ouabain in terms of digoxin, together with their respective fiducial limits, are now calculated.

The formula for calculating $M$, log potency ratio is:

$$M = \bar{x}_S - \bar{x}_U - \frac{\bar{y}_S - \bar{y}_U}{b}$$

where $\bar{x}_S$ and $\bar{x}_U$ are the mean doses of the 'standard' and 'unknown' respectively, and $\bar{y}_S$ and $\bar{y}_U$ the mean responses. $b$ is the slope of the regression. Since in the present case $\bar{x}_S = \bar{x}_U$, the equation is reduced to:

$$M = \frac{\bar{y}_U - \bar{y}_S}{b}$$

The general formula for the variance of $M$, $(V_M)$, is given by the expression:

$$V_M = \left[ \frac{s^2}{b^2} \left\{ (1 - g) \left( \frac{1}{n_S} + \frac{1}{n_U} \right) + \frac{M^2}{S_{xx}} \right\} \right] \Big/ (1 - g)^2$$

where

$$g = \frac{t^2 s^2}{b^2 S_{xx}}$$

and $S_{xx}$ is the sum of deviations of $x$, and $N_S$ and $N_U$ are the total number of observations associated with the 'standard' and 'unknown' preparations respectively:

therefore

$$g = \frac{(2 \cdot 028)^2 (0 \cdot 033025)}{0 \cdot 1839(36)} = 0 \cdot 0205$$

Since $g$ is less than $0 \cdot 1$ it may be ignored.

*Potency ratio of digitoxin in terms of digoxin, and its fiducial limits*

From *Table 5.37*:

$$b = \frac{-15 \cdot 435}{36} = -0 \cdot 4288 \qquad b^2 = 0 \cdot 1839$$

$$\text{Log}_2 \text{ potency ratio, } M' = \left[ \frac{31 \cdot 847 - 37 \cdot 527}{18} \right] \Big/ -0 \cdot 4288 = 0 \cdot 7358$$

$\text{Log}_{10}$ potency ratio, $M = 0 \cdot 7358(0 \cdot 3010) = 0 \cdot 2215$

Ignoring $g$,

$$V_M = \frac{s^2}{b^2} \left[ \frac{1}{n_S} + \frac{1}{n_U} + \frac{(M')^2}{S_{xx}} \right] = 0 \cdot 1796 \left[ \frac{1}{18} + \frac{1}{18} + \frac{(0 \cdot 7358)^2}{36} \right] = 0 \cdot 022648$$

$$s_{M'} = \sqrt{0 \cdot 022648} = \pm 0 \cdot 1505$$
$$s_M = \pm 0 \cdot 1505(0 \cdot 3010) = 0 \cdot 0453, \text{ in terms of log}_{10}$$

For $\quad P = 0 \cdot 95, \quad t = 2 \cdot 028$ for 36 d.f.

Therefore $ts_M = \pm 0 \cdot 0453(2 \cdot 028) = \pm 0 \cdot 0919$

$\text{Log}_{10}$ limits of error $(P = 0 \cdot 95)$ are $M \pm ts_M = 0 \cdot 2215 \pm 0 \cdot 0919$, *i.e.* $0 \cdot 1296$ and $0 \cdot 3134$.

Therefore potency ratio of digitoxin in terms of digoxin is $1 \cdot 67$ with limits of error $(P = 0 \cdot 95)$ from $1 \cdot 35$ to $2 \cdot 06$.

The potency ratio of ouabain in terms of digoxin, and its fiducial limits calculated in the same way as that described for digitoxin, is 1·42 with limits of error (P = 0·95) from 1·16 to 1·74.

Thus on the isolated guinea-pig ventricle, using the time to the maximum inotropic response, digitoxin and ouabain have potencies not significantly different from each other, but both are more active than digoxin under these conditions of assay.

### Duration of effect

While it is usually necessary to determine the approximate length of time for which a single dose of a drug maintains its effect, in some cases the duration of action may have particular significance. Thus with anaesthetics, both local and general, and with muscle relaxants, the choice of drug will vary according to whether a long or a short duration of action is required. Some adjustment of duration may be achieved by variation of the dose, since it is a fairly general rule that higher doses have a more prolonged action. The influence of changes of dose on duration of effect may vary considerably however from one drug to another[64], and in any case such a procedure makes no allowance for the varying intensity of effect achieved, and the risks attaching to it, at different dose levels.

Various studies[64,65] have shown that the logarithm of the duration may be normally distributed, and more or less linearly related to log dose. Estimates of duration at two or more levels of effect (say at the ED50 and ED95) give a reasonable indication of the relative potencies of drugs possessing similar action.

### Time-effect integral as a measure of total action

An attempt is sometimes made to obtain an empirical measure of the 'total action' of a drug treatment by assessing the area under the time–response curve. This may be carried out by using a planimeter, squared paper, or by cutting out the tracing and weighing the paper. Winter and Flataker[66] measured responses of rats at $\frac{1}{4}$, $\frac{1}{2}$, 1 and 2 hours after injection of an analgesic, and assessed the 'total analgesia' by simple geometric means.

This approach is of value in pharmacological research. Its application to screening procedures would perhaps be in some doubt, but for the wide acceptance of the test for local anaesthetics[67]. In this technique doses of the drugs are injected intra-cutaneously into the shaved skin of guinea-pigs. The resulting weals are tested for local anaesthesia by a succession of 6 pin-pricks at 3–5 second intervals, repeated every 5 minutes up to 30 minutes following injection. The number of pricks out of 6 failing to produce a response at each time of testing is used as a measure of the intensity of anaesthesia at that time. These scores are added up for the six times of testing and their sum used as a response metameter for the construction of dose–response lines. For the four anaesthetics quoted, the lines are substantially linear, although for one of them (cinchocaine, Nupercaine) the effect of the lower two doses was over within the test period, while that of the two higher doses persisted. Had testing proceeded until the responses had returned completely at all dose levels, it is likely that some means of rectifying the data would have been necessary.

## Non-parametric Comparisons

In the analyses described so far, it has been assumed that for estimation of errors and tests of significance the normal distribution may be applied. Where necessary, transformations of dose and response were made enabling this requirement to be met. In some situations however the transformation required may be obtained only after lengthy investigation. In such instances tests of significance may be used which make no assumption about the nature of the underlying distribution of the assessments of response.

The techniques for applying non-parametric tests are numerous and diverse. Textbooks such as those by Siegel[68] and Fraser[69] review the practical and theoretical backgrounds respectively. In the past these methods have been avoided by pharmacologists, but recently, in spite of their limitations, they are being used in situations where parametric methods are of dubious validity. The examples given illustrate the type of use for such procedures.

### Dichotomous observations

When the presence or absence of a specific attribute is observed in the members of two groups, the situation of double dichotomy exists and is presented in a $2 \times 2$ table (*Table 5.39*).

*Table 5.39.* General form of double dichotomy

|  | + | − | Totals |
|---|---|---|---|
| Group 1 | a | b | a + b |
| Group 2 | c | d | c + d |
| Totals | a + c | b + d | a + b + c + d |

$a$, $b$, $c$ and $d$ represent the respective frequencies within the classification. The groups commonly correspond either to two forms of treatment to be compared, or to treated and control animals. The positive responses may indicate death, or the observation of any feature not observed in the negative set.

If the proportions showing positive responses, $\dfrac{a}{a + b}$ and $\dfrac{c}{c + d}$, are dissimilar it is required to estimate with what probability such a contrast is equalled or exceeded by chance. This probability can be obtained by a $\chi^2$ approximation when the numbers are large. Since this rarely obtains, it is necessary to compute the probability directly ('The exact treatment of $2 \times 2$ Tables', Fisher[70]).

The probability of the observed contrast is:

$$\frac{(a + b)!(c + d)!(a + c)!(b + d)!}{a!b!c!d!(a + b + c + d)!}$$

This value is added to similar estimates derived from extreme sets of contrasts possible within the fixed marginal totals.

An example of this is given below.

*Table 5.40.* Hypothetical case of double dichotomy situation

| | Observed | | | More extreme case | | |
|---|---|---|---|---|---|---|
| | Dead | Alive | Totals | Dead | Alive | Totals |
| Treatment A | 2 | 5 | 7 | 1 | 6 | 7 |
| Treatment B | 7 | 1 | 8 | 8 | 0 | 8 |
| Totals | 9 | 6 | 15 | 9 | 6 | 15 |

The probability is given by

$$p = \frac{7!8!9!6!}{15!}\left(\frac{1}{2!5!7!1!} + \frac{1}{1!6!8!0!}\right)$$

$$= 0.0336 + 0.0014 = 0.0350$$

The apparently greater toxicity of Treatment B compared with that of Treatment A is therefore significant at the 5 per cent ($P = 0.05$) level.

This technique may be applied to a wide range of data. One further application is given from the field of chemotherapy. Frequently treatment given to infected animals interferes with the course of the disease only in so far as symptoms or death are delayed compared with controls. As an alternative to the estimation of metameters of survival time, treated and control groups may be compared at suitable time intervals by the $2 \times 2$ method. *Table 5.41*

*Table 5.41.* Example of survival times of treated and control groups of animals

| | Total in group | Survivors at day | | | | | | | | | | | |
|---|---|---|---|---|---|---|---|---|---|---|---|---|---|
| | | 7 | 8 | 9 | 10 | 11 | 12 | 13 | 14 | 15 | 16 | 17 | 18 |
| Treated group | 6 | 6 | 6 | 6 | 5 | 3 | 1 | 1 | 1 | 1 | 1 | 1 | 0 |
| Control group | 10 | 10 | 2 | 0 | 0 | 0 | 0 | 0 | 0 | 0 | 0 | 0 | 0 |
| p | — | — | 0.0035 | 0.0001 | 0.0014 | 0.0357 | 0.3750 | — | — | — | — | — | — |

shows the numbers of mice in such an experiment surviving at daily intervals, and the probability of the daily contrasts between treated and control groups.

Significant contrasts have therefore been observed from day 8 to day 11.

Tables of solutions for double dichotomy data have been published by Finney[71], and Mainland, Herrera and Sutcliffe[72].

Combination of the results from two or more independent sets of comparisons, each in the form of a $2 \times 2$ contingency table, is often required.

Rümke[40], using the letter symbols for frequencies given previously for each of the contingency tables, computed

$$A_h = \frac{ad - bc}{(a + b)(c + d)} \quad \text{and} \quad B_h = \frac{(a + c)(b + d)}{(a + b)(c + d)(a + b + c + d - 1)}$$

From these $S(A_h)/\sqrt{S(B_h)}$ was calculated as a normal deviate with unit variance. The probability of the value being equal to, or greater than, that observed, was obtained from a table of the normal distribution.

### Polychotomous observations

In the quantal response situation it frequently occurs that more than one symptom of effect can be recorded. For example, in a toxicity test, animals may be observed as sick or moribund as well as dead or alive. The type of computation for such data proposed by Gurland, Lee and Dahm[73], involving

Table 5.42. The calculation of ridit values[77] (effect = severity of injury)

| Intensity of effect | Observed frequency (1) | (2) | (3) | (4) | Ridits (5) |
|---|---|---|---|---|---|
| None | 17 | 8·5 | 0 | 8·5 | 0·047 |
| Minor | 54 | 27·0 | 17 | 44·0 | 0·246 |
| Moderate | 60 | 30·0 | 71 | 101·0 | 0·564 |
| Severe | 19 | 9·5 | 131 | 140·5 | 0·785 |
| Serious | 9 | 4·5 | 150 | 154·5 | 0·863 |
| Critical | 6 | 3·0 | 159 | 162·0 | 0·905 |
| Fatal | 14 | 7·0 | 165 | 172·0 | 0·961 |
| Total | 179 | | 179 | | |

minimum $\chi^2$ procedures, is described by them as simpler than the maximum likelihood approach of Aitchison and Silvey[74], and Ashford[75]. Even so it is impractical to apply such a method in most screening situations. The suggestion that each symptom be given a unit score and analysis of variance carried out on these scores[35] is a more acceptable procedure.

The recent increase in studies of animal behaviour has led to the type of situation where observations on normal animals reveal patterns of behaviour, each being made up from an assembly of observable reactions[76]. The frequency of occurrence of each reaction has been an inverse measure of the amount of information it contributed. A scoring schedule was devised in which each reaction was weighted inversely, according to its frequency in normal animals. Total scores within each pattern were obtained for the members of treated and control groups, and the effects of the treatment assessed by a standard $t$ test on the mean scores for the two groups.

In an analogous situation Bross[77] devised the 'ridit' as a means of establishing a system of scores. If among the members of a reference group an effect may be observed to occur in varying degrees, the frequencies with which each 'degree' is recorded are tabulated in ascending order of effect. The method of calculation of ridit values is shown in Table 5.42.

The entries in column (2) are one-half of those in column (1). Column (3) carries the cumulative totals from column (1), displaced one downwards. Column (4) contains the sums of the entries in columns (2) and (3). Column (5) gives the ridits obtained by dividing the entries in column (4) by the total frequency, 179.

The ridit values established from such a reference group are used as scores, allotted to the members of treated or control groups according to the intensities of effects observed. Normal statistical tests may then be applied to the mean ridits for such groups. Bross indicates the interesting probability aspects of mean ridit scores and their differences. He states, for example, that the interpretation to be placed on the finding that an experimental group has a mean ridit score of 0·27, is that this is the probability that a member of such a group shows a more intense effect than a member of the reference group.

The value of the ridit approach has yet to be established in pharmacology. It may find application where the responses to experimental treatments are measurable only in a subjective fashion, and show an increase or decrease of intensity compared with a large body of reference data. This is likely to be the case in many behavioural studies and also in the histological findings from chronic toxicity tests.

*Observations in rank order*

Where the magnitudes of effects either cannot be numerically assessed, or if they can, the nature of the distribution is obscure, then it is unlikely that the techniques such as those of Norton[76] and Bross[77] may be used, because of inadequate reference data. Large inter-experiment variation, for example, seriously undermines the usefulness of a reference group. Comparisons of treatment effects will then most efficiently be made solely on the data from each experiment. Numerous tests are available for problems of this sort, each having its appropriate experimental design. The three examples which follow indicate something of the variety of approach.

*The Mann–Whitney U test*[78]—Although the *t* test for the significance of the difference between the means of two groups of numerical data is not particularly sensitive to deviations from normality of the distributions from which they are derived, it is occasionally unwise to employ this test on either the observed values or on any simple transformation of them. One such case occurs in the screening of substances for activity against parasitic infections. Counts of parasites among members of control or treated groups are often distributed in a complex fashion, and to define a suitable transformation of the counts for each experiment would be impractical. The Mann–Whitney 'U test' would appear to be appropriate in such experiments to test the significance of the difference between two groups. In *Table 5.43*, counts of an intestinal worm found in members of a treated and control group are listed, together with their overall rank numbers, 1 being the rank of the lowest count, 2 the next highest, and so on. Counts of equal size share the appropriate rank numbers.

The following value is calculated:

$$U_1 = n_1 n_2 + \frac{n_1(n_1 + 1)}{2} - R_1 = (5)(6) + \frac{(5)(6)}{2} - 19 \cdot 5 = 25 \cdot 5$$

where $n_1$, $n_2$ are the numbers within the two groups, and $R_1$ the sum of the ranks in the groups of $n_1$ observations.

A second estimate $U_2$ may similarly be derived, or more simply from the relationship:

$$U_2 = n_1 n_2 - U_1 = 30 - 25 \cdot 5 = 4 \cdot 5$$

The smaller of the two estimates of $U$ is used to assess the significance of the contrast between the groups. Tables given by Mann and Whitney[78]

Table 5.43. Ranking of worm counts in treated and control animals

| Treated group | | Control group | |
|---|---|---|---|
| Worm count | Rank | Worm count | Rank |
| 133 | 2 | 4946 | 9 |
| 1660 | 3 | 2570 | 7 |
| 0 | 1 | 8000 | 11 |
| 2340 | $5\frac{1}{2}$ | 6820 | 10 |
| 4933 | 8 | 2268 | 4 |
| | | 2340 | $5\frac{1}{2}$ |
| Total | $19\frac{1}{2}$ | Total | $46\frac{1}{2}$ |

for groups up to $n_1 = n_2 = 8$, and extended by Auble[79] up to groups of 20, show the probability associated with the value of $U$ for the respective values of $n_1$ and $n_2$ (as listed $n_2 \geqslant n_1$).

From the table for groups of 6 and 5, values of $P$ for $U = 4$ and $U = 5$ are respectively given as 0·013 and 0·021. By direct interpolation, the probability of a value as low as 4·5 or lower occurring by chance is 0·017. A significant effect therefore can be assumed to have been demonstrated.

*Complex analysis by rankings*—The Mann–Whitney U test is only appropriate for the direct comparison of two groups of data. In the more general case the technique of variance analysis may be employed on the rank numbers themselves. Although it is customary to transform the rankings to scores corresponding to ranked normal deviates (for tables see Fisher and Yates[10], Pearson and Hartley[80]), Van Strik[81] showed that the observed rank numbers may be used without such conversion. In his examples the ranks related to degrees of tissue proliferation, judged subjectively by histological examination of uterine sections from immature rabbits treated with varying doses of progesterone or synthetic steroids. As he points out, the analysis may break down if the contrasts between treatments are excessive, either because the log dose interval is too great, or the compounds examined produce widely differing responses. Two examples are given below.

*Tests applicable to paired comparisons*—(a) *The sign test*—When the comparison between two treatments is made subjectively, such that the animals given one treatment appear more affected than those given the other, the technique of making the comparison in pairs of animals may be appropriate. Each pair contains one animal from each of the two treatments, and in the sense

17                                            247

that '$+$' might indicate an assessment in favour of one treatment, and '$-$' in favour of the other, the 'sign test' is then applied to determine whether the observed frequency of $+$ and $-$ results among $n$ observed pairs is compatible with the null hypothesis of no difference between treatments. With this hypothesis the probability of $+$ and $-$ would be 0·5, and for a one-tailed test of significance the partial sums of the expansion of the binomial $(0·5 + 0·5)^n$ would give the successive probabilities of $n$, $n - 1$ or more, $n - 2$ or more, etc., $+$'s occurring by chance. These values may be computed directly or obtained from tables (Siegel[68], National Bureau of Standards[82]).

(b) *The Wilcoxon 'matched pairs signed ranks' test*[83]—With the sign test it may be possible to assess the degree of difference associated with the sign. For example, Janssen[84] adopted a scoring system in comparing rats in a behavioural study, in which scores of 1, 2 and 3 were given according to the degree of certainty associated with the allocation of $+$ or $-$. Score 1 represented a consciously highly subjective conclusion, score 2 a reasonably clear picture of difference, and score 3 a strong conviction of a difference due to drug action. In this example the scores represent differences between the members of each pair of rats. Under different circumstances the behaviour of each rat might be scored, the difference between rats being given the corresponding sign and magnitude of the difference between the scores. The score values associated with differences are then ranked without regard to sign, ties being given the average of the tied ranks, and rank values the sign corresponding to the difference scores. The sums of the ranks having positive sign and negative sign are separately obtained. The smaller of the two, designated $T$, is used for the test of significance. Critical levels of $T$ for various degrees of significance are tabulated against $N$, the number of non-zero differences[68,83].

The sign test may be used not only to determine the significance of treatment effects, but also to demonstrate the concordance between pairs of observers[84]. Observers must be kept in ignorance as to the treatment groups from which the rats came. Jannsen[84] gives a simple procedure for such a 'blind' trial.

## INTERACTIONS BETWEEN DRUGS

The mechanism of joint drug action is largely in the province of speculative research. Since however it is recognized that two or more drugs administered simultaneously to a patient or an animal may either act independently of one another, or show an interaction indicative of antagonism or potentiation, there are many reasons why the screening of drugs should include tests to reveal possible interactions.

The advantages of demonstrating a lack of interaction are twofold. Firstly, in substituting a new drug for an old, the transfer may sometimes best be made by overlapping the two treatments, reducing the dose of the old treatment while increasing that of the new. Secondly, if the available drugs produce a pattern of undesirable side-effects whilst achieving a desired effect, a mixture may enable the therapeutic response to be obtained with fractional doses of each, and so reduce the likelihood of undesirable side-effects.

Apart from the obvious provision of pharmacological antidotes, a recognition of antagonism between drugs may provide the clinician with a warning that the mixture of certain compounds may result in the abolition of the effect one or the other was intended to induce. Similarly, knowledge of a positive interaction, resulting in the potentiation of an effect, may be of vital importance. Depending on whether the effect is desirable or not, the mixture may be advantageous or dangerous.

It will be appreciated that the substances being examined for their interaction with compounds passing through the screening process, should include all drugs that may be used in clinical practice simultaneously with any new therapeutic agent.

Some examples follow which illustrate something of the variety of procedures used to demonstrate drug interactions.

## Drug Antagonism Measured by Direct Assay

The comparative potency of several analeptics has been determined by a direct assay procedure in guinea-pigs[85]. Thiopentone or pentobarbital was infused intravenously until respiratory arrest occurred, and the doses of analeptic (picrotoxin, cyclohexylethyl-triazol or leptazol) required to re-start respiration and to produce muscular twitching were determined by slow intravenous infusion. These doses of the analeptics were analysed by the direct assay procedure described for the assay of $d$-tubocurarine by the rabbit head-drop method (page 194).

## Drug Antagonism Measured by Quantitative Assay

Schild obtained estimates of the antagonistic activity of neoantergan, benadryl, pethidine and atropine to both histamine and acetylcholine on isolated guinea-pig gut[86]. Activities were measured in pA units, where $pA_x$ was defined as 'the negative logarithm to base 10 of the molar concentration of an antagonistic drug which will reduce the effect of a multiple dose ($x$) of an active drug to that of a single dose'. It is independent of the concentration of the antagonist. For example, if a concentration of $10^{-5.8}$ molar pethidine reduces the effect of 2 $\mu$g histamine to that produced, in the absence of pethidine, by 1 $\mu$g histamine, $pA_2$ pethidine-histamine = 5·8.

The method consists of finding two concentrations of the antagonistic drug, one reducing the effect of a double dose of the active drug to slightly less, and the other to slightly more than the effect of a single dose. The concentration corresponding to $pA_2$ is then computed by graphical interpolation on a log scale.

A constant submaximal response to the stimulant drug is obtained. Then the gut is bathed in Tyrode solution containing the antagonist, and the injection of the stimulant dose which follows is doubled. This double-dose is added at regular intervals on 5 occasions, washing out between each addition, to observe whether the effect of the antagonist increases with increasing length of contact. The bath fluid is then changed to Tyrode, without antagonist present, to test for persistence of antagonistic effect. Finally, a maximal response to the stimulant drug is obtained. Responses are expressed as a percentage of this maximal response. The procedure is repeated using a fresh piece of gut for each concentration of antagonist.

pA values may also be determined indirectly by measuring in a comparative assay the activity of an unknown antagonist in terms of one whose pA is already known, and computing the unknown pA by adding to the known pA the logarithm of the ratio of molar activity of the two antagonists. For example, $pA_2$ (atropine-histamine, 2 min) = $pA_2$ (pethidine-histamine,

Table 5.44. $pA_2$ values assessed directly and indirectly

|  | $pA_2$ (2 min contact) (Direct assessment) | Comparison on same gut (2 min contact) (Indirect assessment) | $pA_2$ (14 min contact) (Direct assessment) |
|---|---|---|---|
| Pethidine-histamine | 5·78 |  | 6·13 |
| Atropine-histamine | 5·73 |  | 5·64 |
|  | — |  | — |
| Log ratio $\dfrac{\text{pethidine}}{\text{atropine}}$ | 0·05 | 0·34 | 0·49 |

2 min) $- 0·34 = 5·78 - 0·34 = 5·44$, where 0·34 is the log potency ratio of pethidine/atropine, obtained by comparative assay. In these experiments, comparative assays were conducted using a $(2 + 2)$ dose procedure in a randomized block design on one piece of gut. Two doses of each antagonist with a constant dose ratio between high and low concentrations were used. One dose was injected into the bath 2 minutes before a constant dose of histamine. Following the antagonist-histamine response, the bath was washed out and the constant dose of histamine repeated at 3 minute-intervals,

Table 5.45. Reproducibility of $pA_2$ values

| Experiment No. | $pA_2$ Values—2 minutes | | $pA_2$ Neoantergan $-pA_2$ Benadryl |
|---|---|---|---|
|  | Neoantergan | Benadryl |  |
| R.205 | 8·91 | 7·94 | 0·97 |
| R.206 | 8·61 | 7·66 | 0·95 |
| R.207 | 8·65 | 7·75 | 0·90 |

washing out between doses until the contraction to histamine had returned to the initial height. The cycle was repeated with other doses. The reduction in height of contraction immediately following each dose of antagonist was linearly related to log dose of antagonist. The log potency ratio of pethidine/atropine determined by the direct and indirect assay procedures is shown in Table 5.44.

The log ratio of pethidine/atropine assessed indirectly lies closest to that calculated directly from the $pA_2$ values after 14 minutes. This may be because the effects of the antagonists are never completely removed in spite of repeated washings. To overcome this difficulty Schild suggested that $pA_2$ values be determined for each antagonist on separate pieces of gut from the same animal, and that the difference between the two $pA_2$ values be taken as a measure of the difference in activity between the two antagonists. The following example shows the reproducibility of this procedure (*Table 5.45*).

While the $pA_2$ values for each antagonist vary from one experiment to another, the variation between the differences in $pA_2$ values is extremely small. It is possible, however, that a Latin square procedure instead of a random block design might have reduced the variation in response due to carry-over effects from one dose of antagonist to another.

Schild has extended his studies of pA measurements to devise tests which determine whether an antagonist is acting competitively or non-competitively[87].

Adrenaline and noradrenaline antagonize the contractile response of the isolated uterus and colon of the rat to carbachol. Unlike the antagonists used by Schild, the effects of adrenaline and noradrenaline may readily be abolished by washing, so that it is possible to carry out satisfactory comparative assays using the $(2 + 2)$ dose procedure on the same muscle preparation[88]. A dose of carbachol producing a submaximal response is determined, and with each alternate dose, a dose of adrenaline (standard) or adrenaline-like substance (unknown) added in the order determined by a 4-dose randomized block design. The height of contraction, or some function of it, is linearly related to log dose of adrenaline. Gaddum and Lembeck[88] determined the mean height of contraction of the uterus to carbachol alone in each randomized block, and expressed each response to carbachol + adrenaline (for standard and unknown) as a percentage of this mean value. The results obtained using this procedure applied to 4 randomized blocks are shown in *Table 5.46*, together with the results obtained from three other

*Table 5.46*. Assay of adrenaline using the isolated rat uterus. Comparison of results obtained from four different metameters

| Methods of analysis | Potency as % of standard | Limits of error (P = 0·95) as % of standard | Statistical* weight |
|---|---|---|---|
| Contraction after U or S as % of mean contraction to carbachol within each randomized block (Gaddum and Lembeck)[88] | 80·7 | 71·6–90·9 | 1903 |
| (1) Contraction after U or S | 80·4 | 70·5–91·6 | 1585 |
| (2) Contraction after U or S as % of contraction before U or S | 87·7 | 79·5–96·7 | 2834 |
| (3) Contraction after U or S corrected for contraction before U or S | 85·4 | 76·7–95·0 | 2466 |

* Statistical weight = Reciprocal of the variance. The higher the weight the more precise the assay.

metameters; (*1*) the data analysed by ignoring the response to the fixed dose of carbachol alone (as suggested by Gaddum and Lembeck), (*2*) the data analysed by expressing each response as a percentage of the response to the preceding fixed dose of carbachol, and (*3*) by correcting the response to the preceding fixed dose of carbachol by covariance analysis. None of the estimates of potency differs significantly from the other, but the more precise estimates are obtained when responses to carbachol + adrenaline are corrected for the immediately preceding response to the fixed dose of carbachol alone.

This design was adopted for the assay of laudexium, based on its ability to antagonize the stimulant action of the agonists, acetylcholine and suxamethonium on the isolated frog rectus muscle preparation[46]. Correction of the response to laudexium + agonist for the preceding response to the fixed dose of agonist by covariance analysis, gave results which were not significantly different from those obtained by simple percentage-wise correction, so that for ease of calculation the latter metameter was used.

### Drug Antagonism Measured by Time Response

Time-Response metameters have also been used to compare the activities of drug antagonists. Weatherall and Weatherall[89] screened a series of dithiols for comparative activity based on their ability to prolong the survival time of rats poisoned with phenylarsenoxide or oxophenarsine. The mean increase in log survival time produced by different doses of dimercaprol in phenylarsenoxide-poisoned rats was linearly related to log dose of dimercaprol. With other dithiols this relationship was linear but not always parallel to the line for phenylarsenoxide alone, but the differences were not large so that approximate comparisons of ten dithiols were made.

### Drug Potentiation Measured by Quantal Response

The comparative potencies of promethazine hydrochloride and hexamethonium bromide in potentiating the hypoglycaemic response of mice to insulin may be determined quantally.

Fasted mice weighing 12–14 g were divided into six groups each of 24 animals. Two groups were injected subcutaneously with hexamethonium bromide (250 $\mu$g/mouse), two were similarly injected with promethazine hydrochloride (100 $\mu$g/mouse), and the remaining 2 were used as controls. Each pair of groups were then injected subcutaneously with insulin, one group with a 'high' dose and the other with a 'low' dose. Preliminary

Table 5.47. Effect of promethazine and hexamethonium on insulin convulsions in mice

|  | Insulin | | Insulin + Promethazine | | Insulin + Hexamethonium | |
|---|---|---|---|---|---|---|
| Test No. 1 Dose of Insulin (mu/mouse) Convulsions/24 | 20 16 | 12 5 | 12 18 | 7·2 7 | 12 23 | 7·2 12 |
| Test No. 2 Dose of Insulin (mu/mouse) Convulsions/24 | 24 15 | 14·4 7 | 14·4 19 | 8·64 8 | 14·4 20 | 8·64 12 |

experiments showed that the doses of promethazine and hexamethonium were the largest possible doses which failed to produce convulsions or death. The mice were maintained at 34°C for 75 minutes, and the number of convulsions occurring in each group was recorded (*Table 5.47*).

The results were calculated by probit analysis as described on page 204. The estimates from the two tests were compatible. ($\chi^2$ was not significant with either drug, promethazine hydrochloride $P > 0.8$ and for hexa-methonium bromide $P > 0.9$). The estimates when combined showed that promethazine hydrochloride potentiates the convulsive action of insulin 3·1 times (limits of error $P = 0.95$ from 2·6 to 3·7 times) and hexamethonium bromide potentiates it 3·9 times (limits of error $P = 0.95$ from 3·3 to 4·7 times), with the doses of each employed.

## 'THE FINAL CHOICE'

In spite of the low probability that any single chemical compound taken at random possesses a specified pharmacological action, once an active substance has been discovered, intensified chemical effort centred around its particular structure often leads to a series of compounds possessing the required activity in varying degrees. It must then be decided which is the most suitable compound. Factors such as the cost of manufacture, which includes the availability of raw materials, may not be ignored in making this decision. In a more scientific sense, the many aspects of pharmaceutical presentation may also be taken into account, including stability, solubility and palata-bility. The most important factor however is the pharmacological 'profile' possessed by the substance. The advantages of a multiple line screening procedure are evident when studying this factor. It is rare for a drug to exhibit one action only at all dose levels. Usually several actions are found, within which may be defined the main therapeutic action, side-effects occurring at dose levels in the therapeutic range, and frequently additional toxic or otherwise undesirable actions which manifest themselves with increasing frequency and intensity at higher doses.

### Pharmacological Profiles

Because of the many ways in which drugs may vary from one another in their actions, any attempt to describe this situation is inevitably over-simplified.

When an established drug is available as a standard of reference, the device of expressing activities as ratios compared with the standard assists in the preliminary interpretation of data. If the ratios obtained for more than one type of action are statistically indistinguishable from one another, this constitutes evidence of a correlation between the various types of action of the particular drugs tested. Other drugs may be found, however, which exert a differential effect on the different response systems. In a study of analgesics, for example, Green[90] listed the potencies of a series of compounds relative to morphine, tested both for their ability to elevate the pain threshold and to depress the respiratory rate in rats. In spite of a wide range of activities among the compounds (from 1/10 to 10 times that of morphine), no significant difference was detected between the relative activity measured by the action on pain threshold and that on respiration, except for pethidine where the $t$ test gave a probability of 0·07.

The straightforward statistical approach breaks down when the dose-response lines are not parallel for the drugs being compared. Green[90] found that the lines relating dosage to a measure of intestinal motility showed marked degrees of non-parallelism, although none of the drugs tested failed to inhibit the bowel movements of rats at sufficiently high dose levels. In these circumstances resort must be made to such measurements as the effects of equi-active doses or of threshold doses necessary to produce an effect.

The pharmacological picture becomes more complicated when more tests are taken into account. Many publications demonstrate the skill with which such situations may be resolved. Lister[91], for example, examined 3 related compounds by 15 distinct experimental procedures, and showed that the route of administration and the species used may considerably influence the relative potencies of the drugs.

When marked species differences are observed in the relative incidence or severity of undesirable effects, it is usual to employ the least favourable species as a guide to indicating the possible outcome of administering a new drug to man. The issue is not whether the compounds can produce undesirable effects, but whether they are likely to do so in any marked degree at the dose levels employed to induce their therapeutic action. This may be masked when relative activities are divorced from the actual dose levels employed in the testing.

### The Therapeutic Index

As a measure of the margin of safety for a drug, Ehrlich proposed the ratio of the smallest effective dose to the largest tolerated (non-lethal) dose. With advances in the theories on probability this definition has had to be rephrased. For many purposes of drug assessment, particularly with quantal responses, emphasis came to be placed on the ED50 and the LD50. Many workers took the ratio of these two estimates as measuring the therapeutic index. Such a measure seriously departs from Ehrlich's original conception. The statement that a margin of safety can be expressed by the ratio of the dose which is effective in only half of its recipients, to that which kills half its recipients makes it clear that the language employed may be statistical, but is far removed from clinical practice. To bring back something of the idealized therapeutic index, Brock and Schneider[92] proposed the ratio:

$$T.I. = \frac{LD5}{ED95}$$

so that the doses considered do at least anticipate as low a death rate as 5 per cent with a 95 per cent probability of therapeutic effect. They inverted the relationship, so that the index increases in magnitude as the therapeutic value (or margin of safety) increases. Brock and Schneider's formula, which they designate as 'Ehrlich's index', results in values less than the ratio LD50/ED50. Its full significance lies in the interpretation to be placed on data derived from non parallel dose–response lines. In *Figure 5.10* are represented the regressions on dose for the therapeutic effect and lethal action of 2 drugs, whose ED50 and LD50 values respectively are identical, but the slope of the lines for substance A is greater than that for B. Whereas the ratio LD50/ED50 is 8·0 for both drugs, the therapeutic index given by LD5/ED95 is 2·0 for substance A and 0·5 for substance B. The latter value dispels any illusions of a safety margin which the ratio of 8·0 might have induced. Some overlap of the distribution of effective and toxic threshold doses demonstrated by substance B will, in theory, always occur. Brock and Schneider suggested that the percentage of lethal responses to be expected at the ED95 dose level be designated the *Coefficient of Danger*. In the example this value is 5 per cent, representing the percentage probability of a toxic response at a 'fully-active' dose level.

In spite of the necessity of making an assumption about the nature of the distribution of threshold doses, and the relatively larger errors associated with the estimation of LD5 and ED95 compared with the median response doses, the Ehrlich index must be of greater practical use than the ratio

*Figure 5.10.* Graphic calculation of 'therapeutic index' for two substances (A and B) possessing different slopes. For discussion see text.

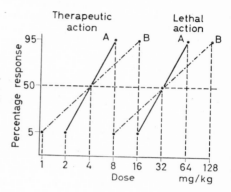

LD50 to ED50. Examining the same problem Foster[93] has earlier proposed a 'standard safety margin' (SSM) defined as:

$$\text{SSM} = \left(\frac{\text{LD1}}{\text{ED99}} - 1\right)(100)$$

The formula is probably too complex for general acceptance, and is better considered as simply $\frac{\text{LD1}}{\text{ED99}}$. While the use of LD1 ensures a greater measure of freedom from toxicity, modern practice is likely to relate this to a dose rather less than the ED99, say the ED95, as the degree of inactivity which may be tolerated is greater than the admissible degree of toxicity.

### Chronic Toxicity

One of the inherent difficulties of extrapolating to man information derived from animal screening tests is that in estimating the probability of toxic reactions in man, the numbers of animals on which such estimates may be based are severely limited. Without the intrusion of other factors the error attaching to any assessment of probability is often too large to be ignored. Supporting evidence is therefore sought from tests in which animals of various species are repeatedly given doses considered to be well above the corresponding therapeutic doses to be used in man.

Statistical appraisal of the value of chronic toxicity tests is difficult. Such tests should be adequately provided with control animals on dummy treatments, otherwise the numerous hazards encountered while maintaining animals in good condition for long periods may be attributed to drug effect. If any signs of pathological condition are detected, which are not a direct consequence of the required therapeutic action of the drugs, it is still a matter for the pharmacologist to decide whether the particular changes must act as a danger signal preventing the use of the drugs in man.

Even completely negative findings in a chronic toxicity experiment leave unanswered the question of whether enough animals or species were used. The answers to such questions may only be arrived at in the form of hindsight when untoward reactions are in fact observed in man.

The ideal duration of chronic studies is difficult to assess. More prolonged experiments are called for when the drugs are intended for administration to man over long periods. It is argued that the difference in the life span of laboratory animals and man gives a proportionately greater significance in animals to each month of testing. Even if this is not so, progress would be seriously impaired if it were not used as a working hypothesis.

### Cumulation and Tolerance

The repeated administration of a drug daily to the same animals is not infrequently associated with changes in the responsiveness of the animals. This may take the form of accumulation of the drug in the body, leading to apparently greater responses as the blood levels rise, or it may follow the reverse path leading to increased tolerance to the drug. Such changes are of significance if they reflect possible similar reactions in man. They are important when considering the results of chronic toxicity studies.

While experiments to investigate this problem can assume any degree of elaboration, the schedule described by Lim, Rink, Glass and Soaje-Echague[94], appears to be sufficiently discriminating for many practical purposes. Using quantal responses they obtained the LD50 and ED50

Table 5.48. C-LD50 as percentage A-LD50[94]

| Cumulation | | No change | | Tolerance | |
|---|---|---|---|---|---|
| emetine | 5 | ectylurea | 91 | phenobarb. Na | 137 |
| reserpine | 6 | acetylsalicylic acid | 100 | prochlorperazine | 150 |
| digitoxin | 11 | nalorphine | 102 | phenmetrazine | 174 |
| triple bromides | 71 | | | meprobamate | 178 |
| | | | | pentobarb. Na | 300 |
| | | | | morphine | 362 |
| | | | | chlorpromazine | 408 |
| | | | | phenaglycodol | 467 |
| | | | | 1-phenylephrine | 800 |

estimates in a variety of pharmacological tests, following a single administration of the drugs. The values were designated as A — LD50 and A — ED50, for the acute responses. In further trials daily dosing commenced at 9 per cent of the A — LD50 given to the whole group of animals (5 male and 5 female). After each four-day period the dose was increased 1·5 fold. The aim was to ensure that the animals survived $24 \pm 4$ days. If rapid cumulative effects foreshortened the test unduly, it was begun again at an appropriate fraction of the original starting dose. From the daily observations of responses C-ED50 and C-LD50 values were computed, the 'C' prefix denoting 'subchronic', because the total duration of exposure to drug treatment was less than that normally adopted for 'chronic' toxicity tests. The way in which these estimates are derived is perhaps open to criticism, since it is assumed that animals dying at one dose level, would have died at subsequent higher dose levels. While this might not seriously bias the median dose estimates, the assumed numbers may lead to underestimation of the limits of error. It is preferable to regard the dose at which each animal died as a direct measurement of its threshold, and calculate the mean log threshold in the ordinary way. Pharmacological responses other than death may only be measured on the survivors. Since doses are referred to throughout as percentages of the A-LD50, changes indicative of cumulation or tolerance are readily detected. Some of the C-LD50 values quoted are given in *Table 5.48*.

### Estimation of the Safe Dose

Assuming that the logarithms of threshold doses are normally distributed, the doses which are expected to have an arbitrarily selected low probability of effect may be calculated from estimates of the mean and standard deviation[95]. It is suggested that 3 standard deviations below the mean might be regarded as the logarithm of the maximum tolerated dose. In a later unpublished communication, Trevan, in discussing the estimation of the LD1/1,000,000, had doubts whether such concepts could ever apply in practice. In particular he felt that the probability, among human recipients of a drug, of individual hyper-sensitivity or idiosyncrasy leading to a fatal reaction vitiates the calculations based on otherwise homogeneous normal distributions. The trial of every new drug in man constitutes a risk. Gaddum[96], working on the same basic assumptions as Gray, Trevan, Bainbridge and Attwood[95], modified the proposed estimate from 3 to 6 standard deviations below the mean. In terms of probability of death this decreased the chance from 1/742 to about 1/1,000,000,000. Such calculations must be based on data derived from the most sensitive sub-human species tested, and errors of estimation must be taken into account. The choice of an appropriate dose metameter may also be critical; it is assumed that quantal responses are transformed into probits.

When a non-lethal toxic action may be measured quantitatively, such that the effect is linearly related to log dose with a slope, $b$, and constant standard deviation at all levels of response, $\pm s$, a threshold dose may be determined as that at which the response is $ts$. This is the smallest effect which is significant against a control base line. Using the index of precision $\lambda = \dfrac{s}{b}$ the value of log (threshold dose) $- 6\lambda$ would give the logarithm of the 'safe-dose'. This alternative is to be preferred to estimates based on lethal effects.

The decision to test a new drug in man, and the selection of the dose to be employed, must remain with the clinician, who can only be guided by all the evidence available to him. His responsibility for the well-being of the human subject is so great that it must divorce him from any restraint imposed by purely statistical argument. As each human trial follows another without untoward reactions, so the clinician turns his attention more to the evaluation of the therapeutic response. An apparently useful drug may only be said to have passed the final stage of screening when its relative safety and its therapeutic value have been demonstrated.

## REFERENCES

1. PATON and ZAIMIS *Brit. J. Pharmacol.* 1949, **4,** 381
2. STONE, TORCHIANA, NAVARRO and BEYER *J. Pharmacol.* 1956, **117,** 169
3. SCHNEIDERMAN *Quantitative Methods in Pharmacology* (Ed. De Jonge): North Holland, 1961, p. 232
4. DAVIES *Bull. Inst. int. Statist.* 1958, **36,** 226
5. ARMITAGE and SCHNEIDERMAN *Ann. N.Y. Acad. Sci.* 1958, **76,** 896
6. DUNNETT *Quantitative Methods in Pharmacology* (Ed. De Jonge): North Holland 1961, p. 212
7. GADDUM *Pharmacol. Rev.* 1953, **5,** 87
8. VARNEY, LINEGAR and HOLADAY *J. Pharmacol.* 1949, **97,** 72
9. DUTTA and MACINTOSH *Analyst* 1949, **74,** 588
10. FISHER and YATES *Statistical Tables for Biological, Agricultural and Medical Research* 3rd Edn: Oliver and Boyd, London and Edinburgh, 1948
11. FINNEY *Statistical Method in Biological Assay:* Charles Griffin, London, 1952, p. 44; *a*, p. 624 seq. *b*, p. 489 *c*, p. 208 seq. *d*. p. 123 seq.
12. JACOBSEN and LARSEN *Acta pharm. tox. Kbh.* 1951, **7,** 35
13. MARESH and FARAH *J. Pharmacol.* 1947, **90,** 304
14. TREVAN *Proc. roy. Soc.* B. 1927, **101,** 483
15. GADDUM *Spec. Rep. Ser. med. Res. Coun., Lond.* 1933 no. 183
16. FINNEY *Probit Analysis:* Cambridge University Press, 1952 *a*, p. 103 seq. *b*, p. 226 seq.
17*a*. SPEARMAN *Brit. J. Psychol.* 1908, **2,** 227
17*b*. KÄRBER *Arch. exp. Path. Pharmak.* 1931, **162,** 480
18. THOMPSON *Bact. Rev.* 1947, **11,** 115
19. REED and MUENCH *Amer. J. Hyg.* 1938, **27,** 493
20*a*. DRAGSTEDT and LANG *J. Pharmacol.* 1928, **32,** 215
20*b*. BEHRENS *Arch. exp. Path. Pharmak.* 1929, **140,** 237
21. IRWIN and CHEESEMAN *J. Hyg., Camb.* 1939, **39,** 574
22. WEIL *Biometrics* 1952, **8,** 249
23. HORN *Biometrics,* 1956, **12,** 311
24. ABBOTT *J. econ. Ent.* 1925, **18,** 265
25. BLISS *Ann. appl. Biol.* 1935, **22,** 134
26. BARTLETT *Suppl. J. roy. Stat. Soc.* 1937, **4,** 137
27. MILLER and TAINTER *Proc. Soc. exp. Biol. N.Y.* 1944, **57,** 261
28. DE BEER *J. Pharmacol.* 1945, **85,** 1
29. LITCHFIELD and WILCOXON *J. Pharmacol.* 1949, **95,** 99
30. EISENBERG *Biometrics* 1952, **8,** 120
31. HEMMINGSEN *Quart. J. Pharm.* 1933, **6,** 187
32. FINNEY *J. Pharmacol.* 1952, **104,** 440
33. LITCHFIELD and WILCOXON *J. Pharmacol.* 1953, **108,** 18
34. KNUDSEN and CURTIS *J. Amer. statist. Ass.* 1947, **42,** 282
35. CLARINGBOLD and EMMENS *Quantitative Methods in Pharmacology* (Ed. De Jonge): North Holland, 1961, p. 72
36. WARNER and COLLIER *Biometrics* 1960, **16,** 491
37. COLLIER, WARNER and SKERRY *Brit. J. Pharmacol.* 1961, **17,** 28
38. DIXON and MOOD *J. Amer. statist. Ass.* 1948, **43,** 109
39. BROWNLEE, HODGES and ROSENBLATT *J. Amer. statist. Ass.* 1953, **48,** 262
40. RÜMKE *Arch. int. Pharmacodyn.* 1959, **119,** 10
41. GREEN and YOUNG *Brit. J. Pharmacol.* 1951, **6,** 572
42. MOGEY, TREVAN and YOUNG *Analyst* 1949, **74,** 577
43. ASKOVITZ *J. Amer. statist. Ass.* 1957, **52,** 13
44. HAMBURGER *Acta pharm. tox., Kbh.* 1945, **1,** 112

45. PENNEFATHER *J. Pharm., Lond.* 1961, **13,** 60
46. BRITTAIN, CHESHER, COLLIER and GRIMSHAW *Brit. J. Pharmacol.* 1959, **14,** 158
47. ROCHA E SILVA and ROTHSCHILD *Brit. J. Pharmacol.* 1956, **11,** 252
48. CHILD and ZAIMIS *Brit. J. Pharmacol.* 1960, **15,** 412
49. WINEGRAD and RENOLD *J. biol. Chem.* 1958, **233,** 267
49a. STEWART and NEVILLE—Unpublished data
50. WOOD *Analyst* 1946, **71,** 1
51. EMMENS *Medical Research Council (Lond.), Special Report Series* 1939 no. 234
52. O'BRIEN and MORGAREIDGE *J. Nutr.* 1939, **18,** 277
53. BERGMAN and TURNER *Endocrinology* 1939, **24,** 656
54. BATES, RIDDLE and MILLER *Endocrinology* 1940, **27,** 781
55. BOX and CULLUMBINE *Brit. J. Pharmacol.* 1947, **2,** 38
56. LAWRENCE and WEBSTER *Brit. J. Pharmacol.* 1958, **13,** 330
57. FENTON *Biochem. J.* 1961, **81,** 570
58. PERRY *Spec. Rep. Ser. med. Res. Coun., Lond.* 1950, no. 270
59. BARTLETT *Proc. roy. Soc.* A 1937, **160,** 268
60. LILJESTRAND *J. Pharm., Lond.* 1949, **1,** 78
61. VOS JR. *J. Amer. pharm. Ass. Sci. Edn.* 1943, **32,** 138
62. THOMPSON *J. Pharmacol.* 1944, **80,** 373
63. STEWART *J. Pharm., Lond.* 1958, **10,** 741
64. YOUNG *Brit. J. Pharmacol.* 1951, **6,** 273
65. BROWN *J. Pharm., Lond.* 1961, **13,** 679
66. WINTER and FLATAKER *J. Pharmacol.* 1950, **98,** 305
67. BÜLBRING and WAJDA *J. Pharmacol.* 1945, **85,** 81
68. SIEGEL *Non Parametric Statistics:* McGraw-Hill, New York, 1956
69. FRASER *Non Parametric Statistics:* John Wiley, New York, 1957
70. FISHER *Statistical Methods for Research Workers:* Oliver and Boyd, London, 1944
71. FINNEY *Biometrika* 1948, **35,** 145
72. MAINLAND, HERRERA and SUTCLIFFE *Statistical Tables for Use with Binomial Samples:* N.Y. Univ. Coll. of Medicine, 1956
73. GURLAND, LEE and DAHM *Biometrics* 1960, **16,** 382
74. AITCHISON and SILVEY *Biometrika* 1951, **44,** 131
75. ASHFORD *Biometrics* 1959, **15,** 573
76. NORTON *Psychotropic Drugs* (Ed. Garattini and Ghetti): Elsevier, Amsterdam, 1957, p. 73
77. BROSS *Biometrics* 1958, **14,** 18
78. MANN and WHITNEY *Ann. math. Statist.* 1947, **18,** 50
79. AUBLE *Bull. Inst. educ. Res. Indiana Univ.* 1953, **1,** no. 2
80. PEARSON and HARTLEY *Biometrika, Tables for Statisticians:* Cambridge University Press, 1954
81. VAN STRIK *Quantitative Methods in Pharmacology* (Ed. De Jonge): North Holland, 1961, p.88
82. UNITED STATES NATIONAL BUREAU OF STANDARDS *Applied Mathematics* Series no. 6, 1952
83. WILCOXON *Some Rapid Approximate Statistical Procedures*, American Cyanamid Co., Stamford, Conn., 1949
84. JANSSEN *Psychopharmacologia* 1960, **1,** 141
85. THORP *Brit. J. Pharmacol.* 1947, **2,** 93
86. SCHILD *Brit. J. Pharmacol.* 1947, **2,** 189
87. ARUNLAKSHANA and SCHILD *Brit. J. Pharmacol.* 1959, **14,** 48
88. GADDUM and LEMBECK *Brit. J. Pharmacol.* 1949, **4,** 401
89. WEATHERALL and WEATHERALL *Brit. J. Pharmacol.* 1949, **4,** 260
90. GREEN *Brit. J. Pharmacol.* 1959, **14,** 26

91. LISTER *Brit. J. Pharmacol.* 1960, **15,** 254
92. BROCK and SCHNEIDER *Quantitative Methods in Pharmacology* (Ed. De Jonge): North Holland, 1961, p. 264
93. FOSTER *J. Pharmacol.* 1939, **65,** 1
94. LIM, RINK, GLASS and SOAJE-ECHAGUE *Arch. int. Pharmacodyn.* 1961, **130,** 336
95. GRAY, TREVAN, BAINBRIDGE and ATTWOOD *Proc. roy. Soc.* B. 1931, **108,** 54
96. GADDUM *Brit. J. Pharmacol.* 1956, **11,** 156
97. SNEDECOR *Statistical Methods* 5th Edn: Iowa State College, 1956, p. 35

# 6

# ANTICONVULSANT DRUGS

A. Spinks and W. S. Waring

## INTRODUCTION

Epilepsy (epilambanein, to take hold of) is an illness that seizes the patient. The nature of this seizure led to its early recognition as a unique and terrible affliction: it is mentioned in the Babylonian civil code of Hammurabi (2080 B.C.) and early Hebrew scripts. Full clinical descriptions were first given in the Hippocratic monograph, 'On the Sacred Disease' (ca. 400 B.C.) A good description of a major seizure also occurs in the New Testament (Mark, IX: 17).

The early authorities recognized all the clinical features of major seizures, and also the occurrence of minor forms of epilepsy, particularly brief interruptions of consciousness. In the nineteenth century, major and minor seizures became known respectively as grand mal and petit mal[1]. These were differentiated from focal epilepsy by Hughlings Jackson, who also recognized the essential relationship between the various epilepsies and explained their protean manifestations in terms of an abnormally intense, disorderly neuronal discharge originating in functionally variable regions of the brain. The signs and symptoms depend on the motor, sensory, autonomic and mental functions of those regions of the brain in which the discharge arises or to which it spreads. If the discharge is violent, prolonged and ubiquitous, the maximal tonic-clonic seizure of grand mal develops; if it is limited in strength or area or duration, various sorts of minor seizure occur.

The cause of the abnormal discharge is imperfectly understood. A distinction is frequently made between symptomatic epilepsy in which a traumatic, infectious, neoplastic or, rarely, emotional, cause is known or suspected, and idiopathic epilepsy in which there is no known cause. In idiopathic epilepsy it is natural to suspect an hereditary origin, but though there is strong evidence, particularly from work on monozygotic twins[2], that a constitutional predisposition may be conferred genetically, it cannot be said unequivocally that epilepsy is inherited. The nature of the neuronal abnormality that confers abnormality of discharge is also uncertain. The abnormal neurones are alive, and in consequence an epileptogenic zone may exist around, but never within, an area of necrotic tissue. Frequently the brain of an idiopathic epileptic appears normal anatomically and histologically. It seems probable that the safety margin between normality and epileptogenic abnormality is relatively small since an epileptiform electroencephalogram may be elicited in about 4 per cent of non-epileptics by a flickering light[3].

The concept of relatively slight abnormality is also supported by the fact that the patient may be normal between attacks. Indeed many great men have been epileptics. Known or suspected sufferers include Julius Caesar, Caligula, the apostle Paul, the prophet Mahommed, Napoleon, Paganini, Dostoievsky, Nobel and Van Gogh. Though the 'normality' of some of these personages is doubtful, the inclusion of Paganini and Van Gogh at least demonstrates that dexterity is not necessarily impaired between attacks. The inclusion of St. Paul, though questionable, is interesting because epilepsy compelled exclusion from the office of priest in the Middle Ages[4].

The popular notion that grand mal is associated with low intelligence is not supported either by the occasional occurrence of the disease in great men, or by the results of Stanford-Binet and similar tests. However, such studies are difficult to assess because the populations tested are nearly always highly selected. An association with personality disorder has also been claimed, and is common in frontal lobe, temporal and hypothalamic epilepsy. When these areas are not primarily involved there may be little or no disorder of personality.

Epileptic taxonomy is a popular diversion, and many classifications are available. The simple scheme of Gibbs and Stamps[5] is very satisfactory for the present purpose, of illustrating specific actions of drugs. The following definitions are based on it.

*Grand mal* is characterized by the occurrence of maximal seizures associated with generalized tonic-clonic convulsions, loss of consciousness, autonomic hyperactivity and, in about 50 per cent of patients, premonitary aurae. The EEG during the attack is characterized by high voltage-fast activity. In 50 per cent of patients it may be normal between attacks though, in some of these, electroencephalographic abnormality may be evoked by sensitizing procedures. When the EEG is abnormal between seizures the abnormality is variable: the record may display focal spikes, spike and wave, 6 or 14 per second waves, and so on. This suggests that the essential feature of grand mal is not a specific localization of initial discharge, but an abnormal ease of generalized spread of an initial discharge of variable location. Additional evidence in favour of this hypothesis is the possible association of grand mal attacks, that is maximal seizures, with any type of sub-maximal seizure. Grand mal is the commonest single form of epilepsy, and the most distressing.

*Petit mal*, formerly descriptive of any mild seizure, is now commonly restricted to brief, frequent (5–100/day) attacks of impaired consciousness, without aurae, but associated frequently with staring and eye movements, and more rarely with loss of posture and arm jerks. There is an increasing tendency to include as an essential criterion the occurrence in the EEG of a regular 3 per second spike and wave pattern. Petit mal, as defined, occurs most commonly before puberty, and is relatively rare in adults. It is frequently complicated by grand mal, and the spike and wave pattern is then often mixed with multiple spikes. True petit mal has no specific aetiology: infection is sometimes suspected.

*Psychomotor seizures* are characterized by confusion, and elaborate, but poorly co-ordinated and purposeless, movements or behaviour patterns. During the attack the patient may smack his lips, run, dance or jump and shout. The EEG displays high voltage 6/sec and flat 4/sec waves in widely separated areas, though much evidence indicates an anterior temporal origin. Psychomotor epilepsy is frequently complicated by psychiatric illness. A traumatic cause is likeliest.

*Myoclonic epilepsy* is characterized clinically by sudden sharp jerks of head, limbs or trunk lasting about a second, and occurring in bursts of four or five at 3–6 second intervals. The EEG may be normal even during an attack, which suggests an extrapyramidal origin; the abnormality if present is a disorganized pattern of slow waves mixed with multiple high voltage spikes. Myoclonic epilepsy is frequently accompanied by grand mal, less frequently by petit mal, and rarely by psychomotor seizures.

In the first year of life, and almost never after four, a more complicated and more protracted series of jerking movements of eyes, body and arms may occur. These are called *infantile spasms* and are almost always associated with a continuous EEG abnormality of high voltage slow waves and spikes (hypsarhythmia), and with feeble mindedness. *Febrile seizures* also are restricted to children, in this instance from 3 to 10, and occur only during fever.

*Jacksonian seizures* are characterized by a sensory or motor march, *e.g.* a twitch in the thumb may spread thence to other muscles in conformity with the conventional plot of these muscles on the motor cortex. Though this motor march, or an analogous sensory march, may suggest a cortical focus, the actual point of origin may be temporal or occipital, as indicated by the EEG or by premonitory psychic or visual aurae. Many Jacksonian seizures, particularly those of occipital origin, fade before puberty.

The incidence of epilepsy is about 4 per 1,000; it is the commonest neurological disease. The incidence of the main types is shown in *Table 6.1*.

*Table 6.1.* Incidence of main types of epilepsy*

| Type | Percentage incidence | Patients in Britain† |
|------|----------------------|----------------------|
| Grand mal (Gm) | 48 | 96,000 |
| Psychomotor (Ps) | 5·8 | 12,000 |
| Jacksonian | 3·9 | 7,800 |
| Petit mal (Pm) | 2·9 | 5,800 |
| Focal | 2·8 | 5,600 |
| Febrile | 1·4 | 2,800 |
| Infantile | 1·1 | 2,200 |
| Myoclonic | 0·3 | 600 |
| Gm. + Ps. | 15 | 30,000 |
| Gm. + Pm. | 6·0 | 12,000 |
| Gm. + Other | 3·6 | 7,200 |

* From data on 11,612 patients given by Gibbs and Gibbs[6].
† Calculated from Gibbs's data assuming an overall incidence of 0·4% and a population of 50 million.

The early history of epilepsy treatment is a record of dismal failure; and worse, since some of the remedies tried, for example, ashes of asses' hooves, stork's dung and the warm blood of a gladiator[7], must have increased the sufferer's misery. The first effective remedy, bromide, was introduced by Locock in 1857[8] and confirmed in 1868 by Clouston, whose admirable trial has recently been discussed by McIlwain[9]. Clouston defined the optimal dose of bromide, and demonstrated its action by measuring reduction in fits during some months' treatment, compared with control periods before and after treatment. Limited use of bromide continues to-day.

The next important advance occurred in 1912 when Hauptmann[10] tried the new sedative phenobarbitone (*I*) in epilepsy. Its great value was recognized at once, and it is still one of the best drugs available. The other important anti-epileptic drugs have been discovered through the use of

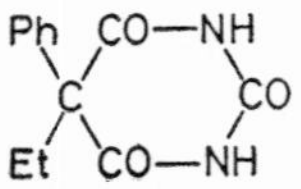

*(I)* Phenobarbitone (1912)

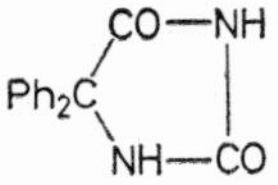

*(II)* Phenytoin (1938) 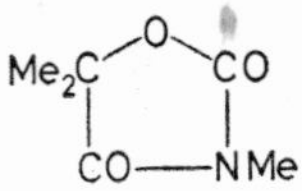     *(III)* Troxidone (1944)

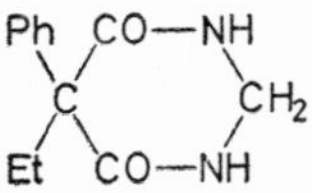

*(IV)* Primidone (1952)

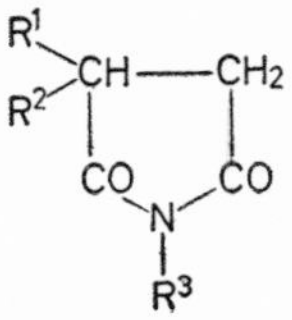

*(V)* Phensuximide (1951), $R^1$=H, $R^2$= Ph, $R^3$= Me
*(VI)* Methsuximide (1956), $R^1$= Me, $R^2$= Ph, $R^3$= Me
*(VII)* Ethosuximide (1958), $R^1$= Me, $R^2$= Et, $R^3$= H

anticonvulsant tests in animals. The first successful test of this type was conducted by Merritt and Putnam[11–13], who screened about seventy compounds against electrically induced convulsions in cats, and selected 5,5-diphenylhydantoin (phenytoin, Dilantin, *II*) as the best. It was highly effective in man, and was non-sedative. It is still the most frequently used specific anticonvulsant, though it often causes side effects, some of them serious.

The main utility of the three drugs so far discussed is in grand mal. The fifteen years after the introduction of phenytoin produced a rapid proliferation of assay methods, and tests of compounds by more than one method led to the discovery of drugs with a new specificity of action. The first important example was troxidone (Tridione, trimethadione, *III*), made as a potential analgesic by Spielman[14], and found by wider central nervous tests to be a useful anticonvulsant[15]. Clinical trial[16,17] showed that it was valueless in grand mal but outstanding in petit mal, and it is still widely used.

After phenytoin and phenobarbitone, the most frequently used anti-epileptic drug is primidone (Mysoline, *IV*) which was discovered by Bogue and Carrington[18] and introduced by Handley and Stewart[19]. It is effective in grand mal, psychomotor epilepsy and Jacksonian seizures, but less useful in petit mal.

The remaining anti-epileptic drugs of outstanding importance form a single group, the succinimides. They are mainly used against petit mal. The first was phensuximide (Milontin, $N$-methyl-$\alpha$-phenylsuccinimide, $V$)[20–22], the second methsuximide (Celontin, $\alpha,N$-dimethyl-$\alpha$-phenyl-succinimide, $VI$)[23] and the most recent ethosuximide ($\alpha$-ethyl-$\alpha$-methyl-succinimide, Zarontin, $VII$). Although few clinical reports have appeared[24–27], it seems probable that ethosuximide is the best drug yet found for the treatment of petit mal.

Although only the six drug types mentioned have come into wide use, the intensification of industrial, chemical and pharmacological research that began in the thirties, and has continued at an increasing rate ever since, has led to the publication of data on thousands of potential anticonvulsant drugs. Their discovery by animal tests is relatively easy, but only a small proportion of the drugs thus discovered eventually prove useful and safe in man. In these circumstances it is reasonable to suspect inadequate knowledge of how anticonvulsants act, of what structures confer this action simultaneously with low toxicity, and of methods that correlate well with clinical usefulness. The first object in this review is to examine the correctness of this suspicion by discussing methods of testing anti-epileptic drugs, and available knowledge of their mode of action. The second object is to discuss the types of structures that have been tested, and the preparation of the most important of them.

## METHODS OF TESTING ANTICONVULSANTS

There has been little fundamental progress since Goodman and his colleagues reviewed methods of testing anticonvulsant drugs in 1948[28,29], though many papers have been published. Indeed, the number of methods of testing anticonvulsants much exceeds the number of successful anticonvulsants. The most used methods cause seizures in animals either electrically or by administering a chemical convulsant, particularly leptazol. Neurophysiological techniques, and chronic epilepsies of animals, have been used only rarely.

Electrical seizures are usually induced by stimulation through corneal or ear electrodes. Though brief rectangular pulses of 300 c/s are more efficient, a 50 or 60 c/s sinusoidal wave stimulus is satisfactory for most purposes, and is almost invariably used[30]. The apparatus should provide constant current, independent of electrode and animal impedance. A high resistance in series achieves a sufficiently constant current[30], but the required voltage is undesirably high. An alternative arrangement makes the animal the anode load of a pentode valve, the screen grid of which is maintained at a constant voltage. The currents commonly used to elicit major seizures in rats or mice are potentially highly dangerous to the operator, who must be protected by appropriate safety switches.

When a subliminal current is applied to the head and then gradually increased, the successive effects are: ($i$) brief jerk as the current is applied, ($ii$) running, hopping and squealing, ($iii$) stunning, ($iv$) minimal or 'threshold' seizure, identified by the occurrence of just detectable clonus of facial muscles, and rhythmical twitches of whiskers and ears, (v) severe whole-body clonus, (vi) the well-defined pattern of the maximal electroshock seizure: hind limb tonic flexion; hind limb tonic extension; whole-body clonus; relaxation; and, finally, post-convulsant depression, during which the animal is partly refractory to a second supramaximal stimulus.

The two electrical methods in most frequent use measure threshold current necessary to elicit stage (iv), or deliver a supramaximal stimulus to elicit the maximal seizure. In the latter variant the end-point commonly observed is full tonic extension of the hind limbs: its absence is the criterion of anti-convulsant action. This is the maximal electroshock seizure or MES test[31,32]. The threshold test is commonly referred to as the MET (minimal electro-shock threshold) or NET (normal electroshock threshold) test[33,34]. Both tests may be varied according to taste without greatly altering the amount of information gained. Variants will therefore be discussed only briefly.

Both may be carried out in a variety of species: rats[30,33], mice[34–38], cats[12,21,35–37], guinea-pigs[39] and rabbits[40] have been most often used. The characteristics of electroshock seizures in some other species have been described[41–44]. For most purposes, and particularly for screening, mice are preferred. However, many drugs are less active (in mg/kg) in mice than in rats. A notable exception is phenytoin.

The commonest form of the MES test is that introduced by Goodman's group: a supramaximal 50 or 60 c/s shock of 0·2 or 0·3 sec duration is applied to mice or rats. Frequently used currents are 50 mA and 150 mA respectively[30,34]. The animal is recorded as protected or unprotected from hind limb tonic extensor spasm, and no finer detail is readily observed. One popular variation is the use of several current strengths so that sub-maximal seizures and variations in duration of seizure component and recovery time, and in drug action may be observed[32,39,45,46]. A modification introduced by Bogue and Carrington[18] measures the energy in milliwatt seconds necessary to elicit tonic extensor spasm of the rat hind limb: precise measurement is facilitated by using large matched groups of rats and a relatively low current of 7·5 mA, so that reaction time is increased to 4–10 sec.

The two most important variants of the MET test are the hyponatraemic test and the so-called 'psychomotor' test. Hyponatraemia induced by injec-tion of glucose reduces electroshock threshold[33,34,47]. The reduced threshold is raised by anticonvulsant drugs, including phenytoin which is inactive in the ordinary MET test[33].

The 'psychomotor' or PSM test was introduced by Toman[48–50]. Rec-tangular 0·2 msec pulses at 6/sec were applied to mice through corneal electrodes for periods of 3 sec and caused initial stunning and then automatic behaviour. Toman claimed that the test was useful in screening drugs for psychomotor epilepsy, mainly because phenacemide, which is highly effective in psychomotor epilepsy, was picked out by the test. Later, Good-man and coworkers[51,52] showed that many drugs were active in the PSM test but not in clinical psychomotor epilepsy, and that the psychomotor test selected much the same drugs as the MET or hyponatraemic test. A recent study by Fink and Swinyard[38] confirms the identity of drug effects in the so-called psychomotor and hyponatraemic tests.

Though antagonism of chemical convulsants by drugs had often been studied previously[53-55], it was probably the discovery of troxidone by Everett and Richards[15] that led to wide use of leptazol in screening test. They showed that troxidone prevented leptazol convulsions (and also those induced by picrotoxin, strychnine, thujone and electrical shock), and that phenytoin in single doses was ineffective against leptazol seizures. The specific value of troxidone in petit mal, the inactivity of phenytoin in petit mal, the occurrence of spike and wave patterns in the electroencephalogram after leptazol[56-58], and the activity of succinimides in leptazol tests and in petit mal[21,58], have led to the assumption that leptazol tests, and particularly leptazol threshold tests, select drugs likely to be active in petit mal, whereas elimination of the tonic extensor component of the electroshock seizure selects drugs likely to be active in grand mal.

There are almost as many leptazol tests as there are electroshock tests. Many of them are based on that of Orloff, Williams and Pfeiffer[59], who used an intermittent intravenous infusion of leptazol in mice and recorded the doses that elicited three successive signs: first, a sharp twitch of the whole body; second, clonus; third, a tonic flexor, tonic extensor sequence similar to that of the MES test, and usually lethal. The effects of drugs on each might be studied. Most later users of this method have introduced only minor variations[45,60-63]. A similar method may also be applied to cats or rabbits, and the appearance or absence of spike and wave patterns in the EEG may then be used to select drugs for test against petit mal[57,58]. In all these tests a minimal seizure threshold, analogous to that of the MET test, is being measured. Effects on the pattern of the seizure, particularly the elimination of the tonic extensor component, may also be observed, but these are studied more conveniently by giving a large intravenous dose of leptazol[46,64]. This is the maximal leptazol (metrazole) seizure or MMS test, equivalent to the maximal electroshock or MES test. In the MMS test, however, the seizure sequence is clonic-tonic not tonic-clonic[64].

The leptazol tests so far described are probably the most useful. However, simpler variants have been widely used, particularly the subcutaneous or intraperitoneal administration of leptazol. According to dose, minimal clonic, severe clonic, clonic-tonic, or lethal seizures may be elicited and the effects of drugs observed[15,18,34,36,46,60,65].

The predictive value of the electrical and leptazol tests has been discussed by several authors. Chen and Ensor[36] studied the effects of nine anticonvulsants against electrical seizures in cats, rats and mice and subcutaneous leptazol seizures (clonic, *i.e.* threshold, seizures) in rats. There was good agreement between electrical shock activity in cats and mice, but rats differed markedly from these species. Drugs that eliminated the tonic extensor component of the maximal electroshock seizure were active against grand mal, and drugs that were weak in anti-leptazol property were ineffective in control of petit mal. These empirical correlations have been widely employed in screening programmes: however, the drugs used by Chen and Ensor for test evaluation were discovered as a consequence of using those, or similar, tests for drug evaluation.

The usefulness of the different tests has been analysed more theoretically by Goodman and his colleagues[28,31,34,64]. They have emphasized the difference between effects on threshold and pattern, and between effects on focus and on spread. Threshold is used in its strict sense, that is the threshold to a minimal (hence clonic) seizure, and pattern is used in the special sense of elimination of the tonic extensor component of maximal seizures. They and others[30,66-69] have emphasized the ability of drugs in use for grand mal to block the tonic extensor component, and they have suggested that this reflects the ability of such drugs to block generalized seizure spread. They distinguish between this action and an ability to raise the threshold for convulsive discharge: this might be related to the ability of a drug to reduce initiation of clinical convulsions. Analysis of differences in action of eight drugs on the MES and MMS tests[64] suggests that the MES test involves mainly seizure spread, and the MMS test spread and initiation of convulsive discharge. Tests have been analysed more empirically by other workers, and there is much controversy about the precise relationships of different tests[45,46,60,70].

It is probable that differences between standard tests depend chiefly on two pairs of variables: electrical or leptazol, maximal or threshold. The likeliest neurophysiological correlations are between maximal electrical seizure and spread, and between leptazol threshold test and initiation of convulsive discharge. These two experimental seizures are probably the most distinctive and useful available. The other two combinations of the two variables (MET and MMS tests) are probably less distinctive and less useful, in that each detects mixed effects on spread and on initial discharge threshold. None of the tests, however, is fully satisfactory. Most workers feel more confident of clinical success in grand mal, predicted by an MES or similar test, than in petit mal, predicted by a leptazol threshold test. However, it is widely recognized that even the former prediction is erroneous more often than not. Thus Gruber found that only four of eleven compounds with significant activity in animal tests had significant activity in man, and only two were comparable in efficacy to known drugs[71]. It is possible that some 'wastage' of this type is due to different metabolism of the drug by man, rather than to a deficiency in the test. Nevertheless, increased understanding of the meaning of available tests, and the development of new ones, are urgently needed.

Other tests have been little used for drug discovery. The most familiar of these is perhaps the anti-strychnine test. Its recent use has been mainly in the detection of so-called polysynaptic depressants of the mephenesin type[45,72].

The use of neurophysiological tests at present is mainly to study mode of action, and they are considered briefly under that heading. Suppression of after-discharge has been used as a test method, but was considered inferior to standard mouse tests[73].

Chronic epilepsies may readily be induced in animals. One well-known technique is to place a foreign substance, e.g. alumina cream, metal powder or talc on the motor cortex. Contralateral focal seizures develop first and may become progressively more generalized, so that eventually grand mal seizures occur. The seizures may persist for several years[74-78]. Though monkeys are almost always used, the method has been applied to mice and rats[79]. The severity of the chronic epilepsy is extremely difficult to evaluate and occasional observation is usually supplemented by challenge of some kind such as prodding, or injection of semicarbazide, leptazol or picrotoxin[80-83]. It is this factor no doubt that has prevented wide use of the technique. However, Morrell, Bradley and Ptashne[83] have recently studied actions of drugs on the chronic epilepsy induced by local freezing of the cortex. Extension of this useful approach is desirable, particularly since the neurophysiological techniques used allow analysis of effects of drugs on focus and on spread of discharge. It might also be possible to study actions of drugs in chronic epilepsy, if automatic recording techniques were developed. A damped jiggle cage or automatic EEG analyser might be tried.

Audiogenic seizures have been used to study actions of anticonvulsant and other drugs[84-89]. The nature of these seizures has been reviewed by Riley and Spinks[90]. The two main components are a running seizure, succeeded by a clonic-tonic-clonic seizure. Anticonvulsants seem much more effective against the tonic extensor component of the maximal audiogenic seizure than they are against the running component[88]. The method offers no obvious advantage over electrical tests. The same is probably true of seizures caused by high oxygen pressures[91].

In summary, it is probable that two simple tests in mice, an MES or similar test, and a leptazol threshold test, are now, as they were 15 years ago, the best tests available; and it is very doubtful whether any of the supplementary tests that have been described, for example, the hyponatraemic test, the psychomotor test, the anti-strychnine test or the audiogenic test, add anything useful to the two main tests. It is also very doubtful whether tests in other species such as rat, cat or rabbit add much to the mouse tests. Their chief use is probably to point to possible differences in absorption or metabolism in different species, and to study actions in greater detail. Improvement in test methods must probably await improved understanding of the nature of epilepsy, and of the mode of action of anticonvulsants. This will be gained by neurophysiological and biochemical studies rather than by elegant variation of existing tests. Chronic epilepsies deserve more attention than they have received, but their immediate utility is probably in neurophysiological and biochemical research rather than in drug testing.

The test methods selected must of course be supplemented by adequate toxicity tests. Most anticonvulsants that have been tried in man have caused side-effects, and successful anticonvulsants may have to be administered daily for many years. The likeliest form of toxicity is central nervous. The habit of determining a ratio between effective dose and that causing minimal evidence of ataxia or other neurological defect is well established and should remain so. Suitable methods of measuring neurotoxicity are readily available[34,90]. The elimination of other types of detectable toxicity by adequate chronic toxicity tests[92-94] is also essential. After this has been done the chance of encountering toxicity in man, particularly of the hypersensitivity type, still seems exceptionally high in this class of drug. Many examples are given later.

## MODE OF ACTION OF ANTICONVULSANTS

Many theories of anticonvulsant action have been proposed. Some of the most interesting of the suggested actions are those on humoral transmission by acetylcholine, noradrenaline, hydroxytryptamine, dopamine or $\gamma$-amino-butyric acid; on oxidative metabolism of brain; and on nerve membrane.

## Involvement of Acetylcholine

Specific chemical substances probably mediate excitatory and inhibitory transmission in the brain, but the number and nature of central transmitters are unknown. However, some may be postulated, particularly acetylcholine. The biochemical evidence for this, reviewed by Hebb[95] and Florey[96], consists mainly of studies of the distribution of acetylcholine, choline acetylase and cholinesterases in brain. Acetylcholine is present in most parts of the brain, though to a much less extent in cerebellum. The amount found is dependent on the activity of the brain just before death: it is increased by anaesthesia or sleep, and is decreased by excitement or convulsions[97-102]. Moreover, seizures and hyperactivity may cause accumulation of free acetylcholine in cerebrospinal fluid and cortical saline pools (see review by Stone[102]). These facts are consistent with the hypothesis that acetylcholine is an excitatory transmitter in most parts of the brain. It follows from this hypothesis that inhibitors of choline acetylase or antagonists of acetylcholine should be central depressants, including perhaps anticonvulsants, and that antagonists of cholinesterase should be central stimulants or convulsants. It is also reasonable to look for disturbance of acetylcholine metabolism in epilepsy.

There is much evidence that excessive amounts of acetylcholine may cause neuronal hyperactivity, tremors and seizures. In particular, cholinesterase inhibitors such as tetraethyl pyrophosphate (TEPP) cause accumulation of acetylcholine; and tremors and generalized convulsions result from the administration of high doses of these inhibitors[102-105]. Topical application of acetylcholine to some areas of exposed cortex evokes spike activity, particularly after sensitization by leptazol, strychnine or eserine[106-110]. These observations, and measurements of acetylcholine concentration during different physiological states, suggest that acetylcholine is mainly an excitatory transmitter. Inhibitory effects that have been seen may perhaps depend on excitation of an inhibitory centre: thus application to some 'suppressor' areas of cortex may cause diminution of cortical excitability[111], as may electrical stimulation or strychnine[112].

Tower and Elliott have reported diminished formation *in vitro* of bound acetylcholine in human epileptogenic cortex[113] and cortex of cats suffering from seizures induced by methionine sulphoximine[114]. Giachetti and Piva have reported similar findings in dogs[115]. Raised cholinesterase concentrations possibly indicating adaptation to increased amounts of free acetylcholine, have also been reported in experimental and human epileptogenic cortex[76, 113]. However, Pappius and Elliott[116] have recently failed to confirm many of the findings of Tower and Elliott, and though Tower[104] has suggested possible reasons for the discrepancy, it seems unlikely that altered acetylcholine metabolism is a cause of human epilepsy. The central actions of those drugs that simulate or antagonize peripheral actions of acetylcholine also fail to prove the importance of cholinergic transmission to epilepsy or anticonvulsant action. The best support is probably provided by the proconvulsant or convulsant properties of anticholinesterases, already referred to. Somewhat weaker support is provided by the confusion, hyperreflexia, tremors and convulsions that may be caused by muscarinic and nicotinic drugs such as pilocarpine, arecoline or nicotine itself. Drugs that antagonize the peripheral muscarinic actions of acetylcholine, such as atropine and scopolamine, have been claimed to have anticonvulsant effects[117,118] though some studies have failed to demonstrate such actions of atropine[102,119,120] or benactyzine[120,121] against electrical or leptazol seizures. However, atropine is active against seizures induced by tetraethyl pyrophosphate[102]. It is usually considered to be ineffective in clinical epilepsy[102]. The anti-nicotinic drugs, pempidine and mecamylamine, have very feeble actions against electroshock[122] though they strongly antagonize nicotine seizures[122,123], as does benactyzine[124]. They also cause tremor[122]. No anticonvulsant of proved value has known atropine-like or pemidine-like activity.

The evidence given above seems to justify the conclusion that acetylcholine is a transmitter, probably mainly of excitation, at a variety of central nervous synapses, but certainly not at all synapses. The central actions of acetylcholine antagonists are consistent with an important role of acetylcholine at some specialized sites, including basal ganglia, and mesodiencephalic reticular formation; but selective block solely of cholinergic transmission seem insufficient to produce complete antagonism of seizures, unless these are initiated by specific activation of cholinergic neurones, for example, by anticholinesterases, or nicotine. It is improbable that any clinically useful anticonvulsant acts by interference with cholinergic transmission.

### Involvement of 5-Hydroxytryptamine, Noradrenaline or Dopamine

5-Hydroxytryptamine, and 5-hydroxytryptophane decarboxylase, by which it is formed, are present mainly in rhinencephalon and diencephalon. Cortex contains much less and cerebellum almost none. Monoamine oxidase, which inactivates it, is fairly evenly distributed throughout the central nervous system[125–127]. 5-Hydroxytryptamine has not been proved to be a central nervous transmitter. The evidence is mainly pharmacological: for example, a number of drugs having potent central, and particularly specific psychotropic actions, antagonize or release, or are structurally related to, 5-hydroxytryptamine.

The anticonvulsant drugs, phenytoin, methoin, troxidone, paramethadione, phensuximide, phenacemide, primidone, phenobarbitone and sodium bromide, all increase the concentration of 5-hydroxytryptamine in brain by about 50 per cent or more[128]. However, meprobromate, reputedly effective in epilepsy[129], does not raise 5-hydroxytryptamine concentrations, and pentobarbitone, hexobarbitone and ether, which are not good anticonvulsants, do. The effect is attributed by Anderson and Bonnycastle[130] to a non-specific reduction of central nervous function: this would result in reduced liberation of transmitters, and hence a rise in the bound stores. This view is supported by the finding of Prockop, Shore and Brodie[131] that lower, but still anticonvulsant, doses of phenytoin do not raise brain amine levels.

Nevertheless, the anticonvulsant actions of amineoxidase inhibitors, and the proconvulsant actions of reserpine must be considered. The demonstration by Zeller[132] that iproniazid is a potent monoamineoxidase inhibitor, led to the rapid development of other more potent inhibitors. They raise brain levels of 5-hydroxytryptamine, noradrenaline[133] and dopamine[134]. Conversely, reserpine lowers concentrations of all three amines in brain[135,136]. Reserpine is proconvulsant[45,137–139] and amineoxidase inhibitors block the tonic extensor component of electrical seizures in rats[131,140], though they seem less effective against leptazol seizures. Iproniazid has been shown to reinforce the action of troxidone, phenacemide and phenobarbitone against maximal electroshock in mice[141], and the proconvulsant action of reserpine is antagonized by monoamineoxidase inhibitors[142,143].

As Kobinger[142] and Prockop, Shore and Brodie[131] emphasized, it is uncertain that the effects of reserpine or the monoamineoxidase inhibitors on seizures are due to the changes in known brain amines. Nevertheless, it is interesting that there appears to be anticonvulsant synergism between the 5-hydroxytryptamine precursor, 5-hydroxytryptophane, and iproniazid[131, 142,143] though probably not between the noradrenaline precursor, 3,4-dihydroxyphenylalanine, and iproniazid[131,142,143]. Moreover, the time course of anticonvulsant action is closely similar to that of the increase in concentrations of noradrenaline and 5-hydroxytryptamine in brain[131], and it has been claimed that 5-hydroxytryptamine itself has some action against seizures induced in mice by high oxygen pressures[144].

In view of the high activity of monoamineoxidase inhibitors in electroshock tests, it is disappointing that Perlstein[145] found pheniprazine, one of the most potent, to be inactive in 31 out of 34 epileptic patients. However, it is toxic and the dose given may have been insufficient.

Rather oddly there has been much less study of noradrenaline or adrenaline than of 5-hydroxytryptamine. Noradrenaline is present in highest concentration mainly in the hypothalamus, dorsal pons and medulla oblongata[146,147]. The assumption that it may be a central nervous transmitter rests, as for 5-hydroxytryptamine, mainly on pharmacological evidence. Intravenously administered adrenaline blocks leptazol convulsions[148], but it is uncertain whether this action is central in origin, and it has been suggested[149] that activation of sino-aortic pressure receptors is responsible. The sympathomimetic amphetamine also has anticonvulsant properties in rats[40,150], but not in mice[150] or cats[12], and has been reported effective in petit mal[151].

The occurrence of noradrenaline and 5-hydroxytryptamine in brain might be considered too localized to support a theory that either is involved in seizures or anticonvulsant action. However, the hypothalamus, in which both occur, may possibly have specific importance to the origin or spread of seizures. Thus, hypothalamic stimulation may precipitate or aggravate convulsions[152], and seizures caused by anoxia or hypoglycaemia have been attributed to reduced cortical inhibition of subcortical centres, including the hypothalamus[149]. Since the amineoxidase inhibitors and reserpine alter amine concentrations in the hypothalamus and some other subcortical centres, it is just possible, though unlikely, that some seizures are due to an alteration of noradrenaline or 5-hydroxytryptamine metabolism, and that some anticonvulsants correct this alteration specifically.

So far there is insufficient evidence to show whether dopamine (3-hydroxytyramine) is involved in epilepsy or anticonvulsant action. Its recently discovered inhibition of the crayfish stretch receptor[153] may lead to an exploration of its role in seizures, analogous to that already postulated for γ-aminobutyric acid. It is present in highest concentration in the caudate nucleus, putamen, and globus pallidum. Concentrations in hypothalamus are moderate and there is little elsewhere[147,154,155]. This distribution suggests that dopamine is concerned in the causation of paralysis agitans rather than epilepsy. Further, the same objection applies to dopamine as to the other potential transmitters already discussed: most useful anti-epileptics seem to act on all neurones, not just those in a specific area of the brain.

### Involvement of γ-Aminobutyric Acid

In 1953 Florey[156] found a substance, Factor I, in brain, that was able to inhibit impulse generation in a stretch receptor preparation of crayfish abdominal muscle. Bazemore, Elliott and Florey[157–159] demonstrated its identity with γ-aminobutyric acid, which had already been detected in brain some years earlier[160,161]. It is formed from glutamic acid by the action of glutamic acid decarboxylase[162,163] and is widely distributed throughout the brain in concentrations ranging from 40 to 1,000 $\mu g/g$; most of this seems to be bound or occluded in some way[164,165]. Since it is inhibitory on the crayfish stretch preparation in concentrations of 1·5–5 $\mu g/ml$[165], its much higher concentration in brain suggests that it may be the (or a) hypothetical inhibitory 'transmitter'. If it were, then impairment of its production or release might lead to excessive firing and seizures. An alternative hypothesis is that its role is solely or mainly nutritive. It was known from the early work of Roberts[166] that transamination with α-ketoglutarate may occur to yield glutamate and succinic semialdehyde[167–169]. The latter compound enters the tricarboxylic acid cycle *via* succinic acid. The main function of γ-amino-butyric acid may be to provide an alternative to oxidative decarboxylation of α-ketoglutarate. There is recent evidence in support of this idea[169a].

The evidence for an inhibitory function of γ-aminobutyric acid includes abolition or severe depression of cortical surface-negative responses to electrical stimulation or strychnine[170–173], sometimes with enhancement of surface positive responses. In these experiments rather large concentrations of γ-aminobutyric acid were applied topically. It is usually agreed to be ineffective or only feebly effective systemically, presumably because of failure to penetrate the blood brain barrier[174,175]. Marked central effects of intravenous administration have, however, been observed after local 'destruction' of the barrier by freezing[176].

Doubt about the ability of γ-aminobutyric acid to reach the brain has been avoided by Curtis and Watkins[177] who applied it ionophoretically to the external surface membrane of spinal motoneurones, interneurones and Renshaw cells. Intracellular recording from motoneurones showed no change in resting membrane potential, but excitatory and inhibitory postsynaptic potentials were both reduced, and orthodromically or antidromically evoked spike potentials were depressed or blocked. Activation of Renshaw cells (inhibitory to the motoneurone) by synaptic excitation, or by ionophoretic application of acetylcholine, was also blocked. These results are characteristic of a non-specific depression of neuronal activity, probably by an increase in membrane conductance, and are not characteristic of a specific inhibitory transmitter. They tend to support the suggestion of Curtis, Phillips and

273

Watkins[178] and also Kuffler and Edwards[179] that the action of $\gamma$-aminobutyric acid is a general one on the soma, and not, as previously claimed by Purpura and others[170,180] exerted exclusively at axo-dendritic synapses. A relatively specific effect on the most superficial cortical elements[173,181] may also be doubted.

The accumulating evidence from these experiments on the vertebrate central nervous system strongly opposes the idea that $\gamma$-aminobutyric acid is a specific inhibitory transmitter. Even the invertebrate evidence has been weakened by the finding[153] that 3-hydroxytyramine (dopamine) is about one hundred times as active as $\gamma$-aminobutyric acid on the crayfish receptor. Even if $\gamma$-aminobutyric acid is not a specific transmitter it might be a general regulator of central nervous activity, and it remains possible that reduction in its action leads to convulsions, and increase to anticonvulsant effects. There is some evidence that relates more directly to these possibilities.

It was shown between 1940[182] and 1952 that pyridoxine deprivation, caused by dietary deficiency or treatment with thiosemicarbazide or semicarbazide, induced convulsions[182–186]. Killam and Bain[187] then found that semicarbazide-induced seizures in rats were associated with a decrease in the amount of $\gamma$-aminobutyric acid in the brain, and with reduced activity of glutamic acid decarboxylase, which is dependent on pyridoxal phosphate[188]. Killam, Dasgupta and Killam later reported[189–191] that intraventricular administration of $\gamma$-aminobutyric acid raised the threshold for electrically evoked hippocampal seizures. Roberts, Rothstein and Baxter[192] discussed other evidence for the association of pyridoxal deprivation or $\gamma$-aminobutyric acid depletion with seizures, including antagonism between picrotoxin and $\gamma$-aminobutyric acid on the crayfish preparation[193], and sensitization to experimental epilepsy by semicarbazide and picrotoxin[80,194]. Various hydrazine derivatives other than semicarbazide and thiosemicarbazide cause seizures, e.g. benzoylhydrazide, thiocarbonhydrazide and isoniazide[195]; as do some pyridoxine analogues, e.g. 4-methoxymethylpyridoxine[196] which also causes a fall in level of $\gamma$-aminobutyric acid. The main doubt is whether these seizures are associated with change in $\gamma$-aminobutyric acid, or with some other consequence of pyridoxal inactivation. Recent evidence suggests the latter.

Thus, Purpura, Girado, Smith and Gómez[174,197] froze the cortex with ethyl chloride and produced epileptogenic foci associated with local loss of blood brain barrier. Intravenous $\gamma$-aminobutyric acid reduced paroxysmal discharges arising from such foci. However, they found later[198] that concentrations of glutamic acid, glutamine and glutathione, but not $\gamma$-aminobutyric acid, were reduced in these epileptogenic sites, and that suppression by $\gamma$-aminobutyric acid of paroxysmal discharges from the epileptogenic sites was not necessarily associated with changed concentrations of glutamic acid, glutamine, glutathione or $\gamma$-aminobutyric acid[176]. Conversely paroxysmal discharges may be unaffected by systemic $\gamma$-aminobutyric acid, despite dramatic increases in concentration of the amino acid in epileptogenic sites. Further evidence of dissociation of seizures from $\gamma$-aminobutyric acid concentration is provided by Baxter and Roberts. They found that hydroxylamine, an inhibitor of $\alpha$-ketoglutaric $\gamma$-aminobutyric transaminase[199], raised cerebral γ-aminobutyric acid concentrations[200], and reduced sensitivity of the cat and monkey cortex to electrical stimulation[201]. However, when hydroxylamine and thiosemicarbazide were given together, the latter induced convulsions when γ-aminobutyric acid concentrations were raised[202].

Tower[203] claims that the low levels of glutamic acid found after incubation of cortex from human epileptogenic foci, or from brains of cats treated with convulsants, may be restored to normal by addition of γ-aminobutyric acid which was also deficient in slices of both types. However, brain concentrations of glutamine, glutamate or γ-aminobutyrate are scarcely affected *in vivo* by administration of convulsants such as leptazol or picrotoxin, or by electroshock[196].

Anticonvulsant effects of γ-aminobutyric acid and of its lactam 2-pyrrolidinone have been observed in mice by Hawkins and Sarett[204], and the former has been claimed by Tower to have shown activity in four out of fourteen human epileptics[203]. Both authors used very high doses, and the clinical effect was modest. Possible actions of anticonvulsant drugs *via* γ-aminobutyrate have been proposed. Thus Marazzi[205] claimed that phenytoin and phenacemide, though not troxidone, markedly enhance and prolong the inhibition by γ-aminobutyric acid of the response to transcallosal stimulation. Vernadakis and Woodbury[206] have shown that phenytoin raises the abnormally low level of γ-aminobutyrate in the brain of the adrenalectomized rat, though not in the normal rat. Elliott and van Gelder[207] found no effect by phenytoin, pentobarbitone, or acetazoleamide on the concentration of γ-aminobutyric acid in brain.

The total evidence on γ-aminobutyric acid seems to justify the following conclusions. First, the likeliest function of γ-aminobutyrate in brain is as an intermediate in the 'shunt' pathway from γ-ketoglutarate to succinic semialdehyde, and it is improbable that γ-aminobutyrate is a specific inhibitory transmitter. Second, it is possible, but not very probable, that the level of γ-aminobutyrate plays a non-specific part in the regulation of central nervous excitation, and, it is possible, but unproved, that some seizure states may be caused by an abnormality of γ-aminobutyrate metabolism or concentration. Lastly, there is no good evidence to show that any important anticonvulsant acts by influencing the metabolism, concentration or action of γ-aminobutyrate.

Apart from γ-aminobutyric acid itself, some related compounds have to be considered as possibly associated with seizures. In 1956 Hayashi described the antagonism of some experimental seizures by γ-amino-β-hydroxybutyric acid and proposed that it was the 'real inhibitory principle' of brain[208]. He claimed that it was about ten times as active as γ-aminobutyric acid, which in some circumstances was convulsant[209]. More recently he has claimed that it prevents seizures induced by injection into the carotid or ventricle of an 'excitatory transmitter' from dog CSF, taken during electrically induced seizures[210]. γ-Amino-β-hydroxybutyric acid is about half as active on the crayfish receptor as γ-aminobutyric acid[158]. However, Leven, Lovell and Florey[211] have been unable to find it in brain in spite of the contrary claim of Ohara, Sano, Koizumi and Nishinuma[212] and its alleged importance must be doubted.

γ-Guanidinobutyric acid is probably present in brain[211,213] and has Factor I activity[214]. However, experiments by Purpura and others[197] suggest that its cerebral effects may be excitatory.

γ-Aminobutyrylcholine has been detected in brain[215,216]. No relationship to seizures or anticonvulsant action has so far been disclosed.

## Oxidative Metabolism of Brain

This subject has been reviewed by Tower[104], Hunter and Lowry[217], McIlwain[218] and Brody[219]. The actions of drugs on cerebral oxidative metabolism have been extensively studied since Quastel and Wheatley[220] first showed that narcotics depress the respiration of brain slices *in vitro*. Depression of oxidative metabolism might theoretically cause, or contribute to, anticonvulsant action, since oxygen consumption increases, and the oxygen tension of the brain falls, during convulsive discharges[221], and since convulsive neurones are more sensitive than normal neurones to anoxia[222]. The idea that narcotics and some other central depressants act by depressing cerebral respiration has, however, been criticized[217] because of the excessively high concentrations, usually 1 to 10 mM, required. More recently, interest has turned to the possibility that central depressants reduce oxidative phosphorylation in concentrations lower than those at which oxygen consumption is reduced, *i.e.* 'uncouple' oxidative phosphorylation as dinitrophenol does[223]. Many drugs, including some barbiturates and thiobarbiturates[224], ether[225], methadone[219], gramicidin[226], chlortetracycline[227], aspirin and salicylate[228], mepacrine[223], hexachlorophene[219] and chlorpromazine[229], have been shown *in vitro* to reduce the number of high energy phosphate bonds produced per atom of oxygen consumed. The alarming variety of pharmacological actions displayed by these drugs evokes grave doubt that any of the actions is a consequence of the biochemical effect. Closer analysis of the exact nature and point of action of the uncoupling[219, 230–232], may perhaps resolve some of these doubts, though it does not seem to have done so yet. Moreover, there are other cogent objections to the theory at least as far as hypnotics or anaesthetics and anticonvulsants are concerned. Thus phenobarbitone in reasonable concentrations does not block the synthesis of energy-rich phosphates[224,232] though 5-(1,3-dimethylbutyl)-5-ethylbarbituric acid, which has convulsant as well as some depressant properties[224], does uncouple. Anaesthesia, even by pentobarbitone—a potent uncoupler *in vitro*[224]—causes an increase not a decrease in the level of adenosinetriphosphate in brain[233], and leptazol causes a decrease[233]. These observations are consistent with the idea that in the whole animal the utilization, not the formation, of energy-rich phosphate is depressed by anaesthesia, and enhanced by convulsions. Work on electrically stimulated brain slices points to the same conclusion. McIlwain, Greengard and Forda[234,235] showed that methoin, troxidone and phenytoin in concentrations of the same order as those attained *in vivo* (*e.g.* phenytoin 0·1 to 0·4 mM) did not reduce respiration of brain slices *in vitro* when these were unstimulated or when respiration was increased by dinitrophenol, potassium chloride or 50 cycle per second current. However, all three compounds reduced the increased oxygen consumption that resulted from simulation at 2,000 c/s. This suggests that the effect on respiration was secondary to an effect on excitability. Reduction of phosphocreatine levels by high frequency stimulation was unaffected by troxidone at 1 mM concentration, though Cohen and Heald[232] showed block by 0·8 mM phenobarbitone of phosphocreatine utilization and oxygen consumption by stimulated slices[232].

All these observations suggest that neither uncoupling of phosphorylation, nor the depression of oxygen consumption, is concerned in the action of anticonvulsants.

### Carbonic Anhydrase Inhibition

The mode of action of one type of anticonvulsant, the carbonic anhydrase inhibitors related to acetazolamide, is partly understood. Carbonic anhydrase, a zinc-containing enzyme of molecular weight ca. 30,000, catalyses the reversible reaction: $H_2O + CO_2 \rightleftharpoons H_2CO_3$.

It is present in high concentration in red blood cells, gastric mucosa and renal cortex, and in lower concentration in the brain and pancreas. Its

(VIII) Acetazolamide

function in red cells is to facilitate elimination of carbon dioxide in expired air[236]. Its function in the gastric mucosa and kidney is probably to provide $H^+$ ions for secretion, or for exchange with $Na^+$ in the distal tubule[237,238].

Mann and Keilin first showed[239] that sulphanilamide was a potent inhibitor of carbonic anhydrase. Study of other sulphonamides led eventually to the introduction of acetazolamide (VIII), which was about sixty-five times as active an inhibitor as sulphanilamide, and found wide use in medicine as an oral diuretic[240,241]. The diuretic action is associated with base loss and metabolic acidosis. Acidosis was known to be effective clinically in epilepsy[242] and this fact led Bergstrom, Carzoli, Lombroso, Davidson and Wallace[243] to test acetazolamide in epilepsy. They, and subsequently others[244,245], showed that it was moderately effective. Up to about 1954–5 it was generally assumed that the anticonvulsant action of acetazolamide was secondary to metabolic acidosis[246], though Yeoman[247], who reported that sulphanilamide was effective in a single mixed petit mal/major patient, had previously found a ketogenic diet ineffective in the same patient. Moreover, acidosis, or alkalosis, has little effect on electroshock[248,249], though more on audiogenic seizures[246,250]. Acetazolamide is effective against both[246,251,252].

In 1955 Millichap, Woodbury and Goodman[253] showed that the anticonvulsant action of acetazolamide was due to inhibition of brain carbonic anhydrase, and was not a consequence of the metabolic acidosis. The evidence was that acetazolamide was an effective anticonvulsant in nephrectomized mice, and that the relative anticonvulsant potency of acetazolamide and sulphanilamide could be correlated with inhibition of brain carbonic anhydrase. Thus, acetazolamide was only twice as potent an anticonvulsant in mice, though one hundred times as active on the enzyme in vitro at 0°C: however, sulphanilamide attained concentrations in brain about fifty times those reached by similar doses of acetazolamide. They also reported that the time of peak anticonvulsant activity corresponded with the time of peak inhibition of brain carbonic anhydrase. In fact, their curves were very flat and this last conclusion was challenged by Gray, Maren, Sisson and Smith[249], who nevertheless produced evidence in support of Millichap, Woodbury and Goodman's hypothesis. Thus, methazolamide (5-acetamido-4-methyl-1,3,-4 thiadiazole-2-sulphonamide or methyl-acetazolamide), like acetazolamide, was active in nephrectomized mice, and was a more effective anticonvulsant than acetazolamide, in accordance with its greater ability to penetrate the blood brain barrier. They suggested, however, that metabolic or respiratory acidosis (the latter caused by impaired pulmonary carbon dioxide exchange)[240] contributes to the effect; and showed that acidosis, caused by ammonium chloride, increases the anticonvulsant action of methazolamide, as it does that of acetazolamide[252]. Later Gray, Rauh and Shanahan[254] showed that both carbonic anhydrase and methazolamide were present in the same, supernatant, fraction of differentially centrifuged brain homogenates, and that the drug concentration was sufficient to cause maximal inhibition of the enzyme. Gray[249] has also studied the enzymatic and anticonvulsant actions of fourteen compounds of the acetazolamide type, and showed that the three most active compounds included the two most active inhibitors of carbonic anhydrase; the third was inactive *in vitro* but was metabolized to a potent inhibitor *in vivo*. It has also been shown by Koch and Woodbury[255] that nitrate ion, which is a moderately effective inhibitor of carbonic anhydrase[256], is anticonvulsant. Bromide also inhibits the enzyme[256].

Two other types of inhibitor, ethoxzolamide (6-ethoxybenzthiazole-2-sulphonamide) and 5-chlorotoluene-2,4-disulphonamide, have been shown to be active anticonvulsants[257–259]. Activity of chlorothiazide in epilepsy has also been claimed by Italian workers[260] though Ligou and Nahas[261] found that it had little effect on cerebral carbonic anhydrase, and Beyer[262] found that it was absent from the cerebrospinal fluid. A related thiazide-type diuretic, bendrofluazide, which is not a potent inhibitor, has no effect on electrical seizures in rats[263].

The evidence so far available justifies a belief that potent inhibitors of cerebral carbonic anhydrase are anticonvulsant. There is no evidence that other well-known anticonvulsants inhibit carbonic anhydrase: for example, diphenylhydantoin, phenobarbitone, primidone and troxidone do not[253,264]. Since the exact function of brain carbonic anhydrase is not known, the reasons why inhibition should result in anticonvulsant action without other marked central nervous effects[240,241], is uncertain. Nevertheless some interesting possibilities have been suggested by Gray, Maren, Sisson and Smith[249] and Koch and Woodbury[255,265]. They proposed that the anticonvulsant effect of an inhibitor is due to an increase in the concentration of carbon dioxide within brain cells. It was already known that administration of excessive concentrations of carbon dioxide prevents convulsions[149,266–268], and that hyperventilation precipitates epileptic attacks. Koch and Woodbury[255] showed that carbon dioxide and acetazolamide blocked maximal electrical seizures in rats at doses of 2·2 per cent and 2 mg/kg respectively; effective doses of both were higher in mice. They also showed that tolerance to acetazolamide and to hypercapnia developed concurrently. The effects of the two agents on the electroshock seizure were also similar. Later[265] they studied the effects of carbon dioxide and of acetazolamide on concentrations of $Na^+$, $K^+$, $Cl^-$ and $HCO_3^-$, in brain. They claimed that acetazolamide decreased the intracellular sodium concentration, and increased the ratio of extracellular to intracellular sodium, and that uptake of radioactive sodium by brain was reduced by acetazolamide. These claims were cited in support of the idea that acetazolamide may be anticonvulsant because it reduces permeability of the neuronal membrane to sodium. Their results require confirmation by additional experiment, which is undoubtedly justified since this study, with that of the same authors on phenytoin, is the most searching yet undertaken in this field.

## Neurophysiological Actions

A symposium[269] describes recent work on the epileptic discharge and confirms the generally held opinion that the basic characteristics are excessively high frequency of discharge, and hypersynchrony of bursts of impulses[270,271]. It seems probable that sustained depolarization is the main property of the membrane that leads to 'epileptic' discharge in a single cell. It is possible that this sustained depolarization causes oscillations of membrane potential that initiate rhythmical bursts[273,274] of cell discharge, though experimental injury is an alternative cause of oscillations that have been observed[270,272]. Other hypothetical mechanisms have been discussed by Eidelberg and French[275], Gloor[276], Ward[277], Morrell[278], Schmidt[279] and Jasper[271]. The nature of the metabolic cause of membrane instability is unknown.

How hypersynchrony, and recruitment of hitherto normal neurones into the epileptic pool, occur is also obscure. Repeated bombardment of normal neurones from a distant primary focus may lead to continuance of epileptic discharge in these neurones after discharge from the focus ceases[270,271]. This phenomenon is analogous to the self-sustaining, epileptiform after-discharge, readily elicited in many areas of the brain by local electrical stimulation at moderately high frequencies[280-284]. The wave-forms of this after-discharge are similar to those of spontaneous seizure discharge in the same region[281,284]. Moreover, when after-discharges are elicited repetitively there is a fall in threshold, increased duration of discharge, and wider spread to distant structures, including sub-cortical structures[282]. This facilitation seems closely similar to the slow but progressive generalization of localized spontaneous seizure activity, observed in man by Delgado and Hamlin[281]. Well-established properties of neurones may be sufficient to explain spread, for example, high maximal frequency of discharge, spatial and temporal summation, post-tetanic potentiation, etc.[66,285]. There are, however, two points of great uncertainty. First, it is not known whether the focal epileptogenic discharge and the electrically induced after-discharge are caused by repetitive self-propagating discharges of individual neurones, or by restimulation of neurones through reverberating circuits[270,282,286]. The sensible view is perhaps that both are involved: certainly excessive stimulation may lead to repetitive discharge in individual neurones, the 'rebound spike' of peripheral nerve being an example[287,288]. The major difficulty is the very high rate of discharge of some single cells in epileptogenic foci, up to 300 per second in man and monkey[289]. One possibility is that massive dendritic potentials are generated, with sufficient synchrony to precipitate high frequency discharges in cells encompassed within the resulting fields[290]. The second uncertainty concerns the existence or non-existence of a centrencephalic (*i.e.* deep, midline) pacemaker that 'drives' the whole brain during generalized seizures. Since this point is of great importance to theories that anticonvulsants might act specifically on particular parts of the brain, it must be considered a little more closely. The best evidence for the existence of such a centrencephalic pacemaker is, first, the observation that the cortical electroencephalogram is bilaterally synchronous during generalized seizures[291–294], and that this synchrony is not prevented by section[295] or congenital absence[296] of the corpus callosum; and, second, the observation that electrical stimulation of medial nuclei of the thalamus elicits the appearance in the cortical EEG of 3 per second spike-and-wave complexes closely similar to those seen in clinical petit mal[291,297–299]. However, the location and importance of the hypothetical centrencephalic pacemaker remain uncertain[294,299–301]. Until this centre[294] has been proved to exist, and has been identified, a single location of anticonvulsant action, even against petit mal, cannot be confidently defined. So far as major (motor) seizures are concerned it is clear that cortex, pyramids, extrapyramidal system, and cord are directly involved[43,301–305], and that a variety of influences including sleep, emotion and hormonal status may profoundly influence spread. The anatomical and physiological parameters of the proconvulsant actions of sleep[306] and emotion[307] have been partly defined. When all these studies on the spread or potentiation of seizures, and the diverse anatomical locations of initiating foci, are considered, it becomes evident that an anticonvulsant might theoretically act on all or any part of the brain and cord[66]. It is difficult even to name areas worthy of special study: nevertheless, studies of location of action of known anticonvulsants have been concerned mainly with neo-cortex, rhinencephalon, thalamus and cord.

In 1957 Esplin[308] showed that the maximal seizure pattern was modified profoundly by dorsal root section, suggesting that the pattern might be imposed by spinal reflex factors, including input from muscle afferents. Later he showed[43,44] that stimulation of the entire cord, by means of a cathode inserted into the severed end from $C_1$ to $C_4$, evoked a sequence of hind limb movements indistinguishable from those observed during a maximal electrical seizure (MES) in the intact animal, or during grand mal seizures in man. Identity of spinal seizure pattern with MES pattern was proved in cat, rabbit, rat, hamster and mouse. Thus the MES pattern was probably a natural response of the cord to intense general stimulation. He also tested anticonvulsants on these spinal seizures and found carbon dioxide, phenobarbitone, phenytoin and troxidone effective: however, though phenobarbitone was as effective as in the intact animal, troxidone was only slightly effective, and phenytoin had to be given in larger doses than to the intact animal. It may be assumed from these results, first, that phenytoin and phenobarbitone have anticonvulsant actions at cord level, and second, from the quantitative discrepancies between actions in decerebrate and intact animals, that they act at higher levels also. An action at higher levels is also demonstrated by effects on locally evoked after-discharges, discussed below.

Other effects of anticonvulsants on the spinal cord have been studied. Stille[309,310] showed that phenytoin facilitated the patellar reflex and depressed the flexor reflex: during the second experiment it reduced the contralateral patellar reflex. Phenobarbitone depressed all three responses. Phenytoin was considered to be a specific interneuronal depressant and phenobarbitone a more general synaptic depressant. Esplin[311] stimulated dorsal root L7 or S1 or peripheral nerve, and recorded reflex action potentials from the homosegmental ventral root. Phenytoin reduced the polysynaptic discharge markedly, and the monosynaptic spike slightly, these results agreeing with most of Stille's. It slightly deepened synaptic depression, when this was induced orthodromically, but not when it was induced antidromically: its effect was therefore on the presynaptic terminals. It also increased transmission failure during repetitive stimulation, and caused a powerful and long-lasting depression of post-tetanic potentiation (PTP). Effects on transmission in the stellate ganglion were consistent with these: thus, it only slightly reduced maximal postganglionic pulses, and slightly deepened synaptic depression. Its effects were more marked during repetitive stimulation of sufficient weakness to permit a large subliminal 'fringe', when it enhanced transmission failure, and markedly reduced PTP. A possible mechanism of PTP (other than the swelling of Endfüsse discussed by Eccles and Rall[312]) is the electrical mechanism of Lloyd[313]. He proposed that an increase in afferent spike potential caused PTP. This increase might be effective if invasion of axonal ramifications has a low safety factor[314,315], so that many rami remain uninvaded in the absence of tetanus-induced increase in spike height. Following Brown and Holmes[316], Esplin was able to demonstrate post-tetanic enhancement of action potentials in C fibres of the cat vagus *in vivo* and reduction of this enhancement by injection of phenytoin. This again emphasizes the possibility that anticonvulsant action might be selective for *discharges of high frequency*.

Later, Esplin and Curto[317] showed that troxidone did not affect PTP, though it profoundly deepened synaptic depression following an orthodromic but not an antidromic volley. This action, which was much greater than that of phenytoin, was considered consistent with the ability of troxidone to raise minimal seizure (clonus) threshold: phenytoin does not raise this threshold, but seems to prevent seizure spread, perhaps through its action on PTP.

Many authors[83,280,283,318,319] have studied the effects of anticonvulsants on after-discharges induced by electrical stimulation, or on discharges from epileptogenic foci. There are many discrepancies among the results, some possibly due to differences in animal species or in technique. They prohibit confident answers to many of the most important questions: for example, whether action of a particular drug is most marked on discharging focus, or on spread of discharge; or whether any drug has a selective action on a particular part of the brain. Nevertheless, two important properties of the anticonvulsants phenytoin, troxidone and phenobarbitone have been established: they have some ability to depress paroxysmal discharges in many areas of the brain, and display this action at doses which are well below the neurotoxic doses, or those which markedly affect the normal EEG: some specificity of action on the paroxysmal discharge has consequently been demonstrated.

A specificity of this type has also been demonstrated by experiments *in vitro*. The most impressive are those of McIlwain and his colleagues[234,235] already referred to on page 276. These show that methoin, troxidone and phenytoin reduce enhanced oxygen consumption of brain slices only when this is elicited by stimulation at high frequency. Analogous observations have been made on isolated nerve. Toman[287] stimulated frog sciatic nerve so as to elicit a 'rebound spike' 3–6 msec after the first spike. This rebound spike was blocked by 0·05 mM phenytoin, and phenobarbitone and phenurone were effective at 1 mM or less. When the nerve was stimulated repetitively by supramaximal shocks, the threshold fell to about half the normal value and recovered only slowly: some anticonvulsants prevented this prolonged hyperexcitability. When frog nerve was soaked in neutral isotonic sodium phosphate solution for an hour, and therefore depleted of $Ca^{++}$ and $Mg^{++}$ among other ions, a single supraliminal shock elicited a synchronized repetitive discharge. This hyperexcitability was blocked by phenytoin, which also prevented the increased entry of sodium that occurred under these conditions. We have been unable to trace a detailed account of this work, and ignorance of the exact experimental conditions and of reproducibility and magnitude of results makes assessment difficult. Morrell and colleagues[288] have carried out comparable experiments *in vivo*. They recorded from tibial nerve of the anaesthetized rabbit, and stimulated the foot pad. They were able to produce a 'rebound spike', similar to Toman's, by 10 msec stimulation of the foot pad, and this 'rebound spike' was blocked by intravenous injection of phenytoin; the enhanced excitability of oxalated nerve was also reversed by phenytoin injection. Korey[320] showed that phenytoin and methoin could reduce spontaneous firing elicited in isolated squid axon by reducing external $Ca^{++}$ and $Mg^{++}$ concentration. Korey and Toman observed little effect of phenytoin on the normal single spike, but this was much reduced or abolished in Morrell's studies. Perhaps deterioration of preparation contributed to this rather surprising result.

The interesting results of these three groups of workers are consistent with the reported usefulness of phenytoin[321–325] and primidone[326] in trigeminal neuralgia, and of the former in lightning pains of tabes dorsalis[327]. Though a central analgesic action of phenytoin in trigeminal neuralgia has been considered[309], conventional analgesic tests suggest that only neurotoxic doses have such an action[328]. Though the abnormality in trigeminal neuralgia is not certainly peripheral[329], one plausible hypothesis might be that the primary defect is a shortened refractory period: in slow pain fibres this might lead to repetitive discharge from the trigger receptors: this repetitive discharge might be blocked by phenytoin, as in the experiments of Toman, Korey and Morrell. This idea is supported by the actions of phenytoin on cardiac arrhythmias. Harris and Kokernot[330] showed that it abolished ectopic beats induced in dogs by coronary ligation. It also abolishes arrhythmias induced by ouabain[331], hypothermia[332], adrenaline-cyclopropane[333] and aconitine or delphinine[334]. The last study showed clearly that atrial flutter and fibrillation were stopped abruptly by intravenous injection of 5 mg/kg. The obverse of this experiment has been carried out by Roumanian workers[335]. They tested quinidine on seizures because of its effects on carbohydrate metabolism and found it active. It seems probable that antifibrillatory and anticonvulsant drugs have related modes of action.

The evidence so far presented in this section suggests strongly that phenytoin reduces hyperexcitability of all excitable cells. One obvious common characteristic of tic douloureux, of fibrillating atrial muscle and of central epileptic discharges, is excessive frequency of discharge. It seems reasonable to suppose that the drug acts by an accentuation of Wedensky inhibition, so that the maximal discharge rate is severely reduced. One possible primary action on membrane might be an increase in the relative or absolute refractory period. Extension of the experiments initiated by Toman seems very desirable. The available evidence hardly justifies attempts to define the mode of action of other anticonvulsants such as troxidone or phenobarbitone. Nevertheless, their actions too may depend on an effect on membrane characteristics which is relatively specific for the hyper-excitable rather than the normal neurone. It might be possible eventually to correlate pharmacological action with action on membrane through a series of drugs of the type non-sedative anticonvulsant (*e.g.* phenytoin), sedative anticonvulsant (*e.g.* phenobarbitone, meprobamate), and weakly anticonvulsant sedative (*e.g.* barbitone). The chemical analogy throughout such a drug series supports this idea.

Some attention has recently been given to an interpretation of possible actions on nerve membrane in terms of ion movements. The most important work is that of Woodbury. Following demonstration that seizure susceptibility varies inversely with extracellular sodium concentration[336,337], he showed[265,338] that phenytoin had the following effects: it prevented the decrease in electrical seizure threshold induced by hyponatraemia; it raised the ratio of cerebral extracellular to intracellular sodium concentration, and increased the rate of movement of radiosodium into and out of brain cells; it raised the ratio of intracellular to extracellular potassium. It was considered that the changes in sodium concentration ratio were much better correlated with electrical seizure threshold than were the changes in potassium concentration ratio, and it was proposed that phenytoin modifies convulsions by increasing extrusion of sodium from brain cells. There is amplification and discussion of these ideas in a recent symposium publication[66,285].

*Hormones*

A variety of hormones affect experimental or clinical seizures. Exacerbation of seizures just before or during menstruation in a proportion of patients is well known[339], and they may decline after the menopause or after ovariec-tomy[339]. Equine oestrogen has been shown to elicit paroxysmal discharges from cortical epileptogenic lesions[339]. Progesterone on the other hand is anticonvulsant[340].

Adrenalectomy increases susceptibility to seizures, and desoxycortico-sterone or aldosterone reduce susceptibility[337,341–343]. Desoxycorticosterone has some activity in epilepsy[344–346]. Cortisone, hydrocortisone and ACTH, on the other hand, lower electroshock threshold. Corticosterone blood level is raised in epilepsy, but phenytoin does not modify it[347].

Thyroidectomy raises electrical shock threshold, and thyroxine powerfully reduces it, though dinitrophenol does not[337].

The relevance of some of these results to the action of phenytoin has been discussed by Woodbury[337]. He showed that it caused an increase in adrenal weight, a rise in liver glycogen and a fall in adrenal ascorbic acid, and that an effect of phenytoin on electroshock threshold could be unmasked by adrenalectomy or by measuring threshold at a time when the antagonistic actions of released glucocorticoids had subsided.

It seems probable that no important anticonvulsant acts primarily by modifying hormone secretion: however, an effect on secretion might modify anticonvulsant action, e.g. that of phenytoin, and provide a variety of false leads in screening tests.

## METABOLISM OF ANTICONVULSANTS

Optimal use of every drug demands a knowledge of its fate in the body, and the fate of anticonvulsants is exceptionally interesting and important because many of the drugs in common use are converted to active metabolites in the body. The field has been reviewed by Maynert and van Dyke[348], Raventós[349] and Butler[350,351].

### Phenobarbitone

Phenobarbitone may be estimated by extraction into chloroform or ether, transfer to alkaline buffer, and ultraviolet spectrophotometry[352–358]. Unless special methods are used, the $p$-hydroxy metabolite is included in the measurement[358].

Good absorption of orally administered phenobarbitone may be assumed from the appearance in the urine of about a quarter of the dose as phenobarbitone[359], and perhaps twice as much as the $p$-hydroxy metabolite $(IX)$[360, 361], and from indirect calculations that 70–90 per cent is absorbed[357]. The drug is distributed almost uniformly throughout the tissues including the brain[352,362–364]. Penetration into white matter of brain is slower than into grey; there is no localization of the drug in any part of the grey matter[365].

The half life of phenobarbitone in human plasma is about five days[355,358, 359,366]. This exceptionally high persistence is a consequence of protein binding of about 40 per cent in plasma[358,359,367,368], extensive tubular reabsorption, particularly from acid filtrates[358,366,369–372] and relatively slow metabolism[360,373]. It results in the maintenance of almost constant concentrations by conventional dosage schedules[355]. The therapeutic plasma concentration in adult epileptics is about $25 \pm 10$ $\mu g/ml$[352,355,374,375]. Toxic concentrations in acute poisoning are probably 50–90 $\mu g/ml$[352,376,377]. However, tolerance to the side effects of phenobarbitone develops during continued dosing while plasma concentrations are still increasing[355] up to a plateau, which is reached after about 12 days; and patients on chronic phenobarbitone dosage can tolerate, without obvious symptoms, blood concentrations that cause coma in acute poisoning[378]. Though the activity of drug-metabolizing rat liver microsomal enzymes increases after pretreatment with phenobarbitone[379–381], Butler[355] observed no statistically significant change in half-life after many months' administration to man.

The major metabolite in man and dog is the $p$-hydroxy derivative $(IX)$[360,382,383]. It is conjugated in the dog, probably mainly as the glucuronide[360], but much of it is excreted unchanged in man[360,383]. No other metabolite is known, though experiments with $^{14}$C suggest that some ring opening may occur[384].

The enzymes responsible for the hydroxylation of phenobarbitone are unknown but seem likely to be the NADPH (TPNH) dependent system of liver microsomes. Dorfman and Goldbaum[373] could detect no disappearance of phenobarbitone during incubation with liver or kidney slices or liver brei, but their analytical method would very probably fail to distinguish

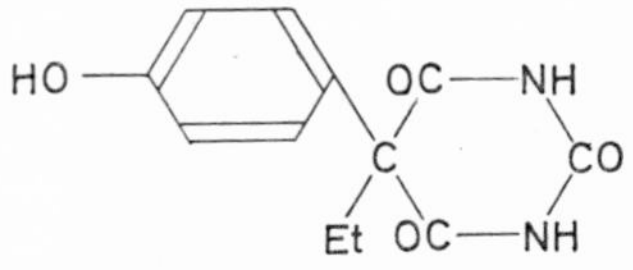

*(IX)*

between phenobarbitone and its *p*-hydroxy derivative. Though there has been much controversy about the effects of hepatectomy or liver damage on the activity of phenobarbitone, convincing experiments by Walker and Wynn Parry[385] suggest that the liver is responsible for metabolism of the drug in the rat. The hydroxy derivative is relatively non-toxic[360], and has only feeble anticonvulsant activity[386].

### Methylphenobarbitone

Methylphenobarbitone and phenobarbitone have different absorption spectra and may be estimated simultaneously by a modification of the method for phenobarbitone[357]. Calculations by Butler suggest that about half of the orally administered drug may be absorbed in man and dog[351,357]. The levels in tissues are unknown but the volume of distribution in the dog, 105–200 per cent, is about twice that of phenobarbitone: localization in fat has been suggested, but not proved[350,387]. Renal clearance is extremely slow and only traces of the drug appear in the urine[351,357]. It is demethylated to phenobarbitone in dog, rat and man[351,357,387,388]. This conversion is virtually complete in the dog, but a second metabolic conversion, resulting in more rapid elimination, probably occurs in the rat[387]. In man, daily administration of methylphenobarbitone in therapeutic doses results in a steady increase in concentration of phenobarbitone in the plasma up to levels of about 30 $\mu$g/ml, known to be therapeutic. Levels of unchanged drug show little build-up and remain between 5 and 15 $\mu$g/ml[351]. These results have naturally led Butler to suppose that the therapeutic and toxic effects of methylphenobarbitone are due to phenobarbitone.

Methylphenobarbitone has only half to two thirds of the anticonvulsant activity of phenobarbitone in MES, electroshock seizure threshold, hypona-traemic and leptazol tests in rats; further, it is about two thirds as neuro-toxic, and peak activity occurs later than for phenobarbitone, and at a time when phenobarbitone will have accumulated in the plasma. These observa-tions[34] are consistent with Butler's suggestion. The two drugs are similar in activity in mice, but metabolism in this species has not been defined, and it is possible that conversion to phenobarbitone is more efficient, or an alternative metabolic conversion less efficient, than in the rat.

In man methylphenobarbitone is about a third as potent as phenobarbitone[389], and the two drugs seem equivalent in activity and toxicity. The total evidence suggests strongly, but does not prove unequivocally, that methylphenobarbitone is itself inactive and is activated *in vivo* by conversion to phenobarbitone.

### Metharbitone (methylbarbitone)

Spectrophotometric methods, similar to those for methylphenobarbitone, allow simultaneous estimation of plasma concentrations of metharbitone and its metabolite barbitone[390]. Its absorption and distribution are unknown, though the volume of distribution, 122 per cent, suggests moderate localization in tissues. The drug is demethylated to barbitone in dog and man[351,388,390,391]. Therapeutic doses in four patients have been shown by Butler to give build-up of barbitone in the plasma until a concentration of about 25 $\mu$g/ml was attained after two weeks. The concentration of unchanged metharbitone never exceeded a fifth of this[351]. It was suggested that the methyl compound is itself inactive and is activated by demethylation. Proof requires more data, particularly on the comparative anticonvulsant potencies of the two compounds, and on their comparative effectiveness in epilepsy, against which barbitone has commonly been considered useless.

### Primidone

No method of estimating primidone in blood or tissues has been published, though colorimetric methods have been used in our laboratories (Thorp, private communication). Primidone is extracted into a mixture of methyl acetate and chloroform at pH 5·5; after washing with buffer at pH 11·8, the solvent is evaporated, and the residue nitrated, reduced, diazotized and coupled with naphthylethylenediamine. This method measures primidone plus its metabolite PEMA (see below). The latter may be removed from

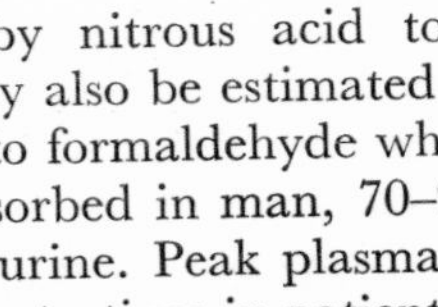

$$\underset{\text{Et}}{\overset{\text{Ph}}{\diagdown}} \overset{\text{CONH}_2}{\underset{\text{C}}{\diagup}} \overset{\text{CONH}_2}{\diagdown}$$

(X) PEMA

extracts after conversion by nitrous acid to alkali-soluble $\alpha$-phenyl-n-butyric acid. Primidone may also be estimated specifically by hydrolysis in 80 per cent sulphuric acid to formaldehyde which is estimated colorimetrically. Primidone is well absorbed in man, 70–90 per cent of the oral dose being accounted for in the urine. Peak plasma concentrations are attained within 4–6 hours, and concentrations in patients receiving 0·75 g b.i.d. vary between 5 and 20 $\mu$g/ml. Plasma protein binding is less than 20 per cent. Distribution in tissues and body fluids is almost uniform[392].

The major metabolite of primidone is phenylethylmalondiamide (PEMA), which constitutes 50–70 per cent of the human urinary excretion of the drug at normal doses. This metabolite is only about one fortieth as active an anticonvulsant as primidone itself[392,393]. This observation, and enhancement of activity of primidone by hepatectomy[394] and by coadministration of SKF 525-A[392], suggested that primidone itself is the active agent. However, Butler and Waddell[395] later showed that primidone is converted to phenobarbitone and its metabolite, $p$-hydroxyphenobarbitone, in dog and man. Concentrations of phenobarbitone measured in the plasma of patients receiving primidone were high enough to exert therapeutic and neurotoxic effects[395,396]. It was suggested that 15 per cent of primidone might be converted to phenobarbitone in man, and 5 per cent in dogs[395]. Since it has been claimed[397,398] that primidone is about one-fifth as potent as phenobarbitone against generalized or focal clinical seizures, we must consider the possibility that primidone is itself inactive and becomes activated *in vivo* by transformation to phenobarbitone.

Several observations prove that primidone itself has anticonvulsant action; the most important being that primidone is much more active than phenobarbitone in MES and similar pattern tests, though less active in a number of other tests[18,399]. The ratio of neurotoxic to effective dose is higher for primidone than for phenobarbitone[399]. Radouco-Thomas and his colleagues[39] have shown by detailed analysis of anticonvulsant action in guinea-pigs that the patterns of action of primidone and phenobarbitone are dissimilar. Scarinci[400] showed that intravenous primidone suppressed clonus induced by application of strychnine to motor cortex; it was much more active than intravenous phenobarbitone. He later showed[401] that intravenous primidone enhanced synchrony in all cortical EEG leads, and reduced the frequency of spikes elicited by application of strychnine to the cortex. Unpublished work in our laboratories has shown that the frequency of strychnine spikes may also be reduced by topical application of primidone to exposed cortex of monkey or rabbit.

Frey and Hahn[402] measured phenobarbitone levels in mice and in dogs receiving single or repeated doses respectively of primidone or phenobarbitone. At similar phenobarbitone levels primodone had the greater anticonvulsant effect against leptazol. They concluded that half to two thirds of its anticonvulsant effect must be attributed to the unchanged compound. Leptazol tests are among those in which primidone is markedly inferior to phenobarbitone in potency: it is therefore probable that more than two thirds of the activity against maximal electrical seizures is due to unchanged primidone.

At least four anticonvulsant compounds are present in patients receiving primidone: these are primidone itself, phenobarbitone, phenylethylmalondiamide and $p$-hydroxyphenobarbitone. The data do not allow calculation of the proportion of the total effect due to each compound, but it is improbable that phenylethylmalondiamide and $p$-hydroxyphenobarbitone (which is less active than phenobarbitone[386]) have marked effects. Since it has been widely reported that primidone is able to control patients who had not been controlled by phenobarbitone[403-411], it seems likely that the total effect is that of primidone itself plus a contribution from phenobarbitone. Exact measurement of that contribution is desirable but would be a formidable task.

## Phenytoin

Phenytoin may be estimated spectrophotometrically after extraction with chloroform and re-extraction into alkaline buffer[353,354]. A colorimetric method, involving nitration, reduction, diazotization and coupling[412], and a titrimetric method[413] have also been described. Phenytoin sodium is slowly but almost completely absorbed by the rat[412]. Oral doses of 100 mg/kg give peak plasma concentrations of about 20 $\mu$g/ml after 6–8 hours. The drug is almost uniformly distributed throughout rat tissues, with the highest concentrations in liver, kidney and fat. The brain concentration resembles that in plasma[412,414]. The concentration in saliva is high and possibly relevant to the occurrence of gingival hyperplasia during phenytoin therapy[414]. The effective therapeutic concentration in human plasma is probably 10–15 $\mu$g/ml; side effects appearing above 30 $\mu$g/ml[354,374,375,412,415–417]. The half-life in human plasma is about 24 hours[354,412] and there is

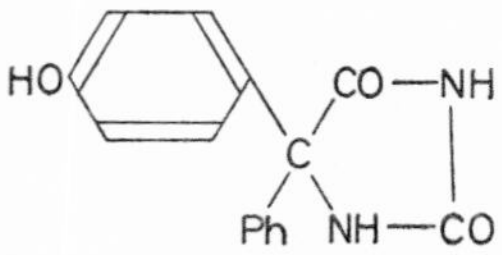

HO—⟨C₆H₄⟩—C(Ph)—CO—NH / NH—CO

(XI)

build-up for the first 5–6 days' administration of therapeutic doses[375]. Less than 5 per cent of administered phenytoin appears unchanged in the urine of rat, dog or man[412,414,418–420]. The major identified urinary metabolite is conjugated 5-$p$-hydroxyphenyl-5-phenylhydantoin (XI). About half of the orally administered drug appears in the urine in this form in dog and man, and about a quarter in the rat[414,419,420]. Man probably hydroxylates one of the phenyl groups only; the dog probably hydroxylates either, with a slight preference for that not hydroxylated by man[419]. Traces only of the free phenol appear in the urine of man, dog or rat: the main conjugate is probably a glucuronide in all three species[420].

The fate of the remainder of the drug is unknown, Maynert found traces only of diphenylhydantoic acid and $\alpha$-aminodiphenylacetic acid in dog urine by $^{15}$N dilution experiments[420], though an earlier report claimed[418] that they were major metabolites. A second phenolic metabolite has been detected in rat urine, but not identified.

## Methoin

Methoin (XII) has not been estimated in blood or tissues, but its metabolite, 5-ethyl-5-phenylhydantoin (Nirvanol, XIII) may be estimated spectro-photometrically after extraction into ether and thence into alkaline buffer[421]. Very little is known of the absorption or distribution of methoin. Studies with $^{14}$C labelled drug in mice have shown that total radioactivity, which must include metabolites, is almost uniformly distributed, except for abdominal fat in which concentrations are low[422,423]. Little or no unchanged methoin appears in dog or human urine[424]. The major metabolite in dog, man and mouse is 5-ethyl-5-phenylhydantoin (XIII)[424].

The $p$-hydroxy derivative (*XIV*) of (*XIII*) is also formed in dog and man[421] and is excreted as the glucuronide in dog urine. Phenylethylglycine (*XV*) is a possible third metabolite in the mouse[425] and dog[426]. Vigne and Fondarai[425] claim that the amounts of urinary metabolites in the mouse are 5 per cent as unchanged methoin, 60 per cent as (*XIII*), and up to 40 per cent as (*XV*).

There are some interesting differences in stereochemical specificity between dog, rat and man. The hydantoin (*XIII*) excreted by man is almost

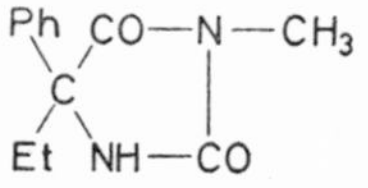

Ph CO—N—CH₃
 \ / |
  C |
 / \ |
Et NH—CO

(*XII*) Methoin

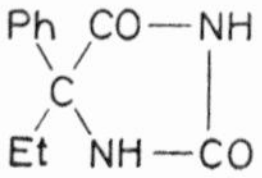

Ph CO—NH
 \ / |
  C |
 / \ |
Et NH—CO

(*XIII*)

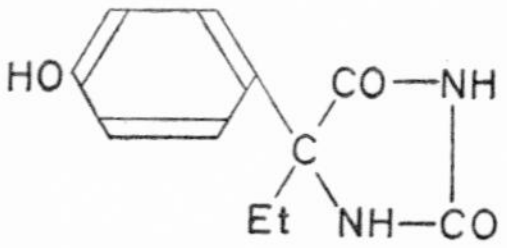

HO—⟨ring⟩—CO—NH
        \ / |
         C |
        / \ |
       Et NH—CO

(*XIV*)

Ph CO₂H
 \ /
  C
 / \
Et NH₂

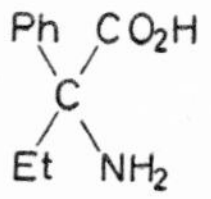

(*XV*)

entirely the (—) isomer, though there is only a slight excess of this isomer in dog urine[424]. (—)-Methoin is converted by the rat to (*XIII*) much more rapidly than is (+)-methoin. On the other hand (+)-(*XIII*) leaves rat blood much more rapidly than does (—)-(*XIII*), and may be further metabolized more rapidly than the latter. If this happened also in man it would explain the presence of almost pure (—)-(*XIII*) in human urine[427]. However, (*XIV*) (one of the two known metabolites of *XIII*) is excreted as the (+) isomer by the dog, and as (±) by man[428], whereas the opposite would have been expected from the rotations of urinary (*XIII*) in these species. These results illustrate the complexity of species differences in drug metabolism. Such differences undoubtedly contribute powerfully to the difficulty of predicting clinical effect from results in one or two species of laboratory animals. Demethylation of methoin to (*XIII*) is much reduced by hepatectomy, and may be assumed to occur in the liver[429]. The administration of therapeutic doses of methoin to man results in the accumulation of (*XIII*), until plasma concentrations of about 25 $\mu g/ml$ are attained after 14 days. Since (*XIII*) was known to be an effective, but toxic, antiepileptic drug, Butler suggested that treatment with methoin is no more than a devious means of giving (*XIII*)[350,351]. However, Chen and Ensor[36] found (*XIII*) only half as active as methoin in an MES test in rats, though the two were equally active in mice. The rat result might or might not be due to better absorption of methoin or to bad timing of electroshock challenge. The actual active agents in methoin-treated animals or patients can only be defined by measuring concentrations of both and correlating the measurements with activity. Until this elaborate research has been performed judgment must be deferred.

## Troxidone

Troxidone (*III*) has been estimated in tissue homogenates by adding alkali to release carbonate, and measuring the latter manometrically after acidification[430]. Its metabolite 5,5-dimethyloxazolidine-2,4-dione (DMO, *XVI*) has been estimated spectrophotometrically after acidification of urine or plasma, extraction into ether, and thence into alkaline buffer[431,432]; this method does not measure troxidone.

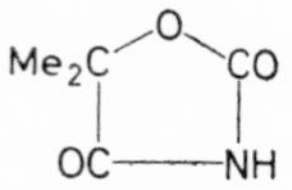

$$Me_2C \overset{O}{\diagup \diagdown} CO$$

(XVI)

Troxidone reaches very high concentrations in the blood, of the order of 1 mg/ml after intraperitoneal administration of 1 g/kg to mice, and is almost uniformly distributed through the tissues, including the brain. These concentrations fall fairly rapidly, and the drug is degraded when incubated with slices of several tissues, including the liver[430]. Concentrations of its metabolite DMO in human plasma suggest that absorption of therapeutic doses is almost complete.

DMO was first identified in dog urine by Butler[433]. Its plasma concentration in the dog is much the same whether DMO itself or an equimolar dose of troxidone is given, suggesting that the conversion is almost complete. Renal excretion of DMO by man is very slow when the urine is acid: the drug is not bound to the plasma protein, so that tubular reabsorption and little or no further metabolism must be assumed. The plasma half life is about 12 days[431,432]. Rapid clearance may, however, be achieved by giving sodium bicarbonate. In these circumstances nearly all the administered DMO can be found unchanged in dog urine[432].

Paramethadione, like troxidone, is demethylated to 5-ethyl-5-methyl-oxazolidine-2,4-dione (*XVII*)[434] and Dimedione is de-ethylated to DMO (*XVI*)[435].

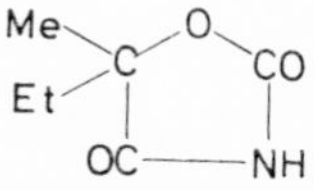

$$\overset{Me}{\underset{Et}{\diagdown}} C \overset{O}{\diagup \diagdown} CO$$

(XVII)

Little is known of the comparative activity of the *N*-alkyl compounds and their metabolites. It seems probable that DMO and troxidone have similar anaesthetic activity, and that paradione is twice as active as its metabolite[436]. It has been suggested by Butler[350,351,437] that the very high concentrations of DMO, and of 5-ethyl-5-methyloxazolidine-2,4-dione, attained in the plasma of patients receiving the 3-methyl compounds, are effective against epilepsy. The case for this is certainly strong, but more knowledge of relative activity and relative blood concentrations is required. Work on this and related problems would be greatly facilitated if it were possible to block the microsomal drug-oxidizing system completely and specifically. We agree with Swinyard, Madsen and Goodman[438] and Thorp, Hurst and Martin[439] that SKF 525-A is insufficiently specific in its effects to give reliable data.

## Phensuximide

Phensuximide may be extracted into chloroform, oxidized to $N$-methyl-$\alpha$-phenylmaleimide by iodine, and determined by measuring the fluorescence of this oxidation product[440]. The drug is well absorbed from the rat gastro-intestinal tract. The maximum blood concentration is attained about $1\frac{1}{2}$ hours after dosing; the half-life in the blood is about 3 hours. There is relatively uniform distribution throughout the tissues and body fluids, including brain and cerebrospinal fluid, and no obvious localization in cortex, thalamus, cerebellum, hippocampus or medulla[440].

Little or no unchanged drug appears in rat urine, but studies with [14]C-labelled drug showed that about 80 per cent of an oral dose of 55 mg/kg appeared in the urine as metabolites within 3 days. The $N$-methyl group appeared to be present in the major metabolites: these were thought to be simple hydrolysis products in which the succinimide ring had been disrupted at one of the nitrogen bonds. Two possible structures are (*XVIII*) and (*XIX*) below[440]:

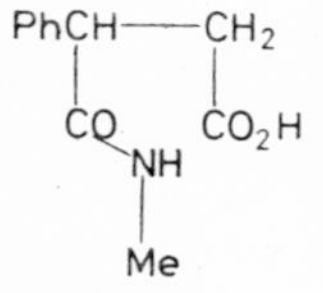

(*XVIII*) 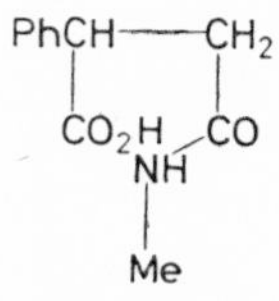          (*XIX*)

The therapeutic concentration in human plasma is probably about 10 $\mu$g/ml. The half-life in serum is about 3–4 hours (our calculation from data of Glazko, Dill, Wolf and Miller[440]), and there is no accumulation of drug during a therapeutic course. Human urine contains two metabolites that give a colour reaction with iodine: one or both were thought likely to be phenolic derivatives, since the $p$-hydroxy derivative of phensuximide gave a similar colour[440].

## Acetazolamide

Acetazolamide (*VIII*) has been estimated by measuring inhibition of red cell carbonic anhydrase by heated tissue homogenates[441]. Spectrophotometric methods have been applied only to aqueous humour[442], apparently because the drug cannot be extracted from tissues[441]. Absorption of oral doses of less than 20 mg/kg by the dog is complete. A dose of 20 mg/kg gives peak plasma concentrations of about 30 $\mu$g/ml, falling to zero within 6 hours. The drug persists longer in red cells, presumably because of its affinity for carbonic anhydrase. Maren and his colleagues believe that the dog inactivates about 30 per cent and the rat about 70 per cent[240]: no metabolite is known. Acetazolamide reaches only low concentrations in the C.S.F.[240,443], but those in brain are higher, particularly in hypothalamus, hippocampus and caudate nucleus[443]. The bearing of these concentrations on the mode of action of acetazolamide is discussed on page 278.

## Summary

The important anticonvulsants seem to have the following common characteristics: first, they are fairly uniformly distributed throughout the body; second, with the exception of troxidone, the effective plasma concentrations appear to be of the order of 10–20 $\mu$g/ml (0·05–0·1 mM). Since, with the exception of acetazolamide, they are closely related to each other chemically, these properties may be coincidental. Nevertheless, they might also be consequences of the physical properties that confer anticonvulsant action. This possibility merits study.

## ANTICONVULSANT DRUG THERAPY

A comprehensive review of anticonvulsants has recently appeared[444], which lists all compounds that have been tested up to the end of 1958. The medical treatment of epilepsy has recently been reviewed by Williams[445], and Simpson[446].

### Barbiturates

Phenobarbitone (*I*) is probably the most powerful anticonvulsant known, but its use is limited by its sedative and hypnotic effects. New analogues include tri-alkyl barbituric acids. One of these, 5,5-diethyl-1-methylbarbituric acid (metharbital, Gemonil, *XX*, R = Me) is reported[447] to be particularly effective for the control of massive spasms in very young children

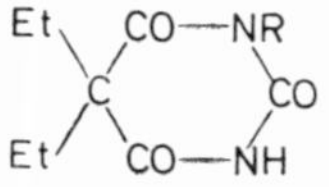

*(XX)* 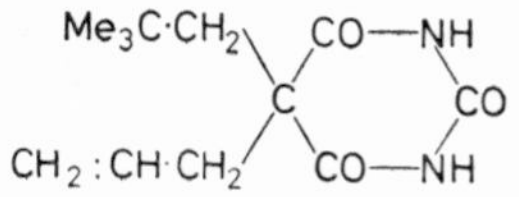                    *(XXI)*

and in patients showing EEG evidence of severe brain damage. In animals the drug is effective against leptazol induced seizures, but is less active against electroshock. It has low toxicity and side effects are infrequent.

*N*-Phenylbarbitone (Pyrictal, *XX*, R = Ph) was the most potent of a group of sixty new compounds tested as anticonvulsants in animals. Its action proved to be rapid in onset and its toxicity low. A trial in epileptic patients showed a response in febrile and clonic, but not in major, seizures. It has been claimed to have a better margin of safety than phenobarbitone and to deserve further evaluation against febrile seizures, hyperpyrexia and minor epilepsies[448,449].

5-Allyl-5-neopentylbarbituric acid (nealbarbitone, Nevental, *XXI*)[450,451] has been shown to prevent leptazol-induced convulsions in experimental animals, but it failed to give adequate control of seizures in man[452].

A comprehensive review of barbituric acid hypnotics has recently appeared, which includes an account of the chemistry of this class of compound[453]. 5,5-Disubstituted barbituric acids are generally prepared by condensation of disubstituted malonic esters with ureas in the presence of sodium alkoxides[454]. Thiourea or guanidine may be used in place of urea to give the corresponding 2-thio- or 2-imino-barbituric acid respectively. Only the very reactive alkyl halides (*e.g.* allyl or benzyl halides) will substitute directly into the 5-position of barbituric acid. The preparation of unsymmetrically substituted, 5,5-dialkylbarbituric acids depends on obtaining

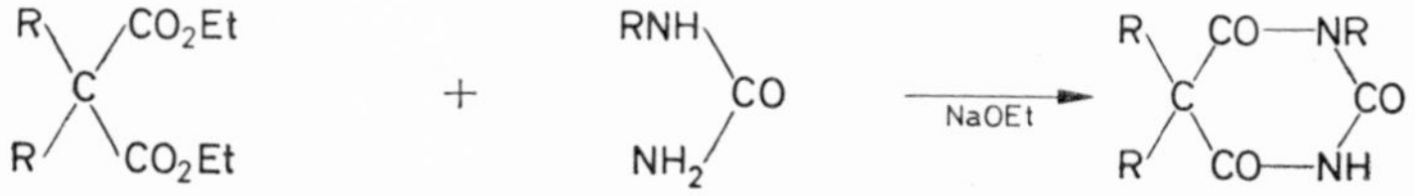

the appropriate malonic ester pure and in good yield, and this is often difficult. Diethyl phenylmalonate, required for the synthesis of phenobarbitone, may be obtained by condensing ethyl phenylacetate with ethyl carbonate in the presence of sodium ethoxide[455,456]. The product is then alkylated and condensed with urea.

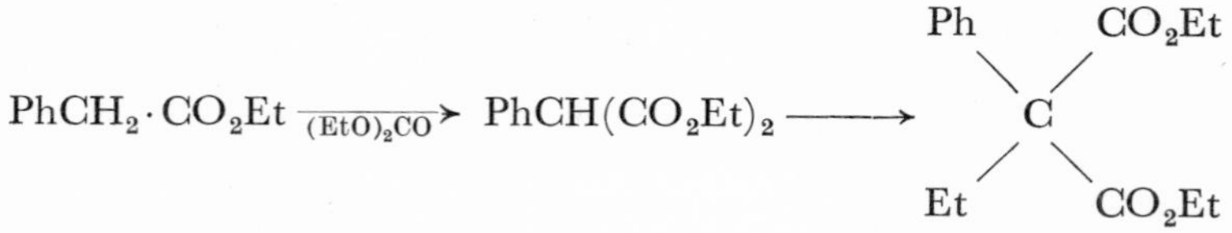

$$PhCH_2 \cdot CO_2Et \xrightarrow{(EtO)_2CO} PhCH(CO_2Et)_2 \longrightarrow$$

*N*-Alkyl or *N*-aryl 5,5-substituted barbituric acids are best obtained by condensation of the appropriate malonic ester with *N*-mono-substituted ureas. A new synthesis of 2-thiobarbituric acids avoids the use of *N*-alkylthioureas, which are not easy to prepare on a large scale. The process involves the reaction of a disubstituted cyanoacetyl chloride with potassium thiocyanate in toluene, followed by reaction with an amine, and then cyclization and hydrolysis[457].

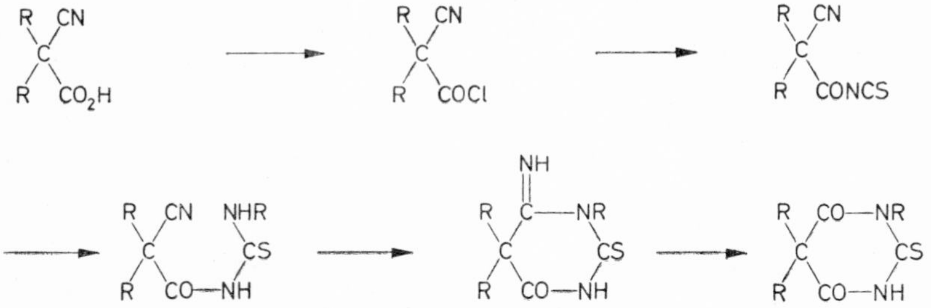

2-Thiobarbituric acids are intermediates in the preparation of anticonvulsants of the primidone type.

### Hydantoins

The position of 5,5-diphenylhydantoin (phenytoin, Dilantin, *II*) as the hydantoin of choice in the treatment of grand mal has not been seriously challenged since it was first introduced in 1938. It is widely used in grand mal, and is sometimes effective in psychomotor attacks, but it may aggravate petit mal. The side effects include ataxia and skin rashes, and a characteristic spongy hypertrophy of the gums. Its use in epilepsy is similar to that of phenobarbitone (with which it is frequently combined) and it has the advantage that unlike phenobarbitone it is not sedative.

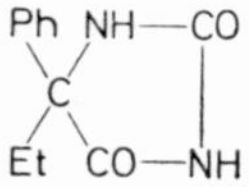

$$\begin{array}{cc} Ph & NH-CO \\ & \diagdown C \diagup \quad | \\ Et & CO-NH \end{array}$$

*(XXII)*

5-Ethyl-3-methyl-5-phenylhydantoin (methoin, Mesantoin, *XII*) has been used clinically since 1947 with some success against grand mal and psychomotor epilepsy, but its usefulness is limited by toxic side effects. Methoin is as effective as phenytoin in the treatment of grand mal, and does not cause gingival hyperplasia; but it frequently causes skin reactions. The chief danger, however, is of blood dyscrasias, some of which have proved fatal. The toxic effects of methoin are perhaps due to its metabolic demethylation to Nirvanol (5-ethyl-5-phenylhydantoin, *XXII*) [421] which is no longer used in the treatment of chorea and epilepsy because of toxicity.

Numerous hydantoins are still being made and tested as anticonvulsants but none so far described seems likely to displace phenytoin.

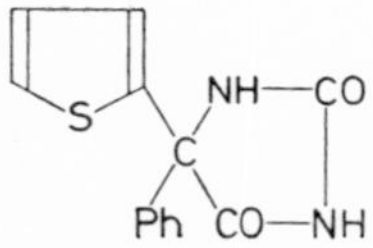

$$\begin{array}{cc} & NH-CO \\ \diagdown S \diagup C \quad | \\ Ph & CO-NH \end{array} \qquad \begin{array}{cc} & NH-CO \\ PhCH \quad | \\ CO-NR \end{array}$$

*(XXIII)* 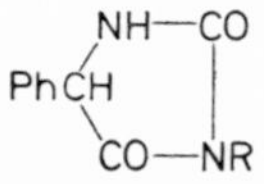       *(XXIV)*

5-Phenyl-5-(2-thienyl)hydantoin (phethenylate, Thiantoin, *XXIII*)[458,459] was found to have activity of the same order as phenytoin, and an early trial reported it to be of value in grand mal. Wider use, however, revealed severe toxic effects[459a].

3-Methyl-5-phenylhydantoin (Nuvarone, *XXIV*, R = Me) was claimed to be effective against grand mal, and less toxic than methoin, but there have been few clinical reports so far[460].

Ethotoin (Peganone, *XXIV*, R = Et)[461] is the *N*-ethyl homologue of Nuvarone, and is reported to be less toxic than the latter. It is effective in grand mal and to a lesser extent in psychomotor epilepsy[462]. Patients who had been refractory to maximal doses of phenytoin, or shown undesirable side effects, had phenytoin slowly substituted by ethotoin. None showed any ataxia, diplopia or gum hyperplasia. Another trial showed a good effect in 50 per cent of cases[463] and no significant abnormalities were found in the blood or urine during the first two years of treatment[464]. The addition of ethotoin allowed the dosage of phenytoin to be reduced, thus eliminating ataxia and gum swelling[465]. Although ethotoin is not so powerful an anticonvulsant as phenytoin it may well prove useful because of its freedom from side effects.

Pesomin (Anirrit, 5-methyl-5-(1,2-dibromo-2-phenyl ethyl)hydantoin, *XXV*) was introduced in Europe as an appetite depressant[466,467]. Trial by Robinson[468] in epileptics who failed to respond to phenobarbitone, phenytoin, and primidone, gave definite improvement in half, but leucopenia occurred in one case: use of Pesomin will need careful control by routine blood counts.

5-(3-Phenanthryl)-5-methylhydantoin (Bagrosin, *XXVI*) was claimed to be the best of a large number of hydantoins tested as anticonvulsants; it was

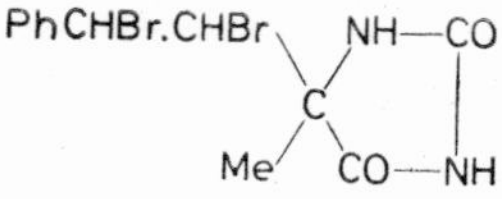

*(XXV)*

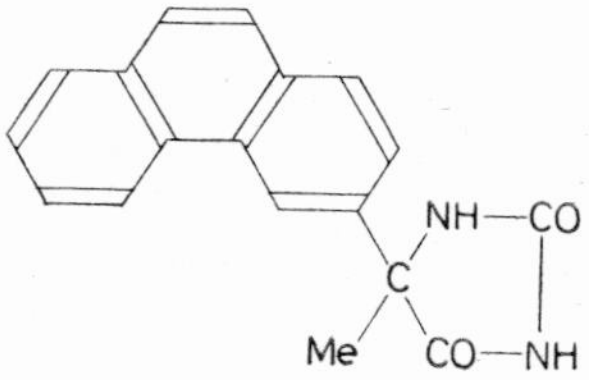

*(XXVI)*

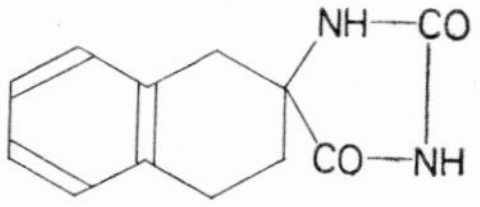

*(XXVII)*

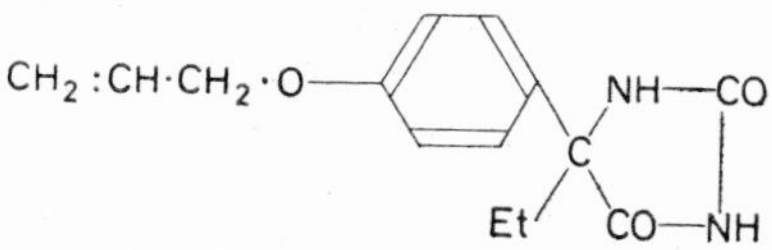

*(XXVIII)*

active against electroshock and leptazol induced seizures, and had a therapeutic ratio twice that of phenytoin[469,470]. The pyrenyl and acenaphthenyl analogues were inactive. Bagrosin showed no activity when given orally to mice. Rats were pretreated intraperitoneally for several days. A clinical trial[471] suggests that it is active and safe, but sedative.

The spirohydantoin from 2-tetralone, 7,8-benzo-1,3-diazaspiro-[4,5]-decane-2,4-dione (tetrantoin, Spirodon, *XXVII*) and its 3-alkyl derivatives[472] were reported to be active against electroshock and leptazol seizures and to have low oral toxicity[473]. No significant changes were observed in chronic toxicity studies[474]. Clinical trials showed that tetrantoin was effective against grand mal and particularly useful against psychomotor and focal attacks. Toxic reactions, however, occurred in a high proportion of the patients and included rash, nausea, confusion, ataxia, and leucopenia[475,476].

5-*p*-Allyloxyphenyl-5-ethylhydantoin (*XXVIII*), a derivative of Nirvanol, showed activity in experimental animals in electroshock and leptazol seizures, and was tested in 20 epileptics. It was reported satisfactory in grand mal, and claimed to cause euphoria without drowsiness[477].

5-Ethyl-1-methyl-5-phenylhydantoin (N.3, methetoin, *XXIX*) has recently had a two year clinical study as an anticonvulsant. It had earlier been found that this compound was only partially converted into Nirvanol in the dog[478]. It was the most promising of a group of alkylated Nirvanol derivatives[479] and a preliminary trial showed it to be active in grand mal[480]. In a careful trial on 89 patients, nearly all of whom had previously proved refractory to other anticonvulsants, a large proportion benefited by the treatment, and complete control was obtained in 50 per cent. The drug was most effective in major seizures and is tentatively regarded as more effective than methoin and ethotoin[481]. There was no evidence of disturbed blood or liver function.

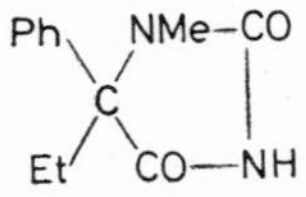

(XXIX)

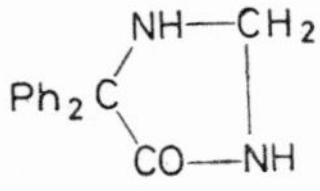

(XXX)

5,5-Diphenyltetrahydroimidazolin-4-one (Glior, XXX), although not a hydantoin, may be conveniently considered here because of its relationship to phenytoin and 5,5-diphenyl-2-thiohydantoin, from which it is prepared. The compound bears the same relationship to phenytoin as primidone does to phenobarbitone. It was reported to be less neurotoxic than phenytoin[482]. It was used in addition to other drugs in 29 refractory cases of grand mal and petit mal: improvement in 60 per cent was claimed[483]. An earlier trial had shown an effect in psychomotor epilepsy[484]. It was well tolerated, except that overdosage produced a cerebellar syndrome which regressed when the dose was reduced. It is recommended that the compound be used in conjunction with other anticonvulsants.

Thiohydantoins have been less intensively studied than have their oxygen analogues, perhaps because 5,5-diphenyl-2-thiohydantoin is less active than phenytoin, or because of the structural similarity between thiohydantoins and the thyrotoxic thiouracils. However, the antithyroid activity of 2-thiohydantoins varies markedly with the nature of the 5-substituent and may be completely suppressed[485]. In a study of the anticonvulsant activity of a series of 3,5-disubstituted 2-thiohydantoins, it was found that the 3-alkyl-5-isobutyl compounds were active against leptazol seizures[486], and 3-allyl-5-isobutyl-2-thiohydantoin (XXXI) was about seven times as active as troxidone[487]. In a preliminary study it was given to 23 refractory epileptics, mostly suffering from grand mal, and about half improved. Trial in non-refractory cases was advocated. Side effects included dizziness, drowsiness and abdominal discomfort, but there were no blood dyscrasias[488].

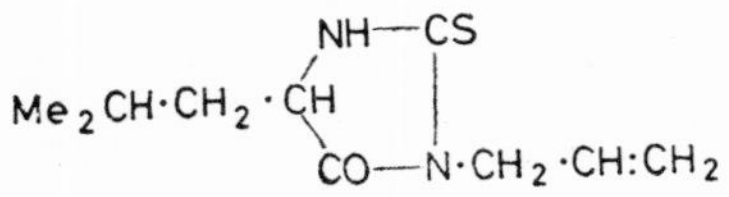

(XXXI)

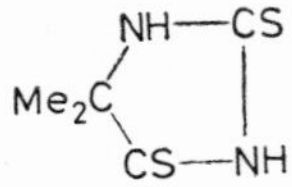

(XXXII)

5,5-Dimethyl-2,4-dithiohydantoin (XXXII) has been proposed for the treatment of epilepsy[489] and has been on trial in several European countries under the name of Thiomedan. In animals it was active against leptazol seizures but relatively poor against electroshock. It was reported to be effective against grand mal[490], but its acceptance requires further evaluation.

An unusual nostrum is now available under the proprietary name Revertonal: it contains 5-t-butyl-5-phenylhydantoin, with caffeine for day medication, and 5-isopropyl-5-phenylhydantoin with belladonna for night medication. It is said to be useful for the treatment of grand mal and psychomotor epilepsy[491].

Neo-Citrullamon contains α-amino-δ-diphenylhydantoylvalerianic acid as active ingredient. This substance is claimed to have an excellent anti-convulsant effect in mice when given intravenously. It is less toxic than phenytoin and intravenous use has been recommended in status epilepticus, psychomotor epilepsy, and during neurosurgery[492].

5-Substituted hydantoins and some 1-substituted hydantoins may be prepared by heating the α-ureido-acids obtained from α-amino-acids and alkali cyanates, with hydrochloric acid[493]. α-Amino-acid amides or nitriles

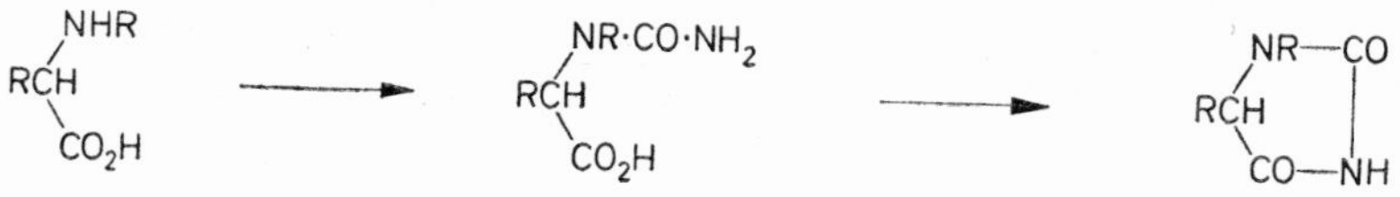

may also be used. The ureido-acids obtained from α-amino-acids and organic isocyanates are similarly cyclized to 3-substituted hydantoins. 3-Substituted

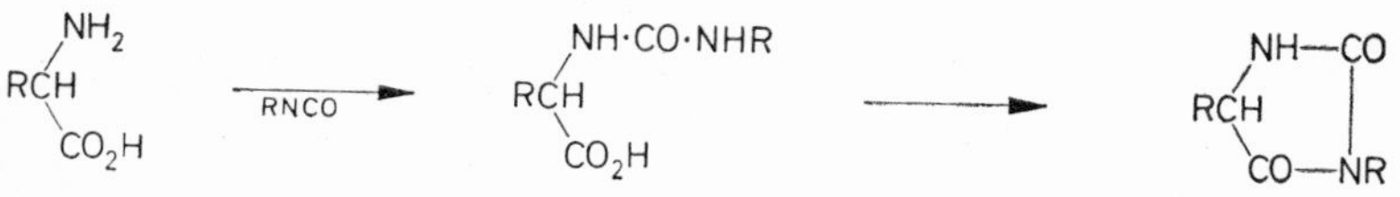

hydantoins are also obtained by direct alkylation of hydantoins. The most important method for making hydantoins is the Bucherer-Bergs synthesis of 5-substituted hydantoins in which a ketone or aldehyde is heated with ammonium carbonate and sodium cyanide in aqueous alcohol. The method has been widely used and extended to relatively unreactive ketones[494,495].

The chemistry of hydantoins has been fully reviewed by Ware[496].

### Oxazolidine-2,4-diones

3,5,5-Trimethyloxazolidine-2,4-dione (troxidone, trimethadione, Tridione, *III*) is principally effective in petit mal, and gives better results in children than in adults. It is ineffective against grand mal. Although the acute toxicity of troxidone is low, prolonged administration may cause blurring of vision in bright light, gastric irritation and skin eruptions. There have been rare cases of aplastic anaemia and some fatalities, and it is now considered essential to check blood counts frequently. Many other oxazolidine-2,4-diones have been described and some may find special uses. Paramethadione (Paradione, 3,5-dimethyl-5-ethyloxazolidine-2,4-dione, *XXXIII*) although considered to be less active than troxidone, is sometimes effective where the latter has failed. It may also be less dangerously toxic. Dimedione (5,5-dimethyl-3-ethyloxazolidine-2,4-dione, *XXXIV*) and aloxidone (Malidone, 3-allyl-5-methyloxazolidine-2,4-dione, *XXXV*)[497], are similar to troxidone but less powerful.

297

5,5-Diphenyloxazolidine-2,4-dione, (Epidon, *XXXVI*) differs from the foregoing analogues in that it is ineffective in petit mal and active in grand mal. The 5,5-diaryloxazolidine-2,4-diones do not possess the hypnotic and sedative properties which characterize the 5,5-dialkyl-compounds[498].

The pharmacology of troxidone and other medicinally useful oxazolidinediones has been reviewed[499]. The most useful method of preparing

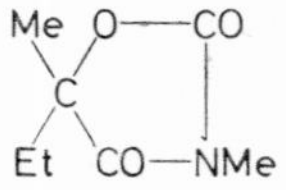

*(XXXIII)*

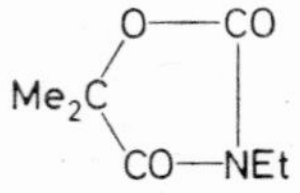

*(XXXIV)*

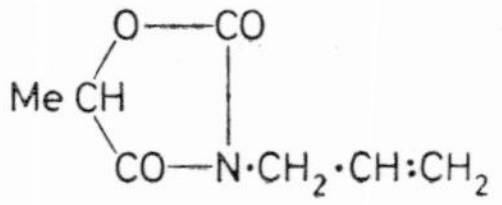

*(XXXV)*

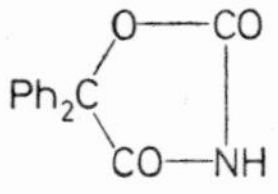

*(XXXVI)*

oxazolidine-2,4-diones appears to be that described by Stoughton[500]: esters of α-hydroxy acids are condensed with urea in the presence of sodium ethoxide, and the products are alkylated with alkyl sulphate or halide.

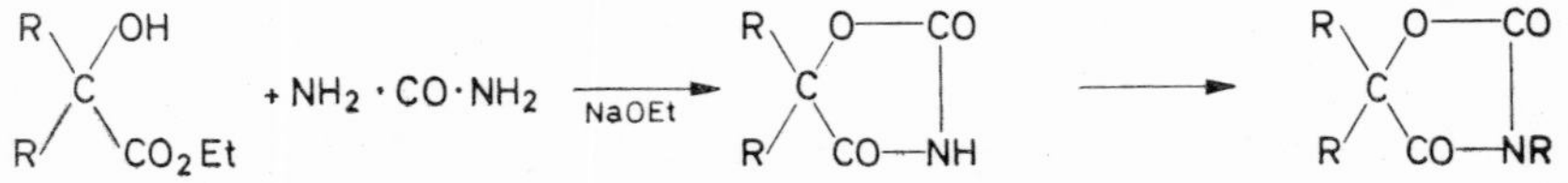

An alternative synthesis utilizes condensation of the amides of α-hydroxy acids with ethyl carbonate[501].

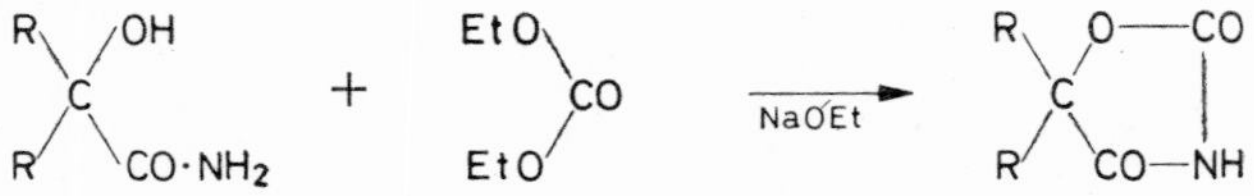

The chemistry of the oxazolidine-2,4-diones has been well reviewed[502].

### Succinimides

After extensive testing of many succinimides, *N*-methyl-α-phenylsuccinimide (phensuximide, Milontin, *V*) was selected for trial in petit mal on the basis of its ability to prevent leptazol-induced convulsions in animals in non-depressive doses[20,21]. In 50 patients with petit mal, it equalled troxidone in therapeutic efficiency and was relatively non-toxic[22]. In a later trial the efficiency was confirmed, but a much higher rate of toxicity was observed and signs of glomerulo-tubular damage were discovered in 48 per cent of the patients[503].

The discovery of phensuximide was followed by that of $N,\alpha$-dimethyl-$\alpha$-phenylsuccinimide (methsuximide, Celontin, *VI*). The action of methsuximide in psychomotor attacks was first noted incidentally during trial in petit mal[23]. In a more fully reported trial in 136 patients, mostly children who had not responded to other anticonvulsant drugs, methsuximide was found to be effective in controlling minor motor and psychomotor seizures. The frequency of spells in some cases of petit mal was also reduced, but patients with major motor seizures were unaffected[504]. Later trials confirmed its activity against petit mal and psychomotor epilepsy, but occasionally, there was a high incidence of ataxia, rash, drowsiness and nausea[505-507]. No changes were observed in blood or urine.

(*XXXVII*)          (*XXXVIII*)

Phensuximide has not proved as effective as the oxazolidinediones in the treatment of petit mal, and tolerance is apt to develop after early success. Methsuximide has been shown to be more toxic and has similar disadvantages. However, evidence is accumulating to suggest that a new analogue, $\alpha$-ethyl-$\alpha$-methylsuccinimide, (ethosuximide, Emeside, Zarontin, *VII*), may be a much more effective and less toxic treatment for petit mal than either of the phenylsuccinimides. Ethosuximide was selected for trial on the basis of its protective action against leptazol seizures in rats: it was about twice as active as phensuximide and four times as active as troxidone. Improvement of 80 out of 100 patients receiving daily doses of 1 to 2 g of ethosuximide has been achieved, with complete control of attacks in 43 per cent over a period of two years[24]. The most frequently reported side effects in less than 20 per cent of patients were nausea, gastric distress, drowsiness, dizziness and headache, and many of these disappeared if the dosage was somewhat reduced. There were no serious blood dyscrasias. Ethosuximide appeared to be much more effective in pure petit mal than in other types of seizure. Myoclonic and psychomotor attacks were not improved or were accentuated[25,26,508]. In another trial complete and lasting control was achieved in over one-third of 60 patients[27].

$N,\alpha$-Dimethyl-$\alpha$-ethylsuccinimide (*XXXVII*), a methyl derivative of ethosuximide, has been used for two years in comparison with methsuximide and was found to control 50 per cent of patients, mainly with petit mal, who had not responded satisfactorily to phensuximide. There were no serious toxic reactions, and the drug was regarded as superior to phensuximide and much less toxic than methsuximide[509]. An earlier and smaller trial had been less favourable[26].

$\alpha$-Ethyl-$\alpha$-phenylsuccinimide (*XXXVIII*) was less effective than methsuximide against petit mal[510].

Phensuximide ($N$-methyl-$\alpha$-phenylsuccinimide) may be synthesized by a series of reactions starting from benzaldehyde and ethyl cyanoacetate. The intermediate ethyl benzalcyanacetate is treated with cyanide, and the succinonitrile derivative so formed is hydrolysed by acid to α-phenylsuccinic acid. The *N*-methylsuccinimide is obtained by heating the acid with methylamine[20].

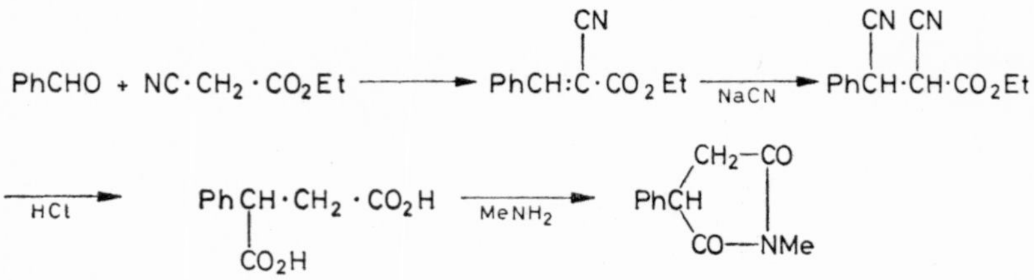

$$PhCHO + NC \cdot CH_2 \cdot CO_2Et \longrightarrow PhCH\text{:}\overset{\displaystyle CN}{C} \cdot CO_2Et \xrightarrow{\text{NaCN}} PhCH \cdot \overset{\displaystyle CN}{CH} \cdot CO_2Et$$

$$\xrightarrow{\text{HCl}} PhCH \cdot CH_2 \cdot CO_2H \atop \underset{\displaystyle CO_2H}{|} \xrightarrow{\text{MeNH}_2} PhCH \underset{\displaystyle CO\text{---}NMe}{\overset{\displaystyle CH_2\text{---}CO}{<}}$$

The intermediate succinonitrile derivative may be alkylated and converted to α,β-disubstituted succinimides[511].

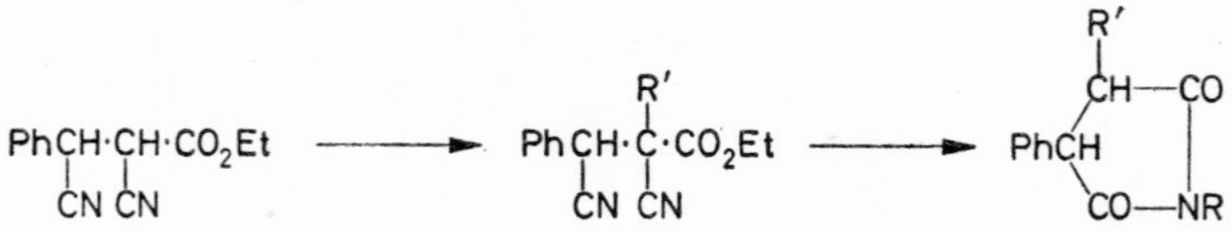

$$\underset{\displaystyle CN \ CN}{PhCH \cdot CH \cdot CO_2Et} \longrightarrow \underset{\displaystyle CN \ CN}{PhCH \cdot \overset{\displaystyle R'}{C} \cdot CO_2Et} \longrightarrow PhCH \underset{\displaystyle CO\text{---}NR}{\overset{\displaystyle \overset{\displaystyle R'}{CH}\text{---}CO}{<}}$$

α,α-Disubstituted succinimides may be synthesized by similar methods starting from ketones and ethyl cyanoacetate. A convenient simplified procedure is described by Smith and Horwitz[512].

## *Other Cyclic Amides*

### *Hexahydropyrimidinediones*

The anticonvulsant properties of 5-ethyl-5-phenylhexahydropyrimidine-4,6-dione (primidone, Mysoline, *IV*) have been described by Bogue and Carrington[18] and Goodman, Swinyard, Brown, Schiffman, Grewal and Bliss[399]. Primidone was most effective in protecting rats against maximal electrical seizures and had about the same activity as phenacemide and troxidone against leptazol seizures. In animals it had remarkably low toxicity. Clinical trial showed primidone to be highly effective in controlling grand mal with few sides effects[19] and occasionally to reduce the frequency of petit mal attacks[410,513]. It appeared to combine the high anticonvulsant activity of phenobarbitone with low toxicity. Nausea, dizziness, drowsiness and mild ataxia were sometimes encountered at the beginning of treatment, but passed off in a few days if treatment was continued.

The most serious but very rare toxic effect has been megaloblastic anaemia: it responds to therapy with folic acid or occasionally cyanocobalamin (vitamin $B_{12}$)[514-518]. Phenytoin and phenobarbitone produce a similar effect.

Primidone was first prepared by hydrogenolysis of 5-ethyl-5-phenyl-2-thiobarbituric acid with Raney nickel, but other reducing agents may be used, and the same product is obtained by electrolytic reduction of phenobarbitone itself. Reduction in alcohol with nickel containing less adsorbed hydrogen yields 2-alkoxy-derivatives which can be converted by further reduction into primidone[519].

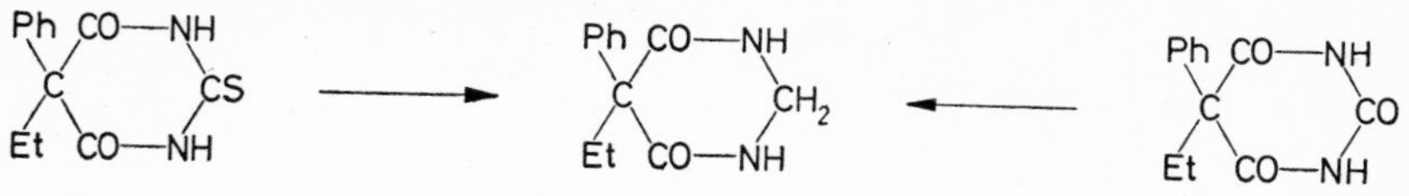

Primidone can also be prepared by the reaction of $C$-ethyl-$C$-phenyl-malondiamide with boiling formamide or formic acid at high temperature. Cyclization of $N$-formylmalondiamide probably yields an intermediate tetrahydropyrimidine, which is then reduced by excess formic acid or formamide to the hexahydropyrimidine[519].

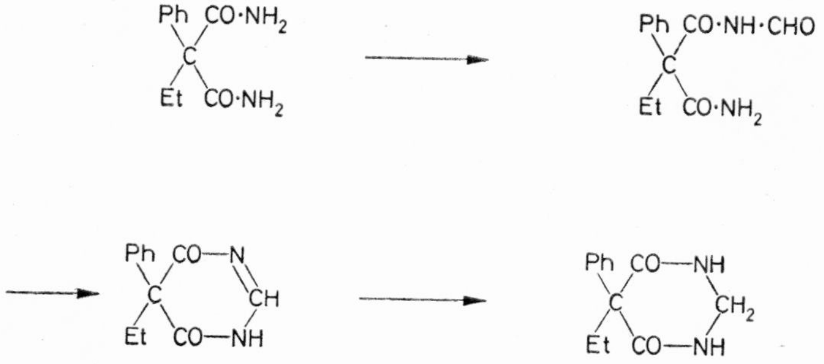

The intermediate malondiamides were prepared from the corresponding malonyl chlorides and ammonia, or by hydrolysis of the corresponding cyanoacetamides with sulphuric acid.

In view of its formal relationship to a diacylmethylenediamine structure, primidone is remarkably stable: it is unchanged by boiling in 5 per cent hydrochloric acid or 2N-sodium hydroxide, and cannot be methylated by methyl sulphate and alkali.

Analogues of primidone in which the benzene ring is substituted, and also some 2-alkoxy derivatives, have been described as anticonvulsants in patents[520-522]. The $N$-acyl derivatives have also been described[523,524].

*Glutarimides*

Further replacement of carbonyl and imide by methylene groups in the barbituric acid structure leads to glutarimides, and α-methyl-α-phenyl-glutarimide (*XXXIX*, R = Me) has been shown to be active against leptazol convulsions[525].

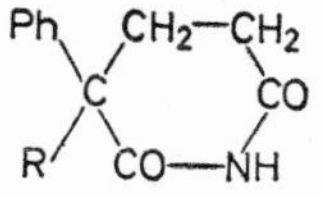

(XXXIX)

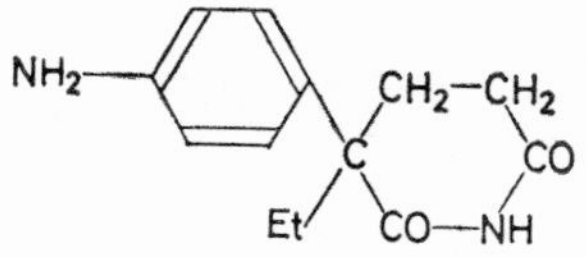

(XL)

Preliminary trial of α-($p$-aminophenyl)-α-ethylglutarimide (Elipten, *XL*) which lacks marked sedative effect, gave promising results in major, minor, petit mal and psychomotor epilepsy[526]. In a trial against grand mal and petit mal, or combinations of the two, the drug gave best results against grand mal, and no abnormal changes in blood, urine, blood pressure or liver function were observed[527]. In further trials[528,529] there were no serious toxic effects except some skin rashes. In a two year trial on outpatients using Elipten with other anticonvulsants, it was not found possible to discontinue the other drugs[530]. It was regarded as a useful addition to the treatment of hospital epileptics with small doses of phenobarbitone, phenytoin or primidone; the absence of sedative and toxic effects allowing considerable reduction of the standard medication. However, the development of tolerance in some patients was a major disadvantage.

Substitution of α-ethyl-α-phenylglutarimide (glutethimide, Doriden, *XXXIX*, R = Et) for Elipten was unsatisfactory. It was only active, in high dose, in patients having few seizures[528,531]. It is used chiefly as a hypnotic, but has anticonvulsant properties in animals.

A differently substituted glutarimide, β-ethyl-β-methylglutarimide, (bemegride, megimide) is convulsant, antagonizes the depressant properties of hypnotics, and has been used in human barbiturate coma[532–534].

α-(*p*-Aminophenyl)-α-ethylglutarimide is prepared by hydrogenation of the corresponding nitro-compound, which is obtained by nitration of α-ethyl-α-phenylglutarimide[535]. Alternatively the nitro-compound may be synthesized from phenylethylacetonitrile according to the following scheme:

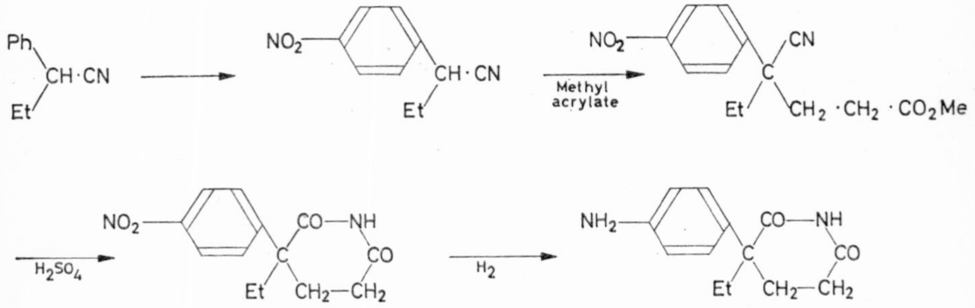

### Pyrrolidones and piperidones

3-Ethyl-3-phenyl-2-pyrrolidone (*XLI*) was the best of a series of 3,3-disubstituted pyrrolidones tested in rats: it showed activity against both electroshock and leptazol convulsions at about one-third of the hypnotic dose. Limited trial demonstrated clinical effect[71,536].

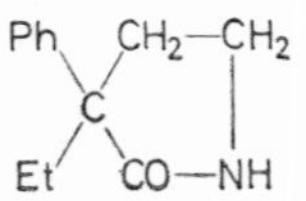

(XLI)

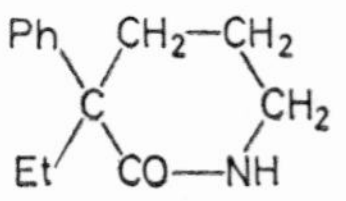

(XLII)

A piperidone derivative, 3-ethyl-3-phenylpiperidin-2-one (*XLII*) had earlier been shown to have some effect in epilepsy[537].

302

*Acyclic Amides*

After examination of a large number of *N*-substituted amides[538], *N*-benzyl-β-chloropropionamide (beclamide, benzchlorpropamide, Nydrane, Hibicon,

$$PhCH_2 \cdot NH \cdot CO \cdot CH_2 \cdot CH_2Cl$$

(*XLIII*)

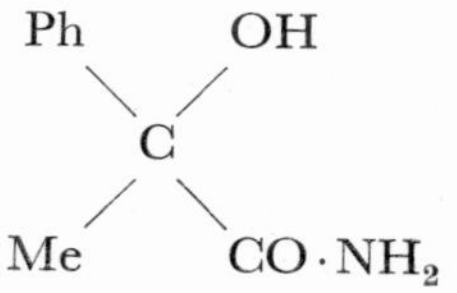

Ph, OH

C

Me, CO·NH$_2$

(*XLIV*)

*XLIII*) was introduced as an anticonvulsant. Reports on the clinical effectiveness of beclamide have been varied and contradictory. It has been claimed to be safe and effective in grand mal and psychomotor epilepsy but not in petit mal[539,540], though Livingston considered that it had little value in the treatment of grand mal[541]. Recent trials have been mildly favourable[542,543]: it was considered that the drug, although not very effective, might occasionally find a use because of its low toxicity.

Atrolactamide (Themisone, *XLIV*) has shown activity against electrical and leptazol convulsions[544]. Trials have proved it to be effective against grand mal and psychomotor epilepsy, but it is suspected of producing serious blood disorders[545].

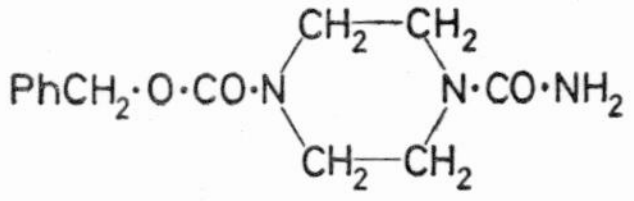

$$PhCH_2 \cdot O \cdot CO \cdot N \overset{CH_2-CH_2}{\underset{CH_2-CH_2}{\diagup\diagdown}} N \cdot CO \cdot NH_2$$

(*XLV*)

A series of benzyl esters of 4-carbamoylpiperazine-1-carboxyclic acid has been described, and tested in rats by an audiogenic method. The most active was named Hibital (*XLV*)[546]. Many other piperazine derivatives have been screened[547]. The compound with highest activity against leptazol seizures was 1-(2-thiazolyl)-4-phenylcarbamoylpiperazine. There is no clinical information about these compounds.

Recently a new acid hydrazide, Diphoxazide, 1-(3,3-diphenyl-3-hydroxy-propionyl)-2-acetylhydrazine, (*XLVI*), which had shown activity against electroshock in experimental animals, was tried for 6 months in 22 patients suffering mainly from grand mal and psychomotor epilepsy. All had failed to respond satisfactorily to other drugs. Half of the psychomotor patients were controlled when the drug was given with other medication. It was not

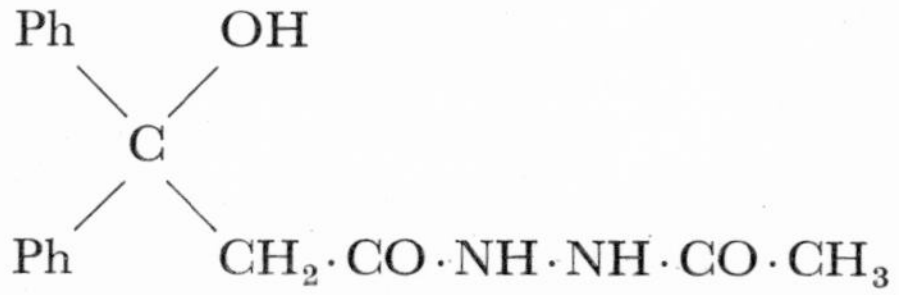

Ph, OH

C

Ph, CH$_2$·CO·NH·NH·CO·CH$_3$

(*XLVI*)

very effective in grand mal. Toxic reactions included albuminuria and a maculopapular rash, but these subsided on withdrawal of the drug[548].

No general method of preparation of acyclic amides can be given. Beclamide, $N$-benzyl-$\beta$-chloropropionamide, was prepared by the acylation of benzylamine with $\beta$-chloropropionyl chloride in the presence of alkali at low temperature[538].

$$PhCH_2 \cdot NH_2 + ClCH_2 \cdot CH_2 \cdot COCl \longrightarrow PhCH_2 \cdot NH \cdot CO \cdot CH_2 \cdot CH_2Cl$$

Atrolactamide is obtained from acetophenone, by conversion to acetophenone cyanhydrin and then hydrolysis to the amide by acid[549].

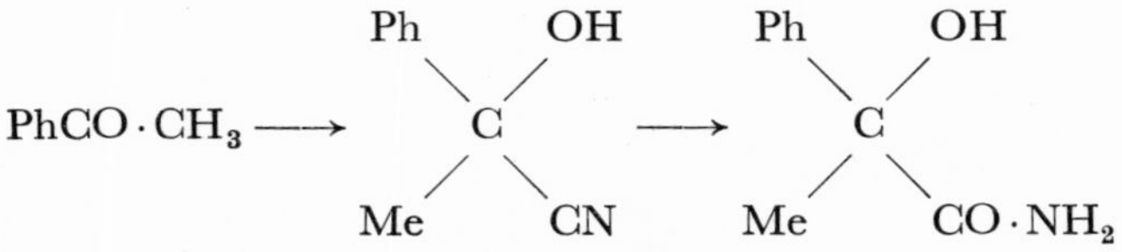

Hibital (benzyl 4-carbamoylpiperazine-1-carboxylate) was prepared from benzyl piperazine-1-carboxylate either by reaction with nitrourea, or cyanate on the hydrochloride. The intermediate benzyl piperazine-1-carboxylate was obtained by the action of carbobenzyloxychloride on piperazine[546].

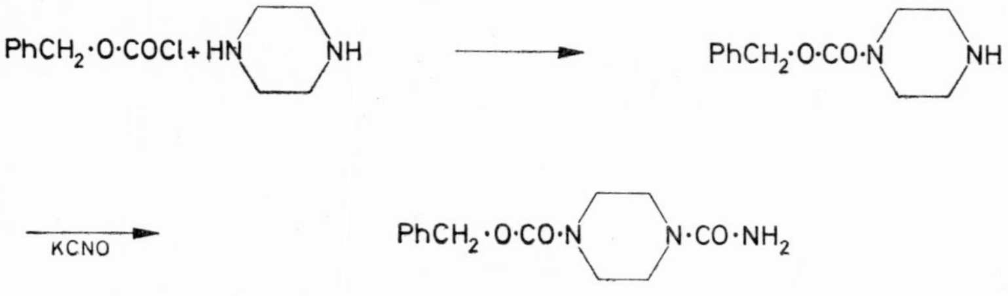

*Acylureas*

Phenylacetylurea (phenacemide, Phenurone, *XLVII*) is a powerful anticonvulsant, showing high activity in electroshock and leptazol tests[550], and in the three major forms of epilepsy[65,551]. Although dangerous side effects

$$PhCH_2 \cdot CO \cdot NH \cdot CO \cdot NH_2 \qquad PhCH \cdot CO \cdot NH \cdot CO \cdot NH_2$$
$$| \qquad\qquad R$$

$$(XLVII) \qquad\qquad (XLVIII)$$

$$PhCH \cdot CO \cdot NH \cdot CO \cdot NH_2$$
$$|$$
$$Et$$
$$(XLIX)$$

such as personality changes, hepatic damage, leucopenia and aplastic anaemia have sometimes been reported, this very potent drug is still used when other drugs are ineffective, and particularly in the treatment of psychomotor epilepsy[552]. Careful clinical observation is necessary, and blood counts and liver function tests should be made regularly.

In an attempt to discover a less toxic derivative of phenacemide, a large number of phenylacetylureas substituted at the α-carbon have been examined, and the α-chloro and α-bromo-derivatives were found to be more active than the parent compound in suppressing electroshock and leptazol seizures[553]. Phenyl-α-chloroacetylurea (Comitiadon, *XLVIII*, R = Cl) was finally selected for toxicity and clinical trials. Rats treated for three weeks with 1 g/kg of phenyl-α-chloroacetylurea daily, showed no sign of toxicity, though the same dose of phenacemide killed rats within seven days. In a three month trial over half of the patients showed a 50 per cent (or more) improvement in all three major types of epilepsy. A later report confirmed the wide spectrum of activity shown by this compound, although some patients were found to need a very high dose to achieve adequate control. There were no blood or urine changes, and sedation or lassitude were absent[554]. In spite of these favourable reports nothing more has been heard of this drug.

α-Phenylbutyrylurea (Pheneturide, *XLIX*) is the ethyl derivative of phenacemide, and it was issued commercially in 1952 as a mixture with phenacemide and phenobarbitone (Trinuride P) or with phenytoin and phenobarbitone (Trinuride H). The pharmacology of α-phenylbutyrylurea has been amply reported[555] and there have been several clinical trials[556,557]. It is said to be clinically effective in grand mal and petit mal, and good results were claimed in psychomotor epilepsy[57]. Skin rashes and hypertension were reported. Its two optical isomers have equal anticonvulsant activity in animals, but the (+)-isomer is stimulant whereas the (−)-isomer is sedative. The slight excitatory effect of the racemate is explained by these observations, and it has been suggested that the (+)-isomer may have a use as a stimulant anti-epileptic[558]. The (+), (−) and (±)-forms have been tried clinically. All three were most useful in temporal lobe epilepsy; not differing significantly in activity, and being equally well tolerated[559].

$$Ph_2CH \cdot NH \cdot CO \cdot NH \cdot COMe \qquad\qquad NH_2 \!\!-\!\!\bigcirc\!\!-\!\! SO_2 \cdot NH \cdot CO \cdot NHBu$$

*(L)*                          *(LI)*

In a preliminary trial, 1-benzhydryl-3-acetylurea (*L*) was claimed to be effective in grand mal but inactive in petit mal. Best results were obtained when it was given in combination with small doses of phenobarbitone. Given alone the drug seemed to cause excessive central nervous stimulation[560].

It is reported that carbutamide (*N*-butyl-*N'*-sulphanilylurea, *LI*) controlled grand mal attacks in a diabetic patient who had previously proved resistant to phenytoin and phenobarbitone. The patient then discontinued the other anticonvulsants, and attacks remained controlled for 14 months under carbutamide alone[561].

The acylureas are prepared simply by heating the appropriate acid chloride with urea, either alone or in a non-polar solvent such as benzene[550].

$$RCOCl + NH_2 \cdot CO \cdot NH_2 \longrightarrow RCO \cdot NH \cdot CO \cdot NH_2$$

## Alcohols

A number of alcohols are known to have anticonvulsant activity in animals, and marked activity has been demonstrated in a series of propanediols[562]. 2,2-Diethylpropane-1,3-diol (Prenderol, *LII*) was a potent inhibitor of chemically induced convulsions, and this relatively simple compound has been shown to be effective in petit mal[563]. Prenderol is fairly non-toxic, but short acting. In man it is oxidized to the inactive 2,2-diethylhydracrylic acid, a process which seems to be general for 2,2-dialkylpropane-1,3-diols. In contrast to the anticonvulsant properties of 2,2-diethylpropane-1,3-diol, a higher homologue 2,2-diethylbutane-1,4-diol was found to be convulsant with a similar action to leptazol, and to be antagonized by Prenderol[564].

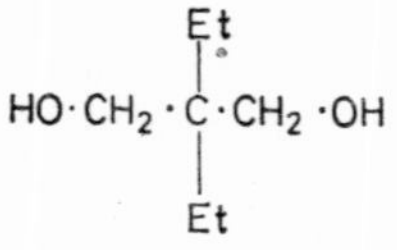

$$\text{HO} \cdot \text{CH}_2 \cdot \underset{\underset{\text{Et}}{|}}{\overset{\overset{\text{Et}}{|}}{\text{C}}} \cdot \text{CH}_2 \cdot \text{OH}$$

(*LII*)

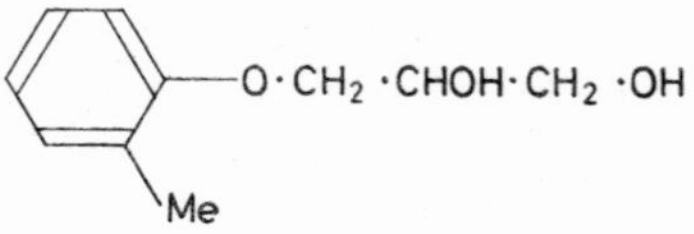

Ph(o-Me)—O·CH$_2$·CHOH·CH$_2$·OH

(*LIII*)

Cl—C$_6$H$_4$—CMeOH·CMe$_2$·OH

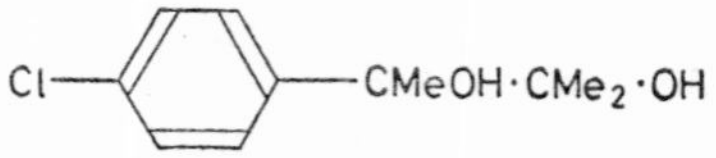

(*LIV*)

Related to this group of propanediols is the muscle relaxant mephenesin (3-*o*-methylphenoxypropane-1,2-diol, *LIII*) which in high doses has been shown to be of value in myoclonic epilepsy[565]. The clinical usefulness of such diols as mephenesin and Prenderol is restricted by their short action, which is probably due to rapid oxidation. Attempts to discover more stable and long acting compounds led to the selection of 2-*p*-chlorophenyl-3-methyl-2,3-butanediol (phenaglycodol, Ultran, *LIV*) from a series of fully substituted ethylene glycols which were active against electroshock and leptazol-induced seizures. The *m*-chloro-analogue was more potent but not so long acting[566]. Phenaglycodol has a significant effect at fairly high doses in epilepsy associated with focal brain damage[567]. Although designed as an anticonvulsant it is mainly used as a tranquillizer.

Some tertiary acetylenic carbinols possess hypnotic and anticonvulsant properties, and one of these, ethchlorvynol (1-chloro-3-ethylpent-1-en-4-yn-3-ol, Placidyl, *LV*) is highly effective against leptazol-induced seizures in mice and rats[568]. It has been tried in mixed grand mal and petit mal epilepsy. Complete or partial control of seizures was achieved in 73 per cent

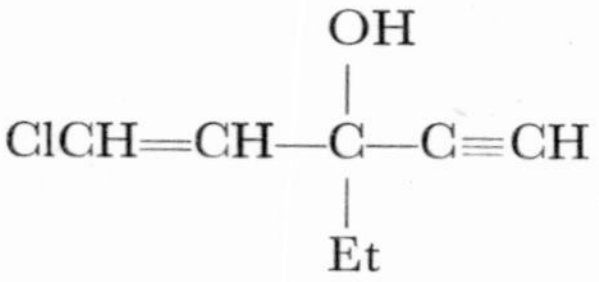

$$\text{ClCH}{=}\text{CH}{-}\underset{\underset{\text{Et}}{|}}{\overset{\overset{\text{OH}}{|}}{\text{C}}}{-}\text{C}{\equiv}\text{CH}$$

(*LV*)

$$\text{Me}{-}\underset{\underset{\text{Et}}{|}}{\overset{\overset{\text{OH}}{|}}{\text{C}}}{-}\text{C}{\equiv}\text{CH}$$

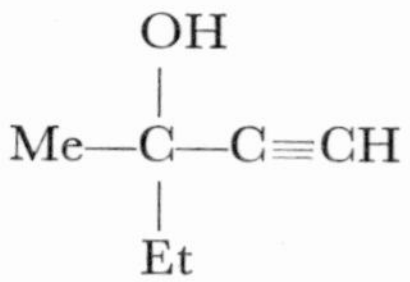

(*LVI*)

of patients. Unfortunately in 26 per cent seizure frequency increased. The only side effect was sedation[569]. 3-Methylpent-1-yn-3-ol (methylpentynol, Atempol, Dormisone, Oblivon, Somnesin, LVI) combines short acting anticonvulsant with sedative action. In one trial methylpentynol controlled grand mal and petit mal attacks in one out of six children for 9 months[570]. The toxic effects observed in an earlier trial[571] were not encountered.

### Carbamates and Allophanates

The tranquillizer meprobamate (2-methyl-2-n-propyl-1,3-propanediol dicarbamate, LVII) is anticonvulsant in experimental animals and relatively long acting[572]. It is reported to be effective in petit mal[129,573,574].

Activity against psychomotor epilepsy has been briefly reported for another tranquillizer, hydroxyphenamate (2-hydroxy-2-phenylbutyl carbamate, LVIII) with a striking absence of side effects, including drowsiness. When given orally to mice it blocked maximal electroshock convulsions, and those caused by leptazol and strychnine[575].

$$\text{n-Pr} \diagdown \diagup \text{CH}_2 \cdot \text{O} \cdot \text{CO} \cdot \text{NH}_2$$
$$\text{C}$$
$$\text{Me} \diagup \diagdown \text{CH}_2 \cdot \text{O} \cdot \text{CO} \cdot \text{NH}_2$$

(LVII)

$$\text{PhCEt} \cdot \text{CH}_2 \cdot \text{O} \cdot \text{CO} \cdot \text{NH}_2$$
$$|$$
$$\text{OH}$$

(LVIII)

$$\text{PhCHEt} \cdot \text{O} \cdot \text{CO} \cdot \text{NH} \cdot \text{CO} \cdot \text{NH}_2$$

(LIX)

Although showing only relatively weak activity against leptazol and electrical convulsions, α-ethylbenzyl allophanate (LIX) was chosen for evaluation in man[576]. It helped about 35 per cent of 64 patients, and was well tolerated[577].

### Carbonic Anhydrase Inhibitors

Inhibition of carbonic anhydrase is correlated with anticonvulsant effect (p. 277). 2-Acetamido-1,3,4-thiadiazole-5-sulphonamide (acetazolamide, Diamox, VIII) has been used successfully in the treatment of grand mal of moderate severity, and as adjuvant therapy in mixed idiopathic epilepsy[578]. Reports, however, have been conflicting: it was said to be useless in chronic adult epileptics and rarely useful in children with petit mal[579,580]. Another trial, lasting three years, demonstrated little benefit in psychomotor or focal seizures, and some benefit in myoclonic and akinetic seizures; effectiveness declined after prolonged treatment[581]. A similar decline in effective control was seen with troxidone.

A recent review of the literature discloses that acetazolamide is mostly used in combination with other anticonvulsants, that its toxicity is low, and that tolerance develops readily[582].

$N^5$-Alkyl and acyl sulphonamido derivatives of acetazolamide have been prepared. The isopropyl and butyryl derivatives (LX, R = CHMe$_2$, R = COC$_3$H$_7$) are active, but the methyl, t-butyl and acetyl derivatives (LX,

307

$R = Me$, $R = CMe_3$, $R = COMe$) are not. Activity appears to depend upon the ease with which the group R is removed in the body.

In small scale trials another carbonic anhydrase inhibitor 6-ethoxy-benzthiazole-2-sulphonamide (ethoxzolamide, Cardrase, LXI) has been

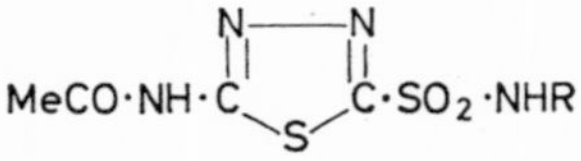

MeCO·NH·C⟨N——N⟩C·SO$_2$·NHR

(LX)

EtO—⟨benzothiazole⟩C·SO$_2$·NH$_2$

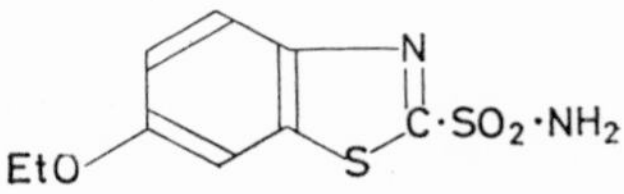

(LXI)

shown to control both grand mal and petit mal seizures. The improvement in patients with psychomotor seizures was significant but less striking. The most common side effect was dizziness, and some patients suffered from drowsiness and headache[257,258,583].

*Sultams*

Sulthiame (N-(4-sulphamoylphenyl)-1,4-butanesultam, Ospolot, LXII) is said to be particularly effective in psychomotor epilepsy and non-sedative.

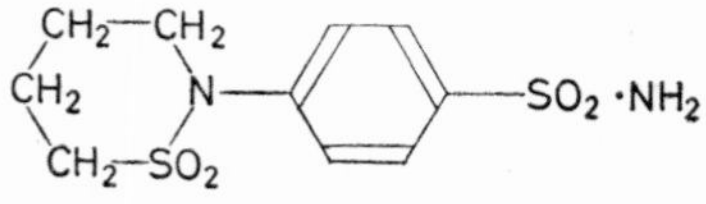

(LXII)

It had little or no effect on pure petit mal[584]. In the remaining forms of epilepsy its main use was in combination with reduced doses of other anticonvulsants. It caused no serious side effects, though a number of patients complained of transient paraesthesiae of extremities and face[585,586].

The pharmacology of sulthiame and analogues has been described in detail[587,588]. It is reported to abolish the tonic component of electroshock convulsions in rats, and to inhibit leptazol convulsions; apparently it is weakly diuretic, and not hypnotic or analgesic[589]. The N-alkyl substituted alkane sultams showed no useful pharmacological properties, and although the N-aryl derivatives had anticonvulsant activity, they were also hypnotic and lowered body temperature. The free p-sulphonamide group raised anticonvulsant potency. Other substituents, or any in other positions, reduced activity or raised toxicity.

A general method of synthesis of this type of sultam has been described[590]: 4-chlorobutane-1-sulphonyl chloride reacts with ammonia or a primary amine, and the resulting 4-chlorobutane-1-sulphonamide is cyclized by base to the sultam.

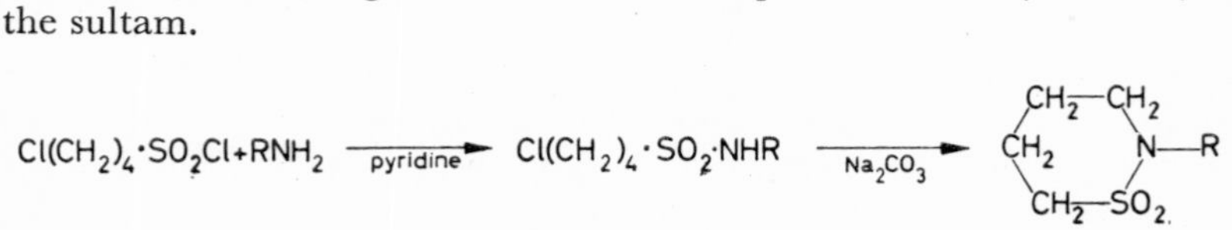

$Cl(CH_2)_4 \cdot SO_2Cl + RNH_2 \xrightarrow{\text{pyridine}} Cl(CH_2)_4 \cdot SO_2 \cdot NHR \xrightarrow{Na_2CO_3}$

Sulthiame may be obtained by using 4-aminobenzenesulphonamide as the appropriate amine in the above synthesis. Alternatively the amino-group of N-(4-aminophenyl)butane sultam may be converted *via* a diazo-reaction

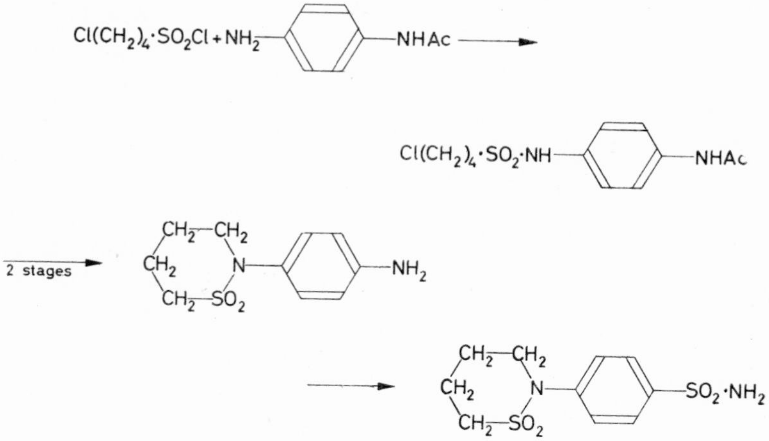

$$Cl(CH_2)_4 \cdot SO_2Cl + NH_2 \text{—} \langle \rangle \text{—} NHAc \longrightarrow$$

$$Cl(CH_2)_4 \cdot SO_2 \cdot NH \text{—} \langle \rangle \text{—} NHAc$$

2 stages $\longrightarrow$

$$\begin{array}{c} CH_2\text{—}CH_2 \\ CH_2 \quad\quad N \\ CH_2\text{—}SO_2 \end{array} N \text{—} \langle \rangle \text{—} NH_2$$

$$\longrightarrow \begin{array}{c} CH_2\text{—}CH_2 \\ CH_2 \quad\quad N \\ CH_2\text{—}SO_2 \end{array} N \text{—} \langle \rangle \text{—} SO_2 \cdot NH_2$$

into a sulphonyl chloride and thence to a sulphonamide[589]. The N-(4-amino-phenyl)butane sultam was active as an anticonvulsant in mice but was hypnotic and lowered body temperature[591]. Unsaturated sultams also have anticonvulsant action[592].

## Drugs for Parenteral Use

In a controlled double-blind trial, Taverner and Bain[593] confirmed the earlier report of Bernhard and Bohm[594] that intravenous lignocaine (Xylocaine, lidocaine, *LXIII*) was effective in status epilepticus. The drug was only active as an anticonvulsant when given intravenously, and this appears to

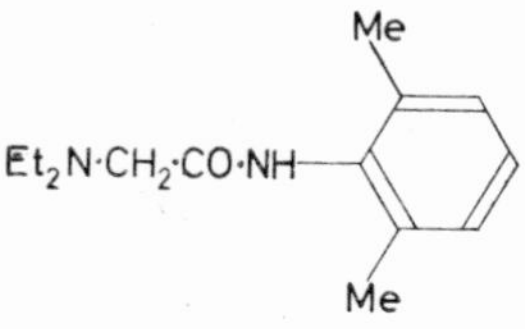

$$Et_2N \cdot CH_2 \cdot CO \cdot NH \text{—} \langle \rangle$$

Me

Me

*(LXIII)*

be true for other local anaesthetics[73,595]. Administration of diphenylhydan-toin sodium, intravenously or intramuscularly, has also been recommended to control status epilepticus[596,597] and McWilliam[598] has achieved good results with it in children. Paraldehyde, intramuscularly, however, is still the drug most often given in this very serious and potentially fatal disorder, although some deaths have been reported after its use. Parenteral barbiturates have also been used but may cause respiratory depression. The use of muscle relaxants, *e.g.* suxamethonium or (+)-tubocurarine, and controlled respira-tion has also been reported[599,600].

## Other Drugs

Chlordiazepoxide (7-chloro-2-methylamino-5-phenyl-3H-1,4-benzodiaze-pine-4-oxide, methaminodiazepoxide, Librium, *LXIV*) was reported to

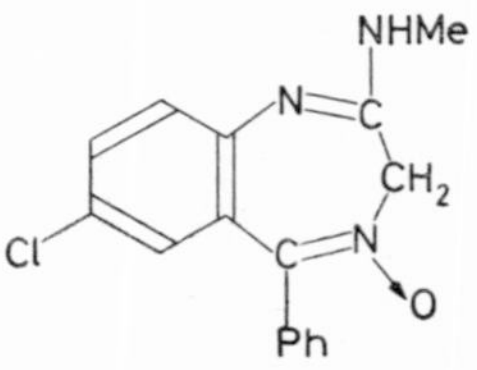

(LXIV) 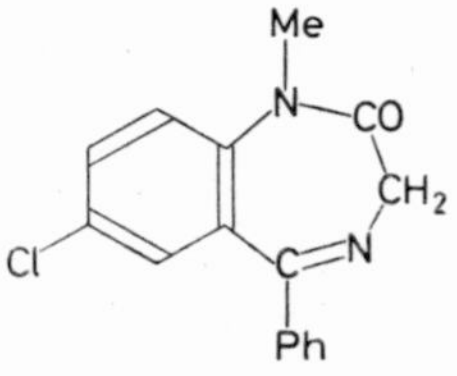                           (LXV)

have anticonvulsant activity in mice[601]. In preliminary trials it was said to have a useful effect on a small group of epileptic patients[602-604]. In a larger trial with 40 epileptic patients no significant anticonvulsant properties could be demonstrated[605].

Diazepam (7-chloro-1-methyl-5-phenyl-3H-1,4-benzodiazepin-2(1H)-one, Valium, *LXV*), a new psychotherapeutic agent of the 1,4-benzodiazepine class, has the same order of toxicity as chlordiazepoxide but is ten times as potent against leptazol and maximal electroshock tests in mice. Human tolerance tests have been carried out; no trial in epilepsy has been reported[606].

A few cases of recalcitrant petit mal have been controlled by treatment with quinacrine (mepacrine). Apart from the yellow discoloration of the skin, no side effects were observed[607].

1-Methyllysergic acid butanolamide was tried in six epileptics, three of whom were refractory to other anticonvulsants. Given by mouth at 6 mg/day, with or without other anticonvulsants, the drug produced a marked reduction in frequency and severity of grand mal attacks, but did not affect petit mal. It had no action against electroshock or leptazol convulsions in rats[608].

Haloperidol (Serenace, Serenase) has been given parenterally at 2 mg/day to 25 epileptics, in addition to previous therapy, with beneficial results in 6 patients. In eleven others it was proconvulsant[609].

## STRUCTURE–ACTIVITY RELATIONSHIPS

Most of the major anticonvulsants of proved clinical value have in their structure an amide or urea unit which is often part of a cyclic system. This amide or urea unit is sometimes further acylated, as in the acyclic phenace-mide molecule, or the cyclic barbiturates, hydantoins and succinimides. The amide nitrogen may carry hydrocarbon substituents. These features may be included in the fragment

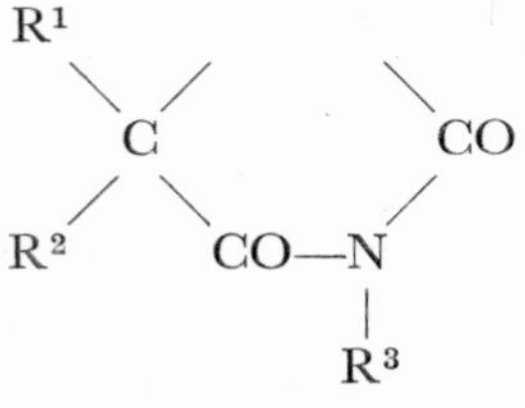

*Table 6.2*

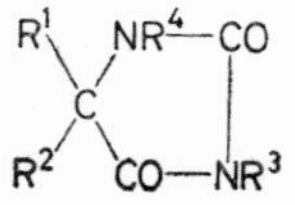

R¹, NR⁴—CO / C / R², CO—NR³

1. Hydantoin

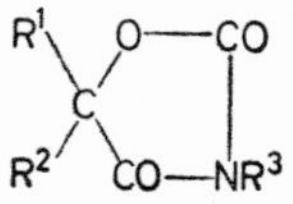

R¹, O—CO / C / R², CO—NR³

2. Oxazolidine - 2,4 - dione

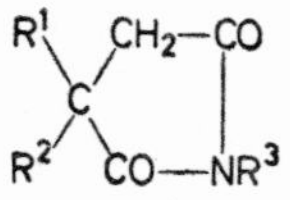

R¹, CH₂—CO / C / R², CO—NR³

3. Succinimide

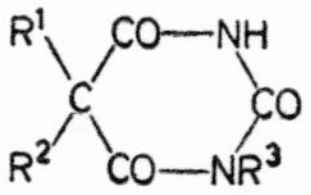

R¹, CO—NH / C / R², CO—NR³ (CO)

4. Barbituric acid

R¹, CO—NH / C / R², CO—NH (CH₂)

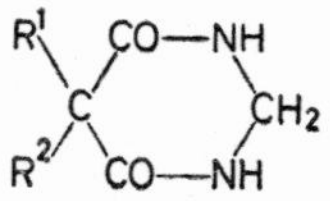

5. Hexahydropyrimidine - 4,6 - dione

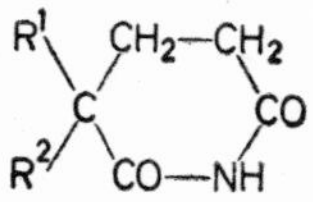

R¹, CH₂—CH₂ / C / R², CO—NH (CO)

6. Glutarimide

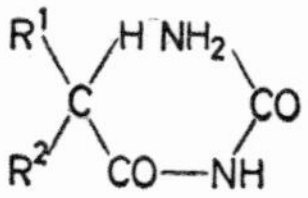

R¹, H NH₂ / C / R², CO—NH (CO)

7. Acylurea

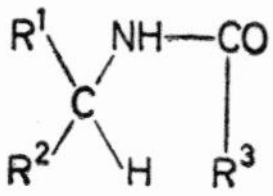

R¹, NH—CO / C / R², H R³

8. Amide (a)

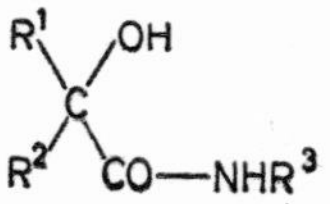

R¹, OH / C / R², CO—NHR³

9. Amide (b)

R¹, O—CO / CH, NH / R², H₂N—CO

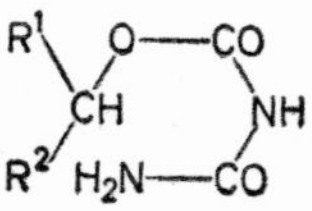

10. Allophanate

*Table 6.3.* Classes of clinically effective anticonvulsants

| Formula (Table 6.2) | Class | Name | Substituents | | | |
|---|---|---|---|---|---|---|
| | | | R¹ | R² | R³ | R⁴ |
| 1 | Hydantoin | phenytoin | Ph | Ph | H | H |
| | | Nirvanol | Ph | Et | H | H |
| | | methoin | Ph | Et | Me | H |
| | | Nuvarone | Ph | H | Me | H |
| | | ethotoin | Ph | H | Et | H |
| | | N.3,methetoin | Ph | Et | H | Me |

*Table 6.3.* Classes of clinically effective anticonvulsants (*contd*)

| | | | R¹ | R² | R³ |
|---|---|---|---|---|---|
| 2 | Oxazolidine-2,4-dione | troxidone | Me | Me | Me |
| | | paramethadione | Me | Et | Me |
| | | dimedione | Me | Me | Et |
| | | malidone | Me | H | $CH_2$:$CHCH_2$ |
| | | Epidon | Ph | Ph | H |
| 3 | Succinimide | phensuximide | Ph | H | Me |
| | | methsuximide | Ph | Me | Me |
| | | ethosuximide | Me | Et | H |
| 4 | Barbituric Acid | phenobarbitone | Ph | Et | H |
| | | methylpheno-barbitone | Ph | Et | Me |
| | | metharbital | Et | Et | Me |
| | | Pyrictal | Et | Et | Ph |
| 5 | Hexahydro pyrimidine-4,6-dione | primidone | Ph | Et | — |
| 6 | Glutarimide | Elipten | $NH_2 \cdot C_6H_4$ | Et | — |
| 7 | Acylurea | phenacemide | Ph | H | — |
| | | Comitiadon | Ph | Cl | — |
| | | pheneturide | Ph | Et | — |
| 8 | Amide (a) | Hibicon | Ph | H | $CH_2CH_2Cl$ |
| 9 | Amide (b) | Atrolactamide | Ph | Me | H |
| 10 | Allophanate | α-Ethylbenzylallo-phanate | Ph | Et | — |

which is common to the structures of hydantoins, oxazolidine-2,4-diones, succinimides, barbiturates, glutarimides, and acylureas.

Those drugs conforming to this structure pattern, and which are particularly effective in grand mal epilepsy, all have at least one benzene or aromatic substituent at the α-carbon atom (*e.g.* $R^1$ = Ph). This group includes phenobarbitone, phenytoin, methoin, and phenacemide, among major anti-epileptic drugs. In some cases the second group at the α-carbon atom is hydrogen ($R^2$ = H) as in phenacemide, or the amide nitrogen may be alkylated with a lower alkyl group, as in ethotoin ($R^3$ = Et). In other instances $R^2$ is an alkyl substituent (frequently ethyl) as in phenobarbitone or methoin, or occasionally halogen as in Comitiadon ($R^2$ = Cl). More rarely $R^1$ and $R^2$ are both aromatic substituents, as in phenytoin and Epidon.

The same amide or acylamide unit also appears in the structures of most of the established drugs in use against petit mal (*e.g.* oxazolidine-2,4-diones and succinimides), but in these compounds the aromatic substituent is less important. Some of the compounds which are most active against petit mal, such as troxidone, paramethadione and dimedione, carry only lower alkyl groups at both carbon and nitrogen atoms of this system. Alkylation of the amide nitrogen is more common in drugs that are useful in petit mal, but such alkylation is not obligatory (*e.g.* ethosuximide has $R^3$ = H).

In a smaller group of antiepileptic drugs (*e.g.* primidone, Atrolactamide) the amide fragment is not acylated

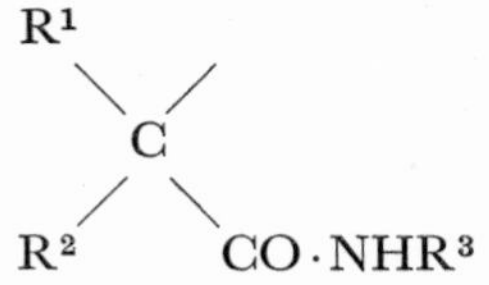

$$R^1 \diagdown \diagup$$
$$C$$
$$R^2 \diagup \diagdown CO \cdot NHR^3$$

312

Amides such as beclamide, the urethanes, and allophanates, which are less effective anticonvulsants, do not contain the same common amide fragment, but they are nevertheless very closely related structures. They may be regarded as being theoretically derived from the partial structures of hydantoins and oxazolidine-2,4-diones.

Drugs which are effective in controlling other forms of epilepsy do not fall into any easy system of classification.

### Hydantoins

The unsubstituted hydantoin ring has in itself no anticonvulsant activity, but when aryl groups are introduced at position 5 the products are often active, the degree of activity depending on the nature and position of other substituents. 5,5-Diphenyl-hydantoin is outstanding against electro-shock and grand mal and in its mildness of side-effects. If one of the phenyl groups of phenytoin is replaced by an alkyl (methyl to butyl), or a heterocyclic substituent (2-thienyl, pyrrolidyl, pyridyl or pyranyl), the activity against electroshock is maintained. The resulting compounds, however, are often more toxic than phenytoin and show more side effects (e.g. Nirvanol, Thiantoin). The effect of substitution on pharmacological action among 5-alkyl-5-arylhydantoins has been discussed with reference to a series of new derivatives[469]. 5-Alkoxymethyl-5-phenylhydantoins and their corresponding thioethers retain much of the activity of Nirvanol, but most other oxygen derivatives are inactive. The 5-phenyl group may itself be substituted, or be replaced by a larger aromatic group such as naphthyl, without losing activity. The 1- and 3-methyl derivatives of phenytoin are much less active than phenytoin itself, but the methylation of Nirvanol produces methoin (5-ethyl-3-methyl-5-phenylhydantoin) which appears to be a safer yet highly potent drug. A recent study of 3,5-di- and 3,5,5-tri-substituted hydantoins showed that the 3-($\beta$-hydroxyethyl) derivatives of phenytoin and Nirvanol have high activity in the electroshock test in mice and a low oral acute toxicity[610].

Among 5-phenylhydantoins a high degree of protection against electro-shock is found in compounds that are alkylated in the 1- or 3-positions. 1-Allyl-5-phenylhydantoin, 3-methyl-5-phenylhydantoin (Nuvarone) and 3-ethyl-5-phenylhydantoin (ethotoin) are examples of this class. Ethotoin is unusual in that it is one of the few effective antiepileptic compounds which has an N-ethyl substituent.

A number of spirohydantoins and spirothiohydantoins derived from large ring ketones have anticonvulsant activity in experimental animals. In contrast to the aryl substituted hydantoins, the spiro-compounds are mainly active against leptazol seizures. Although 5,5-pentamethylenehydantoin is devoid of activity, the higher homologue 5,5-hexamethylenehydantoin protects against leptazol convulsions[611], and 5,5-heptamethylenehydantoin is active in both leptazol and electroshock tests[612]. Among thiohydantoins, the analogous 5,5-heptamethylene-2,4-dithiohydantoin is claimed to be active against leptazol-induced seizures[613,614], while the 2-thiohydantoin has hypnotic and sedative action[615]. The alkyl substituted carbocyclic ring analogues, 5,5-(2 or 3-methylhexamethylene)hydantoins and 2-thiohydantoins also have hypnotic and anticonvulsant properties[616]. The hydantoins derived from 2-decalone, also show activity against leptazol convulsions, and are singularly non-toxic[617].

## Oxazolidine-2,4-diones

This class of compounds was first studied for their analgesic effect, later for their hypnotic action, and eventually for their value in petit mal. All oxazolidine-2,4-diones that are clinically effective in petit mal are active against leptazol-induced convulsions. Substitution in the 5-position of the oxazolidine-2,4-dione ring is essential for high anticonvulsant activity. Lower alkyl substituents at the 5-position favour anticonvulsant and analgesic activity at the expense of hypnotic action, and the anticonvulsant effect is also increased by alkylation of the nitrogen at position 3. Activity is maintained in the 3-methyl series if the alkyl substituents at position 5 are joined to form a spiropentamethylene ring. Introduction of a 5-phenyl substituent in place of the 5-methyl group of troxidone confers little activity against electroshock convulsions, but the activity against leptazol seizures is still maintained. 5,5-Diphenyloxazolidine-2,4-dione (Epidon), however, is active only against electroshock, and has been claimed to be clinically effective in grand mal. The effect of aryl substitution in this series is similar to that in the succinimide group of anticonvulsants, *viz.* to change what is primarily an anti-petit mal type drug into one that is active against grand mal.

If the heterocyclic oxygen atom of an active oxazolidine-2,4-dione (*LXVI*) is replaced by sulphur as in 3,5,5-trimethyl-2,4-dioxothiazolidine (*LXVII*), or by imino as in 3,5,5-trimethylhydantoin (*LXVIII*), activity is lost.

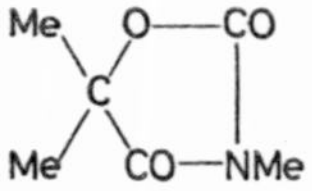

(LXVI) 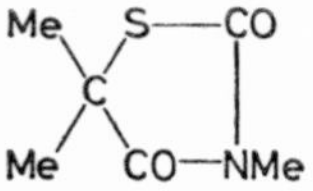          (LXVII) 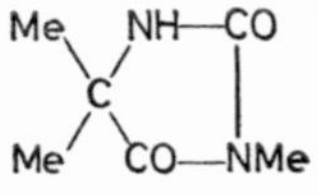          (LXVIII)

## Succinimides

The anticonvulsant succinimides, the structures of which bear a formal resemblance to those of the hydantoins, are mainly used against petit mal. As with hydantoins, the unsubstituted succinimide ring is without activity, but substitution of the $\alpha$-carbon atom by phenyl or lower alkyl groups leads to clinically useful compounds. The imide nitrogen is often methylated (*e.g.* phensuximide, methsuximide) but this is not always necessary for high activity (*e.g.* ethosuximide). All these compounds give high protection against leptazol convulsions in experimental animals, and have little or no effect on electroshock.

In those succinimides carrying only aliphatic substituents on the $\alpha$-carbon, the activity against leptazol convulsions increases with the size of the alkyl groups as far as $\alpha$-butyl-$\alpha$-ethylsuccinimide. High activity is also reached when the α- and N-positions are fully substituted by lower alkyl groups, but in this class optimal activity is often associated with N-methyl derivatives. Alkyl substitution at the β-carbon as well as at the α and N-positions does not reduce activity against leptazol convulsions. A benzene substituent at the α- position causes an increase in the activity against electroshock while retaining the activity against leptazol convulsions. With two benzene substituents, αα-diphenylsuccinimide is active only against electroshock. This influence of aromatic substitution recalls the similar effect of phenyl groups in the oxazolidine-2,4-diones and hydantoins.

Many succinimide derivatives have been described as anticonvulsants, mainly in patent literature[618,619]. They include a chlorinated methsuximide[620], a hydroxylated phensuximide[621] and an amino-derivative, α-(p-aminophenyl)-α-methylsuccinimide[622]. Among spiro-derivatives, the αα-pentamethylenesuccinimides are inactive, but as with the spiro-hydantoins, activity reappears in the larger ring compounds, and a number of αα-heptamethylenesuccinimides have been claimed to be active against electrically induced seizures as well as leptazol convulsions[623]. It is interesting that ααββ-tetramethylsuccinimide has been used clinically as a convulsant in chronic schizophrenics[624]. More distantly related compounds such as αα-pentamethylene-γ-butyrolactones are also stimulants. One of these, as the salt, sodium ββ-pentamethylene-γ-hydroxybutyrate, has received the name of Gevilon[625–627].

*Acylureas*

The successful use of phenobarbitone in the treatment of grand mal epilepsy, encouraged chemists to attempt to design active compounds modelled on the partial structure of the barbiturate ring. The discovery of activity in α-phenylbutyrylurea, an acylic structure which embodied a major part of the phenobarbitone molecule, led to a general study of acylureas, and resulted in the discovery of phenacemide[550]. In general, it was found that straight chain aliphatic acylureas were inactive, and those derived from branched chain aliphatic acids showed optimal anticonvulsant activity at about seven carbon atoms. With increasing molecular weight anticonvulsant activity declined, and hypnotic action appeared. The aromatic series revealed the most potent compound in phenylacetylurea (phenacemide), which showed powerful activity against both electroshock and leptazol-induced convulsions.

The introduction of N-methyl groups into the structure of phenacemide (*XLVII*) does not enhance anticonvulsant activity, and branching the chain at the α-carbon atom (*e.g. XLVIII*, R = Me or Et) increases the sedative but not the anticonvulsant properties. All anticonvulsant activity disappears with larger alkyl groups (*XLVIII*, R = Pr$^i$ or Bu), although some is retained when R = Pr. Diphenylacetylurea (*XLVIII*, R = Ph) which has the nearest formal resemblance to phenytoin is inactive in both tests. The phenyl group of phenacemide cannot be replaced by naphthyl or thienyl, or substituted by methyl or chlorine without loss of activity.

In a series of 1-alkyl-3-aroylureas, peak activity against electroshock and leptazol convulsions in rats was found to occur in 3-benzoyl-1-n-butylurea and in 1-n-butyl-3-o-toluoylurea[628].

## Acyclic Amides

The $\alpha\alpha$-disubstituted malonamide structure is a major fragment of the molecule of a barbiturate or hexahydropyrimidimedione, but few malonamide derivatives show significant activity in experimental animals. A series of dialkylmalondiamides has been examined, and the most active against electroshock was $\alpha$-ethyl-$\alpha$-n-pentylmalonamide (LXIX)[629].

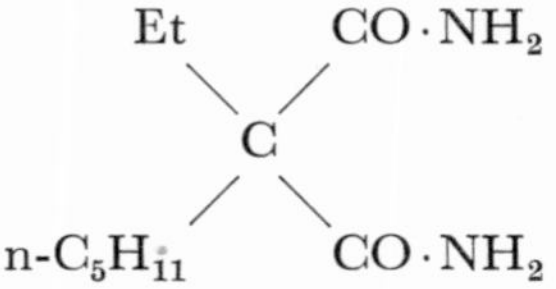

(LXIX) 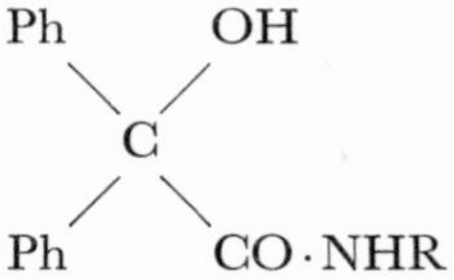　　　　　　(LXX)

Atrolactamide ($\alpha$-methylmandelamide, Themisone, XLIV), which may be regarded as derived from fragmentation of either barbiturate or hydantoin structures, has a powerful anticonvulsant action against both electrical and leptazol convulsions. It is clinically effective in grand mal but is suspected of causing blood changes.

Recently the anticonvulsant and toxicological properties of benzilic amide (LXX, R = H) and six of its N-alkyl derivatives, were studied in mice and rats. These compounds are structurally related to phenytoin in the same way as atrolactamide is related to 5-methyl-5-phenylhydantoin. The parent compound (LXX, R = H) proved to have the most powerful protective activity against electroshock and leptazol convulsions but was neurotoxic. The most suitable derivatives from this point of view were the N-ethyl and N-isopropylamides[630].

## Other Cyclic Amides

Recently, interest has developed in 2-alkyl-3-phenyl-3H-4-quinazolones, following the observation that the hypnotic 2-methyl-3-o-tolyl-3H-4-quinazolone (methaqualone, Melsedin, LXXI) was a potent anticonvulsant, protecting mice against both leptazol seizures and electroshock[631]. Methaqualone was relatively non-toxic, but in high doses caused neurological changes and flaccid paralysis. It is not a diuretic[632]. The most active member

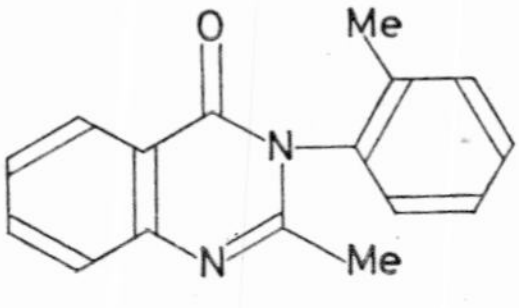

(LXXI) 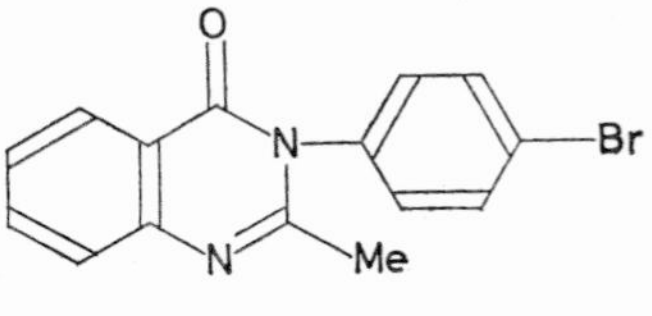　　　　　　(LXXII)

of a series of 2-alkyl-3-aryl-3H-4-quinazolones against leptazol seizures, was 2-methyl-3-p-bromophenyl-3H-4-quinazolone (LXXII). Replacement of the 2-methyl group by ethyl or butyl decreased activity, and analogous thioquinazolones were also less active[633,634].

316

The structure activity relationships in a series of urazoles (*LXXIII*) has been investigated because of the formal similarity of the urazole and hydantoin ring systems. In general the urazoles were most effective against maximal leptazol seizures in mice. At least one phenyl group seems to be necessary at $R^1$ or $R^2$, and the substituent at $R^3$ must be small[635,636].

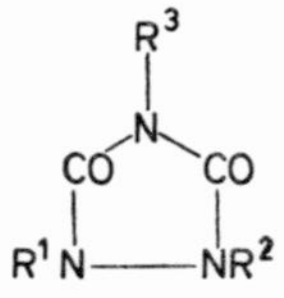

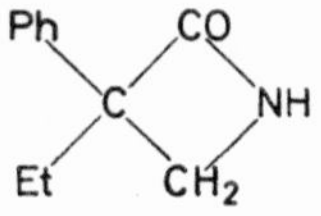

(*LXXIII*)          (*LXXIV*)

It is instructive to observe the persistence of anticonvulsant activity through a group of four, five and six membered cyclic amides differing from each other only by a methylene group. A study of 3,3-disubstituted-2-azetinones (β-lactams) revealed activity in a number of these compounds, one of the most active being 3-ethyl-3-phenyl-2-azetinone (*LXXIV*)[637]. 3-Ethyl-3-phenyl-2-pyrrolidone (*XLI*) was also the most active member of its class in tests against electroshock and leptazol convulsions[71,536]. The isomeric 4-ethyl-4-phenyl-2-pyrrolidone has also been claimed to have anticonvulsant properties[638]. Among six membered cyclic amides, 3-ethyl-3-phenylpiperidin-2-one (*XLII*) has been shown to be clinically effective[537]. This piperidone derivative may be regarded as a partially reduced glutarimide, and thus closely related to glutethimide and Elipten. Peak activity in each series was associated with the phenyl-ethyl-carbon group;

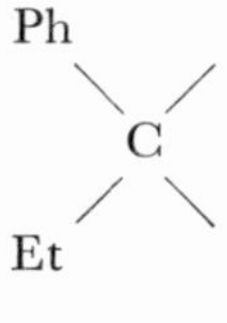

and this grouping is frequently present in anticonvulsant compounds.

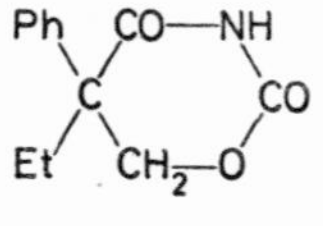

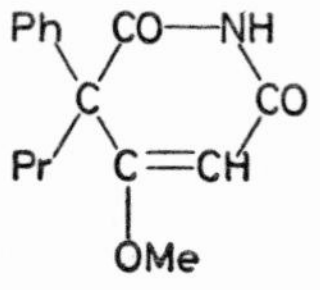

(*LXXV*)          (*LXXVI*)

In a series of 5,5-disubstituted-1,3-oxazine-2,4-diones, the most active compound in the maximal electroshock test was again the 5-ethyl-5-phenyl derivative (*LXXV*), in which a methylene group of the glutethimide molecule

317

has been replaced by an oxygen atom. The 5-methyl and 5-propyl analogues were almost as active as $(LXXV)$, and $N$-methylation enhanced the activity against leptazole convulsions. Some 5,5-dialkyl derivatives, however, were highly convulsant[639]. The best compound with regard to activity and toxicity in a group of 4-alkoxy-3-alkyl-3-phenylglutaconimides examined in the electroshock and leptazole tests was 4-methoxy-3-phenyl-3-propylglutaconimide $(LXXVI)$[640].

## CONCLUSION

Our discussion of structure-activity relationships may be summarized by emphasizing the common structural features of nearly all active anticonvulsants. It seems probable that most of the possible variations on this single theme have been very extensively explored, and it is unlikely that a major advance in therapy will result from further study of the same chemical class. Unfortunately there is as yet no obvious information on which the invention of an entirely novel class of compounds could be based. We therefore think it important to emphasize, as we have done elsewhere in this review, the value of continued, and extended, studies of the mode of action of anaesthetic, sedative and anticonvulsant drugs. A major advance is more likely to result from work of this kind than from further variation of the familiar structures, or from blind screening of thousands of compounds. The second requirement is for more precise and delicate methods of detecting promising anticonvulsants. We do not think that the amount of work of either type currently in progress is sufficient to allow prediction of early improvement in epilepsy treatment. We hope that chance or genius may prove us wrong, for epilepsy is still an imperfectly treated disease.

## REFERENCES

 1. Esquirol *Des Maladies mentales* 1838, **i,** 281
 2. Lennox *Res. Publ. Ass. nerv. ment. Dis.* 1947, **26,** 11
 3. Walter *The Living Brain:* Duckworth, London, 1953, p. 60
 4. Diepgen *Die Theologie und der ärztliche Stand:* Grunewald, Berlin, 1922
 5. Gibbs and Stamps *Epilepsy Handbook:* Blackwell, Oxford, 1958
 6. Gibbs and Gibbs *Atlas of Encephalography* vol. II *Epilepsy:* Addison-Wesley Press, Cambridge, Mass., 1952
 7. Temkin *The Falling Sickness:* John Hopkins Press, Baltimore, 1945
 8. Locock *Lancet* 1857, **i,** 528
 9. McIlwain *Chemotherapy and the Central Nervous System:* Churchill, London, 1957
10. Hauptmann *Münch. med. Wschr.* 1912, **59,** 1907
11. Putnam and Merritt *Science* 1937, **85,** 525
12. Merritt and Putnam *Arch. Neurol. Psychiat., Chicago* 1938, **39,** 1003
13. Merritt and Putnam *J. Amer. med. Ass.* 1938, **111,** 1068
14. Spielman *J. Amer. chem. Soc.* 1944, **66,** 1244
15. Everett and Richards *J. Pharmacol.* 1944, **81,** 402
16. Perlstein and Andelman *J. Pediat.* 1946, **29,** 20
17. Richards and Perlstein *Arch. Neurol. Psychiat., Chicago* 1946, **55,** 164
18. Bogue and Carrington *Brit. J. Pharmacol.* 1953, **8,** 230
19. Handley and Stewart *Lancet* 1952, **i,** 742
20. Miller and Long *J. Amer. chem. Soc.* 1951, **73,** 4895
21. Chen, Portman, Ensor and Bratton *J. Pharmacol.* 1951, **103,** 54

22. ZIMMERMAN *Arch. Neurol. Psychiat., Chicago* 1951, **66,** 156
23. ZIMMERMAN *Arch. Neurol. Psychiat., Chicago* 1956, **76,** 65
24. ZIMMERMAN and BURGEMEISTER *Neurology* 1958, **8,** 769
25. GORDON *Neurology* 1961, **11,** 266
26. VOSSEN *Dtsch. med. Wschr.* 1958, **83,** 1227
27. DE HAAS, LORENZO and STOEL *Epilepsia* 1960, **1,** 501
28. TOMAN and GOODMAN *Physiol. Rev.* 1948, **28,** 409
29. GOODMAN, TOMAN and SWINYARD *Arch. int. Pharmacodyn.* 1949, **78,** 144
30. WOODBURY and DAVENPORT *Arch. int. Pharmacodyn.* 1952, **92,** 97
31. TOMAN, SWINYARD and GOODMAN *J. Neurophysiol.* 1946, **9,** 231
32. TEDESCHI, SWINYARD and GOODMAN *J. Pharmacol.* 1956, **116,** 107
33. SWINYARD *J. Amer. pharm. Ass., Sci. Ed.* 1949, **38,** 201
34. SWINYARD, BROWN and GOODMAN *J. Pharmacol.* 1952, **106,** 319
35. ENSOR and CHEN *Arch. Neurol. Psychiat., Chicago* 1949, **62,** 857
36. CHEN and ENSOR *Arch. Neurol. Psychiat., Chicago* 1950, **63,** 56
37. CHEN, ENSOR and CLARKE *Arch. Neurol. Psychiat., Chicago* 1951, **66,** 329
38. FINK and SWINYARD *J. Amer. pharm. Ass., Sci. Ed.* 1960, **49,** 510
39. RADOUCO-THOMAS, GOLD and RADOUCO-THOMAS *Arch. Ital. Sci. farmacol.* 1954, **4,** 3
40. TAINTER, TAINTER, LAWRENCE, NEURU, LACKEY, LUDUENA, KIRTLAND and GONZALEZ *J. Pharmacol.* 1943, **79,** 42
41. SERVÍT *Epilepsia* 1959, **1,** 95
42. ESPLIN and WOODBURY *Science* 1961, **133,** 1426
43. ESPLIN *Arch. Neurol.* 1959, **1,** 485
44. ESPLIN and FRESTON *J. Pharmacol.* 1960, **130,** 68
45. JENNEY and PFEIFFER *Ann. N.Y. Acad. Sci.* 1956, **64,** 679
46. MITCHELL and KEASLING *J. Pharmacol* 1960, **128,** 79
47. SWINYARD, TOMAN and GOODMAN *J. Neurophysiol.* 1946, **9,** 47
48. TOMAN *Neurology* 1951, **1,** 444
49. EVERETT and TOMAN *Fed. Proc.* 1951, **10,** 293
50. TOMAN, EVERETT and RICHARDS *Texas Rep. Biol. Med.* 1952, **10,** 96
51. BROWN, SCHIFFMAN, SWINYARD and GOODMAN *J. Pharmacol.* 1953, **107,** 273
52. GREWAL, SWINYARD, JENSEN and GOODMAN *J. Pharmacol.* 1954, **112,** 109
53. GROS *Arch. exp. Path. Pharmak.* 1936, **180,** 258
54. KNOEFEL and LEHMANN *J. Pharmacol.* 1942, **76,** 194
55. GOODMAN and LIH *J. Pharmacol.* 1941, **72,** 18
56. GOODMAN, TOMAN and SWINYARD *Amer. J. Med.* 1946, **1,** 213
57. SOREL *Confin. neurol., Basel* 1957, **17,** 16
58. SOREL *Acta neurol. belg.* 1959, **59,** 825
59. ORLOFF, WILLIAMS and PFEIFFER *Proc. Soc. exp. Biol., N.Y.* 1949, **70,** 254
60. CHEN, BOHNER and ENSOR *Proc. Soc. exp. Biol., N.Y.* 1954, **87,** 334
61. McQUARRIE and FINGL *J. Pharmacol.* 1958, **124,** 264
62. RIDLON and BASTIAN *Fed. Proc.* 1958, **17,** 405
63. SALVA, CLEMENTS and ERCOLI *J. Pharmacol.* 1959, **126,** 318
64. GOODMAN, GREWAL, BROWN and SWINYARD *J. Pharmacol.* 1953, **108,** 168
65. EVERETT and RICHARDS *J. Pharmacol.* 1952, **106,** 303
66. WOODBURY and ESPLIN *Res. Publ. Ass. nerv. ment. Dis.* 1959, **37,** 24
67. BÁRÁNY and STEIN-JENSEN *Acta pharm. tox., Kbh.* 1946, **2,** 264
68. BÁRÁNY and STEIN-JENSEN *Arch. int. Pharmacodyn.* 1946, **73,** 1
69. DELAY and SOULAIRAC *C.R. Soc. Biol., Paris* 1944, **138,** 60
70. BASTIAN, KRAUSE, RIDLON and ERCOLI *J. Pharmacol.* 1959, **127,** 75
71. GRUBER, MOSIER and GIBSON *Arch. int. Pharmacodyn.* 1959, **121,** 443
72. BERGER *J. Pharmacol.* 1954, **112,** 413
73. BERRY, SANNER and KEASLING *J. Pharmacol.* 1961, **133,** 357

74. KENNARD *Neurology* 1957, **7,** 404
75. KOPELOFF, CHUSID and KOPELOFF *Arch. Neurol. Psychiat., Chicago* 1955, **74,** 523
76. POPE, MORRIS, JASPER, ELLIOT and PENFIELD *Res. Publ. Ass. nerv. ment. Dis.* 1947, **26,** 218
77. CURE and RASMUSSEN *Electroenceph. clin. Neurophysiol.* 1950, **2,** 354
78. SLOAN, RANSOHOFF and POOL *Electroenceph. clin. Neurophysiol.* 1953, **5,** 320
79. KOPELOFF *Proc. Soc. exp. Biol., N.Y.* 1960, **104,** 500
80. KOPELOFF, CHUSID and KOPELOFF *Proc. Soc. exp. Biol., N.Y.* 1956, **92,** 132
81. CHUSID and KOPELOFF *Fed. Proc.* 1958, **17,** 26
82. FAETH, WALKER, KAPLAN and WARNER *Proc. Soc. exp. Biol., N.Y.* 1955, **88,** 329
83. MORRELL, BRADLEY and PTASHNE *Neurology* 1959, **9,** 492
84. BEVAN and CHINN *J. comp. physiol. Psychol.* 1957, **50,** 311
85. PLOTNIKOFF and GREEN *J. Pharmacol.* 1957, **119,** 294
86. PLOTNIKOFF *Arch. int. Pharmacodyn.* 1958, **116,** 130
87. TRIPOD, BEIN and MEIER *Arch. int. Pharmacodyn.* 1954, **96,** 406
88. FINK and SWINYARD *J. Pharmacol.* 1959, **127,** 318
89. SUTER, KLINGMAN, LACY, BOGGS, MARKS and COPLINGER *Neurology* 1958, **8,** supp. 1, 117
90. RILEY and SPINKS *J. Pharm., Lond.* 1958, **10,** 657, 721
91. CERCHIA, MANTEGAZZINI and PARMA *Arch. Sci. biol., Bologna* 1957, **41,** 420
92. WALPOLE and SPINKS *Evalution of Drug Toxicity:* Churchill, London, 1958
93. PAGET and SPINKS *Quantitative Methods in Human Pharmacology* (Ed. Laurence): Pergamon Press, London, 1959
94. SPINKS *Proc. R. Soc. Med.* 1961, **54,** 203
95. HEBB *Physiol. Rev.* 1957, **37,** 196
96. FLOREY *Ann. Rev. Physiol.* 1961, **23,** 500
97. TOBIAS, LIPTON and LEPINAT *Proc. Soc. exp. Biol., N.Y.* 1946, **61,** 51
98. ELLIOTT, SWANK and HENDERSON *Amer. J. Physiol.* 1950, **162,** 469
99. ELLIOTT and HENDERSON *Amer. J. Physiol.* 1951, **165,** 365
100. RICHTER and CROSSLAND *Amer. J. Physiol.* 1949, **159,** 247
101. CROSSLAND and MERRICK *J. Physiol.* 1954, **125,** 56
102. STONE *Amer. J. phys. Med.* 1957, **36,** 222
103. BURGESS and MACINTOSH *Neurochemistry: The Chemical Dynamics of Brain and Nerve* (Ed. Elliott, Page and Quastel): Thomas, Springfield, 1955, 311
104. TOWER *Neurochemistry of Epilepsy:* Thomas, Springfield, 1960
105. FREEDMAN, BALES, WILLIS and HIMWICH *Amer. J. Physiol.* 1949, **156,** 117
106. FORSTER and MADOW *Amer. J. Physiol.* 1950, **161,** 430
107. HYDE, BECKETT and GELLHORN *J. Neurophysiol.* 1949, **12,** 17
108. MILLER, STAVRAKY and WOONTON *J. Neurophysiol.* 1940, **3,** 131
109. CHATFIELD and DEMPSEY *Amer. J. Physiol.* 1941, **135,** 633
110. HUGHES and ROBINSON *Yale J. Biol. Med.* 1951, **24,** 35
111. BECKETT and GELLHORN *Amer. J. Physiol.* 1948, **153,** 113
112. DUSSER DE BARENNE and MCCULLOCH *J. Neurophysiol.* 1941, **4,** 311
113. TOWER and ELLIOTT *J. appl. Physiol.* 1952, **4,** 669
114. TOWER and ELLIOTT *J. appl. Physiol.* 1953, **5,** 375
115. GIACHETTI and PIVA *Boll. Soc. ital. Biol. sper.* 1958, **34,** 666
116. PAPPIUS and ELLIOTT *J. appl. Physiol.* 1958, **12,** 319
117. CUSHNY *Handbuch der experimentellen Pharmakologie* Vol. 2, pt. 2 (Ed. Heffter): Springer, Berlin, 1924, p. 653
118. SPIEGEL, SPIEGEL-ADOLPH, WYLIS and MARKS *Res. Publ. Ass. Res. nerv. ment. Dis.* 1947, **26,** 84
119. MERRITT and PUTNAM *Epilepsia* 1945, **3,** 51
120. TRIPOD, STUDER and MEIER *Arch. int. Pharmacodyn.* 1957, **112,** 319
121. BERGER, HENDLEY and LYNES *Proc. Soc. exp. Biol., N.Y.* 1956, **92,** 563

122. SPINKS, YOUNG, FARRINGTON and DUNLOP *Brit. J. Pharmacol.* 1958, **13,** 501
123. STONE, MECKLENBURG and TORCHIANA *Fed. Proc.* 1956, **15,** 1590
124. SILVESTRINI *Arch. int. Pharmacodyn.* 1958, **116,** 71
125. BOGDANSKI, WEISSBACH and UDENFRIEND *J. Neurochem.* 1957, **1,** 272
126. PAASONEN and VOGT *J. Physiol.* 1956, **131,** 617
127. PAASONEN, MACLEAN and GIARMAN *J. Neurochem.* 1957, **1,** 326
128. BONNYCASTLE, GIARMAN and PAASONEN *Brit. J. Pharmacol.* 1957, **12,** 228
129. PERLSTEIN *J. Amer. med. Ass.* 1956, **161,** 1040
130. ANDERSON and BONNYCASTLE *J. Pharmacol.* 1960, **130,** 138
131. PROCKOP, SHORE and BRODIE *Ann. N.Y. Acad. Sci.* 1959, **80,** 643
132. ZELLER, BARSKY, DRAGSTEDT, WELLS and ZELLER *Experientia* 1952, **8,** 349
133. BRODIE, SPECTOR and SHORE *Ann. N.Y. Acad. Sci.* 1959, **80,** 609
134. CARLSSON, LINDQVIST and MAGNUSSON *Andrenergic Mechanisms* (Ed. Vane, Wolstenholme and O'Connor): Churchill, London, 1960
135. BRODIE, PLETSCHER and SHORE *J. Pharmacol.* 1956, **116,** 9
136. WEIL-MALHERBE and BONE *J. Neurochem.* 1959, **4,** 251
137. CHEN, ENSOR and BOHNER *Proc. Soc. exp. Biol., N.Y.* 1954, **86,** 507
138. CHEN and BOHNER *J. Pharmacol.* 1956, **117,** 142
139. BIANCHI *Brit. J. Pharmacol.* 1956, **11,** 141
140. CHOW and HENDLEY *Fed. Proc.* 1959, **18,** 376
141. YEN, SILVERMAN and SALVATONE *Fed. Proc.* 1960, **19,** 278
142. KOBINGER *Arch. exp. Path. Pharmak.* 1958, **233,** 559
143. LESSIN and PARKES *Brit. J. Pharmacol.* 1959, **14,** 108
144. LABORIT, BROUSSOLLE and PERRIMOND-TROUCHET *C.R. Soc. Biol., Paris* 1957, **151,** 930
145. PERLSTEIN *Ann. N.Y. Acad. Sci.* 1959, **80,** 551
146. VOGT *J. Physiol.* 1954, **123,** 451
147. SANO, GAMO, KAKIMOTO, TANIGUCHI, TAKESADA and NISHINUMA *Biochim. biophys. Acta* 1959, **32,** 586
148. GELLHORN, DARROW and YESINICK *Arch. Neurol. Psychiat., Chicago* 1939, **42,** 826
149. GELLHORN *Physiological Foundations of Neurology and Psychiatry* Univ. of Minnesota Press, Minneapolis, 1956
150. ALEXANDER and WEAVER *Arch. int. Pharmacodyn.* 1954, **100,** 472
151. LIVINGSTONE, KAJDI and BRIDGE *J. Pediat.* 1948, **32,** 490
152. GELLHORN and BALLIN *Arch. Neurol. Psychiat., Chicago* 1948, **59,** 718
153. McGEER, McGEER and McLENNAN *J. Neurochem.* 1961, **8,** 36
154. BERTLER and ROSENGREN *Acta physiol. scand.* 1958, **47,** 350
155. CARLSSON, LINDQVIST, MAGNUSSON and WALDECK *Science* 1958, **127,** 471
156. FLOREY *Naturwissenschaften* 1953, **40,** 413
157. BAZEMORE, ELLIOTT and FLOREY *Nature, Lond.* 1956, **178,** 1052
158. BAZEMORE, ELLIOTT and FLOREY *J. Neurochem.* 1957, **1,** 334
159. LEVIN, LOVELL and ELLIOTT *J. Neurochem.* 1961, **7,** 147
160. ROBERTS and FRANKEL *Cancer Res.* 1949, **9,** 645
161. ROBERTS, FUKUHARA and VISSER *Fed. Proc.* 1950, **9,** 219
162. ROBERTS and FRANKEL *J. biol. Chem.* 1950, **187,** 55
163. ROBERTS and FRANKEL *J. biol. Chem.* 1951, **188,** 789
164. ELLIOTT and FLOREY *J. Neurochem.* 1956, **1,** 181
165. ELLIOTT and JASPER *Physiol. Rev.* 1959, **39,** 383
166. ROBERTS *Neurochemistry* (Ed. Korey and Nurnberger): Cassell, London, 1956
167. ROBERTS and BREGOFF *J. biol. Chem.* 1953, **201,** 393
168. ROBERTS *Arch. Biochem. Biophys.* 1954, **48,** 395
169. BESSMAN, ROSSEN and LAYNE *J. biol. Chem.* 1953, **201,** 385
169a. McKHANN and TOWER *J. Neurochem.* 1961, **7,** 26
170. PURPURA, GIRADO and GRUNDFEST *Science* 1957, **125,** 1200

171. IWAMA and JASPER *J. Physiol.* 1957, **138,** 365
172. GOLDRING, O'LEARY and HUANG *Electroenceph. clin. Neurophysiol.* 1958, **10,** 663
173. RECH and DOMINO *J. Pharmacol.* 1960, **130,** 59
174. PURPURA, GIRADO, SMITH and GOMEZ *Proc. Soc. exp. Biol., N.Y.* 1958, **97,** 348
175. MARRAZZI, HART and RODRIGUEZ *Science* 1958, **127,** 284
176. BERL, TAKAGAKI and PURPURA *J. Neurochem.* 1961, **7,** 198
177. CURTIS and WATKINS *Inhibition in the Nervous System and γ-Aminobutyric Acid* (Ed. Roberts): Pergamon Press, London, 1960, p. 424
178. CURTIS, PHILLIPS and WATKINS *J. Physiol.* 1959, **146,** 185
179. KUFFLER and EDWARDS *J. Neurophysiol.* 1958, **21,** 589
180. PURPURA and others *Inhibition in the Nervous System and γ-Aminobutyric Acid* (Ed. Roberts): Pergamon Press, London, 1960, p. 495
181. JASPER, GONZALES and ELLIOTT *Fed. Proc.* 1958, **17,** 79
182. CHICK, EL SADR and WORDEN *Biochem. J.* 1940, **34,** 595
183. PATTON, KARN and LONGENECKER *J. biol. Chem.* 1944, **152,** 181
184. DIEKE *Proc. Soc. exp. Biol., N.Y.* 1949, **70,** 688
185. PARKS, KIDDER and DEWEY *Proc. Soc. exp. Biol., N.Y.* 1952, **79,** 287
186. PRESTON *J. Pharmacol.* 1955, **115,** 39
187. KILLAM and BAIN *J. Pharmacol.* 1957, **119,** 255
188. KILLAM *J. Pharmacol.* 1957, **119,** 263
189. KILLAM and KILLAM *J. Pharmacol.* 1958, **122,** 16A
190. KILLAM and KILLAM *J. Pharmacol.* 1958, **122,** 37A
191. KILLAM, DASGUPTA and KILLAM *Inhibition in the Nervous System and γ-Aminobutryric Acid* (Ed. Roberts): Pergamon Press, London, 1960, p. 302
192. ROBERTS, ROTHSTEIN and BAXTER *Proc. Soc. exp. Biol., N.Y.* 1958, **97,** 796
193. FLOREY *Naturwissenschaften* 1957, **44,** 424
194. KOPELOFF, CHUSID and KOPELOFF *J. appl. Physiol.* 1957, **11,** 465
195. PFEIFFER *Inhibition in the Nervous System and γ-Aminobutyric Acid* (Ed. Roberts) Pergamon Press, London, 1960, p. 324
196. GAMMON, GUMMIT, KAMRIN and KAMRIN *Inhibition in the Nervous System and γ-Aminobutyric Acid* (Ed. Roberts): Pergamon Press, London, 1960, p. 328
197. PURPURA, GIRADO, SMITH and GÓMEZ *Electroenceph. clin. Neurophysiol.* 1958, **10,** 677
198. BERL, PURPURA, GIRADO and WAELSCH *J. Neurochem.* 1959, **4,** 311
199. BAXTER and ROBERTS *Fed. Proc.* 1960, **19,** 1
200. BAXTER and ROBERTS *Proc. Soc. exp. Biol., N.Y.* 1959, **101,** 811
201. EIDELBERG, BAXTER, ROBERTS, SALDIAS and FRENCH *Proc. Soc. exp. Biol., N.Y.* 1959, **101,** 815
202. BAXTER and ROBERTS *Proc. Soc. exp. Biol., N.Y.* 1960, **104,** 426
203. TOWER *Inhibition in the Nervous System and γ-Aminobutyric Acid* (Ed. Roberts): Pergamon Press, London, 1960, p. 562
204. HAWKINS and SARETT *Clin. chim. Acta* 1957, **2,** 481
205. MARRAZZI *Inhibition in the Nervous System and γ- Aminobutyric Acid* (Ed. Roberts): Pergamon Press, London, 1960, p. 531
206. VERNADAKIS and WOODBURY *Inhibition in the Nervous System and y-Aminobutyric Acid* (Ed. Roberts): Pergamon Press, London, 1960, p. 242
207. ELLIOTT and VAN GELDER *J. Physiol.* 1960, **153,** 423
208. HAYASHI and NAGAI *Abstr. XX. Internat. physiol. Congr.* 1956, 410
209. HAYASHI *Nature, Lond.* 1958, **182,** 1076
210. HAYASHI *Biochem. Pharmacol.* 1961, **8,** 24
211. LEVIN, LOVELL and FLOREY *J. Neurochem.* 1961, **7,** 147
212. OHARA, SANO, KOIZUMI and NISHINUMA *Science* 1959, **129,** 1225
213. McLENNAN *J. Physiol.* 1959, **146,** 358
214. EDWARDS and KUFFLER *J. Neurochem.* 1959, **4,** 19

215. KURIAKI, YAKUSHIJI, NORO, SHIMIZU and SAJI *Nature, Lond.* 1958, **181,** 1336
216. KEWITZ *Arch. exp. Path. Pharmak.* 1959, **237,** 308
217. HUNTER and LOWRY *Pharmacol. Rev.* 1956, **8,** 89
218. MCILWAIN *Biochemistry and the Central Nervous System:* Churchill, London, 1955
219. BRODY *Pharmacol. Rev.* 1955, **7,** 335
220. QUASTEL and WHEATLEY *Proc. roy. Soc. B.* 1932, **112,** 60
221. DAVIES and REDMOND *Res. Publ. Ass. Res. nerv. ment. Dis.* 1947, **26,** 205
222. GELLHORN and HEYMANS *J. Neurophysiol.* 1948, **11,** 261
223. LOOMIS and LIPMANN *J. biol. Chem.* 1948, **173,** 807
224. BRODY and BAIN *J. Pharmacol.* 1954, **110,** 148
225. HULME and KRANTZ *Fed. Proc.* 1954, **13,** 368
226. CROSS, TAGGART, COVO and GREEN *J. biol. Chem.* 1949, **177,** 655
227. LOOMIS *Science* 1950, **111,** 474
228. BRODY *J. Pharmacol.* 1955, **113,** 8
229. ABOOD *Proc. Soc. exp. Biol., N.Y.* 1955, **88,** 688
230. DAWKINS, JUDAH and REES *Biochem. J.* 1959, **72,** 204
231. LÖW *Biochim. biophys. Acta* 1959, **32,** 11
232. COHEN and HEALD *J. Pharmacol.* 1960, **129,** 361
233. GRENELL *Tranquilizing Drugs* (Ed. Himwich) Amer. Assoc. for the Advancement of Science, Washington, 1957, p. 61
234. FORDA and MCILWAIN *Brit. J. Pharmacol.* 1953, **8,** 225
235. GREENGARD and MCILWAIN *Biochem. J.* 1955, **61,** 61
236. ROUGHTON *J. Physiol.* 1948, **107,** 12P
237. HELLER and GINSBURG *Progress in Medicinal Chemistry*, Vol. I. (Ed. Ellis and West): Butterworths, London, 1961, 132
238. DAVIES and ROUGHTON *Biochem. J.* 1948, **42,** 618
239. MANN and KEILIN *Nature, Lond.* 1940, **146,** 164
240. MAREN, MAYER and WADSWORTH *Johns Hopk. Hosp. Bull.* 1954, **95,** 199
241. MAREN, WADSWORTH, YALE and ALONSO, *Johns Hopk. Hosp. Bull.* 1954, **95** 277
242. KEITH *Amer. J. Dis. Child.* 1947, **74,** 140
243. BERGSTROM, CARZOLI, LOMBROSO, DAVIDSON and WALLACE *Amer. J. Dis. Child.* 1952, **84,** 771
244. LOMBROSO, DAVIDSON and GROSSI-BIANCHI *Epilepsia* 1954, **3,** 123
245. MERLIS *Neurology* 1955, **4,** 863
246. MITCHELL and OGDEN *Amer. J. Physiol.* 1954, **179,** 225
247. YEOMAN *Brit. med. J.* 1938, **ii,** 261
248. HENDLEY, DAVENPORT and TOMAN *Amer. J. Physiol.* 1948, **153,** 580
249. GRAY, MAREN, SISSON and SMITH *J. Pharmacol.* 1957, **121,** 160
250. GINSBURG *Proc. Ass. Res. nerv. Dis.* 1954, **33,** 39
251. WOODBURY and ROLLINS *Fed. Proc.* 1954, **13,** 418
252. MILLICHAP, THATCHER and WILLIAMS *Fed. Proc.* 1955, **14,** 370
253. MILLICHAP, WOODBURY and GOODMAN *J. Pharmacol.* 1955, **115,** 251
254. GRAY, RAUH and SHANAHAN *Biochem. Pharmacol.* 1961, **8,** 307
255. KOCH and WOODBURY *J. Pharmacol.* 1958, **122,** 335
256. ROUGHTON and BOOTH *Biochem. J.* 1946, **40,** 319
257. SOLOMON and HIRANO *Neurology* 1959, **9,** 167
258. MERLIS *Neurology* 1960, **10,** 210
259. DAVID and FELLOWES *J. Pharm., Lond.* 1960, **12,** 65
260. MANCINI and UGHI *Rass. Clin. Terap.* 1959, **58,** 29
261. LIGOU and NAHAS *J. Physiol. Path. gén.* 1959, **51,** 749
262. BEYER *Ann. N.Y. Acad. Sci.* 1958, **71,** 363
263. KOBINGER and KATIC *Arch. exp. Path. Pharmak.* 1960, **238,** 435
264. KELLER *Hoppe-Seyl. Z.* 1957, **309,** 7
265. KOCH and WOODBURY *Amer. J. Physiol.* 1960, **198,** 434

266. WOODBURY, ROLLINS, HENRIE, JONES and SATO *Amer. J. Physiol.* 1956, **184,** 202
267. EVERETT, GOODSELL and TOMAN *Fed. Proc.* 1952, **11,** 343
268. STEIN and POLLOCK *Proc. Soc. exp. Biol., N.Y.* 1949, **70,** 290
269. VARIOUS AUTHORS *Epilepsia* 1961, **2,** 13–91
270. MARSAN *Epilepsia* 1961, **2,** 22
271. JASPER *Epilepsia* 1961, **2,** 91
272. LI *J. Neurophysiol.* 1959, **22,** 436
273. ARVANITAKI *J. Physiol. Path. gén.* 1940, **37,** 895
274. COLE *Arch. Sci. Physiol.* 1949, **3,** 253
275. EIDELBERG and FRENCH *Epilepsia* 1961, **2,** 39
276. GLOOR, VERA, SPERTI and RAY *Epilepsia* 1961, **2,** 42
277. WARD *Epilepsia* 1961, **2,** 70
278. MORRELL *Epilepsia* 1961, **2,** 81
279. SCHMIDT *Epilepsia* 1961, **2,** 89
280. GANGLOFF and MONNIER *Electroenceph. clin. Neurophysiol.* 1957, **9,** 43
281. DELGADO and HAMLIN *Electroenceph. clin. Neurophysiol.* 1958, **10,** 463
282. POGGIO, WALKER and ANDY *Arch. Neurol. Psychiat., Chicago* 1956, **75,** 350
283. STROBOS and SPUDIS *Arch. Neurol.* 1960, **2,** 399
284. CHATRIAN and PETERSEN *Electroenceph. clin. Neurophysiol.* 1960, **12,** 715
285. GERARD *Res. Publ. Ass. Res. nerv. ment. Dis.* 1959, **37,** 67
286. LI, CHOU and HOWARD *Epilepsia* 1961, **2,** 13
287. TOMAN *Electroenceph. clin. Neurophysiol.* 1949, **1,** 33
288. MORRELL, BRADLEY and PTASHNE *Neurology* 1958, **8,** 140
289. WARD *Epilepsia* 1960, **1,** 600
290. SCHMIDT, THOMAS and WARD *J. Neurophysiol.* 1959, **22,** 285
291. PENFIELD and JASPER *Res. Publ. Ass. nerv. ment. Dis.* 1947, **26,** 252
292. MORUZZI and MAGOUN *Electroenceph. clin. Neurophysiol.* 1949, **1,** 455
293. FRENCH *Reticular Formation of the Brain* (Ed. Jasper): Little, Brown, Boston, 1958, p. 491
294. AIRD and GAROUTTE *Epilepsia* 1960, **1,** 337
295. VAN WAGENEN and HERREN *Arch. Neurol. Psychiat., Chicago* 1940, **44,** 740
296. AIRD and GAROUTTE *Neurology* 1958, **8,** 581
297. JASPER and DROOGLEEVER-FORTWYN *Res. Publ. Ass. Res. nerv. ment. Dis.* 1947, **26,** 272
298. HURSH *Arch. Neurol. Psychiat., Chicago* 1945, **53,** 274
299. INGVAR *Acta physiol. scand.* 1955, **33,** 137
300. HAYNE, BELINSON and GIBBS *Electroenceph. clin. Neurophysiol.* 1949, **1,** 437
301. MERLIS and MISRAHY *Epilepsia* 1960, **1,** 527
302. PRUS *Wien. klin. Wschr.* 1898, **11,** 857
303. ADRIAN and MORUZZI *J. Physiol.* 1939, **97,** 153
304. HOEFER and POOL *Arch. Neurol. Psychiat., Chicago* 1942, **50,** 381
305. LOMBROSO and MERLIS *Proc. Soc. exp. Biol., N.Y.* 1953, **82,** 591
306. KAJTOR *Electroenceph. clin. Neurophysiol.* 1961, **13,** 400
307. GELLHORN, BALLIN and KAWAKAMI *Epilepsia* 1960, **1,** 233
308. ESPLIN and LAFFAN *Arch. int. Pharmacodyn.* 1957, **113,** 189
309. STILLE *Arch. exp. Path. Pharmak.* 1960, **238,** 138
310. STILLE *Arch. exp. Path. Pharmak.* 1955, **226,** 172
311. ESPLIN *J. Pharmacol.* 1957, **120,** 301
312. ECCLES and RALL *J. Neurophysiol.* 1951, **14,** 353
313. LLOYD *J. gen. Physiol.* 1949, **33,** 147
314. ECCLES and MALCOLM *J. Neurophysiol.* 1946, **9,** 139
315. KOKETSU *Amer. J. Physiol.* 1956, **184,** 338
316. BROWN and HOLMES *Proc. roy. Soc. B* 1956, **145,** 1

317. Esplin and Curto *J. Pharmacol.* 1957, **121,** 457
318. Delgado and Mihailović *Ann. N.Y. Acad. Sci.* 1957, **64,** 644
319. Vistola and Rosen *Electroenceph. clin. Neurophysiol.* 1960, **12,** 327
320. Korey *Proc. Soc. exp. Biol., N.Y.* 1951, **76,** 297
321. Iannone, Baker and Morrell *Neurology* 1958, **8,** 126
322. Rouques *Pr. méd.* 1951, **59,** 523
323. Albrecht and Krump *Münch. med. Wschr.* 1954, **96,** 985, 1037
324. Dorsey, Hayslip and Anderson *Clin. Med.* 1959, **6,** 1395
325. Braham and Saia *Lancet* 1960, **ii,** 892
326. Albrecht *Medizinische* 1956, 988
327. Green *Neurology* 1961, **11,** 257
328. Swinyard, Smith and Goodman *J. Amer. pharm. Ass., Sci. Ed.* 1954, **43,** 212
329. Kugelberg and Lindblom *J. Neurol. Psychiat.* 1959, **22,** 36
330. Harris and Kokernot *Amer. J. Physiol.* 1950, **163,** 505
331. Mosey and Tyler *Circulation* 1954, **10,** 65
332. Covino, Wright, and Charleson *Amer. J. Physiol.* 1955, **181,** 54
333. White, Megirian and Swiss *Circulat. Res.* 1955, **3,** 290
334. Scherf, Blumenfeld, Taner and Yildiz *Amer. Heart J.* 1960, **60,** 936
335. Steriade and Stoica *Epilepsia* 1960, **1,** 264, 275
336. Swinyard *Amer. J. Physiol.* 1949, **156,** 163
337. Woodbury, *Recent Progr. Hormone Res.* 1954, **10,** 65
338. Woodbury *J. Pharmacol.* 1955, **115,** 74
339. Logothetis, Harner, Morrell and Torres *Neurology* 1959, **9,** 352
340. Costa and Bonnycastle *Arch. int. Pharmacodyn.* 1952, **91,** 330
341. Woodbury *J. Pharmacol.* 1952, **105,** 27
342. Woodbury *Pharmacol. Rev.* 1958, **10,** 275
343. Woodbury and Sayers *Proc. Soc. exp. Biol., N.Y.* 1950, **75,** 398
344. McQuarrie *Amer. J. Dis. Child.* 1946, **72,** 472
345. Aird and Gordan *J. Amer. med. Ass.* 1951, **145,** 715
346. Gordan *Recent Progr. Hormone Res.* 1954, **10,** 104
347. Bray, Kelley, Zapata and Ely *Neurology* 1961, **11,** 246
348. Maynert and van Dyke *Pharmacol. Rev.* 1949, **1,** 217
349. Raventós *J. Pharm., Lond.* 1954, **6,** 217
350. Butler *J. Amer. pharm. Ass., Sci. Ed.* 1955, **44,** 367
351. Butler and Waddell *Neurology* 1958, **8,** suppl. 1, 106
352. Goldbaum *J. Pharmacol.* 1948, **94,** 68
353. Plaa and Hine *J. Lab. clin. Med.* 1956, **47,** 649
354. Svensmark, Schiller and Buchthal *Acta pharm. tox. Kbh.* 1960, **16,** 331
355. Butler, Mahaffee and Waddell *J. Pharmacol.* 1954, **111,** 425
356. Wright and Johns *J. clin. Path.* 1953, **6,** 78
357. Butler *J. Pharmacol.* 1952, **106,** 235
358. Waddell and Butler *J. clin. Invest.* 1957, **36,** 1217
359. Lous *Acta pharm. tox., Kbh.* 1954, **10,** 147
360. Butler *J. Pharmacol.* 1956, **116,** 326
361. Algeri and McBay *Science* 1956, **123,** 183
362. Glasson, Lerch and Viret *Helv. physiol. acta* 1959, **17,** 146
363. Thompson *Lancet* 1950, **i,** 70
364. Koppanyi, Dille and Krop *J. Pharmacol.* 1934, **52,** 121
365. Domek, Barlow and Roth *J. Pharmacol.* 1960, **130,** 285
366. Lous *Acta pharm. tox., Kbh.* 1954, **10,** 261
367. Lous *Acta pharm. tox., Kbh.* 1954, **10,** 166
368. Goldbaum and Smith *J. Pharmacol.* 1954, **111,** 197
369. Brodwall and Stöa *Acta med. scand.* 1956, **154,** 139
370. Wright *Quart. J. Med.* 1955, **24,** 95

371. MOLLARET, MONSALLIER, RAPIN and POCIDALO *C.R. Soc. Biol., Paris* 1958, **152,** 947
372. MOLLARET, RAPIN, POCIDALO and MONSALLIER *C.R. Soc. Biol., Paris* 1958, **152,** 1089
373. DORFMAN and GOLDBAUM *J. Pharmacol.* 1947, **90,** 330
374. PLAA and HINE *Arch. int. Pharmacodyn.* 1960, **128,** 375
375. BUCHTHAL and SVENSMARK *Epilepsia* 1960, **1,** 373
376. LOCKET *Proc. R. Soc. Med.* 1956, **49,** 585
377. FABRE, REGNIER and GRASSET *Ann. pharm. franç.* 1951, **9,** 98
378. LOUS *Ugeskr. Læg.* 1952, **114,** 610
379. CONNEY, DAVISON, GASTEL and BURNS *J. Pharmacol.* 1960, **130,** 1
380. REMMER *Naturwissenschaften* 1958, **45,** 189
381. KRAMER and ARRIGONI-MARTELLI *Arch. exp. Path. Pharmak.* 1959, **237,** 264
382. BUTLER *Science* 1954, **120,** 494
383. CURRY *J. Pharm., Lond.* 1955, **7,** 1072
384. ALIPRANDI and MASIRONI *Ric. Sci.* 1958, **28,** 1611
385. WALKER and WYNN PARRY *Brit. J. Pharmacol.* 1949, **4,** 93
386. CRAIG, HIRANO and SIDEMAN *Fed. Proc.* 1960, **19,** 280
387. BUTLER, MAHAFFEE and MAHAFFEE *J. Pharmacol.* 1952, **106,** 364
388. BUTLER and BUSH *J. Pharmacol.* 1939, **65,** 205
389. FORSTER *Postgrad. Med.* 1960, **27,** 711
390. BUTLER *J. Pharmacol.* 1953, **108,** 474
391. BUSH and BUTLER *J. Pharmacol.* 1940, **68,** 278
392. THORP *3ème Congrès int. Biochim.* Brussels, 1955, communication 15–10, p. 132
393. BOGUE, CARRINGTON and BENTLEY *Acta neurol., belg.* 1956, **56,** 640
394. SWINYARD, TEDESCHI and GOODMAN *J. Amer. pharm. Ass., Sci. Ed.* 1954, **43,** 114
395. BUTLER and WADDELL *Proc. Soc. exp. Biol., N.Y.* 1956, **93,** 544
396. PLAA, FUJIMOTO and HINE *J. Amer. med. Ass.* 1958, **168,** 1769
397. GRUBER, MOSIER and GRANT *J. Pharmacol.* 1957, **120,** 184
398. GRUBER, BROCK and DYKEN *Clin. Pharmacol. Ther.* 1962, **3,** 23
399. GOODMAN, SWINYARD, BROWN, SCHIFFMAN, GREWAL and BLISS *J. Pharmacol.* 1953, **108,** 428
400. SCARINCI *Studi Urbinati.* 1954, **28,** 84
401. SCARINCI *Arch. Sci. biol., Bologna* 1960, **44,** 512
402. FREY and HAHN *Arch. int. Pharmacodyn.* 1960, **128,** 281
403. WILLIAMS *Proc. R. Soc. Med.* 1956, **49,** 589
404. RETTIG *J. nerv. ment. Dis.* 1956, **124,** 607
405. BURTON-BRADLEY *Med. J. Aust.* 1953, **40,** 705
406. SMARTT *E. Afr. med. J.* 1959, **36,** 91
407. KÄFER and POCH *Prensa méd argent.* 1954, **41,** 2786
408. DAVIS *Indian J. Neurol.* 1953, **4,** 179
409. NATHAN *Lancet* 1954, **i,** 21
410. BUTLER *Lancet* 1953, **i,** 1024
411. CAVAZZUTI and LANZONI *Lattante* 1958, **29,** 592
412. DILL, KAZENKO, WOLF and GLAZKO *J. Pharmacol.* 1956, **118,** 270
413. KOZELKA and HINE *J. Pharmacol.* 1941, **72,** 276
414. NOACH, WOODBURY and GOODMAN *J. Pharmacol.* 1958, **122,** 301
415. PLAA, HINE and NELSON *Fed. Proc.* 1956, **15,** 467
416. KOZELKA and HINE *J. Pharmacol.* 1940, **69,** 292
417. BUCHTHAL, SVENSMARK and SCHILLER *Arch. Neurol.* 1960, **2,** 624
418. KOZELKA and HINE *J. Pharmacol.* 1943, **77,** 175
419. BUTLER *J. Pharmacol.* 1957, **119,** 1
420. MAYNERT *J. Pharmacol.* 1960, **130,** 275
421. BUTLER *J. Pharmacol.* 1953, **109,** 340

422. VIGNE C.R. Soc. Biol., Paris 1957, **151,** 1225
423. VIGNE, FONDARAI and CHOUTEAU C.R. Soc. Biol., Paris 1958, **152,** 806
424. BUTLER J. Pharmacol. 1952, **104,** 299
425. VIGNE and FONDARAI Chem. Abstr. 1959, **53,** 20360
426. HINE and KOZELKA J. Pharmacol. 1943, **77,** 180
427. BUTLER and WADDELL J. Pharmacol. 1954, **110,** 120
428. BUTLER J. Pharmacol. 1956, **117,** 160
429. BUTLER and WADDELL J. Pharmacol. 1954, **110,** 241
430. TAYLOR and BERTCHER J. Pharmacol. 1952, **106,** 277
431. BUTLER J. Pharmacol. 1953, **108,** 11
432. WADDELL and BUTLER Proc. Soc. exp. Biol., N.Y. 1957, **96,** 563
433. BUTLER, MAHAFFEE and MAHAFFEE Proc. Soc. exp. Biol., N.Y. 1952, **81,** 450
434. BUTLER J. Pharmacol. 1955, **113,** 178
435. BUTLER and WADDELL Arch. int. Pharmacodyn. 1957, **111,** 308
436. BUTLER and WADDELL J. Pharmacol. 1955, **113,** 238
437. CHAMBERLAIN, BUTLER and WADDELL J. Dis. Child. 1959, **98,** 570
438. SWINYARD, MADSEN and GOODMAN J. Pharmacol. 1954, **111,** 54
439. THORP, HURST and MARTIN J. med. pharm. chem. 1960, **2,** 15
440. GLAZKO, DILL, WOLF and MILLER J. Pharmacol. 1954, **111,** 413
441. MAREN, ASH and BAILEY Johns Hopk. Hosp. Bull. 1954, **95,** 244
442. GREEN, SAWYER and LEOPOLD Arch. Ophthal. 1955, **53,** 478
443. ROTH, SCHOOLAR and BARLOW J. Pharmacol. 1959, **125,** 128
444. CLOSE and SPIELMAN, in HARTUNG Medicinal Chemistry, Vol. V: John Wiley, New York, 1961
445. WILLIAMS Brit. med. J. 1958, **ii,** 1155
446. SIMPSON Canad. med. Ass. J. 1960, **83,** 257
447. PERLSTEIN Pediatrics, Springfield 1950, **5,** 448
448. MILLICHAP Brit. med. J. 1960, **i,** 1111
449. MILLICHAP, HERNANDEZ, ZALES, HALPERN and KRAMER Neurology 1960, **10,** 575
450. U.S. Patent 2,899,435; Chem. Abstr. 1959, **53,** 18074
451. U.S. Patent 2,868,790; Chem. Abstr. 1959, **53,** 13184
452. MELIN Epilepsia 1960, **1,** 521
453. DORAN, in BLICKE and COX Medicinal Chemistry, Vol. IV: John Wiley, New York, 1959
454. FISCHER and DILTHEY Liebigs Ann. 1904, **335,** 334
455. WALKER, LEVINE, KIBLER and HAUSER J. Amer. chem. Soc. 1946, **68,** 672
456. WALLINGFORD, HOMEYER and JONES J. Amer. chem. Soc. 1941, **63,** 2056
457. PEEL Chem. and Ind. 1960, 1112
458. SPURLOCK J. Amer. chem. Soc. 1953, **75,** 1115
459. U.S. Patent 2,591,103; Chem. Abstr. 1952, **46,** 11246
459a. PRYLES, BURNETT and LIVINGSTON J. Amer. med. Ass. 1952, **148,** 536
460. PETERMAN Pediatrics 1954, **14,** 364
461. U.S. Patent 2,793,157; Chem. Abstr. 1957, **51,** 12441
462. LIVINGSTON J. Pediat. 1956, **49,** 728
463. SCHWADE, RICHARDS and EVERETT Dis. nerv. Syst. 1956, **17,** 155
464. MANN Bull. Los Angeles neurol. Soc. 1958, **23,** 130
465. ZIMMERMAN and BURGEMEISTER N.Y. St. J. Med. 1958, **58,** 2054
466. LANE Ther. Umsch. 1955. **10,** 177
467. KUNZ Arch. Pharm., Berl. 1954, **287,** 412
468. ROBINSON Brit. med. J. 1956, **i,** 28
469. NITZ, PERSCH and SCHMIDT Arzneimitt. Forsch. 1955, **5,** 357
470. British Patent 774,394; Chem. Abstr. 1957, **51,** 15591
471. HÄFNER Arzliche Praxis 1954, **6,** No. 30, 7
472. U.S. Patent 2,716,648; Chem. Abstr. 1956, **50,** 7145

473. Faust, Jules, Yee and Sahyun *J. Amer. pharm. Ass., Sci. Ed.* 1957, **46,** 118
474. Seeberg, Hidalgo and Wilken *Fed. Proc.* 1955, **14,** 352, 386
475. Putnam and Jacobs *Neurology* 1957, **7,** 784
476. Frank and Morrell *Neurology* 1958, **8,** 529
477. Lustig and Persch *Arzneimitt. Forsch.* 1954, **4,** 733
478. Butler and Waddell *J. Pharmacol.* 1959, **127,** 171
479. Wolf, Swinyard and Goodman *J. pharm. Sci.* 1962, **51,** 74
480. Kramer, Ybanez, Pauli and Livingston *J. Dis. Child.* 1960, **100,** 605
481. Livingston, Pauli, Kramer and Najmabadi *New Engl. J. Med.* 1961, **265,** 418
482. Goodman, Swinyard, Brown and Schiffman *J. Pharmacol.* 1954, **110,** 403
483. Boudin, Barbizet and Labram *Thérapie* 1959, **14,** 994
484. Millichap, Goodman and Madsen *Neurology* 1955, **5,** 700
485. Kilpatrick, Elmore and Wood *Brit. J. Pharmacol.* 1958, **13,** 350
486. Gesler, Lints and Swinyard *Toxicol. Appl. Pharmacol.* 1961, **3,** 107
487. Gesler, Iwamoto, Parker and Berger *Fed. Proc.* 1959, **18,** 393
488. Davis and Schwade *Fed. Proc.* 1959, **18,** 380
489. Hazard, Cheymol and Smarzewska *C.R. Acad. Sci., Paris* 1948, **227,** 736
490. Hazard and Cheymol *J. Pharm., Lond.* 1950, **2,** 1
491. Helwig *Moderne Arzneimittel:* Wissenschaftliche Verlagsgesellschaft M.B.H., Stuttgart, 1961
492. Uehleke *Nervenarzt* 1959, **30,** 177
493. Boyd *Biochem. J.* 1933, **27,** 1838
494. Bucherer and Lieb *J. prakt. Chem.* 1934, **141,** 5
495. Henze and Speer *J. Amer. chem. Soc.* 1942, **64,** 522
496. Ware *Chem. Rev.* 1950, **46,** 403
497. *U.S. Patent* 2,559,011; *Chem. Abstr.* 1952, **46,** 3086
498. *U.S. Patent* 2,372,861; *Chem. Abstr.* 1945, **39,** 4195
499. Goodman and Gilman *Pharmacological Basis of Therapeutics* 2nd Ed: Macmillan, New York, 1955, pp. 190–195
500. Stoughton *J. Amer. chem. Soc.* 1941, **63,** 2376
501. Wallingford, Thorpe and Stoughton *J. Amer. chem. Soc.* 1945, **67,** 522
502. Clark-Lewis *Chem. Rev.* 1958, **58,** 63
503. Millichap *Lancet* 1952, **ii,** 907
504. Livingston and Pauli *Pediatrics* 1957, **19,** 614
505. Prichard, Murphy and Escardo *Canad. med. Ass. J.* 1957, **76,** 770
506. Scholl, Abbott and Schwab *Epilepsia* 1959, **1,** 105
507. Rabe *Nervenarzt* 1960, **31,** 306
508. Heathfield and Jewesbury *Brit. med. J.* 1961, **ii,** 565
509. Trolle and Kiørboe *Epilepsia* 1960, **1,** 587
510. Zimmerman and Burgemeister *J. Amer. med. Ass.* 1955, **157,** 1194
511. Miller, Scholl and Long *J. Amer. chem. Soc.* 1951, **73,** 5608
512. Smith and Horwitz *J. Amer. chem. Soc.* 1949, **71,** 3418
513. Briggs and Tucker *Lancet* 1954, **i,** 19
514. Newman and Sumner *Blood* 1957, **12,** 183
515. Christenson, Ultmann and Roseman *J. Amer. med. Ass.* 1957, **163,** 940
516. Zbinden *Schweiz. med. Wschr.* 1959, **89,** 1072
517. Benians and Hunter *J. ment. Sci.* 1957, **103,** 606
518. Stokes and Fortune *Aust. Ann. Med.* 1958, **7,** 118
519. Boon, Carrington, Greenhalgh and Vasey *J. chem. Soc.* 1954, 3263
520. *British Patent* 734,511; *Chem. Abstr.* 1956, **50,** 7881
521. *British Patent* 734,512; *Chem. Abstr.* 1956, **50,** 7881
522. *British Patent* 710,266; *Chem. Abstr.* 1955, **49,** 12545
523. *British Patent* 817,877; *Chem. Abstr.* 1960, **54,** 7745
524. *British Patent* 845,235; *Chem. Abstr.* 1961, **55,** 14488

525. MARSHALL and VALLANCE *J. Pharm., Lond.* 1954, **6,** 740
526. LAMBROS *Dis. nerv. Syst.* 1958, **19,** 349
527. CARTER *Dis. nerv. Syst.* 1960, **21,** 50
528. PEARCE *Canad. med. Ass. J.* 1960, **82,** 953
529. LA VECK *Dis. nerv. Syst.* 1960, **21,** 230
530. AGUILAR, MARTIN and McNAUGHTON *Canad. med. Ass. J.* 1961, **84,** 374
531. JOCHHEIM and GERBERDING *Med. Mschr.* 1955, **9,** 808
532. SHAW, SIMON, CASS, SHULMAN, ANSTEE and NELSON *Nature, Lond.* 1954, **174,** 402
533. HARRIS *Lancet* 1955, **i,** 181
534. SHULMAN, SHAW, CASS and WHYTE *Brit. med. J.* 1955, **i,** 1238
535. *British Patent* 829,415; *Chem. Abstr.* 1960, **54,** 9869
536. MARSHALL *J. org. Chem.* 1958, **23,** 503
537. KAUFMANN *Dis. nerv. Syst.* 1950, **11,** 99
538. KUSHNER, CASSELL, MORTON and WILLIAMS *J. org. Chem.* 1951, **16,** 1283
539. HARNED, CUNNINGHAM, CLARK, HINE, KANE, SMITH, VESSEY, YUDA and ZABRANSKY *J. Pharmacol.* 1953, **107,** 403
540. HAWKES *Arch. Neurol. Psychiat., Chicago* 1952, **67,** 815
541. LIVINGSTON *J. Pediat.* 1953, **43,** 673
542. KAYE, JONES and WARRIER *Brit. med. J.* 1959, **i,** 627
543. WILSON, WALTON and NEWELL *Brit. med. J.* 1959, **i,** 1275
544. JENNEY, LEE, WILLIAMS and PFEIFFER *J. Pharmacol.* 1952, **106,** 398
545. STAMPS, MARSHALL, ORLOFF, GIBBS and PFEIFFER *J. Pharmacol.* 1952, **106,** 418
546. GOLDMAN and WILLIAMS *J. org. Chem.* 1953, **18,** 815
547. HOWARD, CONROY, STEWART, and DENTON *J. Amer. pharm. Ass., Sci. Ed.* 1954, **43,** 628
548. MILLIGAN and O'DOHERTY *Med. Ann. D.C.* 1961, **30,** 513
549. STAUDINGER and RUZICKA *Liebigs Ann.* 1911, **380,** 291
550. SPIELMAN, GEISZLER and CLOSE *J. Amer. chem. Soc.* 1948, **70,** 4189
551. TYLER and KING *J. Amer. med. Ass.* 1951, **147,** 17
552. LIVINGSTON and PAULI *New Engl. J. Med.* 1957, **256,** 588
553. JOB, LINDINGER and ZELLNER *Wien. med. Wschr.* 1954, **104,** 46, 911
554. STROTZKA *Wien. med. Wschr.* 1955, **105,** 137
555. GOLD, FROMMEL, RADOUCO, GREDER, MELKONIAN, DELLA SANTE, RADOUCO, VALLETTE and DUCOMMUN *Arch. int. Pharmacodyn.* 1952, **91,** 437
556. ORLOFF, FELDMAN, SHAIOVA and PFEIFFER *Neurology* 1951, **1,** 377
557. SOYTER and FÄSSLER *Schweiz. med. Wschr.* 1956, **86,** 956
558. FROMMEL, GOLD-AUBERT and FLEURY *Arch. int. Pharmacodyn.* 1959, **122,** 15
559. SCHWEINGRUBER and KETZ *Schweiz. med. Wschr.* 1960, **90,** 423
560. PALMER *Neurology* 1954, **4,** 345
561. KOLARIK and MIKULA *Wien. med. Wschr.* 1959, **109,** 691
562. BERGER *Proc. Soc. exp. Biol., N.Y.* 1951, **78,** 277
563. PERLSTEIN *Neurology* 1953, **3,** 744
564. SLATER, LEARY and DRESEL *J. Pharmacol.* 1954, **111,** 182
565. KELLY and LAURENCE *Brit. med. J.* 1955, **i,** 456
566. MILLS, GIBSON and SWANSON *Proc. Soc. exp. Biol., N.Y.* 1957, **96,** 100
567. GRUBER and MOSIER *Proc. Soc. exp. Biol., N.Y.* 1957, **94,** 384
568. P'AN, KODET, GARDOCKI, McLAMORE and BAVLEY *J. Pharmacol.* 1955, **114,** 326
569. CARTER *Epilepsia* 1959, **1,** 110
570. KENNEDY and TROUNCE *Science* 1955, **122,** 515
571. SCHAFFARZICK and BROWN *Science* 1952, **116,** 663
572. BERGER, HENDLEY, LUDWIG and LYNES *J. Pharmacol.* 1956, **116,** 337
573. ABBOTT and SCHWAB *New Engl. J. Med.* 1954, **250,** 197
574. IVANOV *N.Y. St. J. Med.* 1958, **58,** 2529
575. BASTIAN *Pharmacologist* 1960, **2,** 87

576. SPIELMAN, BARNES and CLOSE *J. Amer. chem. Soc.* 1950, **72,** 2520
577. LIVINGSTON *J. Pediat.* 1955, **46,** 394
578. ANSELL and CLARKE *Brit. med. J.* 1956, **i,** 650
579. LIVINGSTON, PETERSON and BOKS *Pediatrics, Springfield* 1956, **17,** 541
580. ROSS *Lancet* 1958, **ii,** 1308
581. LOMBROSO and FORXYTHE *Epilepsia* 1960, **1,** 493
582. CHAO and PLUMB *J. Pediat.* 1961, **58,** 211
583. *British Patent* 795,174; *Chem. Abstr.* 1958, **52,** 20212
584. FLUGEL, BENTE and ITIL *Dtsch. med. Wschr.* 1960, **85,** 2199
585. RAFFAUF *Dtsch. med. Wschr.* 1960, **85,** 2203
586. ENGELMEIER *Dtsch. med. Wschr.* 1960, **85,** 2207
587. FRIEBEL and SOMMER *Dtsch. med. Wschr.* 1960, **85,** 2192
588. WIRTH, HOFFMEISTER, FRIEBEL and SOMMER *Dtsch. med. Wschr.* 1960, **85,** 2195
589. *British Patent* 871,449
590. HELFERICH and KLEB *Liebigs Ann.* 1960, **635,** 91
591. *British Patent* 810,356; *Chem. Abstr.* 1959, **53,** 16068
592. *U.S. Patent* 2,917,512; *Chem. Abstr.* 1960, **54,** 7589
593. TAVERNER and BAIN *Lancet* 1958, **ii,** 1145
594. BERNHARD and BOHM *Acta physiol. scand.* 1954, **31,** Suppl. 114, 5
595. BERNHARD and BOHM *Brit. J. Pharmacol.* 1955, **10,** 288
596. SCHWAB and MURPHY *Epilepsia* 1959, **1,** 227
597. CARTER *Arch. Neurol. Psychiat., Chicago* 1958, **79,** 136
598. McWILLIAM *Lancet* 1958, **ii,** 1147
599. EVANSON *Lancet* 1959, **ii,** 72
600. NISBET *Brit. med. J.* 1959, **i,** 95
601. RANDALL, SCHALLEK, HEISE, KEITH and BAGDON *J. Pharmacol.* 1960, **129,** 163
602. KAIM and ROSENSTEIN *Dis. nerv. Syst.* 1960, **21,** Suppl. 46
603. ROSENSTEIN *Dis. nerv. Syst.* 1960, **21,** Suppl. 57
604. BERCEL *Dis. nerv. Syst.* 1961, **22,** Suppl. 17
605. LIVINGSTON, PAULI and MURPHY *J. Amer. med. Ass.* 1961, **177,** 243
606. RANDALL, HEISE, SCHALLEK, BAGDON, BANZIGER, BORIS, MOE and ABRAMS *Curr. Ther. Res.* 1961, **3,** 405
607. DE MATTOS *J. Med., Porto* 1959, **39,** 802
608. SICUTERI *Medicina Experimentalis* 1960, **2,** 36
609. MADEDDU and LEONE *Minerva med.* 1960, **51,** 2733
610. SCHLÖGL, WESSELY, KRAUPP and STORMANN *J. med. pharm. Chem.* 1961, **4,** 231
611. *British Patent* 884,629; *Chem. Abstr.* 1962, **56,** 13025
612. FRIEBEL and KLATT *Arzneimitt. Forsch.* 1959, **9,** 245
613. *British Patent* 747,951
614. *U.S. Patent* 2,732,380; *Chem. Abstr.* 1956, **50,** 10767
615. *British Patent* 807,679; *Chem. Abstr.* 1959, **53,** 12304
616. *British Patent* 807,678; *Chem. Abstr.* 1959, **53,** 12303
617. *British Patent* 807,676; *Chem. Abstr.* 1959, **53,** 12304
618. MILLER and LONG *J. Amer. chem. Soc.* 1953, **75,** 373
619. *British Patent* 690,728; *Chem. Abstr.* 1954, **48,** 7627
620. *British Patent* 725,945; *Chem. Abstr.* 1956, **50,** 5022
621. *British Patent* 726,208; *Chem. Abstr.* 1956, **50,** 5023
622. *Belgian Patent* 572,773
623. *British Patent* 828,753; *Chem. Abstr.* 1960, **54,** 9799
624. EDWALDS *J. clin. exp. Psychopath.* 1959, **20,** 38
625. ENDERS, VIGELIUS and WESSEM *Naturwissenschaften* 1960, **47,** 84
626. ENDERS, VIGELIUS and WESSEM *Arzneimitt. Forsch.* 1960, **10,** 243
627. ENDERS *Arch. int. Pharmacodyn.* 1960, **127,** 285
628. BEASLEY, PETROV and STEPHENSON *J. Pharm., Lond.* 1961, **13,** 694

629. SCHWARTZ and DOERGE *J. Amer. pharm. Ass., Sci. Ed.* 1955, **44,** 80
630. ALBERT, BOXILL and WEIKEL *J. Pharmacol.* 1961, **131,** 85
631. SWIFT and BECKER *Fed. Proc.* 1959, **18,** 449
632. SWIFT, DICKENS and BECKER *Arch. int. Pharmacodyn.* 1960, **128,** 112
633. BIANCHI and DAVID *J. Pharm., Lond.* 1960, **12,** 501
634. JACKMAN, PETROV and STEPHENSON *J. Pharm., Lond.* 1960, **12,** 529
635. MITCHELL, KEASLING and GROSS *J. Amer. pharm. Ass., Sci. Ed.* 1959, **48,** 122
636. MITCHELL, KEASLING and HIRSCHLER *J. Amer. pharm. Ass., Sci. Ed.* 1959, **48,** 671
637. MAFFII *Farmaco, Sci. Ed.* 1959, **14,** 176
638. *British Patent* 751,072; *Chem. Abstr.* 1957, **51,** 4440
639. MAFFII and SILVESTRINI *Farmaco, Sci. Ed.* 1961, **16,** 39
640. BARGETON and ROQUET *Arch. int. Pharmacodyn.* 1961, **130,** 96

# 7

# LOCAL ANAESTHETICS

S. Wiedling and C. Tegnér

## INTRODUCTION

The evolution of local anaesthetics began with the isolation of cocaine in 1865 by Wöhler's pupil, Albert Niemann. Following Niemann's achievement, many years elapsed before the advent of the first really notable synthetic agent—procaine. This drug, with its relatively low toxicity and its blandness for the tissues, came to dominate most fields of use in local anaesthesia until the introduction of lignocaine some forty years later. In the meantime a large number of compounds possessing local anaesthetic activity—notably, esters of benzoic acid and its $p$-amino derivatives—had been synthesized, but none of them had seriously threatened the supremacy of procaine. Those that did not find clinical usage had in fact been designed essentially for use in certain fields, such as those of topical and spinal anaesthesia.

Lignocaine was synthesized in 1943 by Löfgren, a research chemist at Stockholm University, and was released for general use in 1948. By virtue of its outstanding anaesthetic properties and its low toxicity, lignocaine has since become established as a standard anaesthetic in many parts of the world. Its advent led to an intensive quest for new compounds of the aminoacylanilide type—and to this research work Löfgren and his associates (1946 and later) also made important contributions. Some half-dozen other aminoacylanilides are in clinical use today, besides which numerous compounds of new types have emerged in recent years. The present survey is largely concerned with the period from 1955 to 1961, during which time various aspects of local anaesthetics have been reviewed[1-9].

## CHEMISTRY, LINES OF DEVELOPMENT AND TYPES OF LOCAL ANAESTHETICS

The 'anaesthesiophore' group in cocaine may serve as the starting point for the systemization of the synthetic agents introduced during the last few years (see *Figure 7.1*).

The various types of local anaesthetics differ only in so far as the ester linkage, $-CO_2-$, in the intermediate chain between the benzene nucleus and the amino residue in cocaine, has been exchanged for $-NHCO-$, $-NHCO_2-$, $-NHCONH-$, $-CONH-$, $-CO-$ or $-O-$. Each type will be discussed separately, and a small number of compounds not of these types will also be discussed as a separate group.

### Aminoacylamides

Since the introduction of the first clinically useful aminoacylamide, lignocaine (lidocaine, Xylocaine, Xylotox, Isicaine, *I*), efforts have been made

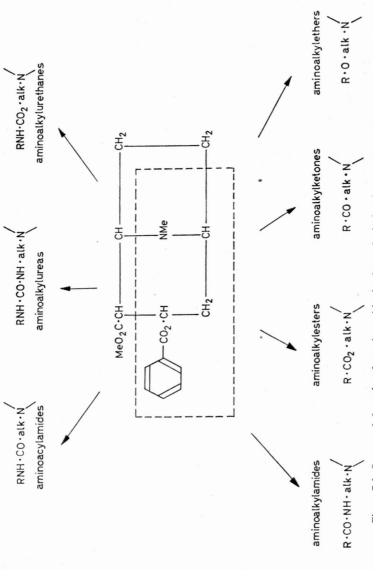

*Figure 7.1.* Structural formula of cocaine with the 'anaesthesiophore' group in the hatched area; also shown are the different types of anaesthetics referable to this basic structure (R = aryl, aralkyl, straight or branched alkyl; alk = alkylene; N< = mono- or di-substituted amino residue).

333

to synthesize compounds with even more favourable pharmacological properties (*cf.* reviews by Killian[5] and Hach[10]). So far, the following compounds* have found clinical usage:

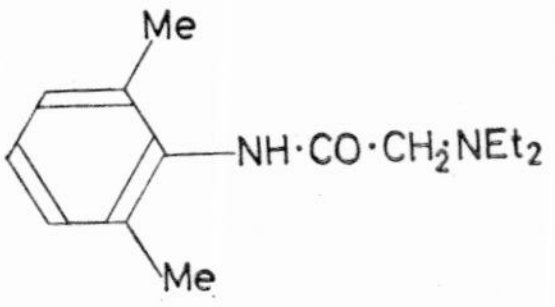

*(I)* Lignocaine

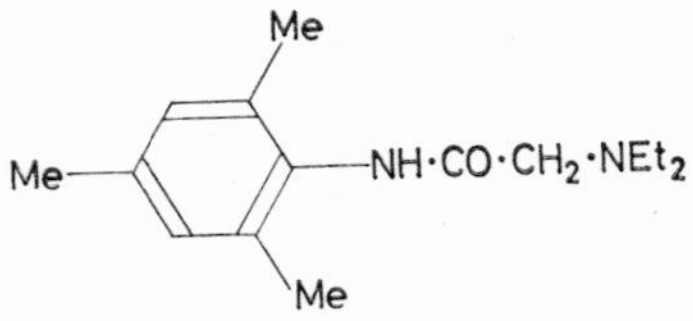

*(II)* Mesocaine

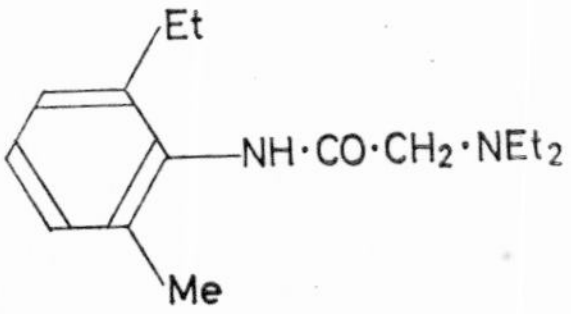

*(III)* Gravocaine

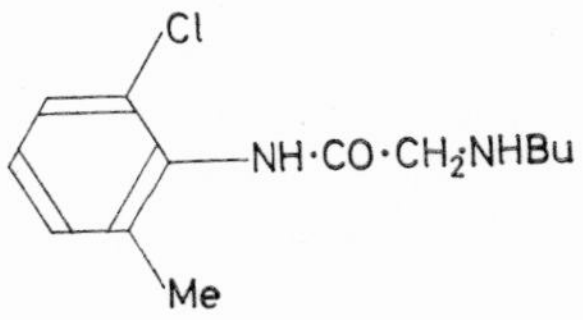

*(IV)* Hostacaine

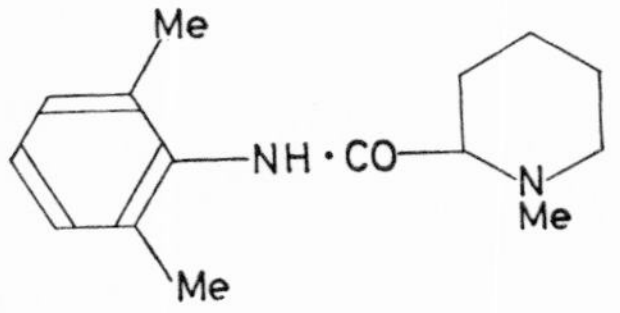

*(V)* Mepivacaine

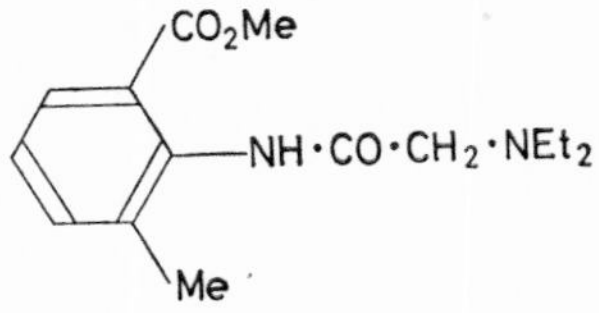

*(VI)* Baycaine

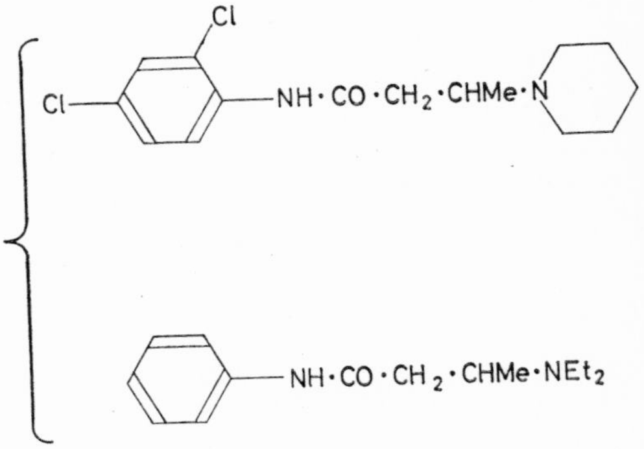

*(VII)* Amplicaine

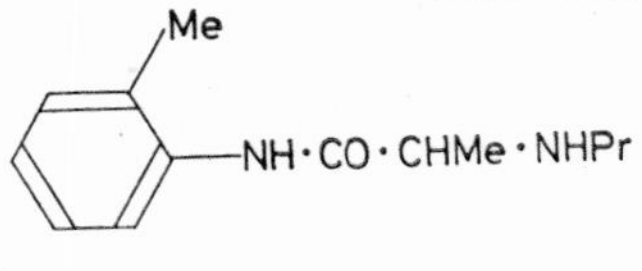

*(VIII)* Citanest

The investigations of recent years have been largely concerned with variations in the aromatic moiety of lignocaine, though to a certain extent new intermediate chains have also been tried. The benzene nucleus of lignocaine may be replaced by an aliphatic radical, but for anaesthetic activity the radical has to contain a tertiary carbon atom[11–13]. The best

* In this review the compounds are represented, chemically, by the structure of the bases, irrespective of the fact that usually a salt is used.

compound of this type (*IX*) was approximately 25 times as active as ligno-caine in surface anaesthesia and 7 times as effective as procaine in infiltration anaesthesia. The morpholino analogue was a poor anaesthetic but produced an analgesic effect in mice[13]. A large number of aminoacylamides of various aminobicycloheptanes were also synthesized[14]. Although these were devoid

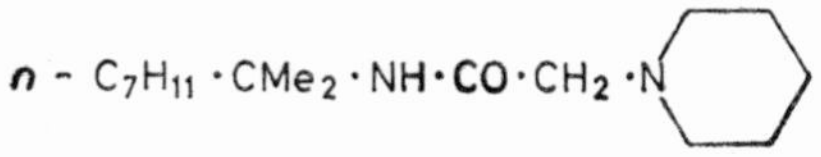

$$n - C_7H_{11} \cdot CMe_2 \cdot NH \cdot CO \cdot CH_2 \cdot N \bigcirc$$

(*IX*)

of surface effects, and showed on intradermal administration only a slight to moderate anaesthetic action, they possessed marked antifibrillatory activity.

Aralkylamines have been the subject of a few investigations. Profft and Jumar[15] prepared $\beta$-piperidinopropioamides of benzyl-, phenethyl-, and 1-phenylethylamine and of a few alkoxy derivatives of these amines. In infiltration anaesthesia, their activity was generally similar to that of Falicaine (see p. 386), but in surface anaesthesia it was much less. Subsequently, Profft[16] found that the mono- and di-alkylpiperidinopropioamides are more potent than the corresponding unsubstituted piperidines. The corresponding $\beta$-diethylaminopropionyl derivatives of similar amines were prepared by Kochetkov and Dudykina[17].

Quite recently, some mono- and bis-acetamides were reported[18], the bisacetamides being exceptionally active surface anaesthetics[19-21]. One compound, oxethazaine (Oxaine, Wy-806, *X*) when tested on rabbit cornea, was ten times as effective as cinchocaine.

$$HO \cdot CH_2 \cdot CH_2 \cdot N(CH_2 \cdot CO \cdot NMe \cdot CMe_2 \cdot CH_2Ph)_2$$

(*X*)

Considerable interest is still centred upon the influence of different aliphatic hydrocarbon radicals in the benzene nucleus. Of the numerous workers who have synthesized anilides or monoalkyl substituted anilides, Löfgren and Tegnér[22] recently described the preparation of a potent compound (Citanest, L 67, *VIII*). Some $N,N'$-bisaminoacylbenzidines (*XI*)

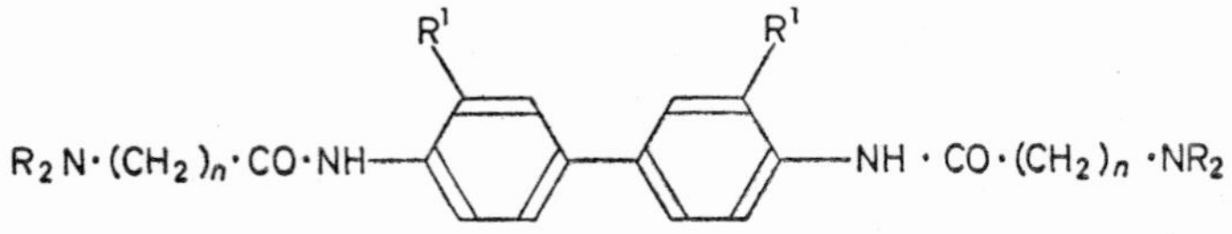

$$R_2N \cdot (CH_2)_n \cdot CO \cdot NH \text{---} \overset{R^1}{\bigcirc} \text{---} \overset{R^1}{\bigcirc} \text{---} NH \cdot CO \cdot (CH_2)_n \cdot NR_2$$

(*XI*)

$$NR_2 = NEt_2, NC_5H_{10}, NC_4H_8O$$
$$R^1 = H, Me, MeO$$
$$n = 1 \text{ or } 2$$

were found to be inactive when tested on the guinea-pig cornea, but produced some effect in infiltration anaesthesia[23]. Of the many dialkyl substituted anilides which have been synthesized, those derived from 2,6-xylidine are of special interest[24,25]. One of these[24] proved to be clinically useful and was introduced under the name of mepivacaine (Carbocaine, *V*). Diverse amides of diethylamino-, morpholino- and piperidino-acetic acid have also been prepared by Dalal and Trivedi[26]. Löfgren, Tegnér and Takman[27] synthesized acetyl and propionylxylidides with different amino groups in the α-position, and when tested on the rabbit cornea, the monoalkylamino compounds possessed the greatest activity, and the effect increased with length of carbon chain. In general, however, the compounds either had too high a toxicity or were inferior to lignocaine in infiltration anaesthesia. Substitution of ethyl groups for the methyl groups in the benzene nucleus of lignocaine yields a compound, the activity of which approximates to that of the dimethyl compound, but which produces distinct irritation[28].

Oelschläger[29] studied a few 2,5-substituted anilides, including compounds of the formula (XII), where R contained two to four carbon atoms. Although

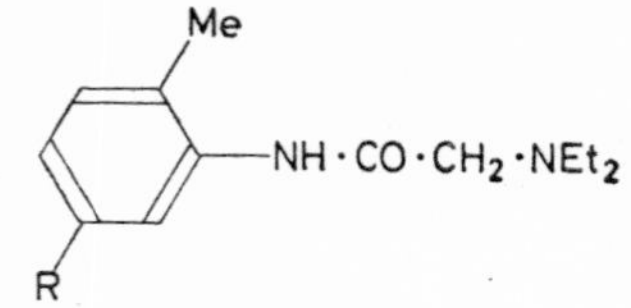

Me

—NH·CO·CH$_2$·NEt$_2$

R

(XII)

they produced a substantial effect in topical anaesthesia (rabbit cornea method), these compounds were inferior to lignocaine for nerve block. Similar compounds in which R is isopropyl were studied by Sen Gupta and Vasudev[30], who found them to possess surface anaesthetic activity.

A comparison of the 2,4- and 2,6-xylidides of diethylamino- and piperi-dinoacetic acid showed that the 2,6-xylidides are approximately twice as active as the 2,4-analogues[31,32]. An imidazolinylaceto-2,6-xylidide, tested by Löfgren and Tegnér[33], was, however, found to possess only slight local anaesthetic activity as compared to lignocaine. Similar results were recorded by Dahlbom and Misiorny[34] in studies on piperazinoacyl-2,6-xylidides.

In recent years the trialkyl substituted anilides have been studied[35–37], and because mesocaine (trimecaine, II) has come into clinical use in East European countries during recent years, syntheses have been extended to mesidides (2,4,6-trimethylanilides) of the general formula (XIII). When

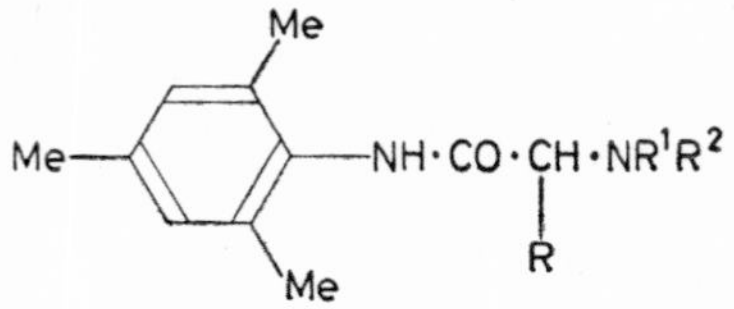

Me

Me—    —NH·CO·CH·NR$^1$R$^2$

Me          R

(XIII)

NR$^1$R$^2$ was diethylamino and R was methyl, ethyl or butyl, the activity, both in topical and in infiltration anaesthesia, rose with the length of R$^1$ and R$^2$, the toxicity increasing concurrently though to a lesser degree. Among the acetyl derivatives (R = H), variations of the amino groups were investigated. All derivatives with secondary amino groups (R$^1$ = H; R$^2$ = butyl, hexyl, cyclohexyl, benzyl) were more active than lignocaine, but, with the exception of the benzyl derivative, they were also more toxic. Compounds in which NR¹R² was a piperidine ring had local anaesthetic properties: of the methylpiperidines, the 3-methyl compound was the best and showed a lower toxicity than lignocaine, as did the 2,6-dimethyl- and 2,4,6-trimethyl-piperidines which possessed substantial anaesthetic activity. Morpholines and ethoxycarbonylpiperazines, on the other hand, exhibited low activity. Exceptionally effective was the dibutylaminoaceto-2,4,6-trimethylanilide (*XIV*) which was approximately 35 times as active as lignocaine in topical

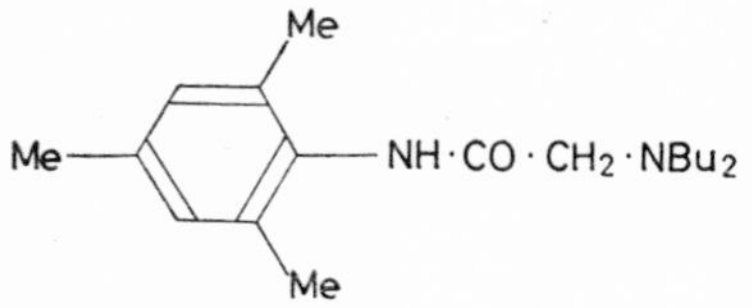

*(XIV)*

anaesthesia, and about four times as active in infiltration anaesthesia. Although irritation was not mentioned in the reports, the toxicity of the dibutyl compound (>4·5 g/kg, white mice)—and of many of the other compounds too—is suggestive of precipitation or of low absorption.

A series of 2,4,6-trimethylanilides with various secondary and tertiary amines in α-position, showed promise in laboratory animals, but when tested in man they proved inferior to lignocaine[27].

The replacement of alkyl by chlorine in the benzene nucleus of amino-acylanilides led to the introduction of Hostacaine (*IV*)[38]. Compounds which contained one chlorine atom and one methyl group in the nucleus, generally produced no major surface effect. Of compounds which differed only in the positions of the substituents, the 2-chloro-6-methyl analogue was superior to its isomers, chiefly by virtue of its higher solubility. The anaesthetic activity, as expected, depended on the length of the alkyl at the amino nitrogen. When the latter was unsubstituted, the compound was devoid of action, but on alkylation the activity increased with the length of the alkyl, concurrently with a rise of the intravenous toxicity. The butyl residue was observed to be the most favourable. The acetyl derivatives, however, proved superior to the other acyl compounds tested. The higher fatty acid derivatives produced greater local irritation coincident with a rise in the subcutaneous toxicity, but no increase in local anaesthetic activity.

At the same time as these investigations, Koelzer and Wehr[39] were studying compounds of a similar type. They concluded that the aminoacylanilides required, for maximal effect, two substituents in the phenyl nucleus, in the 2,6-positions, and they should preferably be one chlorine and one methyl group. Koelzer and Wehr obtained, with the higher fatty acid derivatives, an increase in local anaesthetic effect, but at the cost of severe irritation and greater toxicity (*cf.* Oelschläger *et al.*[40]). In tests on compounds with different substituents at the amino nitrogen, the pyrrolidino derivative (*XV*) was the best. Smith and Hofstetter[41] investigated similar butyric acid derivatives

337

but found them to be irritating. An exception was β-piperidino-2,4-dichloro-butyranilide (*XVI*), which in spite of its longer intermediate chain produced only relatively slight irritation in rabbit eyes. Of the diverse types of compounds studied by Koelzer and Wehr[42], the ethylenediamine derivative (*XVII*) showed the best combination of pharmacological attributes. In

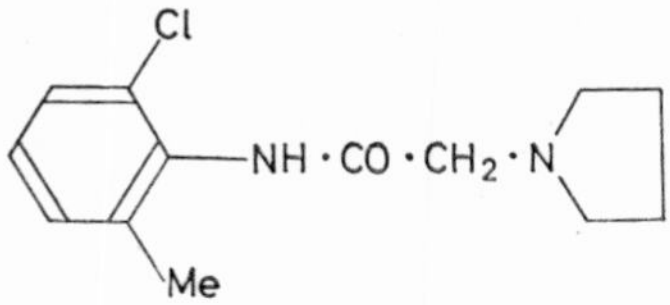

(XV)

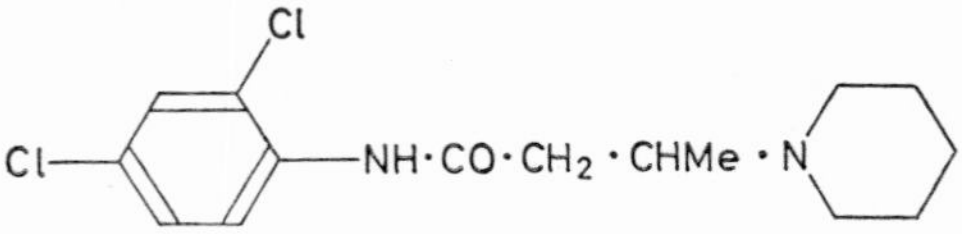

(XVI)

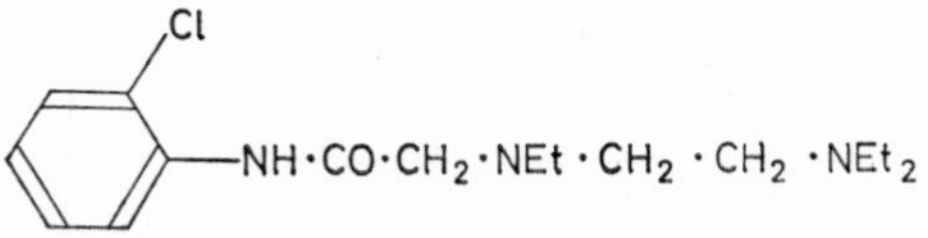

(XVII)

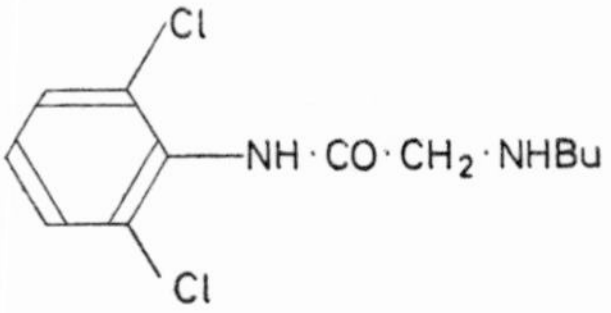

(XVIII)

surface anaesthesia, as well as in nerve block, it was four or five times as active as lignocaine, and less toxic. The compound produced, however, some degree of irritation, both when injected and when applied to the rabbit cornea.

Beke and his colleagues followed up their earlier studies[43] by investigating monohalogen and dihalogen substituted diethylaminoacetanilides[44] and butylaminoacetanilides[45], with and without alkyl groups in the nucleus. Of the latter type, the 2,6-dichloro derivative (*XVIII*), showed favourable properties. Similar compounds, especially the 3-chlorotoluidides, were shown in preliminary clinical tests to equal procaine in potency[46,47]. The few fluoro substituted diethylaminoacetanilides, toluidides and xylidides which have been prepared, showed only slight anaesthetic activity[48-50]. $m$-Trifluoro-methyl-substituted dialkylaminoacetanilides, however, possessed marked anaesthetic activity[51].

The introduction of hydroxy, alkoxy, and aralkoxy groups into the lignocaine molecule has engaged the attention of several investigators[15,39,46,52-58]. This work, however, has so far been unsuccessful. Compounds such as $(XIX)$ and $(XX)$ where R in both instances was methyl, ethyl, propyl, or

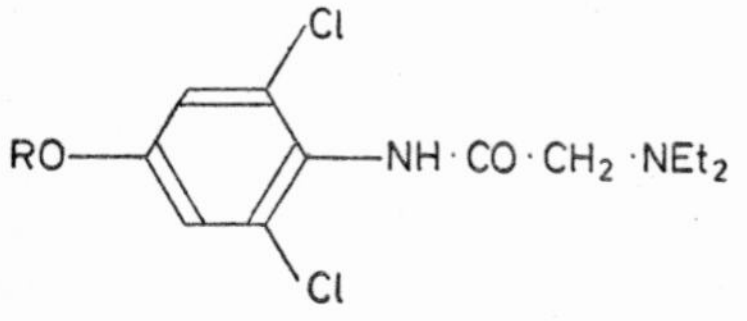

*(XIX)*

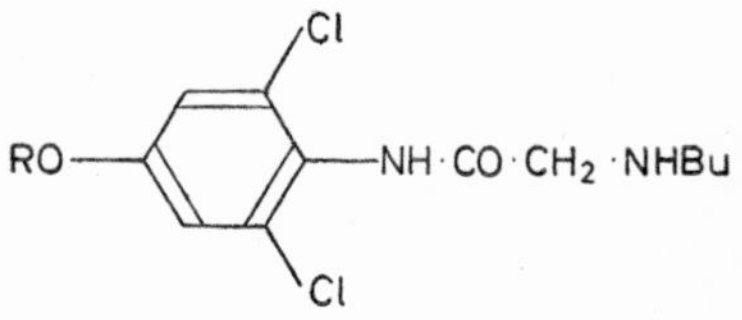

*(XX)*

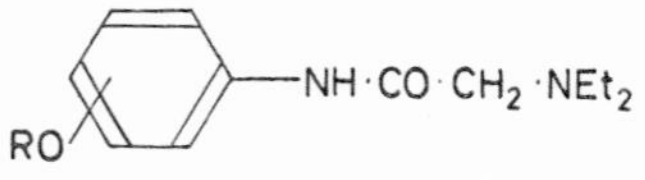

*(XXI)*

R = Ph, CH₂Ph, CH₂·CH₂Ph

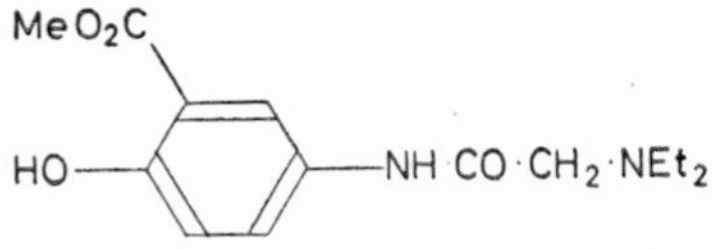

*(XXII)*

butyl, possessed a higher activity than the corresponding unsubstituted compounds, the potency increasing with the length of the alkyl chain[52,53]. The toxicity of the substituted compounds had a maximum at the ethoxy derivative. The higher homologues produced severe irritation. Borovanský, Sekera and Vrba[54] studied $o$-, $m$- and $p$-alkoxy substituted phenyl, benzyl, and phenethyl derivatives of the general type $(XXI)$. The compounds were mostly more active than lignocaine, both when tested on rabbit cornea and in infiltration anaesthesia, and their toxicity was very low[55]. A few $\beta$-morpholino derivatives of alkoxybutyranilides were prepared[56] but had a relatively weak anaesthetic effect. Although the 3,4,5-trimethoxyanilide has also been synthesized[69], no data on its anaesthetic behaviour are available.

Tsatsas and Guioca-Dedopoulou[58] recently reported on the synthesis of $p$-alkoxyanilides of acetic acid and propionic acid containing different amines in $\alpha$- and $\beta$-position. In common with other investigators, they found that the compounds had local anaesthetic action, but caused such severe irritation that the investigations were discontinued. The first anilide to contain an alkoxycarbonyl group in the benzene nucleus was Nirvanine $(XXII)$. Since the revival of interest in anilides through the discovery of lignocaine, detailed investigations into the influence of alkoxycarbonyl substitution have been conducted. Wiedmann and Petersen[59] studied a series of alkoxycarbonyl substituted $\alpha,\beta$-diaminopropionic acid anilides (*XXIII*), where R was an alkyl group (methyl, ethyl, propyl, isopropyl and

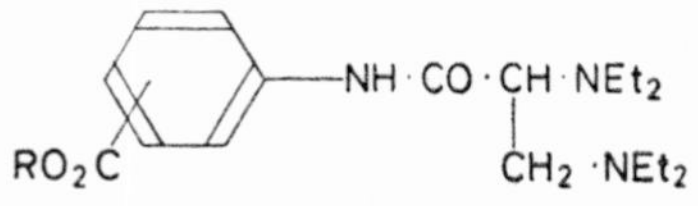

(XXIII)

butyl) and the $CO_2R$ group is in the 2- or the 4-position. They noted that *ortho*-substitution was more favourable than *para*-substitution and that the surface effect increased with the length of the group R, reaching a maximum at propyl. In nerve block, however, the esters had only a low anaesthetic effect. For aminoacylanilides with an ester group in the *para*-position (*XXIV*), a satisfactory relation between effect and toxicity can be obtained

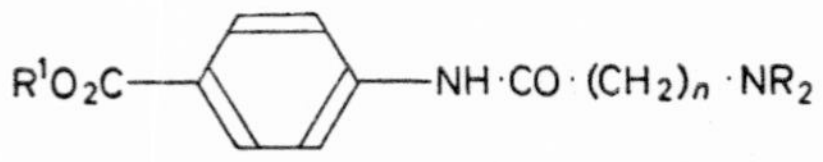

(XXIV)

$NR_2 = NEt_2, NC_5H_{10}, NC_4H_8O$
$R^1 = Pr, Pr^i, Bu$
$n = 1$ or $2$

with compounds of this type[60]. Other compounds of this type, as well as the corresponding *o*- and *p*-dialkylcarbamoyl derivatives have been synthesized[50,56,61]. A detailed study of this type of substitution in about 130 aminoacylanilides has been reported by Epstein and Kaminsky[62,63], among

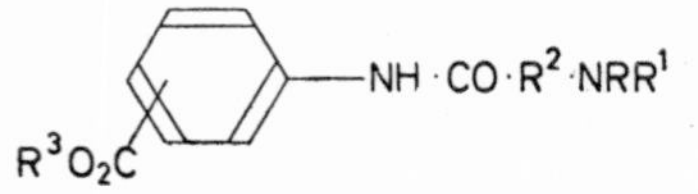

(XXV)

$NRR^1 = $ s - or t- amino group
$R^2 = $ straight or branched alkylene
$R^3 = $ Me to $C_6H_{13}$

others. Systematic variations in different parts of the molecule (*XXV*) led to the following conclusions:

(1) Potency and irritation increased with increasing molecular weight of $R^3$, except that the methyl ester was more active than the ethyl ester. As a rule, normal chains were more potent and irritant than branched chains.

(2) The position of the ester group in the nucleus was significant. The ratio

potency/irritation decreased in the order *meta > ortho > para*, whereas for the ratio toxicity/anaesthetic effect, the order was *ortho > meta > para.*

(3) Variations in the intermediate chain $R^2$ showed that branched chain compounds were somewhat less toxic and irritant than, equal in potency to, or more active than, their straight chain analogues with the same number of carbon atoms. An increase in the length of the intermediate chain resulted in greater irritation and reduced anaesthetic activity.

(4) Variations in $NRR^1$ were difficult to correlate with pharmacological effects. Nevertheless, the introduction of tertiary alkylamino groups reduced the toxicity as compared to the corresponding secondary amino groups with the same number of carbon atoms.

Ester groups combined with alkyls or halogens in the benzene nucleus have been investigated[38]. None of the compounds (*XXVI*) and (*XXVII*) was

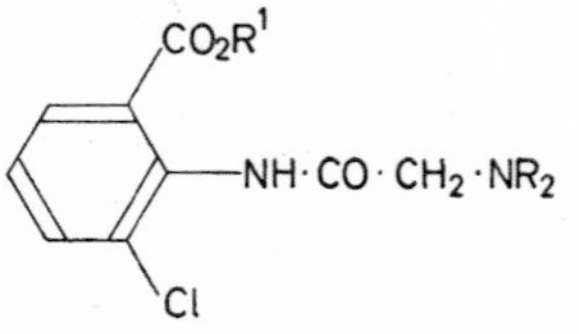

Structure (*XXVI*): benzene ring with $CO_2R^1$ (ortho), $-NH \cdot CO \cdot CH_2 \cdot NR_2$, and $Cl$.

Structure (*XXVII*): benzene ring with $CO_2 \cdot Me$, $-NH \cdot CO \cdot CH_2 \cdot NR_2$, and $Me$.

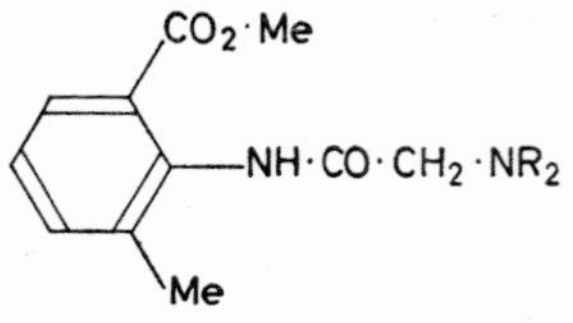

superior to Hostacaine but one compound (*XXVII*, R = Et) was subsequently tested by Wirth and Gösswald[64], who found its properties so satisfactory that it was introduced under the name of Baycaine. Compounds (*XXVIII*) containing both an ester and an alkoxy group in the aromatic

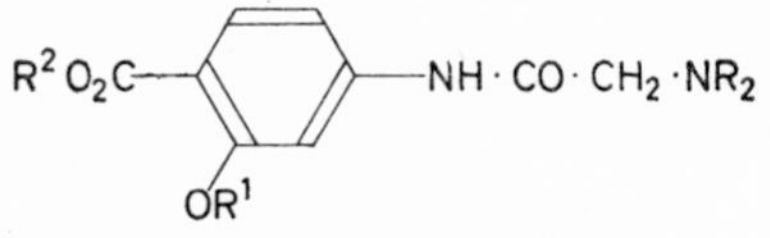

Structure (*XXVIII*): benzene ring with $R^2O_2C-$, $-NH \cdot CO \cdot CH_2 \cdot NR_2$, and $OR^1$.

nucleus, have also been studied[65]. These are related to Nirvanine, but showed relatively low anaesthetic activity.

Introduction of an acyl group into the aromatic nucleus to produce, for example, *m*-acetyl- and *m*-propionylaminoacylanilides, gives compounds without noteworthy surface anaesthetic activity, although equal to procaine in nerve block[66].

The significance of amino groups in the benzoic acid esters had earlier prompted numerous workers[67-70] to study the influence of that group in the aminoacylanilides. Introduction of a *p*-amino group into the molecule of diethylaminoacetanilide[32] and of 2,6-xylidide, contrary to previous reports[69], reduced the anaesthetic effect[32,71]. Alkylation or acylation of the amino group with a radical containing approximately five carbon atoms increased the local anaesthetic effect (rabbit cornea), though coincidently with severe irritation or increased toxicity[71]. A few aminoalkyl substituted anilides have also been synthesized[72]. While being devoid of surface effects these compounds had, in intracutaneous wheals, anaesthetic activity combined with tissue injuries. By introducing a urethane group in the *para*-position of the lignocaine molecule, Tegnér and Willman[73] obtained compounds with a surface anaesthetic effect when tested on rabbit cornea. The best of these compounds was the pentyl derivative (*XXIX*), which was approximately

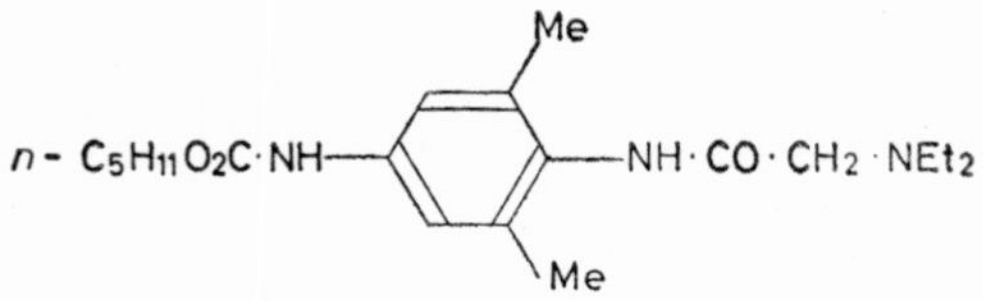

$$n\text{-}C_5H_{11}O_2C\cdot NH - \underset{Me}{\overset{Me}{\bigcirc}} - NH\cdot CO\cdot CH_2\cdot NEt_2$$

(*XXIX*)

$$R^1 Y - \underset{Cl}{\overset{Cl}{\bigcirc}} - NH\cdot CO\cdot CH_2\cdot NR_2$$

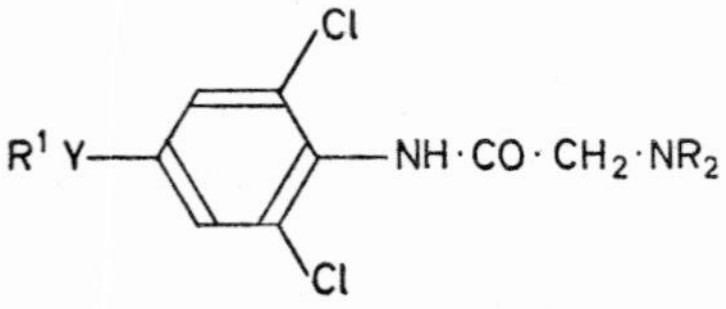

(*XXX*)

$R^1$ = Me, Et, Pr, Bu
$NR_2$ = $NEt_2$, NHBu
Y = O, S

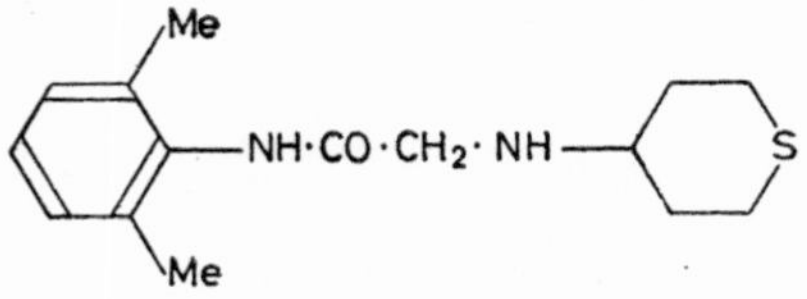

$$\underset{Me}{\overset{Me}{\bigcirc}} - NH\cdot CO\cdot CH_2\cdot NH - \bigcirc S$$

(*XXXI*)

35 times as active as lignocaine. The compound was relatively non-toxic and gave rise to only slight irritation, but showed poor solubility characteristics. A few of the corresponding amides were also tested by Tegnér and Domeij[74] but proved to have a weaker anaesthetic effect. Substitution of sulphur for oxygen atoms in aminoacylanilides has been tried. A few thioacylanilides were compared with the corresponding acyl compounds. In each instance the introduction of sulphur caused either depression or total suppression of the local anaesthetic activity[35,37,75,76]. Similar results were obtained on exchanging alkoxy for alkylmercapto groups in 2,6-dichloranilides of formula (*XXX*)[77,78]. Barkenbus and Wuellner[79] replaced diethylamino by a 4-tetrahydrothiapyranylamino group, *e.g.* in lignocaine to give compound (*XXXI*). Here too the local anaesthetic effect is substantially less if comparison is made with that of the corresponding cyclohexyl derivatives. Recent years have brought further reports on the exchange of the

benzene nucleus in lignocaine for another ring system, *e.g.* naphthalene[53,80,81], tetralin[82], fluorene[83,84], anthraquinone[85], phenanthrene[84], acridine[85], chroman[86], thiazole[87–92], oxadiazole[93], and phenothiazine[94,95]. Of the naphthalene derivatives, which appear to be the most interesting of the above mentioned types of compounds, many of the 2-alkoxy-1-amino derivatives (*XXXII*) were more active than cocaine. The most active of the

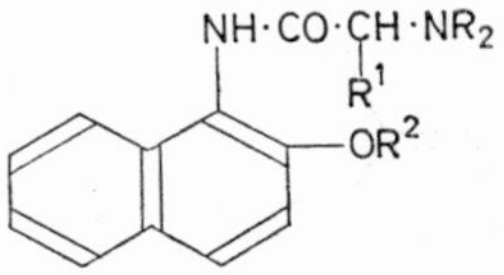

*(XXXII)*

R = Me, Et
R$^1$ = H, Me, Et
R$^2$ = Me, Et, Bu, i -C$_5$H$_{11}$

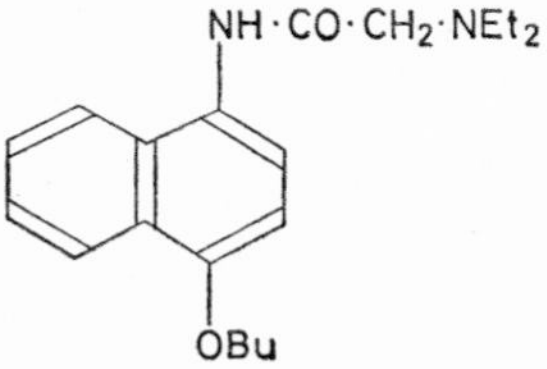

*(XXXIII)*

compounds, however, produced irritation when tested on the rabbit's eye[80]. Other naphthalene derivatives with a surface effect have been studied[96]. Comparison of 1-butoxy-4-diethylaminoacetamidonaphthalene with the corresponding 7-butoxy derivative showed that the latter, in surface and infiltration anaesthesia, was greatly inferior to the 1-derivative[81]. Hydrogenation of the compound (*XXXIII*) to the 5,6,7,8-tetrahydro derivative resulted in an increase in the effect in infiltration anaesthesia, coincident with a reduction of the toxicity.

The influence of variations in the intermediate chain between the amino group and the aromatic nucleus has also been investigated by numerous workers. While branching or lengthening of the acyl group of α-amino-acylanilides improved the effect, lengthening was associated with higher toxicity and greater irritation[35,37,97]. On the whole, the β-aminoacyl compounds apparently behaved similarly. The anaesthetic activity decreased with a change from α- to β-substituted acyls.

Czechoslovakian workers[98,99], working with mesocaine, exchanged the —NHCO— for —NHCH$_2$—, —CO$_2$—, —COCH$_2$—, —OCH$_2$—, —CONHCH$_2$—, —CO$_2$CH$_2$—, —CH$_2$OCH$_2$—, —CH$_2$SCH$_2$—, and —COCH(CH$_2$NEt$_2$)$_2$, observing for nearly all compounds an increased effect both in surface and in infiltration anaesthesia. Tests for intradermal irritability showed, however, some advantages of the amide bond.

By reversing the intermediate chain in lignocaine Larizza and Pellegrino[100] obtained compounds of type (*XXXIV*). In the pharmacological tests these compounds exhibited anaesthetic activity[101] in association with a distinct central depressant action. Alkylation or acylation of the aromatic nitrogen in lignocaine lowered activity[47,102]. Some derivatives of lignocaine in which the amide nitrogen was further substituted, as in cinnamoyl-lignocaine (*XXXV*), have a long duration of action on the rabbit cornea[103].

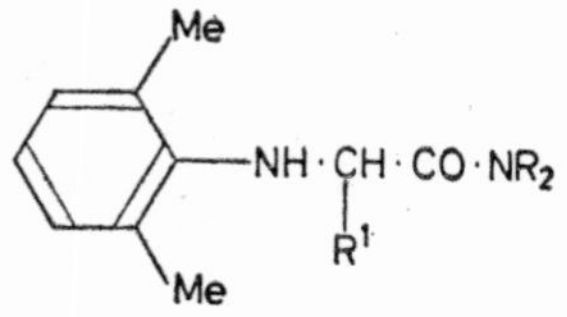

(*XXXIV*)

$NR_2 = NMe_2, NEt_2, NC_4H_8, NC_5H_{10}, NC_4H_8O$
R = H, Me, Et

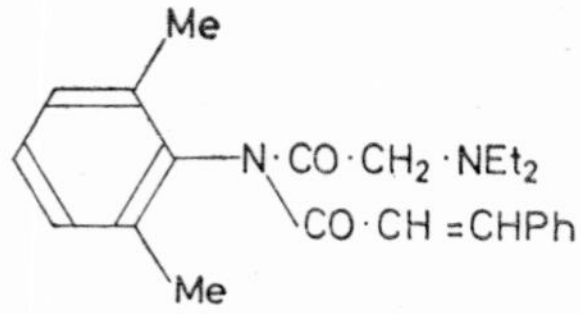

(*XXXV*)

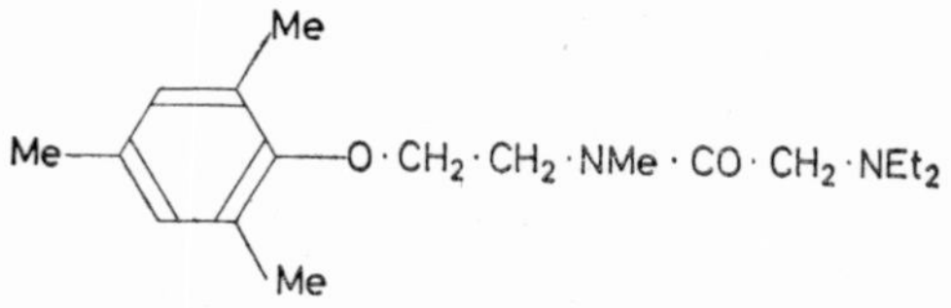

(*XXXVI*)

The many different types of compounds investigated by Koelzer and Wehr[104] included aminoacylphenoxyethylamides, which exhibited anaesthetic activity. While these compounds approximated to cinchocaine in their effect, their toxicity equalled that of procaine. The most active of them was (*XXXVI*), with an activity about three times that of cinchocaine.

## Urethanes and Ureas

Earlier work with this group of compounds has been reviewed by Soehring and Rautmann[105]. Only two urethanes, diperodon (diperocaine, Diothane, *XXXVII*) and Carbacaine (*XXXVIII*)[105a], have so far been clinically introduced as local anaesthetics.

344

Esterification of a series of dialkylamino-alcohols with phenylcarbamic acid gave compounds such as (*XXXIX*), with a variety of substituents at

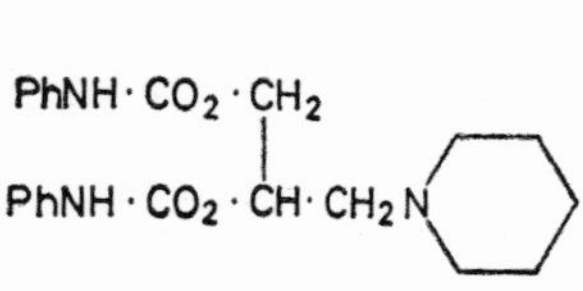

$$PhNH \cdot CO_2 \cdot CH_2$$
$$PhNH \cdot CO_2 \cdot CH \cdot CH_2 N$$

(*XXXVII*) Diperodon

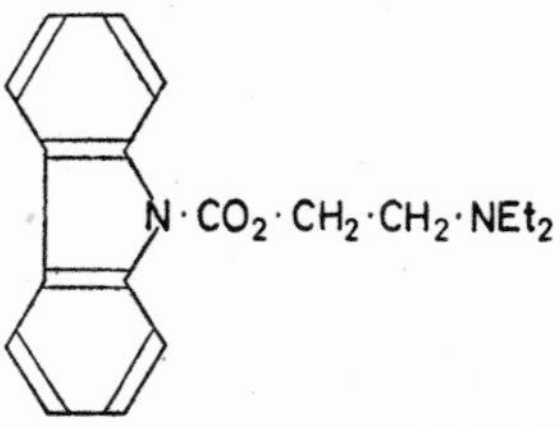

$$N \cdot CO_2 \cdot CH_2 \cdot CH_2 \cdot NEt_2$$

(*XXXVIII*)  Carbacaine

$$CH_2 \cdot NRR^1$$
$$PhNH \cdot CO_2 \cdot CH$$
$$CH_2 \cdot NR^2R^3$$
$$(XXXIX)$$

the amino nitrogen. It was found that while the compounds were, on the whole, active surface anaesthetics—this being particularly true of the dipiperidino derivative—they gave rise to irritation[106]. When the influence of different amino components upon the intravenous toxicity was studied, the following order of rising toxicity emerged:

$$morpholino < NMe_2 < NBu_2 < NEt_2 < NPr_2 < NPr^i_2$$

The study of another short series of carbamates showed that the compound (*XL*) was active on guinea-pig cornea, was slightly irritant, and had

$$PhNH \cdot CO_2 \cdot CHPh \cdot CH_2 \cdot CH_2 \cdot NMe_2$$
$$(XL)$$

a low toxicity[107]. Relatively few workers have investigated substituted phenylcarbamates; a fact which prompted Hutton[108] to study *p*-amino-

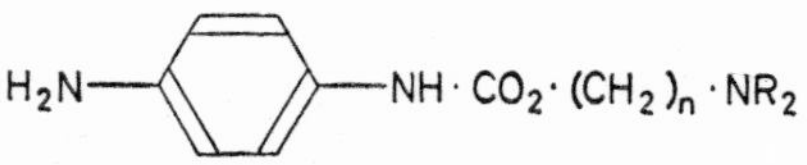

$$H_2N-\!\!\!\!\bigcirc\!\!\!\!-NH \cdot CO_2 \cdot (CH_2)_n \cdot NR_2$$

(*XLI*)

$$NR_2 = NEt_2, NC_4H_8O, NC_5H_{10}$$
$$n = 2,3$$

phenyl derivatives (*XLI*) as well as various mono- and dialkoxyphenyl derivatives. He found them to be fairly active, particularly a veratryl carbamate. Similar compounds with a chloro- or a trifluoromethyl substituent at the *meta* position have been studied[51]. Epstein and Kaminsky[109] investigated *o*-, *m*- and *p*-chloro substituted phenylcarbamates of diethylaminoethanol and of the corresponding isopropanol derivative. They detected no appreciable correlation between the position of the chlorine atom in the nucleus, and the anaesthetic activity. *N*-Substituted 2-aminopropyl derivatives, on the other hand, were generally more active than the corresponding aminoethyl compounds. With different substituents at the amino nitrogen they found that diethylaminoethyl and dibutylaminoethyl esters had a greater anaesthetic effect than the dimethylaminoethyl, diisopropylaminoethyl or

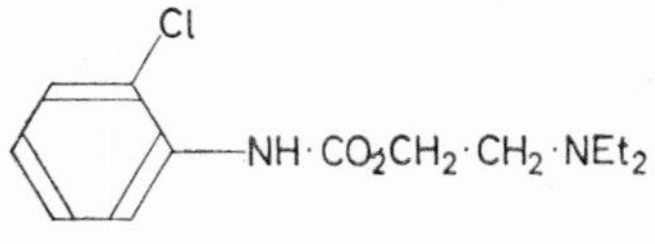

$$\text{Cl} \quad -\text{NH·CO}_2\text{CH}_2\text{·CH}_2\text{·NEt}_2$$

*(XLII)*

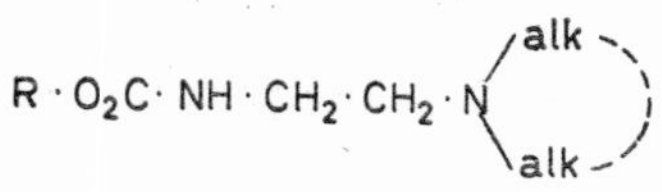

$$\text{R·O}_2\text{C·NH·CH}_2\text{·CH}_2\text{·N}\overset{\text{alk}}{\underset{\text{alk}}{}}$$

*(XLIII)*

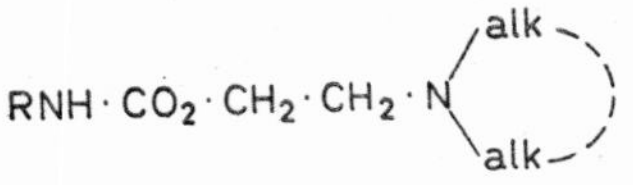

$$\text{RNH·CO}_2\text{·CH}_2\text{·CH}_2\text{·N}\overset{\text{alk}}{\underset{\text{alk}}{}}$$

*(XLIV)*

morpholinoethyl derivatives. The compound *(XLII)* had only one-third the effect of cocaine when tested on the rabbit cornea. Tested by infiltration in guinea-pigs, it was approximately four times as active as procaine. When compared to procaine in sciatic nerve block, it was five times as active without a vasoconstrictor drug, and equally effective with addition of adrenaline. A few chloro substituted urethanes have been reported by Häring[110–112], who studied urethanes of two types; compounds of the general formula *(XLIII)* and compounds in which the carboxylamino moiety had been reversed *(XLIV)*. Aryl and aralkyl esters of the former type *(XLIII)* were prepared. With a longer carbon chain in the aralkyl group, Häring observed an increase in the local anaesthetic effect, but also an increased toxicity, both for the diethylamino and the pyrrolidino derivatives. Substitution with methoxy or amino groups at the aromatic nucleus, yielded compounds with properties inferior to those of corresponding unsubstituted derivatives. Substitution with chloro or methyl groups at the benzene nucleus, on the other hand, resulted in greater anaesthetic potency, which was particularly evident following substitution in the 2,6-positions. The introduction of higher alkyls gave rise to severe irritation (necrosis).

Reversal of the carboxylamino linkage *(XLIV)* generally yielded compounds less irritant and of lower toxicity, but with a more or less unchanged anaesthetic effect. Here too, the pyrrolidino derivatives exhibited satisfactory pharmacological attributes. The only morpholino compound tested was devoid of anaesthetic effect.

Koelzer and Wehr[113] investigated the $N$-aminoalkyl-$N'$-phenylureas, principally of type $(XLV)$ where $R^1$ represented hydrogen, alkyl, aryl or aralkyl, and where $R^2$ represented hydrogen, chlorine or methyl. With

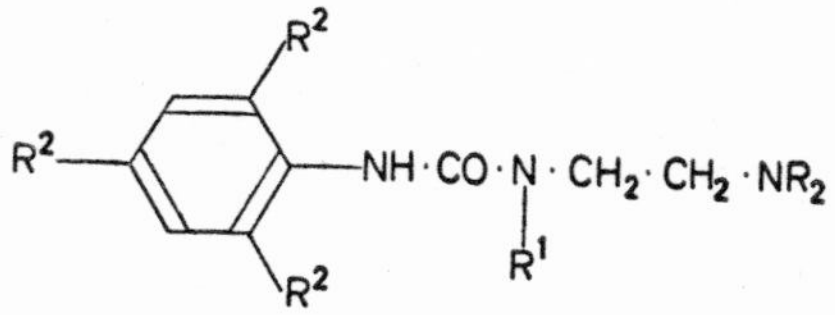

(XLV)

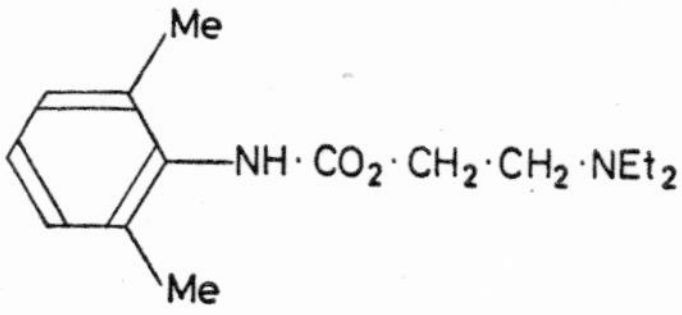

(XLVI)

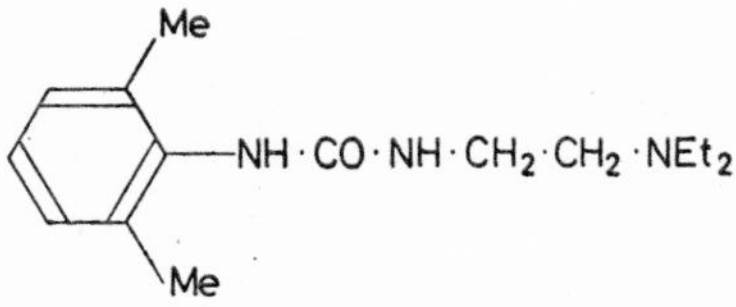

(XLVII)

$R^1$ as hydrogen the compounds frequently showed an anaesthetic effect only at high concentrations, and had a long latency of action. When an alkyl group was introduced, lengthening of its chain was associated with more rapid induction and a higher incidence of anaesthesia, but increasing toxicity. In these respects aryl- and aralkyl-substituted compounds occupied a position between the alkyl-substituted and the unsubstituted derivatives. Sekera and his collaborators have continued their studies of diethyl-aminoethyl carbamates. Their first investigations comprised alkyl and dialkylcarbamates[114–116], and subsequent ones were concerned with aryl-carbamates[55,117–119], which were compared with corresponding anilides. The incorporation of methyl or aralkyl groups at the 2- or the 2,6-positions increased the activity in both surface and infiltration anaesthesia. The compound $(XLVI)$, as compared with lignocaine, had four times the surface effect and about one and a half times the effect in infiltration anaesthesia. The same compounds, as well as other related ones, were synthesized contemporaneously by Dahlbom and Österberg[120], who found them to possess considerably greater toxicity than lignocaine. The urea derivatives $(XLVII)$, corresponding to the urethanes, were devoid of effect at the concentrations tested[120]. Some diarylcarbamates of the general formula (*XLVIII*), where $R^1$ and $R^2$ are H, EtO or BuO, when tested in surface and infiltration anaesthesia, showed high activity. Most active was the *m*-butoxy derivative $(R^1 = H; R^2 = 3\text{-BuO})$, which, in addition to having 75 times the surface

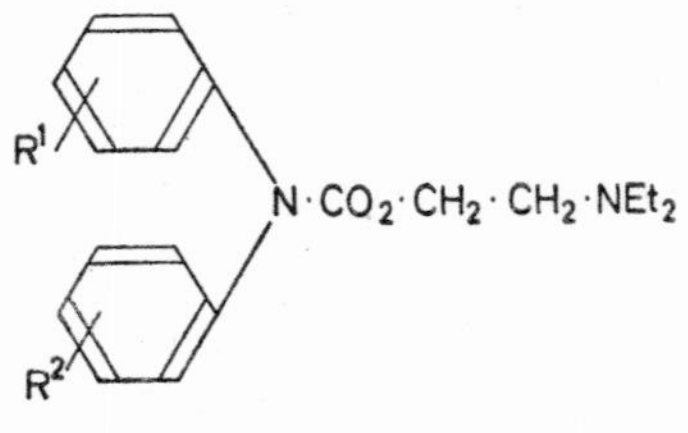

*(XLVIII)*

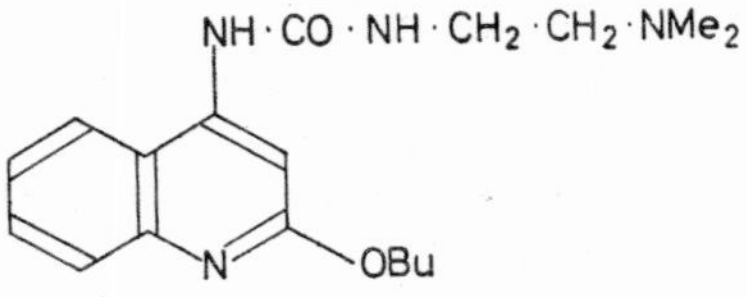

*(XLIX)*

effect of cocaine and, in infiltration anaesthesia, 40 times the effect of procaine, was of relatively low toxicity. Similar pharmacological properties were recorded for aryloxy- and aralkyloxyphenyl-carbamates[119,121]. A number of bisurethanes in which alkyl and alkoxy substituents were introduced into the aromatic nucleus of diperodon (*XXXVII*), showed an elevation of the local anaesthetic effect, the irritation generally showing a corresponding rise[122]. The carbamic acid analogue (*XLIX*) of cinchocaine has a local anaesthetic effect, and a toxicity comparable with that of cinchocaine[123].

*Aminoalkylamides*

Relatively few aminoalkylamides have been synthesized, and only one compound, cinchocaine (dibucaine, Nupercaine, Percaine, *L*), has come into

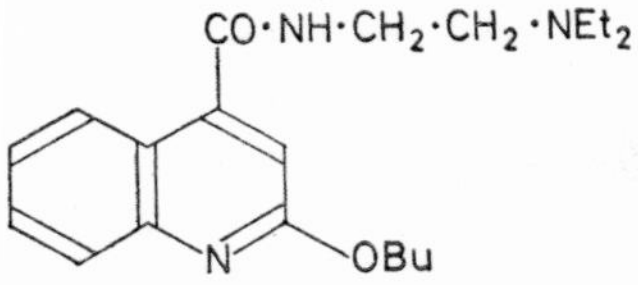

*(L)* Cinchocaine

clinical use on any major scale. This may be attributed to the fact that these amides are less satisfactory anaesthetics than the corresponding esters and

produce greater irritation. Büchi and Perlia[124] synthesized certain cinchocaine homologues and investigated their physical properties in detail.
Sieger, Ziegler, Klein and Sokol studied the diethylaminoalkylamides of
3-hydroxy- and 3-alkoxynaphthalene-2-carboxylic acid (*LI*) and compared

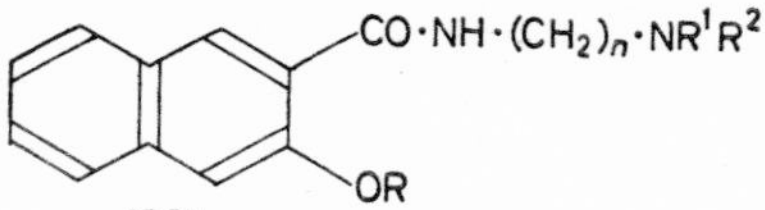

(*LI*)

$R = H, Et, Bu$
$R^1 = H, Et$
$R^2 = Et, Pr^i$
$n = 2, 3$

them with the corresponding esters[125]. Though more stable, the amides were
generally more toxic as well. A few cinchocaine compounds, in which the
butoxy group had been exchanged for a methoxy, ethoxy or an ethoxy-
ethyloxy group, showed reduced toxicity, but this modification also impaired
other essential properties[126].

Häring and Stille[127] studied, in the cinchocaine molecule, the effect of (*1*)
substitution of pyrrolidino for the diethylamino group, and (*2*) transposition
of the butoxy group to 3- position (*o-* to the amide group)—two measures
which, in previous investigations, they had found to augment local
anaesthetic activity. This time, however, the pyrrolidino substitution failed
to alter the activity, but lowered toxicity. The *ortho* substitution, on the
other hand, reduced the surface effect. Of the aminoalkylamides, those
derived from substituted benzoic acids have received the greatest attention
in the last few years[128-131]. The effect on the rabbit cornea of a number of
methylated benzamides of the general formula (*LII*) has been compared

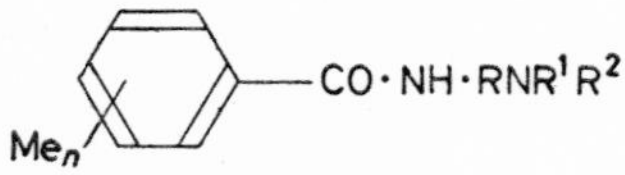

(*LII*)

R = straight or branched alkyl
$NR^1R^2 = NMe_2, NEt_2, NC_4H_8O$

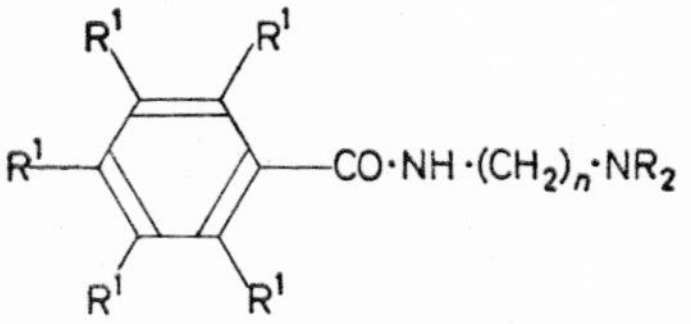

(*LIII*)

with that of lignocaine. Although in general the new compounds were less
active than the reference substance, a few were more active but also more
toxic. Similar compounds were studied by Honkanen[132] in his investigation
of sterically hindered local anaesthetics. For amides of the type (*LIII*)

Honkanen noted the following general associations between structure and action:

(*1*) With variations in the amino component, —NR$_2$, local anaesthesia (surface and infiltration anaesthesia and nerve block) was intensified with increasing length of R, but the solubility of the compounds decreased, and they possessed a higher toxicity and exerted greater irritation.

(*2*) An increase of the number of methylene groups in the intermediate chain from two to three, reduced both the local anaesthetic activity and the toxicity.

(*3*) Di-*o*-substitution in the benzoic acid moiety generally served to augment the activity. The superiority of 2-chloro-6-methyl substituted

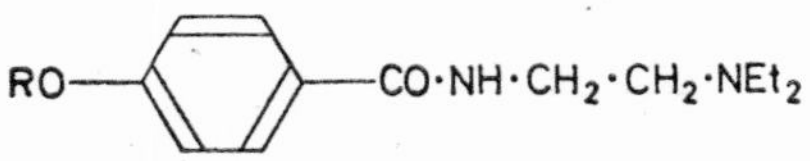

RO—⟨benzene ring⟩—CO·NH·CH$_2$·CH$_2$·NEt$_2$

*(LIV)*

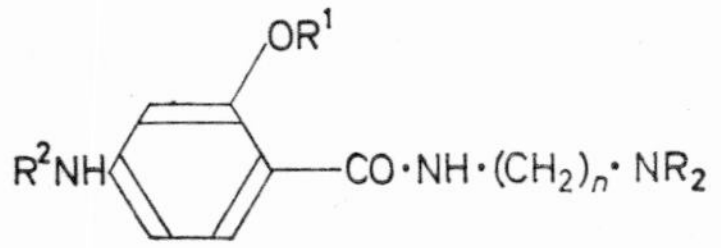

R$^2$NH—⟨benzene ring, OR$^1$⟩—CO·NH·(CH$_2$)$_n$·NR$_2$

*(LV)*

R—⟨benzene ring⟩—CO·NH—⟨benzene ring⟩—NMe$_2$

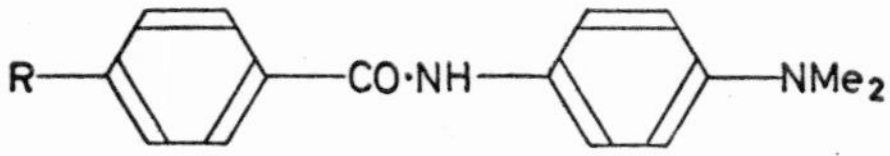

*(LVI)*

R = Me, MeO, NO$_2$, NH$_2$

derivatives over 2,6-dimethyl substituted, as observed in the lignocaine series[38],[39], was not found in the amides investigated.

(*4*) *p*-Alkoxy-substitution enhanced the local anaesthetic effect but increased the toxicity. A maximum effect was recorded with the pentoxy derivatives. An amino group in *meta* position in the acid moiety reduced both the toxicity and the local anaesthetic action, whereas *para* substitution had the opposite effect. When a *p*-amino group was alkylated, the activity increased appreciably, but so did the irritation. Acylation of the amino group, on the other hand, gave an inactive compound. Comparison of esters of *p*-alkoxybenzoic acids and the corresponding amides (*LIV*) showed the latter to have a weaker anaesthetic effect with no effect on toxicity[133]. Another comparative study on compounds of the general type (*LV*) also showed that activity was generally lower than that of the corresponding esters, while the irritation effect and toxicity were unchanged[65],[134]. Many of the higher homologues had an antifibrillatory action. Substitution of a *p*-phenylene for the ethylene component of aroylethylenediamines as in (*LVI*), destroyed the surface anaesthetic property[135]. $o$-Alkoxybenzoic acid amides $(LVII)$ exhibit local anaesthetic properties but the compounds were more toxic and produced greater irritation than did lignocaine. One compound of this

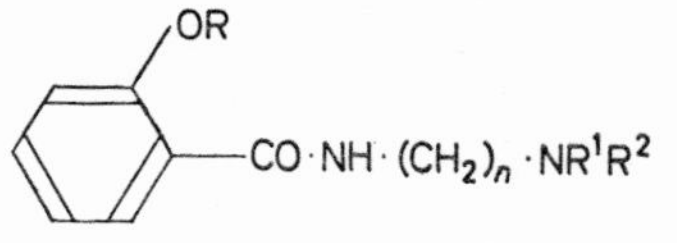

$(LVII)$

structure in which R is butyl, $NR^1R^2$ is pyrrolidino and $n$ is 2, has properties similar to those of lignocaine[137].

As a part of work on psychopharmacological agents, various aryloxyacetic acid amides of several alkylaminoalkylamines were synthesized[138]. According to preliminary tests the compounds possessed slight local anaesthetic activity, notably in the diethylaminoethyl derivatives. Some $N$-(dialkylaminoalkyl)-indolecarboxamides displayed anaesthetic activity, but they were unusable in practice because of side reactions, which included a distinct oxytocic effect[139].

### Aminoalkyl Esters of Carboxylic Acids

Since the introduction of procaine by Einhorn[140], esters of this type have been the subject of intensive study. Carney[141] in an exhaustive survey mentioned more than one thousand esters which had been tested for local anaesthetic properties. Somewhat later, Büchi[142] also presented a review of anaesthetics of this type. Many compounds referable to this group have been employed clinically and some of them are listed in *Table 7.1*.

In order to obtain esters possessing a lower hydrolysis rate, esters of sterically hindered alkyl substituted benzoic acids were prepared[143]. Such derivatives had a longer duration than the corresponding compounds not

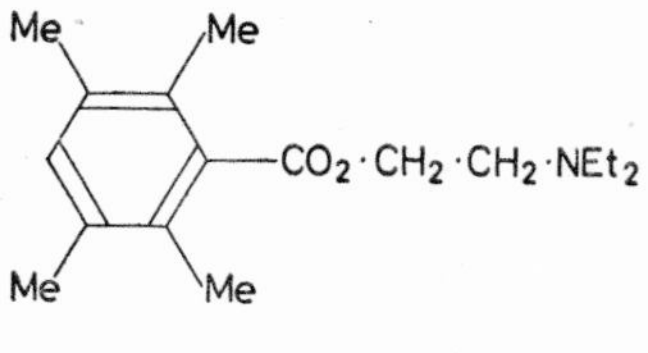

$(LIX)$

sterically hindered. This behaviour was most evident for the tetramethyl derivative $(LIX)$, which was more active than procaine and showed a longer duration both on topical application and on injection.

Investigations of aryl or aralkyl carboxylic acids include those of 4-piperidyl esters $(LX)$ of, for example, benzoic acid, phenoxyacetic acid, cinnamic acid and dihydrocinnamic acid[144]. Samarina[145] tested the activities of some of these compounds, and found that the phenoxyacetic acid esters were inferior to the other esters. Of the esters investigated those of cinnamic

Table 7.1. Local anaesthetics of the ester type.

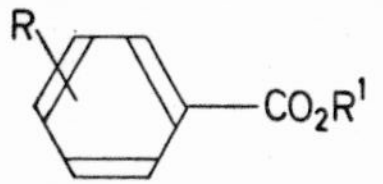

(LVIII)

| Derivative number | R | R¹ | Approved name | Other name |
|---|---|---|---|---|
| 1 | H | $CHMe \cdot CH_2 \cdot NH \cdot C_6H_{11}$* | Hexylcaine | Cyclaine |
| 2 | H | $CH_2 \cdot CMe_2 \cdot NHPr$ | Meprylcaine | Oracaine |
| 3 | H | $(CH_2)_3 \cdot NC_6H_{12}$† | Piperocaine | Metycaine, Neothesin |
| 4 | 4-EtO | $(CH_2)_2 \cdot NEt_2$ | Parethoxycaine | Intracaine, Maxicaine |
| 5 | 4-$C_6H_{11}O$ | $(CH_2)_3 \cdot NC_6H_{12}$† | Cyclomethycaine | Surfathesin, Surfacaine |
| 6 | 4-$NH_2$ | $(CH_2)_2 \cdot NEt_2$ | Procaine | Novocaine |
| 7 | 4-$NH_2$ | $(CH_2)_2 \cdot NPr_2^i$ | | Isocaine |
| 8 | 4-$NH_2$ | $(CH_2)_2 \cdot NHBu^i$ | Butethamine | Monocaine |
| 9 | 4-$NH_2$ | $(CH_2)_2 \cdot NHC_5H_{11}$ | Naepaine | Amylsine |
| 10 | 4-$NH_2$ | $CH_2 \cdot CHBu^i \cdot NEt_2$ | Leucinocaine | Panthesine |
| 11 | 4-$NH_2$ | $(CH_2)_3 \cdot NBu_2$ | Butacaine | Butyn, Butelline |
| 12 | 4-$NH_2$ | $(CHMe)_2 \cdot CH_2 \cdot NMe_2$ | Butamin | Tutocaine |
| 13 | 4-$NH_2$ | $CH_2 \cdot CMe_2 \cdot CH_2 \cdot NEt_2$ | Dimethocaine | Larocaine |
| 14 | 4-NHPr | $CH_2 \cdot CH(OH) \cdot CH_2 \cdot NMe_2$ | Amethocaine | Cornecaine |
| 15 | 4-NHBu | $(CH_2)_2 \cdot NMe_2$ | Tetracaine | Pontocaine, Pantocaine, Anethaine, Decicaine |
| 16 | 3-$NH_2$-2-OH | $(CH_2)_2 \cdot NHBu^i$ | Metabutethamine | Unacaine |
| 17 | 4-NHBu-2-OH | $(CH_2)_2 \cdot NEt_2$ | Hydroxyprocaine | Oxycaine, Oxyprocaine |
| 18 | 4-NHBu-2-OH | $(CH_2)_2 \cdot NMe_2$ | Hydroxyamethocaine | Rhenocaine, Salicaine |
| 19 | 4-$NH_2$-2-OPr | $(CH_2)_2 \cdot NEt_2$ | Propoxycaine | Ravocaine, Pravocaine |
| 20 | 3-$NH_2$-4-OPr | $(CH_2)_2 \cdot NEt_2$ | Propoxymetacaine | Proparacaine, Ophthaine |
| 21 | 4-$NH_2$-2-OBu | $(CH_2)_2 \cdot NEt_2$ | Ambucaine | Sympocaine, Butoxycaine |
| 22 | 4-$NH_2$-3-Cl | $(CH_2)_2 \cdot NEt_2$ | Benoxinate | Oxybuprocaine, Butoxyprocaine, Dorsacaine, Novesin |
| 23 | 4-$NH_2$-2-Cl | $(CH_2)_2 \cdot NEt_2$ | Chloroprocaine | Nesacaine |
| 24 | 3-$NH_2$-2-OBu | $(CH_2)_2 \cdot NEt_2$ | Metambucaine | Metabutoxycaine, Primacaine |

* Cyclohexyl  † 2-methylpiperidino

acid were the most irritant, and among the various methyl substituted allyl (propenyl) compounds the irritation increased with the number of carbon atoms.

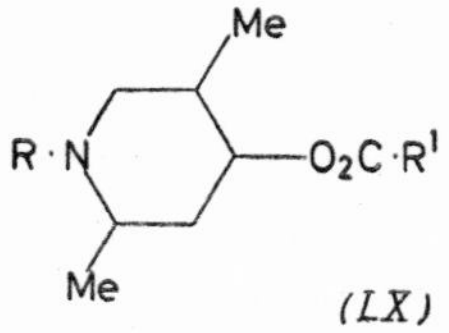

$$R \cdot N \overset{Me}{\underset{Me}{\diamondsuit}} O_2C \cdot R^1$$

(LX)

R = $CH_2 \cdot CH : CH_2$      $R^1$= Ph
     $CH_2 \cdot CH : CHMe$      $CH_2 Ph$
     $CH_2 \cdot CH : CMe_2$      $CH_2 \cdot CH_2 Ph$
         $CH : CHPh$
         $CH_2 \cdot OPh$

Kucheruk[146] reported that the compound (LXI) was two to three times as toxic as procaine but approximately eight times as active.

$$PhO \cdot CH_2 \cdot CO_2 \cdot CEtPh \cdot (CH_2)_2 \cdot NMe_2$$
$$(LXI)$$

Of a large number of diesters of type (LXII)

$$CO_2 \cdot CHPh \cdot CH_2 \cdot NR_2$$
$$|$$
$$X$$
$$|$$
$$CO_2 \cdot CHPh \cdot CH_2 \cdot NR_2$$
$$(LXII)$$

(where X = $CH_2CH_2$; $o\text{-}C_6H_4$; $p\text{-}C_6H_4$, and where R = lower alkyl or $NR_2$ = a heterocycle) studied, those derived from aromatic acids showed only slight anaesthetic activity, whereas the succinic acid esters were more active than lignocaine. Their anaesthetic action, however, was generally accompanied by a curariform effect[147]. Further study of the compounds obtained by esterification of 2-amino-1-phenylethanols and 2-amino-2-phenylethanols with various substituted or unsubstituted benzoic acids, aryloxyacetic acids and heterocyclic carboxylic acids, showed that the local anaesthetic effect was related to the structure. Among the best acids was phenoxyacetic acid, the esters of which were found to possess anaesthetic activity and relatively low toxicity.

Esters of dialkylaminoalkoxyphenyl ethanols were recently investigated and proved to be more active, although somewhat more toxic than the previously investigated esters[148].

Honkanen[132] conducted a very extensive investigation into sterically hindered local anaesthetics of varying type. Among the benzoic acid derivatives of the general formula (LXIII), the anaesthetic effect in surface and infiltration anaesthesia and nerve block was related to the length of the alkyl group $R^1$. Steric blocking of the ester linkage resulted in an elevated anaesthetic effect. As regards $p$-substitution, Honkanen observed that of the alkoxy derivatives, propoxy and isobutoxy were the best in the relevant series. The majority of compounds, however, produced fairly severe irritation. Häring[111] prepared other benzoic acid derivatives, with similar results.

Recently, considerable interest has been focussed on esters of alkoxy and polyalkoxy substituted aromatic acids. Among the mono-substituted

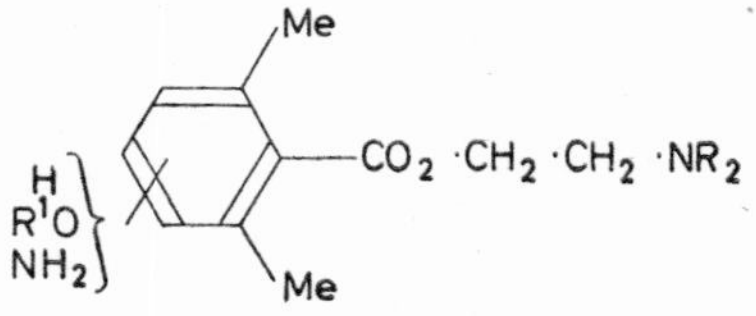

*(LXIII)*

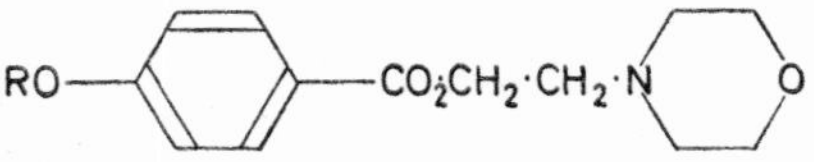

*(LXIV)*

alkoxy-carboxylic acids it was found that the longer the alkyl chain, the better was the anaesthetic effect. While the $p$-methoxy substituted derivative was less active than procaine, the corresponding ethoxy derivative was more active. The introduction of an additional oxygen atom, as in alkoxy-ethoxy compounds, reduced the anaesthetic effect[149]. In some instances, moreover, irreversible anaesthesia appears to have been produced[150].

A series of monoalkoxybenzoic acid esters of morpholinoethanol (*LXIV*) have been reported to be twice as active as procaine on rabbit cornea, and only one half as toxic[151]. On lengthening of the alkyl group, R, the activity first increased and then declined, probably because of solubility factors. The optimum length for an alkyl group apparently depends on the rest of the molecular structure[132,147]. The diethylaminoethyl ester of acetylsalicylic acid, prepared by Szadowska and Ciborska[152], exhibited an anaesthetic effect equal to that of procaine and a toxicity only one-half that of procaine. On the introduction of two alkoxy groups, an increase of the anaesthetic effect was observed upon rabbit cornea. Using esters of dihydrocinnamic acid, a further augmentation of the activity, as compared to benzoic acid, was obtained without demonstrable irritation[153].

The esters of the trialkoxybenzoic acids are often reported to be totally devoid of anaesthetic effect, but this is not true of all compounds of this type[154]. Such compounds (*LXV*) in aqueous solution have a slight anaesthetic effect, probably due to the fact that even at very low concentrations the molecules associated to form inactive aggregates, which when split, as for example by addition of an alcohol (propane-1,2-diol), produced an anaesthetic effect.

Among hydroxy and alkoxy derivatives of polycyclic acids, one (*LXVI*) was more active than lignocaine on rabbit's cornea, and at the same time was somewhat less toxic[125].

The combination of alkoxy groups with amino groups in the benzoic acid moiety has led to the development of numerous clinically serviceable drugs (see *Table 7.1*). For example, several mono- and dialkylaminoethyl

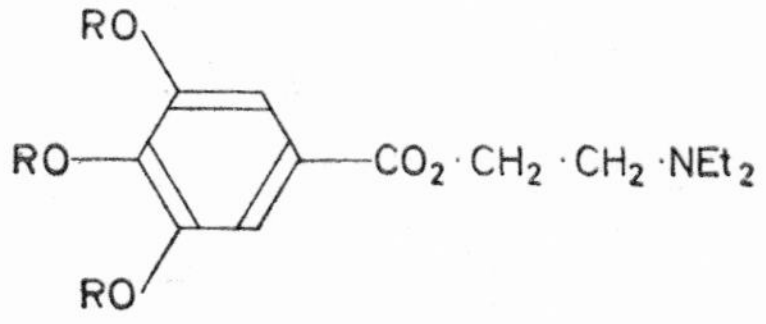

$$RO \begin{array}{c} \\ \end{array} CO_2 \cdot CH_2 \cdot CH_2 \cdot NEt_2$$

*(LXV)*

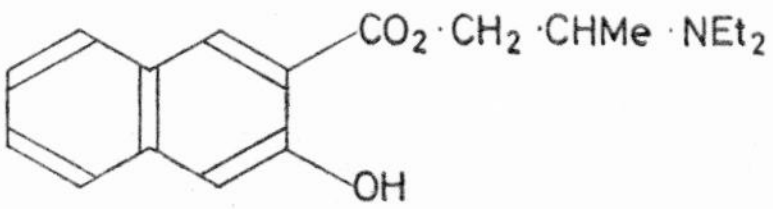

$$CO_2 \cdot CH_2 \cdot CHMe \cdot NEt_2 \\ OH$$

*(LXVI)*

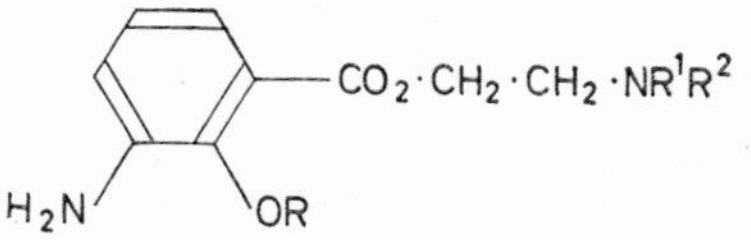

$$CO_2 \cdot CH_2 \cdot CH_2 \cdot NR^1R^2 \\ H_2N \qquad OR$$

*(LXVII)*

esters of 2-, 5- and 6-alkoxy substituted 3-aminobenzoic acids were prepared and tested by Epstein and Meyer[155], a number of them showing local anaesthetic properties. Compound (*LXVII*, R = $C_5H_{11}$, $R^1$ = H, $R^2$ = $C_5H_{11}$) tested on rabbit cornea, was approximately 200 times as effective as cocaine, while a related compound (*LXVII*, R = Bu, $R^1$ = $R^2$ = Et) displayed a combination of properties so impressive that it was introduced clinically under the name of metambucaine (metabutoxycaine, Primacaine). A few 4-alkoxy derivatives isomeric with these compounds were subsequently prepared as also were esters of 3-alkoxy-4-aminobenzoic acids[156].

A study of procaine derivatives containing halogens, alkoxy groups and alkylthio groups at the 2- and the 3-position in the aromatic nucleus, showed that electron-releasing radicals were more effective at the *ortho* than at the *meta* position, whereas electron-attracting groups were more effective at the *meta* position. The most active compounds were methylmercapto and ethyl-mercapto derivatives, which in surface anaesthesia were approximately one and a half times as effective as cocaine[157]. By exchanging the *p*-amino group in procaine and a few closely related derivatives for an alkoxycarbonylamino group, compounds characterized by a high anaesthetic activity on rabbit cornea were obtained[158,159]. Zirm and Pongratz[160] recently described the result of introducing a nicotinoyl group at the $p$-amino group in procaine. They found their new compound to be a less toxic and more active anaesthetic than procaine. In clinical trials it has been used without addition of a vasoconstrictor.

The introduction of 2-chloroprocaine to therapy, brought a revival of interest in esters of halogenated acids. The anaesthetic effect of dimethyl, diethyl and piperidinoethyl esters of $o$-, $m$- and $p$-fluoro-substituted benzoic acids and phenoxyacetic acids, was proved to be less than that of procaine[161].

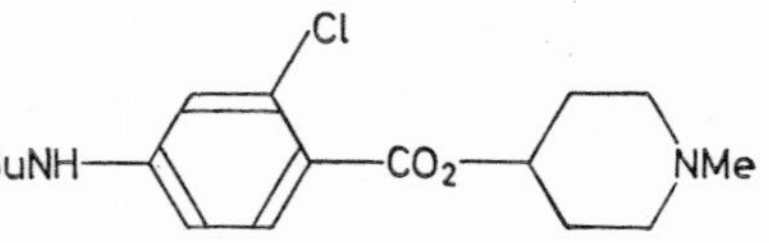

*(LXVIII)*

The most active of them was the dimethylaminoethyl ester of $m$-fluorobenzoic acid. Nearly all of these compounds were found to have local irritant properties, as was consistent with previous experience. However, the piperidino derivatives were exceptions. Reisner and Cordasco[162] continued their investigations of 2-chloro-substituted procaine derivatives, and synthesized 2-chloroprocainamide and 2-chlorothiocaine. These compounds were as active as procaine. Similar substitution in paridocaine has been reported *(LXVIII)*[163]. Basic esters of 3-amino-4-chlorobenzoic acid have also been tested[164], and a few of them have been found somewhat more active than procaine.

Kurihara, Niwa and Ro[165] synthesized dialkylaminoalkyl esters of diphenyl- and diphenylalkoxythio-fatty acids, and compared them with the corresponding fatty acid derivatives. Some of the thio compounds were found to have local anaesthetic activity combined with low toxicity and only slight tissue irritation. A comparative study of thioesters and corresponding esters has been reported by Luduena and Hoppe[166]. Although the thio derivatives were found to be considerably more active, they were also more toxic than corresponding benzoates. The importance of the ester group in molecules such as procaine was further shown by replacing the $—CO_2—$ group by $—CH_2—$, $—CO—$, $—O—$, $—S—$, $—SO—$ and $—SO_2—$. The resultant compounds were devoid of a surface effect and showed substantially reduced activity in nerve block[167].

Some new variations in the amino component have been tried during the last few years. No consistent difference was observed between a series of $\alpha$- and $\beta$-tropine esters of $p$-alkylaminobenzoic acids[168]. As expected, an elevation of the anaesthetic effect was obtained on lengthening the alkyl chain on the $p$-amino group. The most active compound was *(LXIX)* whose action was equal to that of amethocaine, but which proved to have a poorer therapeutic index.

$N$-($\beta$-Hydroxyalkyl)nortropane esters of alkoxy- and amino-benzoic acids and of benzilic acids were more active than procaine in infiltration anaesthesia, but all of them had irritant properties and some were unstable[169].

Linnell and Perks[170] synthesized benzoates, cinnamates and $p$-aminobenzoates of the three hydroxyalkylpyrrolidines (LXX), (LXXI) and (LXXII). The maximum effect of these agents was half that of cocaine.

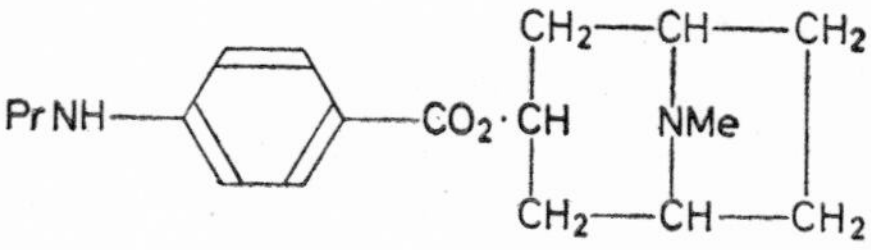

(LXIX)

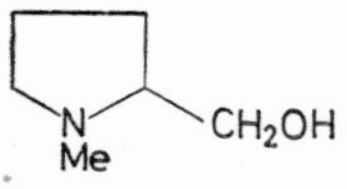

(LXX) 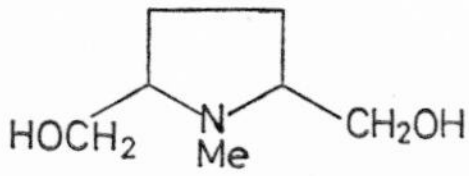　　　　(LXXI) 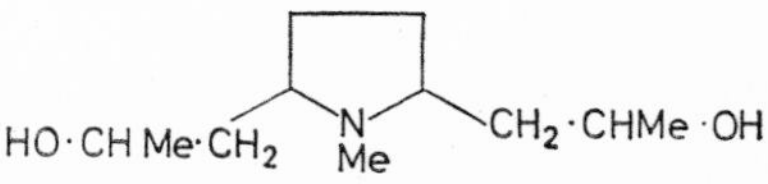　　　　(LXXII)

Frahm and Soehring[171] tested two compounds which they had prepared by exchanging a methylthioethyl for one of the alkyl groups at the dialkylamino function in procaine and in amethocaine respectively. Using intracutaneous wheals they observed a decrease in anaesthetic action, but on topical application (rabbit cornea) there was a slight increase. Both derivatives showed greatly reduced toxicity.

*Aminoketones*

The earliest investigations in this group of compounds were concerned with various hydrogenated or non-hydrogenated heterocyclic ketones[5]. There has been a remarkable paucity of studies during recent years, and only two drugs have, in fact, come into clinical use; namely, Falicaine (LXXIII, R = Pr)

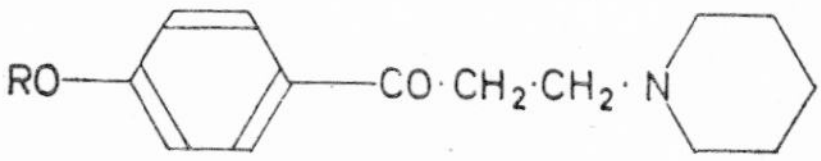

(LXXIII)

and dyclonine (Dyclone, LXXIII, R = Bu). In the last few years the study of aminoketones has centred largely upon these two compounds.

Beani and Fowst in a series of papers[172–174], reported compounds of propiophenone type (LXXIV) in which R was a straight or branched alkyl and R[1] was hydrogen, methyl, ethyl or alkoxy. One compound (LXXIV, R = CH$_2$:CH·CH$_2$; R[1] = Me), which in certain respects showed more favourable properties than Falicaine, was subjected to closer study[174]. This compound, called AMPP, had a lower toxicity than Falicaine, but showed the same irritant properties. The same authors replaced the keto group in $\beta$-piperidinopropiophenone by —CHOH—, —CH$_2$— or —CH=CH—,

357

but found that the optimal anaesthetic effect resided in the ketones[173]. They also observed, however, that the ketones had far greater irritant properties.

Profft continued the investigations[175] that led to the clinical introduction of Falicaine. By incorporating a 4-ethyl group in the piperidino ring and lengthening the *p*-alkoxy chain, he obtained compounds approximating to Falicaine in their anaesthetic activity, but having a substantially longer duration[176]. Profft and Schultz[177] recorded an augmentation of the anaesthetic effect with the $\beta$-pipecoline analogues of Falicaine. When, in addition,

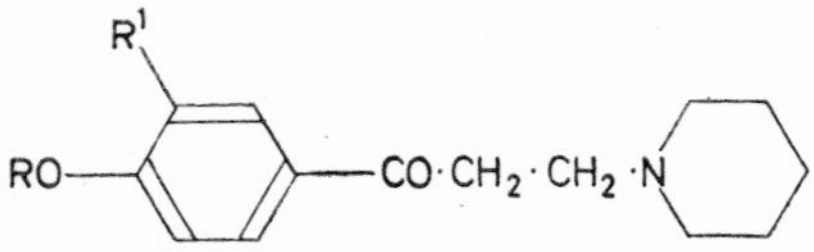

*(LXXIV)*

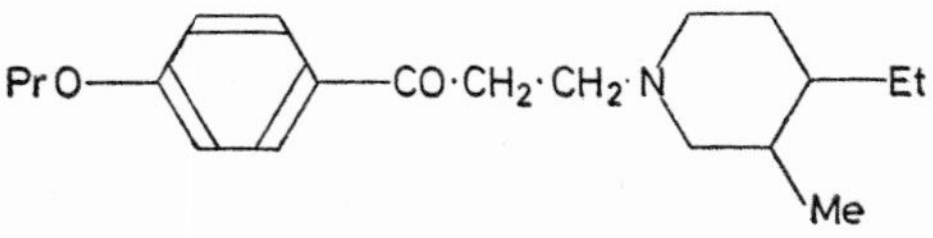

*(LXXV)*

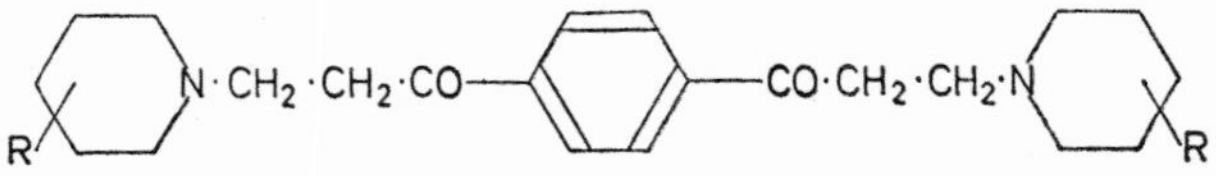

*(LXXVI)*

a 4-ethyl group was introduced, the resulting compound (*LXXV*) was more than twice as active as Falicaine.

Replacement of the benzene nucleus of Falicaine by thiophene[177] produced a substantial decrease in the topical effect. A few thio analogues of morpholino propiophenones have also been synthesized[178].The introduction of sulphur into the molecule reduced the toxicity and increased the anaesthetic effect. When the alkoxy group in Falicaine was replaced by an acyl group[179] the compounds obtained were, in surface anaesthesia, less effective than Falicaine, but approximately four times more active than cocaine. In this series too, alkylation of the piperidino ring, notably at the 4-position, resulted in an increase of the effect. Profft and Hoffmeister[179] observed, with bis compounds of type (*LXXVI*) a further reduction of the surface anaesthetic effect, and noted that in these bis compounds alkylation of the piperidino ring lowered, not increased, activity. Profft and Zschummel[180], continuing their experiments with 4-alkylpiperidinopropiophenones, investigated $\beta$-(4-butylpiperidino) derivatives of *o*- and *p*-alkoxypropiophenone. Amongst the *p*-derivatives were compounds more active than Falicaine, and amongst the

$o$-derivatives they noted unexpectedly high activity. The low water-solubility of most of these compounds, however, has prevented their use in medicine. Some hexamethyleneiminoalkyl ketones ($LXXVII$) have also displayed anaesthetic activity[181].

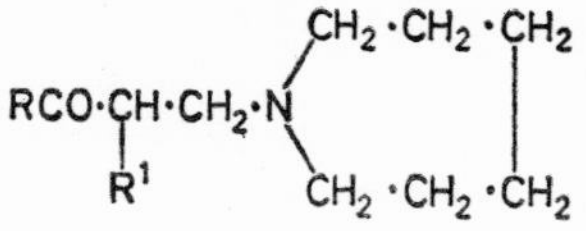

$$RCO \cdot \underset{\underset{R^1}{|}}{CH} \cdot CH_2 \cdot N \underset{CH_2 \cdot CH_2 \cdot CH_2}{\overset{CH_2 \cdot CH_2 \cdot CH_2}{\diagdown}}$$

*(LXXVII)*

$R = Me, Pr^i, Ph, p - BrC_6H_4, p - EtOC_6H_4$
$R^1 = H, Me$

### Amino Ethers

A small number of amino ethers were investigated, though with little success, at the beginning of the present century. Compounds of this type again attracted attention in the early nineteen-fifties, resulting in two clinically useful drugs, pramoxine (Tronothane $LXXVIII$) and dimethisoquin

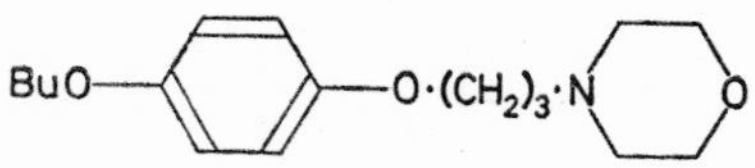

$$BuO \text{—} \underset{}{\bigcirc} \text{—} O \cdot (CH_2)_3 \cdot N \underset{}{\bigcirc} O$$

*(LXXVIII)*  Pramoxine

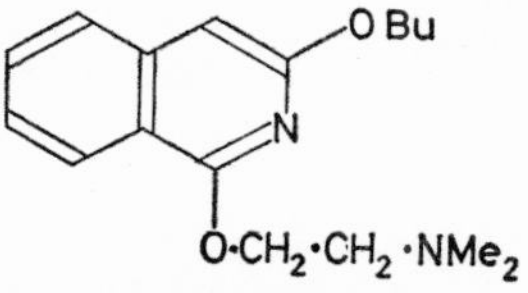

$$\underset{O \cdot CH_2 \cdot CH_2 \cdot NMe_2}{\bigcirc\bigcirc\overset{OBu}{N}}$$

*(LXXIX)* Dimethisoquin

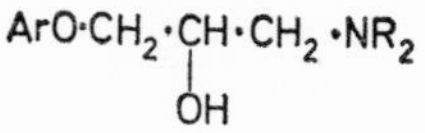

$$ArO \cdot CH_2 \cdot \underset{\underset{OH}{|}}{CH} \cdot CH_2 \cdot NR_2$$

*(LXXX)*

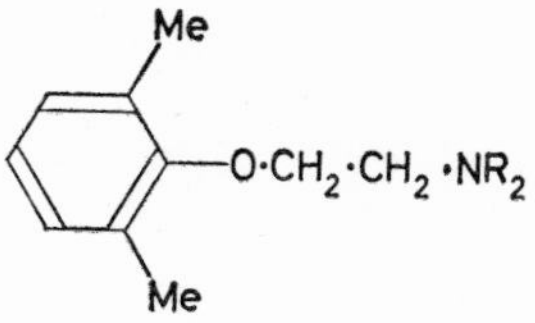

$$\underset{Me}{\overset{Me}{\bigcirc}} \text{—} O \cdot CH_2 \cdot CH_2 \cdot NR_2$$

*(LXXXI)*

$$Ph_2CH \cdot O \cdot CH_2 \cdot \underset{\underset{OH}{|}}{CH} \cdot CH_2 \cdot NR_2$$

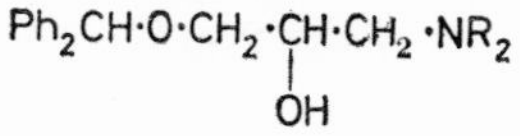

*(LXXXII)*

(Quotane, $LXXIX$). Petrow, Stephenson and Thomas[182], following their studies of aryloxypropane derivatives, prepared derivatives of three different types ($LXXX$), ($LXXXI$), ($LXXXII$), $NR_2$ being a secondary or tertiary amino group. Compounds of type ($LXXX$) showed an appreciable anaesthetic effect on rabbit cornea (*cf.* Ing and Ormerod[183]). The maximum effect observed was with 1-isopropylamino-2-hydroxy-3-$o$-tolyloxypropane, which was more active than procaine but proved to be more toxic. Some of the 2,6-dimethylphenoxy derivatives (type *LXXXI*) had marked surface effects, but owing to the severe irritation none of them was serviceable. The compounds of type (*LXXXII*) were characterized by similar properties. Wheatley and Holrege[184], synthesized a number of dialkylaminoalkyl ethers, mainly of 2,6-di-isopropylphenol, but did not report their pharmacological actions.

The *p*-alkoxy group in compounds of the pramoxine type has been replaced by other substituents, for example, alkoxycarbonyl[151], alkoxycarbonyl-amino[185,186], acylamino[187,188] and alkoxyethoxycarbonylamino[189] but, although many of these were very active, they were also irritant. Further substitution in the benzene ring of aryloxyethylamines, for example, with primary amino and alkoxycarbonyl groups[134], or with primary amino, halogen and alkoxy groups[190-192], has not met with much success.

### Miscellaneous Types

Among the compounds which have come into clinical use the following are worthy of note: phenacaine (Holocain, *LXXXIII*, R = Et), Diocain (*LXXXIII*, R = allyl) and hydroxypolyethoxydodecane (Thesit, *LXXXIV*)

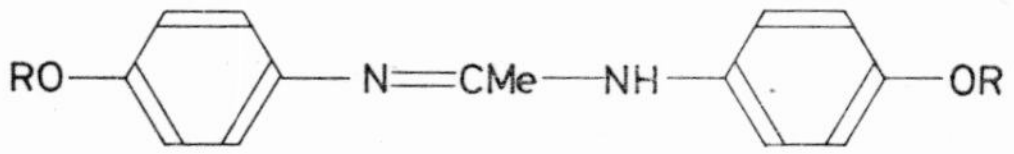

$$RO—\langle\;\rangle—N{=}CMe—NH—\langle\;\rangle—OR$$

*(LXXXIII)*

R = Et , Phenacaine
R = CH$_2$·CH:CH$_2$ , Diocaine

$$C_{12}H_{25}(O\cdot CH_2\cdot CH_2)_n\, OH$$

*(LXXXIV)* Hydroxypolyethoxydodecane

Of nitrogen-free organic compounds, Adler-Hradecky and Kelentey[193] recently investigated *p*-hydroxybenzoic acid esters of alcohols containing from one to twelve carbon atoms. These esters were found to be non-toxic, and those of alcohols with more than four or five carbon atoms exhibited local anaesthetic properties.

Synthesis of new amidine derivatives have been made in the hope of arriving at less irritant compounds. *N,N'*-Disubstituted acetamidines, in which aryl or alkoxyaryl groups were introduced at the nitrogen, were irritant, except for one of them (*LXXXV*) which showed only relatively

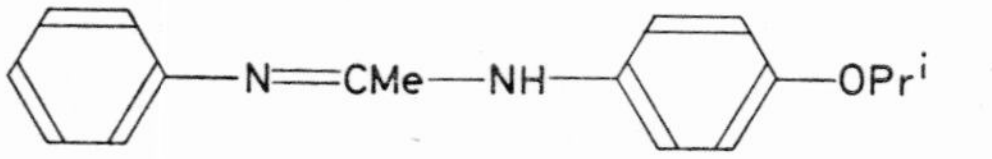

$$\langle\;\rangle—N{=}CMe—NH—\langle\;\rangle—OPr^i$$

*(LXXXV)*

slight irritation and low toxicity, while its anaesthetic potency in various tests was higher than that of procaine[194,195]. Honkanen[132] studied the properties of a large number of amidines of the same type, and found that the incorporation of alkoxy groups resulted in an elevation of the surface anaesthetic effect and a reduction of the toxicity. Introduction of amino instead of alkoxy groups improved the properties in infiltration anaesthesia.

Carelli, Cardellini and Liberatore[196] studied compounds of type (*LXXXVI*)

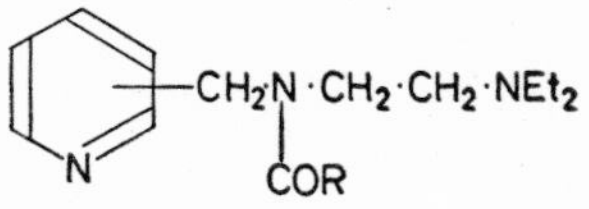

(*LXXXVI*)

R = alkyl, aryl, aralkyl

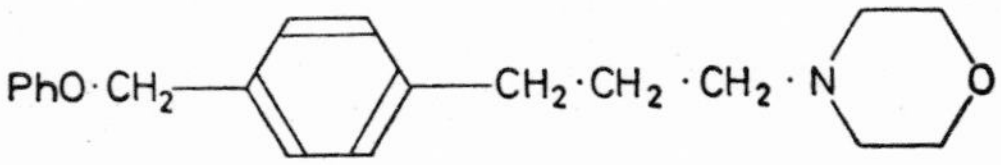

(*LXXXVII*)

as well as the corresponding derivatives in which the diethylamino group had been replaced by aniline. The benzoyl and the cinnamoyl compounds were more active than procaine when tested on rabbit cornea. This was, however, not so with the aliphatic carboxylic acid amides.

Oelschläger[197,198] prepared a series of amines with alkoxy or aryloxy substitution, and of these the phenoxymethyl derivative (*LXXXVII*) revealed favourable properties. It produced little irritation, and was superior to procaine in nerve block.

Chiti[199] recently synthesized ureides, of which the diphenylacetyl derivatives of type (*LXXXVIII*) had a distinct anaesthetic effect when tested on rabbit cornea.

$$Ph_2CH \cdot CO \cdot N \cdot (CH_2)_n \cdot NEt_2$$
$$| $$
$$CO \cdot NH_2$$

(*LXXXVIII*)

Alkoxyphenyl substituted aminopropanols (*LXXXIX*), some of which were subjected to preliminary clinical tests, were synthesized by Epstein[200].

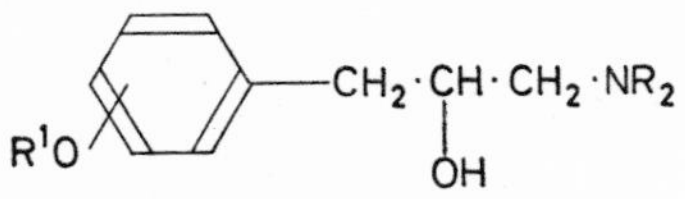

(*LXXXIX*)

He observed that the alkoxy group, when placed at the *ortho* or *meta* position, yielded more active but also more toxic compounds. On lengthening of the alkyl $R^1$ the irritation increased, though to a lesser degree than the anaesthetic effect. With variations of the amino component $NR_2$, Epstein found the allylamino derivative to be the most potent, the aromatic or heterocyclic amines being associated with lower anaesthetic activity.

Masuda and Hamor[201], working with $N$-diethylaminoalkyl derivatives of $o$-benzenedisulphonic acid imide, found that compound ($XC$) on intradermal

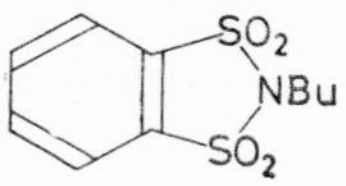

*(XC)*

injection (guinea-pigs) produced anaesthesia of long duration. However, all the other derivatives studied produced severe irritation.

Among the other types of compounds studied may be noted the alcohols ($XCI$) and their $p$-nitro- and $p$-amino-benzoic acid esters, the latter of which

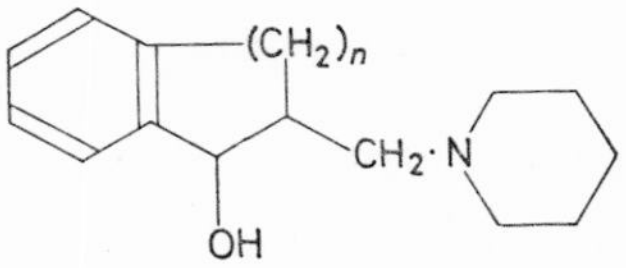

*(XCI)*

$n = 1 - 3$

were active both in surface and in infiltration anaesthesia[202]. The anaesthetic properties of 2-diethylaminoethyl substituted heterocycles (benzimidazole, benzthiazole and quinoline) are reported to be of a similar order to that of procaine[203]. Several heterocyclic compounds of general formula ($XCII$)

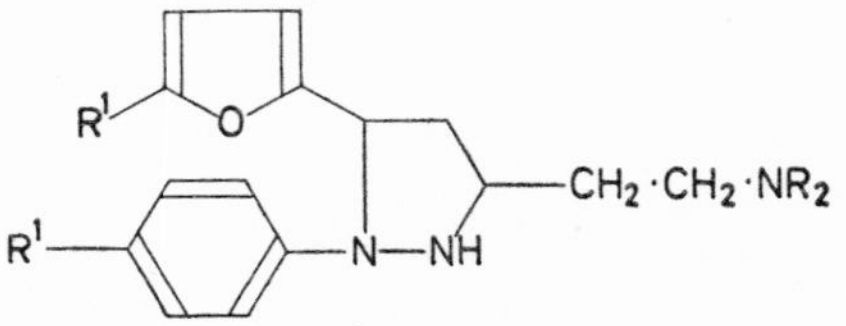

*(XCII)*

$NR_2 = NMe_2, NEt_2, NC_4H_8O$
$R^1 = H, Me$

were found to have no surface anaesthetic properties, but were active in nerve block and infiltration anaesthesia in rats[204,205]. The substances were, however, irritating.

The question as to the local anaesthetic effect of quaternary bases has been studied[206]. It was formerly thought that quaternarization of tertiary bases having local anaesthetic activity served to extinguish the latter, coincident with the appearance of curariform properties. However, benzyl-quaternary derivatives of local anaesthetics such as procaine and amethocaine, while showing a prolonged latency, have a local anaesthetic effect with several times the duration of that of corresponding tertiary bases[206]. A similar increase was demonstrated by Horakova, not only for procaine etho-bromide[207] but also for procaine to which had been added a quaternary salt, as for instance tetraethylammonium bromide[208–210]. The surface anaesthetic effect associated with a tertiary base appears, in general, to be

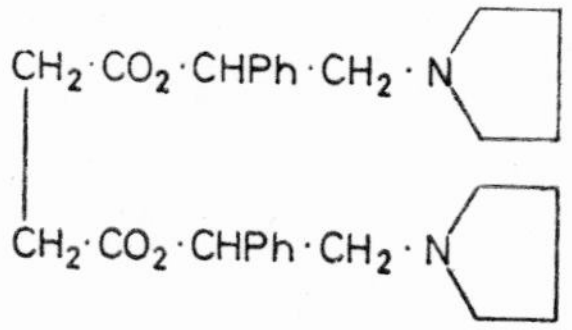

$$CH_2 \cdot CO_2 \cdot CHPh \cdot CH_2 \cdot N$$

$$CH_2 \cdot CO_2 \cdot CHPh \cdot CH_2 \cdot N$$

*(XCIII)*

abolished by quaternarization, and for some compounds differing in type from procaine even the activity in nerve block is apparently reduced[147,211]. As regards the curariform action, the compound *(XCIII)* had, after quaternarization, a substantially reduced curare-like activity[147]—a finding that conflicted with general experience.

### THE RELATIONSHIP BETWEEN STRUCTURE AND LOCAL ANAESTHETIC ACTIVITY

Broadly speaking, the structure of a local anaesthetic may be defined by the general formula:

Lipophilic centre—Intermediate chain—Hydrophilic centre

This formula, which was first propounded by Löfgren[212], comprises the majority of investigated anaesthetics. It also includes, as pointed out by Wiedling[9], some compounds with other pharmacological actions, such as analgesics, quinidine-like compounds, and antagonists to acetylcholine, adrenaline, noradrenaline, histamine, and nicotine. The lipophilic centre usually consists of an aromatic or heterocyclic nucleus, but it may be exchanged for an aralkyl or an alkyl group. In nearly all anaesthetics a secondary or tertiary amino group acts as the hydrophilic centre, even though an alkoxy or a hydroxy group may replace the amino group—as for instance in such alcohols as chlorbutol, benzyl alcohol, and hydroxypoly-ethoxydodecane. The mode of action of these latter compounds, however, usually differs from that of 'true' local anaesthetics. The intermediate chain consists in part of a hydrocarbon bridge attached to the hydrophilic centre and, in part, of an atom or group of atoms such as $—CO_2—$, $—CONH—$, $—NHCO—$, $—NHCONH—$, $—NHCO_2—$, $—CO—$ or $—O—$, attached to the lipophilic centre. Anaesthetics in which the intermediate chain consists solely of a hydrocarbon bridge are also known.

As pointed out notably by Quevauviller[213], a balance between the lipo-philic and the hydrophilic parts of the molecule is essential. If the latter attribute dominates the anaesthetic effect is lost. If, on the other hand, the lipophilic character is unduly marked, the compound is not readily soluble. This intramolecular balance is, for an anaesthetic, a *sine qua non*. It is, moreover, a key factor not merely in the solubility; for, just as is the case with wetting agents—some properties of which may be characterized by an HLB value (hydrophilelipophile balance)—it determines the behaviour of the molecule at interfaces, as for instance cell membranes. The interrelationship of these factors assumes a more complex pattern, however, when the anaesthetic actions of different compounds are considered with special respect to the molecular structure. As Büchi and Perlia[124] have pointed out, this complexity is largely attributable to the fact that the structural formula of a compound does not adequately indicate the form, size nor steric structure, nor the physical properties associated with the pharmacological action. Nor do structural formulae lend themselves to definition of the electron distribution within the molecule. Büchi and Perlia emphasize the importance of those aspects of local anaesthetics which implicate electron theory. Löfgren[212,214] and later Perkow[215] have called attention to the fact that, in all active anaesthetics of ester and amide type, the carbonyl group is activated by a lower electron density at the carbon atom. The electron distribution within the molecule is in turn responsible for those forces (*e.g.* van der Waals', dipole–dipole, hydrogen and ionic bonds) which modify not only the behaviour of the molecule at interfaces, but also association to form larger, anaesthetically inactive aggregates[154]. The fact that an apparently insignificant modification of the molecular structure of a local anaesthetic substantially alters its anaesthetic activity, may frequently be accounted for in terms of electron theory.

There is not the slightest doubt that the physical properties of the molecule are determinant for at least some subdivisions of the course of anaesthesia. Thus, for example, solubility (in aqueous and in lipid phase), dissociation constant, and rate of diffusion are decisive factors in the transport of the molecules to their site of action. The exact behaviour of the molecules on reaching that site still remains unknown.

## MODE OF ACTION OF LOCAL ANAESTHETICS

The mechanism of action of local anaesthetics was recently the subject of a detailed review by Watson[8]. After surveying current theories of the origin and transmission of nerve impulses, Watson outlines the various hypotheses, as well as those concepts of general anaesthesia which have been applied to local anaesthetics—the theories propounded by Overton and Meyer, by Traube and by Warburg, and those which relate to permeability, the coagulation of colloids and proteins, dehydration, acetylcholine, histamine, metabolism, ions, electrical phenomena, and thermodynamic activity. He treats, moreover, other considerations of significance in this context, such as the influence of pH, actions on various nerves and tissues, the structure and properties of local anaesthetic agents, and structural features of the nerves. Also discussed are factors that limit the applicability either of results or theories, such as the influence of pH and temperature, species and tissue differences, and the use of models. Lastly, he seeks to answer or account for a number of pertinent questions and considerations: whether local anaesthesia constitutes a surface activity; what is known about the membrane;

the rôle of myelin; the causes of differential effects; the significance of structure and penetration of local anaesthetics. In his conclusions, Watson cautions against the indiscriminate application to peripheral nerve of observations referable to general anaesthesia of the central nervous system. He emphasizes, furthermore, that a model or an isolated tissue is no substitute for the living cell or tissue in its natural environment.

Sekera and Vrba[216] reported a statistical evaluation of the correlation between some *physico-chemical properties* and local anaesthetic activity. They recorded a correlation between surface activity in buffered and unbuffered solution, displacement adsorption (adsorbate: active charcoal/methylene blue), coefficient of distribution (ether/phosphate buffer) and ability to coagulate colloids (mastix) on the one hand, and anaesthetic activity in surface and infiltration tests and in nerve block, on the other. A correlation between the terminal anaesthetic action and the surface activity of several local anaesthetics was also observed by Pryanishnikova and Pchelin[217].

Kudriashova and Khromov-Borisov[218] as well as Motovilov[219], working on aminoacylanilides, recently found that stereoisomers exhibit conspicuous differences in anaesthetic activity. Since stereoisomers have, aside from their variable behaviour with respect to polarized light, identical physico-chemical properties, a disparity in their anaesthetic potency suggests that their other pharmacological actions exert a modifying influence on their anaesthetic activity[220].

The current theory about the propagation of nerve impulses, that changes in the cell membrane *permeability* to ions determine the action potential, lends support to the view that nerve block is produced by alterations of the permeability\*. The lipids adsorbed on the membrane are 'organized' and, together with inorganic ions, are responsible for the transmission of impulses. On administration of a local anaesthetic, the adsorption equilibrium is disturbed and the conducting layer is disorganized, resulting in cessation of the propagation of impulses. In other words, local anaesthetics block nerve conduction by 'stabilizing' the particular conditions in the cell membrane which, normally, are sufficiently 'labile' to make possible those variations in membrane potential that produce the propagation of impulses. (Shanes[228] has recently surveyed the electrochemical aspects of physiological and pharmacological actions in excitable cells.)

Since the molecular structure of local anaesthetics invariably conforms to the lipophilic-hydrophilic principle, generally with an amino group as the hydrophilic centre, Löfgren[214,227] considers it probable that the amino group comes into contact with an appropriate polar hydrophilic group in the membrane (polar or 'head' association). In his view, moreover, it is not unlikely that the lipophilic component also takes part in the formation of the complex, so that this 'tail', by virtue of van der Waals' forces, interacts with a suitable 'tail' in the membrane, whereby penetration occurs. Problems germane to these theories have, in recent years, been the subject of comprehensive investigations by Skou[229-240].

Skou used five local anaesthetics, procaine, cocaine, tropacocaine, amethocaine and cinchocaine, as well as a general anaesthetic, butanol,

---

\* Several workers[221-226] have studied the influence of local anaesthetics upon permeability in systems other than in peripheral nerves.

which has some local anaesthetic effect. In common with previous investigators, he found that the *minimum anaesthetic concentrations* of the five local anaesthetics declined with increasing pH, whereas that of the non-ionized butanol was independent of pH. The same applied to the *minimum toxic concentrations* as determined by irreversible anaesthesia of peripheral nerve. The relative anaesthetic potencies were not identical with the relative toxic potencies, and the minimum anaesthetic concentrations declined more sharply than the toxic ones with increasing pH. The inference is that the mechanism of toxic action diverges from that of anaesthetic action. The minimum toxic concentrations of the five local anaesthetics were of a similar order to the *haemolyzing concentrations*. It may be surmised, therefore, that the toxic action on peripheral nerves is similar in nature to the haemolytic action on blood cells, *i.e.* cytolysis. The investigations revealed some degree of parallelism between the toxic action, and, to a lesser degree, the anaesthetic action, on the one hand, and the distribution between the solid phase of the nerves and water on the other. This suggests that by studying those factors which condition the *binding in the nerves* it is possible to obtain some information on the site of the toxic action and, perhaps, even on that of the anaesthetic action. One of the factors of relevance to the binding is the capillary activity of the substances. Skou accordingly studied the surface activity on certain models. The capillary-active potencies accorded so closely with the anaesthetic and toxic potencies, that he decided to study the action upon an interface resembling that existing in nerves; namely, a monomolecular layer of nerve lipids on a water surface. The capacity of the five local anaesthetics and of butanol to penetrate into the lipid monolayer, determined as the concentrations in the aqueous phase required to produce the same rise of pressure in the monolayer, showed a fairly close correlation to the anaesthetic potency, and an even closer one to the toxic potency.

The binding of local anaesthetics to nervous and other tissues has also been studied in homogenates by Truant[241], and Truant and Takman[242], who observed that the binding affinity increased in the following order:

procaine < lignocaine < amethocaine < cinchocaine

The sequence was the same in action potential determinations, at which the recovery time was prolonged for amethocaine, hexylcaine and propoxycaine, but short for procaine and lignocaine. Lendle and Mohrmann[243] used the soporific action of local anaesthetics on swimming fish for the purpose of studying the diffusion and binding capacities. Their results, however, were apparently not correlated to the local anaesthetic properties of the drugs investigated. In subsequent investigations Skou[236,237] examined the possibility of a correlation between local anaesthetic potency and *inhibition of acetylcholinesterase* (*cf.* p. 368). For this purpose he used enzymes both from electric eel tissue and from non-haemolyzed human erythrocytes. It is evident from *Figure 7.2* that in neither instance did any correlation exist between the inhibitory effect on acetylcholinesterase, and the blocking action on peripheral nerve.

Condouris[244,245] has recently made an interesting contribution to the knowledge of the mechanism of peripheral nerve block. On investigating the quantitative relations between the concentrations of cocaine and other local anaesthetics as well as of sodium ions, and the degree of conduction block, he arrived at the conclusion that cocaine depresses conduction in peripheral nerves by acting as *antagonist to sodium ions*. Quantitative analysis of the behaviour indicated that the antagonism was competitive. The conduction block produced by cocaine was abolished by raising the concentration of sodium ions around the nerve. The antagonism between sodium

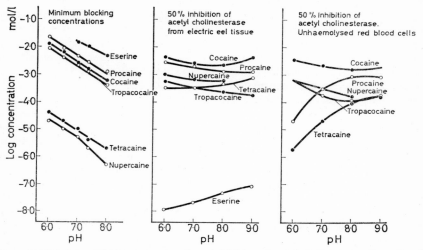

*Figure 7.2.* Minimum blocking concentrations, inhibition of acetyl cholinesterase from electric eel tissue and from human erythrocytes determined at various pH values for five local anaesthetics and eserine[237]. Abscissa: pH. Ordinate: Concentration in M/l.

ions and cocaine was reciprocal and, for both factors, occurred in a wide range of concentrations. The resulting pharmacological action was a function of the ratio of the respective concentrations (*cf.* p. 376).

The *time course of local anaesthesia* with lignocaine and procaine, as well as the concomitant change in conduction velocity, have been the subject of detailed investigations by Rud[246]. Isolated sciatic nerve from *Rana esculenta* was used in his studies. The anaesthetic action of the hydrochlorides increased with concentration and pH. This observation lent weight to the view that the base form of the anaesthetic is the active factor. At identical hydrochloride concentrations and pH, the progress of anaesthesia was twice as rapid with lignocaine as with procaine—a finding attributed to the fact that lignocaine hydrochloride had a dissociation constant ten times that of procaine hydrochloride. The clinical implication was that if rapid onset and minimal toxicity were required, it was advisable to use a solution with as high a pH as possible, rather than increase the hydrochloride concentration.

Although the ability of the base to penetrate cell membranes is the *sine qua non* of anaesthetic activity, certain observations, as pointed out by Goodman and Gilman[247], suggest that anaesthetics act, intracellularly, in the form of cations. This phenomenon was recently illustrated by the findings of Ritchie and Greengard[248], using isolated desheathed vagus nerve from rabbit. The nerve was pretreated with a local anaesthetic until block occurred, after which the anaesthetic was removed. Three local anaesthetics proper, cinchocaine, amethocaine and procaine, as well as two non-specific agents, chlorpromazine and imipramine, were used. Propagation of impulses in the anaesthetized nerve was restored by raising the pH of the surrounding solution from 7 to 9·5. When the pH was lowered again to 7, the block promptly returned. With the long-acting agents this procedure was repeated for hours, simply by allowing the pH to alternate between 9·5 and 7. With the short-acting procaine the results were complicated by the rapid recovery even at pH 7. According to Ritchie and Greengard, the view that local anaesthetics penetrate the tissues in the form of uncharged molecules and exert their action intracellularly as cations, accounts for the fact that nearly all local anaesthetics are amines, with $pK_a$ values falling in a fairly narrow range. The $pK_a$ values for conventional local anaesthetics are such that both the uncharged and the cationic forms are present at physiological pH values. A quaternary ammonium compound or a basic compound with too high a $pK_a$ is not expected to show satisfactory local anaesthetic activity since, at a physiological pH, it is unlikely to reach the conducting system in the nerve membrane in a sufficient amount. On the other hand, a base with too low a $pK_a$, while perhaps having a satisfactory penetrating power, is not likely to be active as a local anaesthetic, because of the relatively insignificant amount which exists as cations at the site of action in the nerve fibres. Recently, Dettbarn[249] studied the pH dependence of procaine, amethocaine and cinchocaine in nerve bundles from crab, and in Ranvier nodes of single fibres from frog sciatic nerve. While the action on the nerve bundles increased with increasing pH, that on the nodes was maximal at pH 7. This observation suggests that the uncharged form is of importance for penetration of the structures which surround the majority of axons.

The theory propounded in the nineteen-thirties, and subsequently defended notably by Nachmansohn[250,251], relating to the significant rôle of *acetylcholine* in the propagation of impulses along the axon, has been critically discussed in various contexts, for instance by Skou[237], Feldberg[252], von Muralt[253], Büchi and Perlia[124], Watson[8] and Schoffeniels[254]. According to this theory, local anaesthetics exert their action via antagonism to acetylcholine. Such a mechanism presupposes competition for a specific receptor. Attempts to identify this receptor have been made by Chagas and his colleagues[255,256] and Ehrenpreis[257], whereby a 'receptor-like' protein was isolated from electric eel tissue. This protein is reported to react with i.a. local anaesthetics[258-260].

An interesting contribution to the question of the mechanism of local anaesthetic action was recently made by Eckert[261], who used eight local anaesthetics of different types. He demonstrated that each of them formed a $\pi$-electron complex with *thiamine*, the local anaesthetic acting as donor and thiamine as acceptor. This observation led him to surmise that local anaesthetics act by blocking thiamine essential to the nerve function (*cf.* [253,262]). In this connection it is worth noting that in rabbit experiments[263], thiamine had an antagonistic action upon local anaesthetics (cinchocaine, procaine, cocaine and lignocaine) in topical and infiltration anaesthesia, as well as in nerve block. Addition of thiamine, however, prolonged the duration of spinal anaesthesia with procaine. According to Horáková and Hach[264], thiamine potentiates the effect of procaine and reduces that of mesocaine in infiltration anaesthesia, but fails to influence the activity of cocaine in surface anaesthesia. The same authors also combined other *water-soluble vitamins* with local anaesthetics and obtained varying results. According to Marras and Farina[265], certain *amino-acids*—aspartic acid, tryptophane, leucine, and cysteine—inhibit the local anaesthetic action of lignocaine, cocaine, cinchocaine and Farmocaine (pharmocaine) on the rabbit's cornea. Electrophoretic studies suggest that this inhibition is due to depression of the mobility of the anaesthetics.

*Specificity*—The compounds which are included in Löfgren's general formula for local anaesthetics (see p. 363) comprise not only the local anaesthetics proper but a large number of agents, the actions of which are dominated by other properties. *Figures 7.3* and *7.4* illustrate the lack of

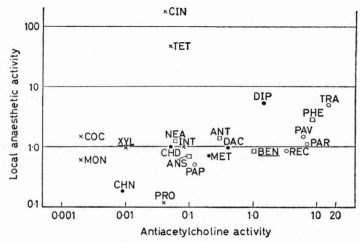

*Figure 7.3.* Local anaesthetic potency (lignocaine = 1) in relation to anti-acetylcholine effect (diphenhydramine = 1). Ordinate and abscissa logarithmic. After Wiedling[9].

*Substances investigated:*

| Group | Abbreviation | Substance | Group | Abbreviation | Substance |
|---|---|---|---|---|---|
| □ | ANS | Antazoline | × | MON | Butethamine |
| □ | ANT | Phenbenzamine | □ | NEA | Mepyramine |
| □ | BEN | Diphenhydramine | ○ | PAP | Papaverine |
| ● | CHD | Quinidine | ○ | PAR | Caramiphen |
| ● | CHN | Quinine | ○ | PAV | Pavatrine |
| × | CIN | Cinchocaine | □ | PHE | Promethazine |
| × | COC | Cocaine | × | PRO | Procaine |
| ● | DAC | Dacorène | ○ | REC | Recipavrin |
| ● | DIP | Diethazine | × | TET | Amethocaine |
| × | INT | Parethoxycaine | ○ | TRA | Hexahydroadiphenine |
| ● | MET | Methadone | × | XYL | Lignocaine |

× = Local anaesthetics ☐ = Antihistaminics ○ = Antispasmodics ● = Other agents correlation between the local anaesthetic activity and the anti-acetylcholine and antihistamine actions of numerous compounds of different categories. Local anaesthetic activity was determined by the discriminatory corneal method in rabbits, and the other actions were recorded using isolated guinea-pig small intestine. An investigation conducted by Naranjo and Naranjo[266] into the local anaesthetic, antihistamine and anti-acetylcholine

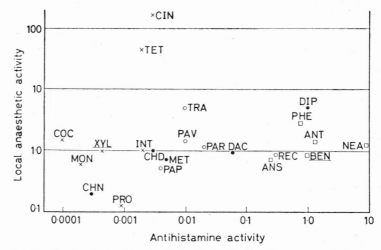

*Figure 7.4.* Local anaesthetic potency (lignocaine = 1) in relation to antihistamine effect (diphenhydramine = 1). Ordinate and abscissa logarithmic. After Wiedling[9]. For substances investigated, see *Figure 7.3*.

actions of a number of antihistaminics yielded similar results. Certain investigators, however, claim to have demonstrated, in homologous series, a more or less pronounced correlation between local anaesthetic and anti-acetylcholine actions[267,268], or between local anaesthetic and antihistamine actions[269]. *Table 7.2* illustrates the values obtained by different workers for the potency of lignocaine in varying antagonistic actions on different effects *in vitro*, all values being recorded in relation to those for procaine. The tabulation is, in other words, a comparison of the two hitherto most representative local anaesthetics. Ratio values vary from 0·1 to 3·0.

Herr and Balogh[274] have recently made a contribution to *the theory of surface anaesthesia*. Investigating the mode of action, they studied the uptake of procaine, cocaine, amethocaine and cinchocaine by isolated cat cornea and vesical mucosa, as well as by cat cornea *in vivo*. The absorption rate and the binding for the four drugs in the cornea increased in the order indicated. Surface anaesthetics thus appear to be characterized by rapid absorption and firm binding to the tissue. The flattening of the dose-effect curve for corneal anaesthesia which, with certain local anaesthetics, occurs at fairly high concentrations[275,276] has been attributed[154] to molecular association. Molecular association may account for the decrease of potency observed in the higher homologues of a series of amine hydrochlorides with surface anaesthetic activity[154]. Molinengo[277], has also investigated the time course for anaesthesia of rabbit cornea, and determined for several local anaesthetics the fixation or absorption constant, the detoxication constant, and the coefficient of distribution.

Table 7.2. Potency of lignocaine in various antagonistic actions on different effects *in vitro*, in relation to procaine ($= 1$).

| Stimulant action | Tissue | Species | Potency | Reference |
|---|---|---|---|---|
| Acetylcholine | Rectus abdominis | Frog | 0·5 | 270 |
| | Ileum | Rabbit | 1·0 | 270 |
| | Ileum | Guinea-pig | 0·2 | 270 |
| | Trachea | Cat | 0·1 | 270 |
| | Small intestine | Guinea-pig | 0·25 | 271 |
| | Small intestine | Rat | 0·3 | 9 |
| Adrenaline | Uterus | Rabbit | 3·0 | 9 |
| Barium ions | Small intestine | Rat | 2·0 | 9 |
| Cholinesterase | Serum | Man | 0·1 | 272 |
| Histamine | Ileum | Guinea-pig | 0·2 | 270 |
| | Small intestine | Guinea-pig | 0·5 | 271 |
| Nicotine | Ileum | Rabbit | 1·4 | 270 |
| | Ileum | Guinea-pig | 0·6 | 270 |
| Peristaltic reflex | Ileum | Rabbit | 1·2 | 270 |
| | Ileum | Guinea-pig | 0·6 | 270 |
| Potassium ions | Rectus abdominis | Frog | 1·0 | 270 |
| | Ileum | Rabbit | 1·6 | 270 |
| | Ileum | Guinea-pig | 2·0 | 270 |
| | Trachea | Cat | 1·3 | 270 |
| Serotonin | Ileum | Guinea-pig | 1·0 | 273 |
| | Trachea | Cat | 1·0 | 273 |
| | Uterus | Rat | 1·0 | 273 |
| Succinylcholine | Rectus abdominis | Frog | 1·0 | 270 |

## SCREENING AND EVALUATION

The choice of method or methods for screening of local anaesthetics is determined by the minimum requirement or requirements to be satisfied. Frequently, no distinction is made between the two concepts, 'screening' and 'evaluation'. When, for example, Geddes[278] and Herr[279] propose the use of a given method or methods—*e.g.* infiltration anaesthesia, nerve block, and surface anaesthesia in laboratory animals—for the purpose of obtaining a standardized evaluation of local anaesthetics, it is screening on the basis of given parameters. Furthermore, quantitative conclusions reached with one method are not necessarily valid for another. The connection between two sets of values obtained for a series of compounds by two different methods is, at most, a statistical correlation. Results referable to one homologous series do not permit deductions concerning the behaviour of another, nor can observations in laboratory animals be safely generalized to humans.

The evaluations of local anaesthetics requires not only determination of

371

their anaesthetic potency by various appropriate methods, but also elucidation of their general and local toxicity, specificity and metabolism[278-281]. A number of new methods or variants of earlier methods have been reported during the last few years. For example, Kreppel and Zipf[282] recorded afferent impulses in the vagus nerves from the lungs of urethane-anaesthetized guinea-pigs, the local anaesthetics being given intravenously before and after administration of veratrine. Petros and Gibilisco[283] used pentobarbital-anaesthetized cats which they stimulated *via* needle electrodes in the canine fossa, the action potentials being conducted *via* electrodes inserted in the gasserian ganglion. Blocking of certain reflex arcs has also been applied to the study of both nerve block and surface anaesthesia. Griffié and Brunel[284] used for this purpose the arc formed by sensory fibres of the trigeminal nerve and motor fibres of the same nerve with terminals in the anterior belly of the digastric muscle. Their experiments were performed on dogs under general anaesthesia. The animals were injected with a local anaesthetic *via* the mental foramen, and the pulp of the lower canine tooth was subjected to electrical stimulation.

Nieschulz, Hoffmann and Popendiker[285] utilized the sneeze reflex, elicited by the introduction of a small brush into the nostrils of guinea-pigs or rabbits. This method permits determination of the effect of surface anaesthetics on the nasal mucosa. It has been used by Åstrom and Persson[286] for studying the actions of lignocaine, Citanest, amethocaine, and cocaine. Problems associated with the use of the corneal method in studies of surface anaesthetics, have been discussed by Charonnat and Lechat[287], Horáková and Roth[288], and Boberg-Ans[289]. Eriksson and Gordh[290], working with finger block, found a correlation between the subjects' age and the duration of anaesthesia. The effect upon the duration was attributed to modified vascularization in the injected area. Dhunér, Edshage and Wilhelm[291] introduced the ninhydrin print technique for the testing of local anaesthetic action. In their opinion the method is reliable for ulnar, median and finger block, but of limited value for other types of nerve block and for intracutaneous wheals. Albért and Löfström[292] studied the possibility of utilizing bilateral ulnar nerve block in humans for evaluation of local anaesthetics. Employing a double blind technique and volunteers of the same age and sex, they were able to make a fairly accurate estimate of latency, duration, muscle paralysis, penetrating power, and potency.

Wiedling[9] recently surveyed the literature and collected data on some 40 determinations of the potency of lignocaine, relative to that of procaine. The general pattern of the results is shown in *Figure 7.5*, in which the different determinations are condensed. For infiltration anaesthesia the relative potency of lignocaine (procaine = 1) as determined by different investigators ranged from 1 to 4, and averaged 2·4. For nerve block the corresponding range was 2 to 4 with a mean of 2·8, and for topical anaesthesia 2 to 21·6 with a mean of 7·5. The results of the *in vitro* experiments, showing a mean of 3·2, were consistent with the mean for nerve blocks *in vivo*. Discrepancies in results were, in all probability, due mainly to the varying discriminatory capacity of the methods employed; this capacity being greater for nerve block than for infiltration anaesthesia, and greatest for topical anaesthesia.

Björn[293], in reviewing aspects of the experimental and clinical evaluation of local anaesthetics in the field of dentistry, discussed experience acquired in recent years with his own method of electrical stimulation of dental pulp[294], a method which had been employed, for example, in the evaluation of several agents referable to the lignocaine group. This method, moreover,

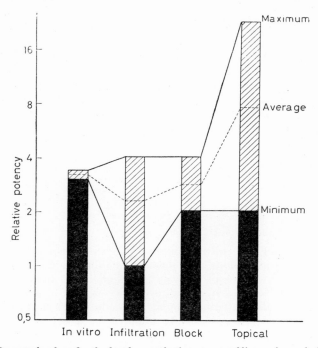

*Figure 7.5.* Reported values for the local anaesthetic potency of lignocaine, relative to that of procaine (logarithmic scale). The shaded parts of the columns indicate the lowest, and the hatched parts the highest activity recorded; the broken line, the mean for each group.

is probably the most useful one available for experimental evaluation, in humans, of local anaesthetics, alone and in combination with vasoconstrictors or other agents.

Statistical and mathematical treatment of the results of pharmacological tests of local anaesthetics has been the subject of studies by Vrba and Sekera[295], Roth[296], Mongar[297], and Chakravarti[298]. The first-mentioned authors reported a graphical method for analysis of experimental data pertaining to topical as well as infiltration anaesthesia. A mathematical modification of this method, permitting statistical analysis, was presented by Roth. Mongar described the use of the randomized blocks in tests of local anaesthetics. Chakravarti discussed an equation founded on theoretical considerations, the underlying theory being that a stimulus applied to a nerve fibre produces a liberation of acetylcholine. Under the catalytic action of cholinesterase, the liberated acetylcholine reacts with phosphocreatine, and thus initiates the adenylphosphate reaction (chain reaction). Since local anaesthetics have structural features in common with acetylcholine, they may compete with it for the enzyme cholinesterase and thereby interfere with the propagation of stimuli. Although the formula is based on unsubstantiated theoretical considerations, Chakravarti claims to have ample confirmation from determinations reported in the literature. Koelzer and Wehr, in a series of papers[39,42,97,102,104,113], reported studies of a large number of new compounds of different types, using a system founded on the determination of motor paralysis of rat sciatic nerve, subcutaneous toxicity in mice, and the tendency of the aqueous solution to form a precipitate on addition of alkali. The last-mentioned value was regarded as a criterion of the degree of irritation (*cf*. 299). Taking the results of these determinations as a basis, they computed an 'average usefulness' (Durchschnittsbrauchbarkeit) and a 'total usefulness' (Gesamtbrauchbarkeit) for each compound. Since these quantities are derived from a few values selected more or less arbitrarily, and valid only for certain given methods, they can only be considered as a form of screening.

## OTHER PHARMACOLOGICAL ACTIONS OF LOCAL ANAESTHETICS

### Actions upon the Central Nervous System

#### Sedative, analgesic, and antitussive actions

Soon after the clinical introduction of lignocaine, it was observed that large doses had a conspicuous central action, manifested in a greater sedative effect and a higher degree of amnesia than had been obtained with other local anaesthetics. Central analgesic properties were also noted at an early stage. By virtue of these attributes lignocaine, administered intravenously or intramuscularly, has been clinically adopted as a central analgesic for intensely painful conditions, or as a supplement to various forms of general anaesthesia, whereby a salutary effect upon postoperative pain has frequently been noted as well[9,300-303]. During studies of lignocaine administered intravenously to supplement thiobarbiturate-nitrous oxide anaesthesia, Steinhaus and Howland[304,305] observed depression of the pharyngeal and laryngeal reflexes. In experiments on rabbits and dogs, lignocaine totally suppressed the cough reflexes attending severe mechanical irritation, without producing respiratory collapse. Neither thiopentone nor pethidine possessed this capacity. Other aspects studied include the apnoeic and hypotensive actions of lignocaine and procaine in dogs and mice under general anaesthesia[306], the effects of intravenously administered lignocaine and succinylcholine on the respiration in dogs[307], the central action of lignocaine as well as its effect upon cardiac output[308], the cardiovascular actions of lignocaine and procaine administered intravenously in humans under general anaesthesia[309], prolongation of the duration of sleep caused by barbiturates[310-312], and the antitussive actions of local anaesthetics[313].

#### Anticonvulsive action

The anticonvulsive effect of lignocaine was first observed by Halldin[314], and many local anaesthetics have since been subjected to detailed experimental and clinical studies[315-332]. As a result, a method of treating status epilepticus by intravenous administration of lignocaine has been devised.

### Anti-arrhythmic Actions

Allied to the nerve blocking capacity of local anaesthetics, is their influence upon the conducting system of the heart. The correcting action of procaine and procaine-amide on cardiac arrhythmias was first demonstrated in the nineteen-forties. Since that time lignocaine has been found, both experimentally and clinically, to produce a similar effect. Using mechanical stimulation, an antifibrillatory action of lignocaine was observed by Carden and Steinhaus and others[333-339]. Similar results were obtained for electrical stimulation[340,341] and for chemical stimulation[14,338-340,342-345]. In the relevant experiments lignocaine was administered both intravenously[14,333-340,344] and locally[341-343,345]. Experimental investigations into the anti-arrythmic actions of the following local anaesthetics have also been reported: amethocaine[336,344,346], cinchocaine[346], dimethocaine[348], hexylcaine[336,344,347], Panthesin[336], Pascain (hydroxyprocaine-p-aminosalicylate)[349], piperocaine[336] and procaine[340,341,346,350].

In 1950 Southworth[350a] reported a case in which ventricular fibrillation produced by heart catheterization was abolished with lignocaine. Hitchcock and Keown[350b] have since presented a series of more than 500 cases of arrhythmia due to mechanical irritation during heart surgery being treated by intravenous administration of lignocaine. In their experience lignocaine is the only agent really effective against such arrhythmia. The intravenous use of lignocaine for ventricular arrhythmia has also been described in a study by Weiss[350c].

Baird and Hardman[351] studied the mechanism of the anti-arrhythmic actions of local anaesthetics on isolated turtle heart, using procaine as the standard. Hardman, Baird and Moore[352] had earlier observed that the negative inotropic effect of procaine was correlated with the concentration of the non-ionized form, and the negative chronotropic effect with the ionized (cationic) form of procaine. Baird and Hardman analysed the influence of pH, procaine cation, non-ionized procaine, and the quaternary 'ethyl-procaine' cation, i.e. the $N$-$(\beta$-$p$-aminobenzoyloxyethyl)-$N,N,N$-triethylammonium ion, on cardiac conduction time, stimulation threshold, and amplitude of contraction, as well as the relation of those parameters to the anti-arrhythmic effect. A direct correlation was noted between procaine cation concentration and both elevation of the stimulation threshold and prolongation of the conduction time. The ionized form thus appeared to be the primary form for an influence upon those parameters. A direct correlation was also observed between the concentration of non-ionized procaine and the negative inotropic activity. Only the non-ionized form of procaine affected the contraction amplitude. Except for the fact that it lacked a negative inotropic action, ethyl-procaine chloride produced the same qualitative effects as procaine cation upon turtle heart. When tested on ventricular tachycardia induced by acetylstrophanthidin in the isolated rabbit heart, ethyl-procaine chloride had an antagonistic action similar to that of procaine, but only about one half as potent.

Baird and Hardman concluded that a close association existed between the anti-arrhythmic action of procaine and the changes produced by that drug in the stimulation threshold, refractory period and conduction time, since each of those parameters was correlated to the procaine cation. Recently Rossignol and Pattani[353] have shown that the blocking action of procaine on the isolated auricle from rabbit was inhibited by an excess of sodium ions (*cf.* p. 367).

## Other Actions

Zipf[354,355], in his reviews of the general, pharmacodynamic actions of local anaesthetics, illustrated the dosimetric pattern of procaine by a graphic representation (*Figure 7.6*). The first group of actions includes blocking of the parasympathetic heart ganglia, inhibition of impulse production and conduction in the heart, endoanaesthesia of inner sensory receptors, and stimulation of the uterus. In this group the intravenous threshold dose is 2 mg/kg, which is comparable with a therapeutic dosage in man. In the second, larger group—spasmolytic action on intestine and other smooth muscle, sensitization to adrenaline, hypotensive action, analgesia, anti-motor and anticonvulsive action—the intravenous threshold dose is approximately 5 mg/kg. In the third group, however, comprising a lissive action on striated muscle and adrenolytic action, the doses calculated for humans must be regarded as toxic. As regards the fourth group—blocking of sympathetic ganglia, anti-acetylcholine action at cellular level, antihistamine, anti-anaphylactic and anti-allergic actions—the threshold doses in experimental animals are 20 mg/kg or over, *i.e.* greatly in excess of the maximum dose in man.

The corresponding actions of lignocaine are outlined in the monograph by Wiedling[9]. Although several aspects of the activity pattern of lignocaine resemble those of procaine, the former drug is the more useful of the two because of its greater stability and, in certain contexts, its higher potency. Procaine, due to its rapid elimination, has a more transient action.

## TOXICOLOGY AND TOLERANCE

### Systemic Toxicity

The data presented in *Figure 7.7* illustrate graphically the results of some forty toxicity determinations of lignocaine in mice, as reported by various authors[9]. For intravenous injection, the LD50 value varied, in the different determinations, between 21 and 62 mg per kilogramme of body weight, the average being 34 mg/kg; for intraperitoneal injection the corresponding range was 120–180 mg/kg and the mean 140 mg/kg, and for subcutaneous injection 230–1,070 and 425 mg/kg respectively. In man, direct determinations of the blood concentrations have recently been conducted[356] for intravenously administered procaine, chloroprocaine, lignocaine and amethocaine, and by Bromage and Robson[357] for lignocaine using various modes of administration. It is important however to record if the local anaesthetic solution used contains only the drug in question, since LD50 determinations in animals are, as Wiedling[9] has pointed out, of dubious value particularly when the anaesthetic agents have been combined with vasoconstrictors[358–360].

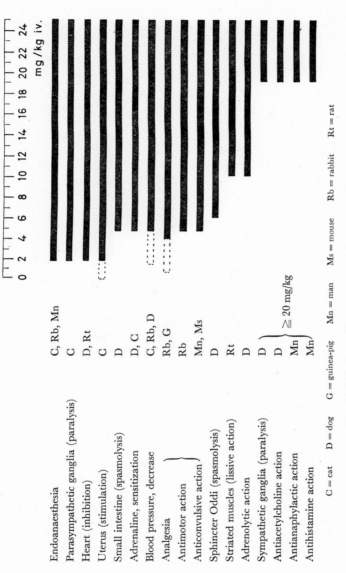

Endoanaesthesia — C, Rb, Mn
Parasympathetic ganglia (paralysis) — C
Heart (inhibition) — D, Rt
Uterus (stimulation) — C
Small intestine (spasmolysis) — D
Adrenaline, sensitization — D, C
Blood pressure, decrease — C, Rb, D
Analgesia — Rb, G
Antimotor action — Rb
Anticonvulsive action — Mn, Ms
Sphincter Oddi (spasmolysis) — D
Striated muscles (lissive action) — Rt
Adrenolytic action — D
Sympathetic ganglia (paralysis) — D
Antiacetylcholine action — D
Antianaphylactic action — Mn } ≧ 20 mg/kg
Antihistamine action — Mn

mg/kg iv.
0 2 4 6 8 10 12 14 16 18 20 22 24

C = cat    D = dog    G = guinea-pig    Mn = man    Ms = mouse    Rb = rabbit    Rt = rat

*Figure 7.6.* Actions of intravenous procaine in animals[354]

377

The clinical toxicity of injected local anaesthetics is more or less reduced by vasoconstrictor drugs, *e.g.* the addition of adrenaline in a moderate concentration to lignocaine solutions retards the absorption to such a degree that the duration may be prolonged tenfold[361]. For estimating the modifying effect of vasoconstrictors on the toxicity of local anaesthetics, a better approach

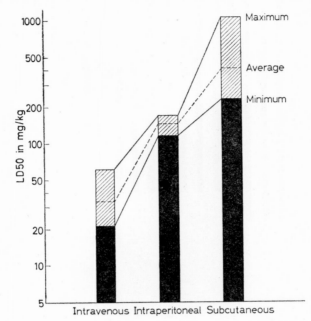

*Figure 7.7*. Survey of values collected from the literature of the acute toxicity of lignocaine in mice using different modes of administration[9].

Ordinate: LD50 in mg per kg body-weight (logarithmic scale). The shaded parts of the columns indicate the lowest, and the hatched parts the highest LD50 values recorded. The broken line refers to the mean for the relevant mode of administration.

than LD50 determinations in small animals is the chemical determination of the blood concentration of the anaesthetic after different modes of administration, with and without addition of vasoconstrictors.

Hoppe and Duprey[362] have reported a comparative study of the intravenous and the intracisternal LD50 for a number of local anaesthetics. The intracisternal toxicities of procaine and procaine-caffeine in rabbits have also been determined by Zipf and Schlickeisen[363]. The toxicity of procaine in albino rats shows a sex difference, both CD50 and LD50 values for intraperitoneal administration were considerably higher in males[364]. The chronic toxicity of procaine in growing rats was investigated by Berger[365], and similar studies with lignocaine have been reported[271]. Cheymol[366,367], using mice, observed a protective effect of procaine against gamma radiation from $^{60}$Co. Winne[368] found that both the CD50 and LD50 values for procaine in mice were unchanged after irradiation. According to Manca[369], premedication with chlorpromazine increased the

378

minimum lethal doses of procaine in rats and rabbits. Bunce[370] reported recently that the toxic actions of the contrast medium acetrizoate in dogs, were reduced by pretreatment with procaine and/or curare. Similar observations had previously been made for lignocaine in patients who, prior to lumbar myelography with the radiopaque substance methiodal, had received an intraspinal injection of the anaesthetic[371], and in dogs which, for corresponding examinations, had been given a mixture of methiodal and lignocaine[372].

The effect of lignocaine on the renal function was studied by De Felice[373]. On intravenous administration in humans and dogs, as well as oral administration in man, the only effect observed was slight water diuresis (not statistically significant) in some subjects.

### Tissue and Cell Toxicity

The histopathological actions of local anaesthetics and related substances were recently the subject of a monograph by Pizzolato and Mannheimer[374], who divided the agents into four groups based on the degree of reactivity of nerve, muscle, and dermal tissue. In group *I* (the lowest reactivity), were placed physiological saline, 1 and 2 per cent lignocaine hydrochloride and procaine hydrochloride (with adrenaline, hyaluronidase, or both), and 0·07 per cent cinchocaine hydrochloride; group *II* comprised distilled water, 5 per cent procaine hydrochloride and 1·5 per cent piperocaine hydrochloride; group *III*, 0·5 per cent cinchocaine hydrochloride, 1 per cent amethocaine hydrochloride, 1 and 2 per cent hexylcaine hydrochloride, and Duracaine (benzocaine and urethane in a water solution;) to group *IV* (the highest reactivity) were referred Efocaine (consisting of procaine, butylcaine, propylene glycol, polyethylene glycol and water) and benzyl alcohol.

In recent years a number of investigators have used injection into different tissues for studying the irritant effects of local anaesthetics. Spencer[375], for example, gave injections into the anterior chamber of rabbit eye; Tait[376] used similar injections as well as intradermal and endoneural injections in rabbits; and Brun[377] gave subcutaneous injections in rabbits and mice. The effect of repeated injections in the same nerve region was investigated by Pizzolato and Renegar[378]. Nilsson and Wendeberg[379] studied the influence of subcutaneous injections upon wound healing in rats. The effects upon capillary resistance after intradermal injections, with trypan blue as indicator, were determined in rabbits[380–383], and in rats[299]. Other workers[376,384–386] investigated the reactions to local application in the conjunctival sac of the rabbit. Tissue cultures of ciliated epithelium from human respiratory organs have been used for the testing of local anaesthetics with respect to toxic properties[387]. Cultures of connective tissue cells and liver cells from mice[382], mesenterium from rat[388], and cultures of HeLa cells and kidney cells from monkeys[389,390] have been similarly used. Marcus and Husa[391] found that a number of clinical local anaesthetics produced haemolysis of human and rabbit red blood cells even in the presence of 0·6 per cent sodium chloride (*cf.* p. 366).

The effect of procaine hydrochloride on the permeability of the rabbit erythrocyte membrane was investigated by Setnikar and Temelcou[392]. An

25

iso-osmotic solution (5·05 per cent) was observed to cause haemolysis, and to render the solution isotonic for red blood cells the addition of 1·3 per cent sodium chloride was required, 0·9 per cent being insufficient; when dextrose was similarly used, 3·3 per cent (0·6 iso-osmolar) sufficed.

## The Relationship between Systemic and Local Toxicity and Anaesthetic Activity

Luduena and Hoppe[393] recorded, in a group of 2-alkoxybenzoate and thiolbenzoate derivatives, a correlation between local anaesthetic potency as determined by intracutaneous injections in guinea-pigs, and systemic toxicity, determined intravenously in mice. Luduena[394], however, found no correlation between intraspinal anaesthetic activity and irritation.

Schmidt[382] subsequently demonstrated, for a number of local anaesthetics in clinical use, a correlation between the irritant properties as determined by the trypan blue method, and the cytotoxic effect on cultured cells from mouse connective tissue or mouse liver, as well as between the intracutaneous local anaesthetic potency and the intravenous toxicity (*cf.* p. 366).

## Allergic Effects

The ability of procaine and allied substances to produce allergic phenomena has long been known, and it is considered to be connected with the *para*-substituted amino group in the benzene nucleus; hence the term 'para allergy'. The use of procaine penicillin has done much to focus attention on this type of hypersensitivity[395]. Hanauer[396] observed that persons hypersensitive to benzocaine also reacted to local anaesthetics of the procaine and the hydroxy-procaine series, as well as to procaine penicillin and sulphanilamides. Lignocaine, on the contrary, produced no reaction. Siegal[397] described a series of repeated local oedemas following injections of procaine; and cross reactions were obtained with procaine penicillin, butethamine and metabutethamine, but not with lignocaine. Fisher and Sturm[398] too, reported a case of procaine allergy in which there was no sensitivity to lignocaine. The absence of cross sensitization between procaine and similar compounds, on the one hand, and lignocaine on the other is attributable to the different structure of, and the lower reactivity associated with, lignocaine. Genuine hypersensitivity to lignocaine appears to be exceedingly rare[399].

## METABOLISM
### Lignocaine

The metabolism of lignocaine has been studied by Hollunger[400-403], and Hollunger and Niklasson[404]. Hollunger showed that in rabbit liver, lignocaine is metabolized oxidatively by an enzymatic system existing in the microsomes and this requires the presence of both oxygen and reduced triphosphopyridine nucleotide (TPN). Under aerobic conditions, 1 mole acetaldehyde per mole lignocaine was formed, $N$-ethylglycylxylidide being detected in the medium. $N$-Ethylglycylxylidide disappeared at approximately the same rate in the presence, as in the absence, of oxygen, whereas lignocaine disappearance was insignificant under anaerobic conditions. Anaerobically, xylidine was formed in an amount commensurate with the

$N$-ethylglycylxylidide loss. Added glycylxylidide was broken down at an extremely slow rate, and practically no glycylxylidine was formed during the metabolism of lignocaine. It was concluded that lignocaine was eliminated mainly *via* oxidative de-ethylation, and its breakdown may be schematized as follows:

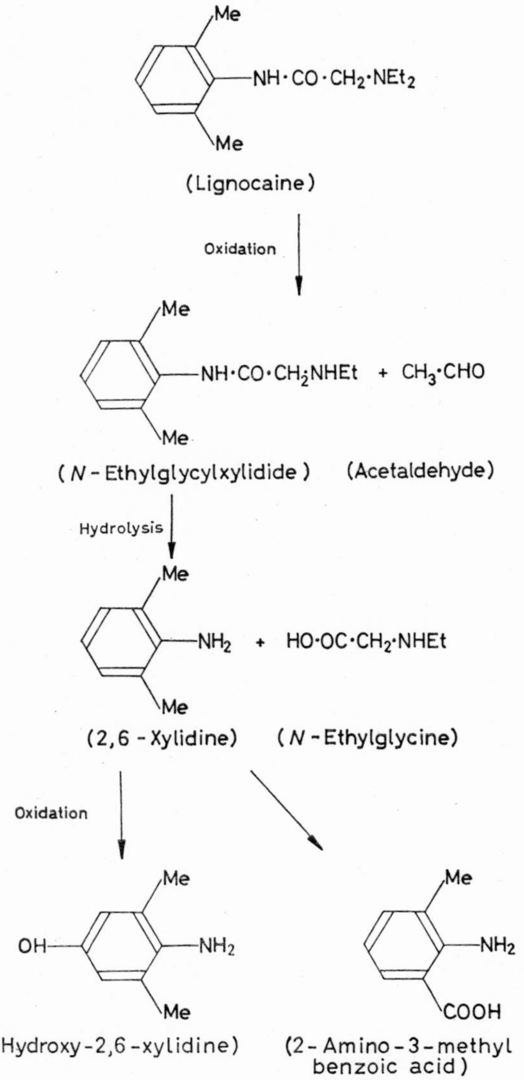

$$\text{—NH·CO·CH}_2\text{·NEt}_2$$

(Lignocaine)

Oxidation ↓

$$\text{—NH·CO·CH}_2\text{NHEt} \quad + \quad \text{CH}_3\text{·CHO}$$

( $N$ - Ethylglycylxylidide )     (Acetaldehyde)

Hydrolysis ↓

$$\text{—NH}_2 \quad + \quad \text{HO·OC·CH}_2\text{·NHEt}$$

(2,6 - Xylidine)     ( $N$ - Ethylglycine)

Oxidation ↓

$$\text{OH—} \quad \text{—NH}_2$$

(4 - Hydroxy - 2,6 - xylidine)

$$\text{—NH}_2 \quad \text{COOH}$$

(2 - Amino - 3 - methyl benzoic acid )

The metabolism of 2,6-xylidine was studied in rats by Lindstrom[405], who administered 150 mg per kilogramme body weight daily by gastric tube. He recovered in the urine relatively large amounts of 4-hydroxy-2,6-xylidine, as well as small amounts of 2-amino-3-methylbenzoic acid.

Hollunger reported, furthermore, the conversion of an amidase from rabbit liver microsomes into a soluble form by freezing and thawing. He found high activity against the secondary amine, $N$-ethylglycyl-2,6-xylidide, a metabolite of the de-ethylation of lignocaine. This amidase was highly specific since it was inactive against both the tertiary amine lignocaine, and the primary amine glycyl-2,6-xylidide. On chromatographic fractionation of solubilized protein from the microsomes, one of the fractions observed was an acetanilide-hydrolysing enzyme. The chromatographic distribution of the aminoacylanilide-, acetanilide-, procaine-, cocaine-, atropine-, and acetylcholine-hydrolysing enzymes in the microsomes, were subsequently elucidated by Hollunger and Niklasson[404]. Geddes[406], and Geddes and Douglas[407], working with lignocaine whose carbonyl group had been labelled with [14]C, and with slices of rat liver, concluded that $N,N$-diethylglycine was the principal metabolic product of lignocaine. Since, however, the $R_f$ values of $N,N$-diethylglycine and $N$-ethylglycine are very close together in the chromatographic system used by those authors, Hollunger[401] suggested that the metabolite may have been the monoethyl rather than the diethyl compound.

### Benzoic Acid Esters

In comparative experiments with human serum, Becker[408] showed that metabutethamine was hydrolysed 30–35 times, meprylcaine, 15–21 times, piperocaine 5–8 times, and butethamine 0·5–0·6 times, as rapidly as procaine. Using paper electrophoresis of human serum, Becker[409] also localized the esterase activity against these local anaesthetics, and suggested that there are several serum cholinesterases with varying degrees of hydrolytic action upon local anaesthetics of ester type. Kalow[410] called attention to species differences in the metabolism of ester-type local anaesthetics due to variability of plasma esterases; for example, procaine is hydrolysed in man, but is excreted intact in the horse.

### Oxethazaine

In studying the metabolism and distribution of oxethazaine, Wiser and Seifter[411] used a sample which had been labelled with [14]C in both carbon atoms of the ethanolamine moiety. Following oral administration in rats, radioactivity appeared in the exhaled carbon dioxide within 30 minutes, and at 28 hours, 20 per cent of the administered radio-activity had been eliminated by that route.

### LOCAL ANAESTHETICS IN CLINICAL USE

During the past decade lignocaine and other aminoacylamides have increasingly superseded procaine and the other ester-type compounds as clinical local anaesthetics, see, *inter alia*, reviews by Björn[3], Adriani[412], and Buděšínský and Protiva[413]. The first group of compounds to be discussed will therefore be the aminoacylamides.

### Aminoacylamides

Lignocaine

Since its discovery in 1943, lignocaine (2-diethylamino-2′,6′-acetoxylidide, lidocaine, Xylocaine, Xylotox, $I$) has been officially entered in several pharmacopoeiae, and its bibliography comprises more than two thousand papers. A detailed survey of its pharmacology was communicated by Wiedling in 1959[9]. Its principal clinical fields of use are described in 'Xylocaine in Anaesthesia'[414], and a full bibliography was published in 1956[415]. Various aspects of lignocaine have been treated in reviews by Björn[3,293], Gray and Geddes[416], and Gruber[4], among others.

The introduction of lignocaine constituted a notable advance in the field of local anaesthetics, and within a comparatively short time its properties were summed up as follows[417]: 'Chemically, the most outstanding property of Xylocaine is its exceptional stability. Indeed, of all local anaesthetics Xylocaine is the most stable. Pharmacologically, Xylocaine is distinguished by its high and specific local anaesthetic activity and by its relatively low toxicity, which gives it a high safety rating as compared both to anaesthetics for parenteral use (e.g. procaine) and to surface anaesthetics (e.g. amethocaine). Its latency is short and it does not produce tissue irritation. Clinically, Xylocaine is notable for its versatility. It lends itself to all forms of regional anaesthesia—spinal, epidural, and caudal; paravertebral, nerve block, field block, infiltration, and surface. It is also serviceable as an intravenous analgesic. Local and general side effects are minimal.'

*Mesocaine*

Mesocaine (2-diethylamino-2',4',6'-acetomesidide, trimecaine, *II*) differs from lignocaine only in so far as an additional methyl group has been incorporated into the benzene nucleus at the *para*-position. It is one of the compounds synthesized by Löfgren in the early nineteen-forties[212,418]. In the investigations conducted at that time by Goldberg[419] and others, it was found to resemble lignocaine in many respects, but was less satisfactory. In recent years mesocaine has attracted a certain amount of interest in East European countries[420–425]. Indeed, it has even been launched as a 'new Czechoslovakian anaesthetic'.

*Gravocaine*

Gravocaine (2-diethylamino-6'-ethyl-*o*-acetotoluidide, *III*) differs from lignocaine only in that one of the methyl groups substituted in the benzene nucleus has been exchanged for an ethyl group. The actions of the two drugs do not differ to any major degree[426]. Unlike lignocaine, however, Gravocaine is a local irritant[427], which probably accounts for the fact that it is not extensively used.

*Baycaine*

Baycaine (2-diethylamino-6'-methoxycarbonyl-*o*-acetotoluidide, *VI*) was synthesized by Hiltmann, and has been tested pharmacologically by Ther[38], and by Wirth and Gösswald[64]. Baycaine appears to be intermediate in action between lignocaine and procaine. It requires a substantially greater addition of vasoconstrictor than the former; 1:25,000 adrenaline, 1:20,000 noradrenaline, or 1:50,000 adrenaline plus 1:50,000 noradrenaline is used in the dental solutions, where the Baycaine content is in each instance 3 per cent.

383

*Hostacaine*

The first of the lignocaine type anaesthetics to be developed outside Sweden was Hostacaine (2-butylamino-6'-chloro-*o*-acetotoluidide, *IV*)[428,429]. The compound was soon found to be a local irritant, besides which it had other side-effects[430–437]. For this reason it is not employed on any major scale.

*Mepivacaine*

Mepivacaine ((±)-*N*-methylpipecolyl-2,6-xylidide, Carbocaine, Scandicaine, *V*) was synthesized by af Ekenstam, Egnér and Petterson[24]. It has been pharmacologically investigated by Ulfendahl[438], Frahm[439], Truant and Wiedling[440], and Henn[441], and has been experimentally tested in humans by Berling[442], and Feldmann and Nordenram[443]. In its properties mepivacaine resembles lignocaine, but with some testing methods, *e.g.* the isolated nerve and the corneal techniques, however, it is distinctly weaker than lignocaine. While, in terms of intrinsic potency, mepivacaine is not superior to lignocaine, it may, with some modes of injection, have a longer duration because of its slower absorption at the injection site. For surface anaesthesia mepivacaine, due to its inferior effect, has been combined with the surface anaesthetic agent hydroxypolyethoxydodecane (Thesit).

The relative toxicity of mepivacaine varies with the mode of injection. The subcutaneous toxicity in mice, for instance, is approximately one-third higher than that of lignocaine, while the interval between injection and death is more prolonged. Determinations after too short an interval accordingly show too low a toxicity for mepivacaine with this mode of administration. The intraperitoneal toxicity also is higher than that of lignocaine, whereas in the case of intravenous injection no significant difference is apparent. Clinically too, the toxicity appears to be equal to or greater than that of lignocaine[444].

*Citanest*

Citanest ((±)-2-propylamino-*o*-propionotoluidide, *VIII*), which in the experimental tests and clinical trials was designated as 'L 67' or 'Astra 1512', is the latest local anaesthetic to be introduced. It was synthesized in 1953 by Löfgren and Tegnér[22]. Pharmacological investigations have been conducted by Wiedling[445], and Åström and Persson[446]; and experimental studies were carried out in humans by Berling and Björn[447], Eriksson[448,449], and Eriksson and Gordh[290]. While similar to lignocaine in its anaesthetic properties, Citanest shows a somewhat greater tendency towards localization at the injection site, and hence requires a smaller amount of supplementary vasoconstrictor. Its toxicity is lower than that of lignocaine—approximately 40 per cent lower in animal experiments. The tissue toxicity is minimal, and the local anaesthetic specificity favourable.

*Amplicaine*

Amplicaine is a mixture of two aminoacylanilides ((±)-3-diethylaminobutyrylanilide and 3-piperidino-2,4-dichlorobutyrylanilide, *VII*). These compounds were synthesized by Smith and Hofstetter[41]. Amplicaine is not extensively used, as it has a relatively long latency, and produces some local irritation[427].

### Aminoalkyl Esters of Benzoic Acids

*Procaine*

Procaine ($\beta$-diethylaminoethyl-$p$-aminobenzoate, Novocaine, *LVIII*—6, *Table 7.1*) has been used for more than half a century. Clinically, it has been superseded to an increasing degree by lignocaine. A review of its pharmacology and metabolism has been given by Giotti[450] and its general actions have been discussed by Zipf[354]. In recent years procaine (as 'Gerovital H₃') has attracted some attention in the domain of geriatrics, because of an alleged 'eutrophic' and 'rejuvenating' action[451–456]. The literature in this field has been critically examined in the British Medical Journal[457] as well as by Chiu[458]. Each of them emphasizes the lack of placebo administration of control series, double blind tests, and statistical analyses. Recent, controlled clinical tests in various types of senile changes have not revealed any appreciable response to procaine as compared with placebos[459–462]. Animal experiments were also negative[463].

Procaine is still a conventional anaesthetic in East Europe and China. In the Soviet Union it is frequently administered *ad modum* Vishnevski (tension crawl infiltration)—a technique which permits, it is reported, doses of up to 3,000 ml of a 0·25 per cent solution with adrenaline 1 : 500,000[464]. Vishnevski's technique is applied in China, where procaine is also used, in conjunction with muscle relaxants and, sometimes, other agents, for intravenous anaesthesia[465].

*Chloroprocaine*

The local anaesthetic activity of chloroprocaine ($\beta$-diethylaminoethyl-2-chloro-4-aminobenzoate, Nesacaine, *LVIII*—23, *Table 7.1*) is similar to that of lignocaine, and it has a similar intravenous toxicity. Like procaine, it potentiates the pressor effect of adrenaline and noradrenaline[427]. It is rapidly broken down in the organism[466], yielding 2-chloro-4-aminobenzoic acid and diethylaminoethanol. The pharmacological properties of chloroaminobenzoic acid apparently are not known. According to clinical investigators, chloroprocaine has a minimum of side-actions[356,467–469]. Under controlled conditions, however, its toxicity is equal to or greater than that of lignocaine at equi-effective doses[470–472].

*Propoxycaine*

Propoxycaine (Ravocaine, Pravocaine, Blockain, WIN 3459, *LVIII*—19, *Table 7.1*), the 2-propoxy derivative of procaine, is a surface and spinal anaesthetic with an activity and a toxicity approximately ten times that of procaine. It has been studied pharmacologically by Luduena and co-workers[380,381,393,394,473,474]. Propoxycaine is employed principally to reinforce the effect of procaine in dental solutions.

*Ambucaine*

Ambucaine (butoxycaine, Sympocaine, WIN 3706, *LVIII*—21, *Table 7.1*) is the 2-butoxy derivative of procaine and, hence, is a homologue of propoxycaine and an isomer of benoxinate. It is a surface anaesthetic possessing about twenty times the activity and toxicity of procaine. Pharmacologically, it has been investigated by Luduena and co-workers[380,381,393, 394,473].

### Propoxymetacaine

Propoxymetacaine ($\beta$-diethylaminoethyl-3-amino-4-propoxybenzoate, proparacaine, Ophthaine, *LVIII—20, Table 7.1*) is an isomer of propoxycaine and, like the latter, is an active surface anaesthetic[475]. It has been used solely for local instillation into the eye.

### Metambucaine

Metambucaine, ($\beta$-diethylaminoethyl-2-n-butoxy-3-aminobenzoate, metabutoxycaine, Primacaine, *LVIII—24, Table 7.1*) was synthesized by Epstein and Meyer[155] and has been pharmacologically studied by Epstein[476]. With various modes of administration its toxicity is equal to, or higher than, that of lignocaine, but its activity appears to be lower[477].

### Meprylcaine

Meprylcaine (2-methyl-2-n-propylaminopropylbenzoate, Oracaine, *LVIII—2, Table 7.1*) was pharmacologically investigated by Truant[478]. In anaesthetic potency it is intermediate between lignocaine and procaine, but more toxic. Meprylcaine, with addition of adrenaline, is employed as a short-acting dental anaesthetic.

## Miscellaneous Types of Agents

### Falicaine

Falicaine, which may be designated chemically as $\beta$-piperidino-4-propoxypropiophenone (*LXXIII*, R = Pr), was developed in East Germany. Its chemistry, pharmacology and clinical application have been described by Profft[479,480]. The compound is not sufficiently stable for sterilization by boiling or autoclaving. Administered subcutaneously Falicaine is approximately ten times as active as procaine, but also about ten times as toxic. In surface anaesthesia, it is roughly equal to amethocaine in potency. Although Falicaine shows a greater tendency than procaine to localization at the site of administration, and may be used without adrenaline, the addition of a vasoconstrictor is nevertheless advisable in order to counteract its hyperaemizing effect. Falicaine has soporific, sedative, and spasmolytic actions.

### Dyclonine

Dyclonine, $\beta$-piperidino-4-butoxypropiophenone (*LXXIII*, R = Bu), is a homologue of Falicaine and, like the latter, was synthesized by Profft[175]. Although it has found acceptance as a surface anaesthetic relatively free from irritant properties, it is quite unsuitable for injection[481–483]. According to Florestano and Bahler[484] it possesses not only surface anaesthetic activity, but also bactericidal and fungicidal actions.

*Hydroxypolyethoxydodecane*

This compound (Thesit, *LXXXIV*) is of theoretical interest, in that it exemplifies a local anaesthetic with a higher alkyl group as the lipophilic centre, and a hydroxyl group incorporated into the hydrophilic centre[212]. The mean molecular weight is approximately 600, *i.e.* $n \simeq 9$. Its pharmacology has been studied notably by Soehring and his associates[485-492], and by Zipf and co-workers[493,494]. The compound is used solely as a surface anaesthetic and, as such, is also combined with mepivacaine to reinforce the latter's effect. When injected, it is damaging to the tissues[427].

*Oxethazaine*

Oxethazaine (*N,N*-bis[*N*-methyl-*N*-(α,α-dimethyl-β-phenylethyl)acetamide] ethanolamine, Oxaine, *X*) was originally discovered as an impurity in a synthesis[18]. Oxethazaine appears to be the most powerful surface anaesthetic known, for on the rabbit cornea its potency is approximately 2,000 times that of lignocaine. Since the compound not only has a high intravenous toxicity and a long latency, but is also not a specific local anaesthetic[20,21], it has come into use only as a symptomatic agent in gastrointestinal disorders such as gastritis, peptic ulcer, oesophagitis, and irritable colon. Its metabolism has been studied by Wiser and Seifter[411].

### Long-acting Local Anaesthetics ('*Depot Preparations*')

With the aim of developing a drug that would have a substantially prolonged duration of action ('depot preparation'), researchers have been working for several years on various additions to, and modifications of, local anaesthetics. They have tried poorly soluble or poorly hydrolysable salts, supplementary agents increasing the viscosity (*e.g.* carboxymethylcellulose, dextran, polyvidone), and various solvents and suspension media; but the required degree of prolongation has been obtained only with the anaesthetic dissolved for example in propylene glycol or urethane solution. These two agents are, however, highly deleterious to the tissues, and the prolonged 'anaesthetic' action is simply a manifestation of more or less protracted nerve damage (*vide* Friberg[495], among others). In recent years numerous authors have cautioned against the use of such agents. The need for circumspection is particularly evident in the case of Efocaine, which is a mixture of procaine, butylcaine, propylene glycol, polyethylene glycol, and water. This preparation has, in recent years, been the subject of several negative clinical reports and similar findings have been reported by Horáková, Hach and Smolková[496] in experimental investigations using Efocaine and Efocaine-like mixtures.

### REFERENCES

1. ADLER *Riv. ital. Stomat.* 1958, **13**, 25
2. ADRIANI *Clin. Pharmacol. Ther.* 1960, **1**, 645
3. BJÖRN *Odont. Revy* 1956, **7**, 305
4. GRUBER *Acta anaesth. scand.* 1961, Suppl. 7, 1
5. KILLIAN *Lokalanästhesie und Lokalanästhetica*: Georg Thieme Verlag, Stuttgart, 1959
6. LOEWE *Arzneimitt. Forsch.* 1956, **6**, 43

7. VANDAM *New Engl. J. Med.* 1960, **263**, 748
8. WATSON *J. Pharm., Lond.* 1960, **12**, 257
9. WIEDLING *Xylocaine. The Pharmacological Basis of its Clinical Use:* Almqvist & Wiksell, Uppsala, 1959
10. HACH *Čsl. Farm.* 1953, **2**, 200
11. BOISSIER, MALEN and DUMONT *C.R. Acad. Sci., Paris* 1956, **242**, 1086
12. MAUGÉ, MALEN and BOISSIER *Bull. Soc. chim. Fr.* 1956, 926
13. BOISSIER, DUMONT and MALEN *Anesth. Analg., Paris* 1956, **13**, 569
14. BOEHME, GRAEME, SCHARPF, SIEGMUND, SCHIPPER and TOBKES *J. med. pharm. Chem.* 1961, **4**, 183
15. PROFFT and JUMAR *Arch. Pharm., Berl.* 1956, **289**, 90
16. PROFFT *Arch. Pharm., Berl.* 1960, **293**, 543
17. KOCHETKOV and DUDYKINA *J. gen. Chem., Moscow* 1959, **29**, 1659
18. FREED, BRUCE, HANSLICK and MASCITTI *J. org. Chem.* 1961, **26**, 2378
19. BEADER, GLASSMAN, HUDYMA and SEIFTER *Proc. Soc. exp. Biol., N.Y.* 1955, **89**, 645
20. GLASSMAN, HUDYMA and SEIFTER *J. Pharmacol.* 1957, **119**, 150
21. GLASSMAN, HUDYMA, RAUZZINO and SEIFTER *Pharmacologist* 1961, **3**, 74
22. LÖFGREN and TEGNÉR *Acta chem. scand.* 1960, **14**, 486
23. SEN GUPTA, NARANG, VIG and BANSAL *J. Indian chem. Soc.* 1957, **34**, 71
24. AF EKENSTAM, EGNÉR and PETTERSON *Acta chem. scand.* 1957, **11**, 1183
25. RINDERKNECHT *Helv. chim. acta* 1959, **42**, 1324
26. DALAL and TRIVEDI *J. Indian chem. Soc.* 1960, **37**, 437
27. LÖFGREN, TEGNÉR and TAKMAN *Acta chem. scand.* 1957, **11**, 1724
28. HARMS, TERSTEEGE and NAUTA *J. med. pharm. Chem.* 1961, **4**, 575
29. OELSCHLÄGER *Arch. Pharm., Berl.* 1957, **290**, 587
30. SEN GUPTA and VASUDEV *J. Indian chem. Soc.* 1956, **33**, 665
31. MOTOVILOV *Pharm. & Toxic.* 1958, **21**, 140
32. KUDRIASHOVA, REMISOV and KHROMOV-BORISOV *J. gen. Chem., Moscow* 1959, **29**, 1211
33. LÖFGREN and TEGNÉR *Acta chem. scand.* 1955, **9**, 493
34. DAHLBOM and MISIORNY *Acta chem. scand.* 1961, **15**, 1367
35. DOFEK and VRBA *Acta fac. pharmaceut. Brunensis et Bratislavensis* 1959, **2**, 141
36. DOFEK and VRBA *Coll. Trav. chim. Tchécosl.* 1960, **25**, 1596
37. DOFEK, SEKERA and VRBA *J. pharm. Sci.* 1961, **50**, 161
38. AUMÜLLER, STEIN and RUSCHIG *Medizin und Chemie*, Bd VI: Verlag Chemie GmbH, Weinheim/Bergstr. 1958, 370
39. KOELZER and WEHR *Arzneimitt. Forsch.* 1958, **8**, 181, 270, 406, 544, 609; 1959, **9**, 683
40. OELSCHLÄGER, SCHMERSAHL and TOPORSKI *Arch. Pharm., Berl.* 1961, **294**, 488
41. SMITH and HOFSTETTER *Helv. chim. acta* 1955, **38**, 1085
42. KOELZER and WEHR *Arzneimitt. Forsch.* 1959, **9**, 167, 262
43. BEKE, LEMPERT and GYERMEK *Acta Chim. Acad. Sci. hung.* 1954, **5**, 143, 151
44. GYERMEK, BEKE and LEMPERT *Acta Pharm. hung.* 1955, **25**, 114
45. BEKE, LEMPERT, SERES and GYERMEK *Mag. chem. Foly.* 1955, **61**, 190
46. EPSTEIN and KAMINSKY *J. Amer. chem. Soc.* 1958, **80**, 1892
47. EPSTEIN and MALATESTINIC *J. Amer. pharm. Ass., Sci. Ed.* 1960, **49**, 80
48. LÖFGREN, LUNDQVIST and LINDSTRÖM *Acta chem. scand.* 1955, **9**, 1079
49. LINDSTRÖM *Acta chem. scand.* 1957, **11**, 962
50. SMITH *Helv. chim. acta* 1959, **42**, 1764
51. MALATESTA, MIGLIACCIO and DIAMANTI *Ann. Chim., Roma* 1960, **50**, 1167
52. LEMPERT, BEKE and HERR *Acta Chim. Acad. Sci. hung.* 1957, **12**, 93
53. HACH, HORÁKOVÁ and HAVLOVÁ *Coll. Trav. chim. Tchécosl.* 1957, **22**, 53

54. BOROVANSKÝ, SEKERA and VRBA *J. Amer. pharm. Ass., Sci. Ed.* 1959, **48,** 402; 1960, **49,** 57
55. SOVA, SEKERA and VRBA *Experientia* 1957, **13,** 495
56. WILDER SMITH *Helv. chim. acta* 1959, **42,** 1771
57. SCHIEMENZ and ENGELHARD *Chem. Ber.* 1959, **92,** 862
58. TSATSAS and GUIOCA-DEDOPOULOU *Bull. Soc. chim. Fr.* 1961, 298
59. WEIDMANN and PETERSEN *J. Pharmacol.* 1955, **115,** 246
60. SEN GUPTA, NARANG, VIG and BANSAL *J. Indian chem. Soc.* 1956, **33,** 902
61. TAKAHASHI, SATODA, FUKUI and MATSUO *J. pharm. Soc. Japan* 1960, **80,** 1579
62. EPSTEIN and KAMINSKY *J. Amer. chem. Soc.* 1957, **79,** 5814
63. EPSTEIN and KAMINSKY *J. Amer. pharm. Ass., Sci. Ed.* 1959, **48,** 150
64. WIRTH and GÖSSWALD *Dtsch. zahnärztl. Z.* 1960, **15,** 1271
65. CLINTON, LASKOWSKY, SALVADOR, BATES and CARROLL *J. Amer. chem. Soc.* 1957, **79,** 2285
66. OELSCHLÄGER *Arzneimitt. Forsch.* 1958, **8,** 532
67. FOSDICK and RAPP *J. Amer. chem. Soc.* 1943, **65,** 2307
68. LÖFGREN and FISCHER *Svensk kem. Tidskr.* 1946, **65,** 219
69. BEKE, LEMPERT and GYERMEK *Acta Chim. Acad. Sci. hung.* 1954, **5,** 151
70. HOFSTETTER and SMITH *Helv. chim. acta* 1953, **36,** 1698
71. DAHLBOM, TEGNÉR and WILLMAN *Acta chem. scand.* 1959, **13,** 1145
72. SEN GUPTA, KAUR and VASUDEV *J. Indian chem. Soc.* 1957, **34,** 893
73. TEGNÉR and WILLMAN *Acta chem. scand.* 1960, **14,** 885
74. TEGNÉR and DOMEIJ *Acta chem. scand.* 1960, **14,** 916
75. LÜNING *Acta chem. scand.* 1957, **11,** 957
76. DOFEK, SVOBODA and VRBA *Čsl. Farm.* 1959, **8,** 431
77. LEMPERT, BEKE and BOROVANSKY *Mag. chem. Foly.* 1956, **62,** 373
78. LEMPERT, BEKE, BOROVANSKY and HERR *Arch. Pharm., Berl.* 1957, **290,** 637
79. BARKENBUS and WUELLNER *J. Amer. chem. Soc.* 1955, **77,** 3866
80. YOKOYAMA, IWATA and TOYOSHIMA *J. pharm. Soc. Japan* 1958, **78,** 123
81. HORÁKOVÁ, HACH, ROTH and MATOUŠKOVÁ-SMOLKOVÁ *Čsl. Farm.* 1956, **5,** 448
82. SENDA and IZUMI *J. pharm. Soc. Japan* 1961, **81,** 964
83. BHARGAVA and NAIR *J. Indian chem. Soc.* 1957, **34,** 42
84. NOVELLI *An. Farm. Bioquím., B. Aires* 1955, **22,** 28
85. ETTEL and NEUMANN *Chem. Listy* 1957, **51,** 1906
86. HACH *Coll. Trav. chim. Tchécosl.* 1959, **24,** 3136
87. BHARGAVA and BALIGA *J. Indian. chem. Soc.* 1958, **35,** 807
88. BHARGAVA and SINGH *J. Indian chem. Soc.* 1960, **37,** 241
89. BHARGAVA and JOSE *J. Indian chem. Soc.* 1960, **37,** 314
90. BHARGAVA and SINGH *J. Indian chem. Soc.* 1961, **38,** 77
91. BHARGAVA and PRASAD *J. Indian chem. Soc.* 1961, **38,** 165
92. BHARGAVA and RAM *J. Indian chem. Soc.* 1961, **38,** 167
93. SILVESTRINI and POZZATTI *Arch. int. Pharmacodyn.* 1960, **129,** 249
94. SPALVA *Pharm. & Toxic.* 1960, **23,** 331
95. HORÁKOVÁ and VOTAVA *Physiol. Boh.-slov.* 1959, **8,** 260
96. NAKAMURA *Shikoku Acta Med.* 1960, **16,** (Suppl.), 93
97. KOELZER and WEHR *Arzneimitt. Forsch.* 1958, **8,** 544
98. HACH, HORÁKOVÁ, REICHELT and HAVLOVÁ *Coll. Trav. chim. Tchécosl.* 1957, **22,** 1887
99. HORÁKOVÁ and HACH *Čsl. Farm.* 1959, **8,** 126
100. LARIZZA and PELLEGRINO *Gazz. chim. ital.* 1959, **89,** 2018
101. LARIZZA, BRANCACCIO and COSCIA *Farmaco, Ed. sci.* 1961, **16,** 693
102. KOELZER and WEHR *Arzneimitt. Forsch.* 1958, **8,** 609
103. CARELLI, CARDELLINI and LIBERATORE *Ann. Chim., Roma* 1961, **51,** 699

104. KOELZER and WEHR *Arzneimitt. Forsch.* 1958, **8,** 761: 1959, **9,** 70, 113
105. SOEHRING and RAUTMANN *Arzneimitt. Forsch.* 1952, **2,** 551
105a. KNOEFEL *J. Pharmacol.* 1933, **47,** 69
106. ROTHSTEIN, GLEY, DE BOISLAMBERT, BINOVIC, STOVEN and DELOR *C.R. Acad. Sci., Paris* 1954, **239,** 284
107. ROSE, SULLIVAN and POHLAND *J. Amer. Pharm. Ass., Sci. Ed.* 1955, **44,** 766
108. HUTTON *J. org. Chem.* 1955, **20,** 855
109. EPSTEIN and KAMINSKY *J. Amer. pharm. Ass., Sci. Ed.* 1958, **47,** 347
110. HÄRING *Helv. chim. acta* 1959, **42,** 1916
111. HÄRING *Helv. chim. acta* 1960, **43,** 104
112. HÄRING *Arzneimitt. Forsch.* 1960, **10,** 475
113. KOELZER and WEHR *Arzneimitt. Forsch.* 1958, **8,** 664
114. SEKERA, HRUBÝ, VRBA and LEBDUŠKA *Chem. Listy* 1950, **44,** 275
115. SEKERA, BOROVANSKÝ and VRBA *Chem. Listy* 1951, **45,** 90; 1953, **47,** 591
116. SEKERA, JAKUBEC and VRBA *Chem. Listy* 1952, **46,** 762

117. SEKERA, HRUBÝ, VRBA and LEBDUŠKA *Čsl. Farm.* 1952, **1,** 12
118. SEKERA, SOVA and VRBA *Experientia* 1955, **11,** 275
119. SEKERA and VRBA *Arch. Pharm., Berl.* 1958, **291,** 122
120. DAHLBOM and ÖSTERBERG *Acta chem. scand.* 1955, **9,** 1553
121. PALÁT, SEKERA and VRBA *Experientia* 1956, **12,** 273
122. DOFEK, SEKERA and VRBA *J. Amer. pharm. Ass., Sci. Ed.* 1959, **48,** 398
123. SEKERA, PAVLIČEK and VRBA *Ann. pharm. franç.* 1958, **16,** 684
124. BÜCHI and PERLIA *Arzneimitt. Forsch.* 1960, **10,** 1, 117, 174, 297, 465, 554, 745, 930, 1016; 1961, **11,** 62, 877
125. SIEGER, ZIEGLER, KLEIN and SOKOL *J. Amer. pharm. Ass., Sci. Ed.* 1958, **47,** 734
126. SEKERA, PAVLIČEK and VRBA *Bull. Soc. chim. Fr.* 1959, 401
127. HÄRING and STILLE *Helv. chim. acta* 1961, **44,** 642
128. LÖFGREN and STOFFEL *Acta chem. scand.* 1959, **13,** 1585
129. LÖFGREN and WÅHLSTAM *Acta chem. scand.* 1961, **15,** 1467
130. LÜNING *Acta chem. scand.* 1959, **13,** 1623; 1960, **14,** 321
131. LÜNING *Svensk kem. Tidskr.* 1960, **72,** 319
132. HONKANEN *Ann. Acad. Sci. fenn.* 1960, Ser. A.II, nr. 99
133. KOLOSY, TEYSSIÉ and VANDERHAEGHE *J. Pharm., Lond.* 1955, **7,** 477
134. CLINTON, LASKOWSKI, SALVADOR and CARROLL *J. Amer. chem. Soc.* 1957, **79,** 2290
135. SEN GUPTA, KAUR and VASUDEV *J. Indian chem. Soc.* 1957, **34,** 528
136. DEMOLIS, SURBER and WAGNER-JAUREGG *Arzneimitt. Forsch.* 1960, **10,** 743
137. HÄRING, STILLE and WAGNER-JAUREGG *Arzneimitt. Forsch.* 1961, **11,** 801
138. THUILLIER, RUMPF and SAVILLE *Bull. Soc. chim. Fr.* 1960, 1786
139. WORMSER and ELKIN *J. pharm. Sci.* 1961, **50,** 976
140. EINHORN *Liebigs Ann.* 1910, **371,** 125, 131, 142
141. CARNEY *Medicinal Chemistry* (Ed. Suter) Vol. I: John Wiley, New York 1951, 280
142. BÜCHI *Arzneimitt. Forsch.* 1952, **2,** 1, 65, 114
143. RABJOHN, FRONABARGER and LINSTROMBERG *J. org. Chem.* 1955, **20,** 271
144. NAZAROV and various collaborators *J. gen. Chem., Moscow* 1959, **29,** 724 and 28 other papers 1951–59; *Izvest. Akad. Nauk, Otdel Khim. Nauk.* 1960, 251, 872, 1605
145. SAMARINA *Pharm. & Toxic.* 1959, **22,** 144
146. KUCHERUK *Pharm. & Toxic.* 1961, **24,** 706
147. SHAPIRO, SOLOWAY, CHODOS and FREEDMAN *J. Amer. chem. Soc.* 1959, **81,** 201, 203
148. SHAPIRO, SOLOWAY, SHAPIRO and FREEDMAN *J. pharm. Sci.* 1961, **50,** 769
149. WINSTEAD, WISHNOFF and BOST *J. Amer. chem. Soc.* 1955, **77,** 772
150. PAVLIČEK, SEKERA and VRBA *Pharmazie* 1958, **13,** 748
151. NAJER, CHABRIER and GIUDICELLI *Bull. Soc. chim. Fr.* 1956, 613

152. SZADOWSKA and CIBORSKA *Diss., Polska Akad. Nauk.* 1957, *IX*, 1: 9/23
153. PERRY, JONES and PRATT *J. Amer. chem. Soc.* 1956, **78**, 3403
154. ROHMANN, ECKERT and HEIL *Arch. Pharm., Berl.* 1959, **292**, 255
155. EPSTEIN and MEYER *J. Amer. chem. Soc.* 1955, **77**, 4059
156. FREIFELDER, MOORE, VERNSTEN and STONE *J. Amer. chem. Soc.* 1958, **80**, 4320
157. KURIHARA, NIWA and TODA *J. pharm. Soc. Japan* 1955, **75**, 215
158. NAJER, CHABRIER and GIUDICELLI *Bull. Soc. chim. Fr.* 1955, 1189; 1956, 1134, 1669
159. GIUDICELLI, NAJER, CHABRIER and JOANNIC *Ann. pharm. franç.* 1956, **14**, 376
160. ZIRM and PONGRATZ *Arzneimitt. Forsch.* 1960, **10**, 412
161. OLÁH, PAVLÁTH, OLÁH and HERR *J. org. Chem.* 1957, **22**, 879
162. REISNER and CORDASCO *J. org. Chem.* 1958, **23**, 1403
163. TACCARDI, RAPUZZI and FERRARI *J. med. pharm. Chem.* 1961, **3**, 525
164. DA RE and VERLICCHI *Farmaco., Ed. sci.* 1958, **13**, 574
165. KURIHARA, NIWA and RO *Ann. Report Tohoku Coll. Pharm.* 1955, **2**, 37
166. LUDUENA and HOPPE *J. Amer. pharm. Ass., Sci. Ed.* 1955, **44**, 393
167. BÜCHI, ENÉZIAN, ENÉZIAN, VALETTE and PATTANI *Helv. chim. acta* 1960, **43**, 1971
168. HAINING, JOHNSTON and SCOTT *J. Pharm., Lond.* 1960, **12**, 641
169. HEUSNER, SCHULZ and ZIELE *Arch. Pharm., Berl.* 1961, **294**, 273
170. LINNELL and PERKS *J. chem. Soc.* 1960, 1036
171. FRAHM and SOEHRING *Arzneimitt. Forsch.* 1957, **7**, 215
172. BEANI and FOWST *Arch. ital. Sci. farmacol.* 1955, **5**, 287
173. BEANI and FOWST *Arch. ital. Sci. farmacol.* 1955, **5**, 296
174. BEANI and FOWST *Arch. ital. Sci. farmacol.* 1955, **5**, 301
175. PROFFT *Chem. Tech., Berlin* 1951, **3**, 210; 1952, **4**, 241; 1953, **5**, 13
176. PROFFT *Arzneimitt. Forsch.* 1958, **8**, 268
177. PROFFT and SCHULZ *Arch. Pharm., Berl.* 1961, **294**, 292
178. ČELADNIK, PALÁT, SEKERA and VRBA *Arch. Pharm., Berl.* 1958, **291**, 3
179. PROFFT and HOFFMEISTER *Liebigs Ann.* 1961, **644**, 84
180. PROFFT and ZSCHUMMEL *Arzneimitt. Forsch.* 1961, **11**, 574
181. KOST, KUDRIN, TERENTIEV and ERSHOV *Vestn., Moskow. Univ., Ser. II.* 1960, **15**, 66
182. PETROW, STEPHENSON and THOMAS *J. Pharm., Lond.* 1956, **8**, 666
183. ING and ORMEROD *J. Pharm., Lond.* 1952, **4**, 21
184. WHEATLEY and HOLDREGE *J. org. Chem.* 1958, **23**, 568
185. CHABRIER, NAJER and GIUDICELLI *Bull. Soc. chim. Fr.* 1955, 1353
186. NAJER, CHABRIER and GIUDICELLI *Bull. Soc. chim. Fr.* 1956, 106
187. CHABRIER, NAJER and GIUDICELLI *Bull. Soc. chim. Fr.* 1955, 1603
188. HACH and HORÁKOVÁ *Chem. Listy* 1957, **51**, 382
189. VIELLEFOSSE, VAYSON DE PRADENNE and COSTEROUSSE *Ann. pharm. franç.* 1957, **15**, 303
190. LUDUENA, HOPPE, PAGE and CLINTON *J. med. pharm. Chem.* 1961, **3**, 545
191. GONZALEZ and LUDUENA *J. med. pharm. Chem.* 1961, **3**, 555
192. PAGE and CLINTON *J. org. Chem.* 1962, **27**, 218
193. ADLER-HRADECKY and KELENTEY *Arch. int. Pharmacodyn.* 1960, **128**, 135
194. TSATSAS, DELABY, QUEVAUVILLER, DAMIENS and BLANPIN *Ann. pharm. franç.* 1956, **14**, 607
195. TSATSAS and DELABY *Ann. pharm. franç.* 1956, **14**, 621
196. CARELLI, CARDELLINI and LIBERATORE *Farmaco, Ed. Sci.* 1960, **15**, 803; 1961, **16**, 375
197. OELSCHLÄGER *Arch. Pharm., Berl.* 1959, **292**, 174
198. OELSCHLÄGER *Arzneimitt. Forsch.* 1959, **9**, 313
199. CHITI *Farmaco, Ed. sci.* 1960, **15**, 29
200. EPSTEIN *J. Amer. chem. Soc.* 1959, **81**, 6207

201. MASUDA and HAMOR J. *Amer. pharm. Ass., Sci. Ed.* 1957, **46,** 61
202. HACH, HORÁKOVÁ and PROTIVA *Chem. Listy.* 1955, **49,** 227
203. LEMPERT and GYERMEK *Mag. chem. Foly.* 1955, **61,** 193
204. ANDRISANO, CHIERICI and CRAVERI *Arzneimitt. Forsch.* 1958, **8,** 706, 767
205. CRAVERI, CREMA and DORMIA *Arzneimitt. Forsch.* 1960, **10,** 925
206. NÁDOR, HERR, PATAKY and BORSY *Nature, Lond.* 1953, **171,** 788
207. HORÁKOVÁ and HACH Čsl. *Farm.* 1957, **6,** 36
208. HACH and HORÁKOVÁ *Experientia* 1956, **12,** 112
209. HORÁKOVÁ and HACH Čsl. *Farm.* 1957, **6,** 442
210. HORÁKOVÁ and ROTH Čsl. *Farm.* 1958, **7,** 289
211. SEKERA, NOVACEK, SALAC and VRBA J. *Amer. pharm. Ass., Sci. Ed.* 1959, **48,** 396
212. LÖFGREN *Ark. Kemi. Min. Geol.* 1946, **22A,** nr. 18
213. QUEVAUVILLER *Prod. pharm.* 1952, **7,** 533, 585
214. LÖFGREN *Studies on Local Anesthetics. Xylocaine, a new synthetic drug:* Ivar Haeggströms Boktryckeri AB, Stockholm 1948
215. PERKOW *Arzneimitt. Forsch.* 1960, **10,** 1020
216. SEKERA and VRBA *Biochem. Pharmacol.* 1959, **2,** 315
217. PRYANISHNIKOVA and PCHELIN *C.R. Acad. Sci. U.R.S.S. Biochem. Sect.* 1959, **126,** 177
218. KUDRIASHOVA and KHROMOV-BORISOV J. *gen. Chem., Moscow* 1960, **30,** 4035
219. MOTOVILOV *Farm. & Toxic.* 1961, **24,** 113
220. TEGNÉR and WILLMAN *Acta chem. scand.* 1961, **15,** 1180
221. DASTUGUE and MONTEIL *Anesth. Analg., Paris* 1955, **12,** 401
222. DASTUGUE, BASTIDE and DECROS *Ann. pharm. franç.* 1959, **17,** 269
223. DASTUGUE, BASTIDE and DECROS *Ann. pharm. franç.* 1959, **17,** 359
224. BASTIDE, MONTEIL, VAISSIER and DASTUGUE *Anesth. Analg., Paris* 1960, **17,** 270
225. DASTUGUE, BASTIDE and VAISSIER *Anesth. Analg., Paris* 1960, **17,** 278
226. SIMON, FÖLDVÁRI and GYÖRGYI *Acta Physiol. Acad. Sci. hung.* 1960, Suppl. **18,** 96
227. TAMMELIN and LÖFGREN *Acta chem. scand.* 1947, **1,** 871
228. SHANES *Pharmacol. Rev.* 1958, **10,** 165
229. SKOU *Acta Pharm. Tox., Kbh.* 1954, **10,** 281
230. SKOU *Acta Pharm. Tox., Kbh.* 1954, **10,** 292
231. SKOU *Acta Pharm. Tox., Kbh.* 1954, **10,** 297
232. SKOU *Acta Pharm. Tox., Kbh.* 1954, **10,** 305
233. SKOU *Acta Pharm. Tox., Kbh.* 1954, **10,** 317
234. SKOU *Acta Pharm. Tox., Kbh.* 1954, **10,** 325
235. SKOU *Lokalanestetika:* Universitetsforlaget, Aarhus 1954
236. SKOU *Acta Pharm. Tox., Kbh.* 1956, **12,** 109
237. SKOU *Acta Pharm. Tox., Kbh.* 1956, **12,** 115
238. SKOU *Biochim. biophys. acta* 1958, **30,** 625
239. SKOU *Biochim. biophys. acta.* 1959, **31,** 1
240. SKOU J. *Pharm., Lond.* 1961, **13,** 204
241. TRUANT *Fed. Proc.* 1957, **16,** 341
242. TRUANT and TAKMAN *Anesth. Analg., Cleveland* 1959, **38,** 478
243. LENDLE and MOHRMANN *Arzneimitt. Forsch.* 1955, **5,** 249
244. CONDOURIS *Biochem. Pharmacol.* 1961, **8,** 97
245. CONDOURIS J. *Pharmacol.* 1961, **131,** 243
246. RUD *Acta physiol. scand.* 1961, **51,** Suppl. 178
247. GOODMAN and GILMAN *The Pharmacological Basis of Therapeutics,* 2nd ed.: Macmillan, New York, 1955
248. RITCHIE and GREENGARD J. *Pharmacol.* 1961, **133,** 241
249. DETTBARN *Biochim. biophys. acta* 1962, **57,** 73

250. NACHMANSOHN *Chemical and Molecular Basis of Nerve Activity:* Academic Press, New York, 1959
251. NACHMANSOHN *Science* 1961, **134,** 1962
252. FELDBERG *Metabolism of the Nervous System* (Ed. Richter): Pergamon,L ondon, 1957, p. 493
253. VON MURALT *Neue Ergebnisse der Nervenphysiologie:* Springer-Verlag, Berlin, 1958
254. SCHOFFENIELS *Arch. int. Physiol. Biochim.* 1960, **68,** 1
255. CHAGAS, PENNA-FRANCA, HASSON, CROCKER, NISHIE and GARCIA *Anais Acad. bras. Cienc.* 1957, **29,** 53
256. CHAGAS, PENNA-FRANCA, NISHIE and GARCIA *Arch. Biochem. Biophys.* 1958, **75,** 251
257. EHRENPREIS *Science* 1959, **129,** 1613
258. EHRENPREIS and KELLOCK *Biochem. Biophys. Res. Comm.* 1960, **2,** 311
259. BARTELS, DETTBARN, HIGMAN and ROSENBERG *Biochem. Biophys. Res. Comm.* 1960, **2,** 316
260. HIGMAN and BARTELS *Biochim. biophys. acta* 1961, **54,** 543
261. ECKERT *Arzneimitt. Forsch.* 1962, **12,** 8
262. VON MURALT *Die Signalübermittlung im Nerven:* Birkhäuser, Bale, 1946
263. HAZARD, CHEYMOL, LECHAT and DELEAU *J. Physiol., Paris* 1960, **52,** 116
264. HORÁKOVÁ and HACH *Čsl. Farm.* 1959, **8,** 193
265. MARRAS and FARINA *Boll. Soc. ital. Biol. sper.* 1960, **34,** 53
266. NARANJO and NARANJO *Arch. int. Pharmacodyn.* 1958, **113,** 313
267. AKOPIAN and SAMVELIAN *Pharm. & Toxic.* 1958, **21,** 460
268. SEKERA and VRBA *Arch. int. Pharmacodyn.* 1960, **125,** 311
269. SEKERA, VRBA and PINOSOVÁ-ČEPELÁKOVÁ *Arch. int. Pharmacodyn.* 1960, **125,** 322
270. SINHA *J. Pharm., Lond.* 1953, **5,** 620
271. WIEDLING *Acta Pharm. Tox., Kbh.* 1952, **8,** 117
272. ADLER, GÁL and VÉGH *Z. Vitamin-, Hormon- u. Fermentforsch.* 1950, **3,** 236
273. SINHA and WEST *J. Pharm., Lond.* 1953, **5,** 370
274. HERR and BALOGH *Arch. exp. Path. Pharmak.* 1957, **232,** 423
275. KEIL and VIETEN *Fortschr. Geb. Röntgenstrahlen* 1952, **3,** 77
276. LAUBENDER and HEIL *Dissertation Heil:* Frankfurt 1956
277. MOLINENGO *Arch. ital. Sci. farmacol.* 1960, **10,** 141
278. GEDDES *Brit. J. Anaesth.* 1955, **27,** 609
279. HERR *Arzneimitt. Forsch.* 1958, **8,** 137
280. THER *Medizin u. Chemie* 1958, **6,** 399
281. MUNCH *Bioassays. A Handbook of Quantitative Pharmacology:* Baillière, Tindall and Cox, London, 1931
282. KREPPEL and ZIPF *Arch. int. Pharmacodyn.* 1955, **101,** 279
283. PETROS and GIBILISCO *J. dent. Res.* 1959, **38,** 348
284. GRIFFIÉ and BRUNEL *C.R. Acad. Sci., Paris* 1959, **248,** 2802
285. NIESCHULZ, HOFFMANN and POPENDIKER *Arzneimitt. Forsch.* 1958, **8,** 539
286. ÅSTRÖM and PERSSON *J. Pharmacol.* 1961, **132,** 87
287. CHARONNAT and LECHAT *Ann. pharm. franç.* 1955, **13,** 410
288. HORÁKOVÁ and ROTH *Čsl. Farm.* 1956, **5,** 527
289. BOBERG-ANS *Acta Ophthal., Kbh.* 1956, **34,** 149
290. ERIKSSON and GORDH *Acta anaesth. scand.* 1959, Suppl. 2, 81
291. DHUNÉR, EDSHAGE and WILHELM *Acta anaesth. scand.* 1960, **4,** 189
292. ALBÉRT and LÖFSTRÖM *Acta anaesth. scand.* 1961, **5,** 99
293. BJÖRN *Nordisk klinisk odontologi* Vol. III, chapter 17: II, p. 1: Forlaget for Faglitteratur, Copenhagen, 1961
294. BJÖRN *Svensk tandläk. Tidskr.* 1946, **39,** Suppl.
295. VRBA and SEKERA *Arch. int. Pharmacodyn.* 1959, **118,** 155
296. ROTH *Arch. int Pharmacodyn.* 1959, **118,** 284

297. MONGAR *Quantitative Methods in Human Pharmacology and Therapeutics* (Ed. Laurence): Pergamon Press, London, 1959, p. 114
298. CHAKRAVARTI *Biometrics* 1960, **16,** 278
299. WEHR and KOELZER *Arzneimitt. Forsch.* 1958, **8,** 88
300. PHILLIPS, NELSON, LYONS, GRAFF, HARRIS and FRAZIER *Anesth. Analg., Cleveland* 1960, **39,** 317
301. SIEBECKER, KIMMEY, BAMFORTH and STEINHAUS *Acta anaesth. scand.* 1960, **4,** 97
302. WAGERS and SMITH *J. Pharmacol.* 1960, **130,** 89
303. BARTLETT and HUTASERANI *Anesth. Analg., Cleveland* 1961, **40,** 296
304. STEINHAUS and HOWLAND *J. Pharmacol.* 1957, **119,** 186
305. STEINHAUS and HOWLAND *Anesth. Analg., Cleveland* 1958, **37,** 40
306. WOODS and HAGGART *Anesthesiology* 1957, **18,** 831
307. DE KORNFELD and STEINHAUS *Anésth. Analg.* 1959, **38,** 173
308. KAO and JALAR *Brit. J. Pharmacol.* 1959, **14,** 522
309. KIMMEY and STEINHAUS *Acta anaesth. scand.* 1959, **3,** 9
310. SMITH, FROMMEL and MORRIS *J. Pharm., Lond.* 1959, **11,** 600
311. MAYKUT and KALOW *Canad. Anaesth. Soc. J.* 1955, **2,** 109
312. HOLTEN and LARSEN *Acta Pharm. Tox., Kbh.* 1956, **12,** 346
313. THER and LINDNER *Medizin u. Chemie.* 1958, **6,** 351
314. HALLDIN *Svenska Läkartidn.* 1954, **51,** 2147
315. BERNHARD and BOHM *Acta physiol. scand.* 1954, **31,** Suppl. 114, 5
316. BERNHARD and BOHM *Experientia* 1954, **10,** 474
317. BERNHARD and BOHM *Brit. J. Pharmacol.* 1955, **10,** 288
318. BERNHARD, BOHM and HÖJEBERG *Arch. Neurol. Psychiat., Chicago* 1955, **74,** 208
319. OTTOSSON *Experientia* 1955, **11,** 453
320. BERNHARD, BOHM, HÖJEBERG and MELIN *Acta Psychiat., Kbh.* 1956, **31,** 185
321. BERNHARD, BOHM and WIESEL *Arch. int. Pharmacodyn.* 1956, **108,** 392
322. BERNHARD, BOHM, KIRSTEIN and WIESEL *Arch. int. Pharmacodyn.* 1956, **108,** 408
323. BERNHARD *Exper. Cell. Res.* 1958, Suppl. 5, 201
324. BOHM, FLODMARK and PETERSÉN *Arch. Neurol. Psychiat., Chicago* 1959, **81,** 550
325. OTTOSSON *Experimental Studies of the Mode of Action of Electroconvulsive Therapy:* Munksgaard, Copenhagen, 1960
326. BLOMBERG, FEGERSTEN, FLODMARK and PETERSÉN *Acta Psychiat., Kbh.* 1961, **36,** 57
327. FRENCH, LIVINGSTON, KONIGSMARK and RICHLAND *J. Neurosurg.* 1957, **14,** 43
328. TAVERNER and BAIN *Lancet* 1958, **2,** 1145
329. TAVERNER *Brit. J. Pharmacol.* 1960, **15,** 201
330. BERRY *Dissertation Abs.* 1961, **22,** 1661
331. BERRY, SANNER and KEASLING *J. Pharmacol.* 1961, **133,** 357
332. ZAPATA-ORTÍZ, CASTRO DE LA MATA and BARRANTES-CAMPOS *Arzneimitt. Forsch.* 1961, **11,** 657
333. CARDEN and STEINHAUS *Fed. Proc.* 1955, **14,** 324
334. CARDEN, STEINHAUS and STEINHAUS *Circulation Res.* 1956, **4,** 680
335. GRAEME, LEHOTZKY, CADMUS, SIEGMUND, CAMPBELL and LU *Fed. Proc.* 1956, **15,** 430
336. HARRIS, AGUIRRE y GUERRA, LIPTAK and BRIGHAM *J. appl. Physiol.* 1956, **8,** 499
337. HITCHCOCK and KEOWN *Fed. Proc.* 1958, **17,** 378
338. STEINHAUS, SIEBECKER and KIMMEY *J. Amer. med. Ass.* 1959, **169,** 8
339. STEPHENSON, COLE, PARRISH and others *Amer. J. Cardiol.* 1960, **5,** 77
340. VAN DONGEN *Arch. int. Pharmacodyn.* 1953, **96,** 45
341. VISENTINI *Arch. ital. Sci. farmacol.*, Serie III, 1955, **5,** 16
342. MELON, CAHN and DUBRASQUET *Anesth. Analg., Paris* 1953, **10,** 425
343. VISENTINI *Arch. int. Pharmacodyn.* 1954, **98,** 302

344. FREDERICKSON and MORRIS *Fed. Proc.* 1955, **14**, 340
345. CAHN *Anaesthesist* 1955, **4**, 207
346. ANGELAKOS and HEGNAUER *J. Pharmacol.* 1959, **127**, 137
347. IZUMIDA *Folia pharm. jap.* 1959, **55**, 691
348. SINGH and SHARMA *Arch. int. Pharmacodyn.* 1961, **131**, 1
349. VINOGRADOV *Pharm. & Toxic.* 1957, **20**, 527
350. WILLIAMS and SZEKERES *Biochem. Pharmacol.* 1961, **8**, 11
350a. SOUTHWORTH, McKUSICK, PEIRCE and RAWSON *J. Amer. med. Ass.* 1950, **143**, 717
350b. HITCHCOCK and KEOWN *Sth. med. J., Nashville* 1959, **52**, 702
350c. WEISS *Anésth. Analg.* 1960, **39**, 369
351. BAIRD and HARDMAN *J. Pharmacol.* 1961, **132**, 382
352. HARDMAN, BAIRD and MOORE *Fed. Proc.* 1957, **16**, 305
353. ROSSIGNOL and PATTANI *J. Physiol., Paris* 1961, **52**, 463
354. ZIPF *Arzneimitt. Forsch.* 1957, **7**, 529
355. ZIPF *Killian: Lokalanästhesie und Lokalanästhetika:* Georg Thieme, Stuttgart, 1959, p. 111
356. FOLDES, MOLLOY, McNALL, and KOUKAL *J. Amer. med. Ass.* 1960, **172**, 1493
357. BROMAGE and ROBSON *Anaesthesia* 1961, **16**, 461
358. HOLLER *Dtsch. zahnärztl. Z.* 1952, **7**, 1198
359. AVANT and WEATHERBY *Proc. Soc. exp. Biol., N.Y.* 1960, **103**, 353
360. STEINHAUS *Anesthesiology* 1957, **18**, 275
361. HULDT *Acta odont. scand.* 1953, **11**, Suppl. 13
362. HOPPE and DUPREY *Pharmacologist* 1960, **2**, 85
363. ZIPF and SCHLICKEISEN *Arzneimitt. Forsch.* 1959, **9**, 137
364. MUNOZ, GUERRERO, PAEILE and CAMPOS *Toxicol. appl. Pharmacol.* 1961, **3**, 445
365. BERGER *C.R. Soc. Biol., Paris* 1960, **154**, 959
366. CHEYMOL, LOVW, CHABRIER and ADOLPHE *Bull. Acad. nat. Méd.* 1960, **144**, 665
367. CHEYMOL, CHABRIER, ADOLPHE and SELIM *C.R. Soc. Biol., Paris* 1960, **154**, 1761
368. WINNE *Arzneimitt. Forsch.* 1961, **11**, 507
369. MANCA *Boll. Soc. ital. Biol. sper.* 1958, **34**, 427
370. BUNCE *Biochem. Pharmacol.* 1961, **8**, 175
371. HIRSCH *Acta orthopaed. scand.* 1959, **29**, 79
372. FUNKQVIST and OBEL *Acta radiol., Stockh.* 1960, **53**, 337
373. DE FELICE *Arch. int. Pharmacodyn.* 1958, **116**, 418
374. PIZZOLATO and MANNHEIMER *Histopathologic Effects of Local Anesthetic Drugs and Related Substances:* Charles C. Thomas, Springfield, 1961
375. SPENCER, SCHEIE and DRIPPS *J. Pharmacol.* 1955, **113**, 421
376. TAIT, REESE and DAVIS *Sth. med. J., Nashville* 1958, **51**, 358
377. BRUN *Acta anaesth. scand.* 1959, **3**, 59
378. PIZZOLATO and RENEGAR *Anesth. Analg., Cleveland* 1959, **38**, 138
379. NILSSON and WENDEBERG *Acta anaesth. scand.* 1957, **1**, 87
380. LUDUENA, HOPPE, NACHOD, MARTINI and SILVERN *Arch. int. Pharmacodyn.* 1955, **101**, 17
381. LUDUENA, HOPPE and BORLAND *J. Pharmacol.* 1958, **123**, 269
382. SCHMIDT, McINTIRE, MARTIN, HAWTHORNE and RICHARDS *Toxicol. appl. Pharmacol.* 1959, **1**, 454
383. SADOVE and KOLODNY *Acta anaesth. scand.* 1961, **5**, 13
384. BEHRENDT *Amer. J. Ophthal.* 1956, **41**, 99
385. BEHRENDT *Internat. J. Anesthesia* 1960, **7**, 14
386. MARR, WOOD, SENTERFIT and SIGELMAN *Amer. J. Ophthal.* 1957, **43**, 606
387. CORSSEN and ALLEN *Anesthesiology* 1960, **21**, 237
388. VOL'FENZON *Tsitologija* 1959, **1**, 641
389. ZINNER, JABLON, SANDERS and SASLAW *J. dent. Res.* 1960, **39**, 226

390. JABLON and ZINNER *J. dent. Res.* 1961, **40,** 678
391. MARCUS and HUSA *J. Amer. pharm. Ass., Sci. Ed.* 1959, **48,** 569
392. SETNIKAR and TEMELCOU *J. Amer. pharm. Ass., Sci. Ed.* 1959, **48,** 628
393. LUDUENA and HOPPE *J. Pharmacol.* 1956, **117,** 89
394. LUDUENA *Arch. int. Pharmacodyn.* 1957, **109,** 143
395. FERNSTRÖM *Acta derm.-venereol., Stockh.* 1959, **39,** 433
396. HANAUER *Dtsch. med. Wschr.* 1955, **80,** 1175
397. SIEGAL *J. Allergy* 1958, **29,** 329
398. FISHER and STURM *Ann. Allergy* 1958, **16,** 593
399. NOBLE and PIERCE *Lancet* 1961, **2,** 1436
400. HOLLUNGER *Acta Pharm. Tox., Kbh.* 1960, **17,** 356
401. HOLLUNGER *Acta Pharm. Tox., Kbh.* 1960, **17,** 365
402. HOLLUNGER *Acta Pharm. Tox., Kbh.* 1960, **17,** 374
403. HOLLUNGER *Acta Pharm. Tox., Kbh.* 1960, **17,** 384
404. HOLLUNGER and NIKLASSON *Biochem. Pharmacol.* 1961, **8,** 5
405. LINDSTROM *Fed. Proc.* 1961, **20,** 243
406. GEDDES *Anesth. Analg., Paris* 1958, **15,** 908
407. GEDDES and DOUGLAS *Fed. Proc.* 1956, **15,** 260
408. BECKER *J. dent. Res.* 1961, **40,** 190
409. BECKER *J. dent. Res.* 1961, **40,** 195
410. KALOW *Biochem. Pharmacol.* 1961, **8,** 111
411. WISER and SEIFTER *Pharmacologist* 1961, **3,** 74
412. ADRIANI *The Pharmacology of Anesthetic Drugs.* 4th ed: Charles C. Thomas, Springfield, Ill., 1960
413. BUDESÍNSKÝ and PROTIVA *Synthetische Arzneimittel:* Akademie-Verlag, Berlin, 1961
414. *Xylocaine in Anaesthesia:* Rotopress, Stockholm, 1957
415. *Xylocaine Bibliography:* Skoglunds, Stockholm, 1955
416. GRAY and GEDDES *J. Pharm., Lond.* 1954, **6,** 89
417. WIEDLING *Anaesthesist* 1952, **1,** 119
418. LÖFGREN and TAKMAN *Svensk kem. Tidskr.* 1946, **58,** 206
419. GOLDBERG *Acta physiol. scand.* 1949, **18,** 1
420. SHURAVLEV and TSHUGAJEVA *Med. Ind., Moscow* 1958, **12,** 21
421. BOROVANSKÝ, SEKERA and VRBA *J. Amer. Pharm. Ass., Sci. Ed.* 1959, **48,** 402
422. HACH, HOCH, HORÁKOVÁ and POKORNÝ *Čsl. Farm.* 1959, **8,** 326
423. PRYANISHNIKOVA *Pharm. & Toxic.* 1959, **22,** 138
424. DOFEK, SEKERA and VRBA *Ann. pharm. franç.* 1960, **18,** 159
425. SOLDATOVA *Pharm. & Toxic.* 1960, **23,** 90
426. ANONYMUS *Dent. Echo, Berl.* 1957, **27,** 33
427. WIEDLING *Unpublished results*
428. THER and HARNISCH *Klin. Wschr.* 1953, **31,** 850
429. HARNISCH *Dtsch. zahnärztl. Z.* 1953, **8,** 1224
430. EDLUND and WIEDLING *Odont. Tidskr.* 1954, **62,** 498
431. HOLLER *Zahnärztl. Rdsch.* 1954, **63,** 154
432. PERSSON *Sverig. Tandläk. Förb. Tidn.* 1955, **47,** 34
433. HAUSER *Dtsch. zahnärztl. Z.* 1955, **10,** 1492
434. HAUSER *Dtsch. zahnärztl. Z.* 1955, **10,** 1751
435. GÄRTNER *Dtsch. zahnärztl. Z.* 1955, **10,** 1053
436. GÄRTNER *Dtsch. zahnärztl. Z.* 1956, **11,** 455
437. TRACKSDORF *Dtsch. zahnärztl. Z.* 1955, **10,** 1494
438. ULFENDAHL *Acta anaesth. scand.* 1957, **1,** 81
439. FRAHM *Anaesthesist* 1958, **7,** 44
440. TRUANT and WIEDLING *Acta chir. scand.* 1959, **116,** 351
441. HENN *Acta anaesth. scand.* 1960, **4,** 125

442. BERLING *Odont. Revy* 1958, **9,** 4
443. FELDMAN and NORDENRAM *Svensk tandläk. Tidskr.* 1959, **52,** 531
444. CALISE *Anaesth. Analg.* 1961, **40,** 551
445. WIEDLING *Acta Pharm. Tox.*, *Kbh.* 1960, **17,** 233
446. ÅSTRÖM and PERSSON *Brit. J. Pharmacol.* 1961, **16,** 32
447. BERLING and BJÖRN *Dtsch. zahnärztl. Z.* 1961, **16,** 1497
448. ERIKSSON *Acta anaesth. scand.* 1960, suppl. 6, 40
449. ERIKSSON *Acta anaesth. scand.* 1961, **5,** 191
450. GIOTTI *Giorn. Gerontol.* 1958, **6,** 289
451. ASLAN *Therapiewoche* 1956, **7,** 14
452. ASLAN *Ther. Umsch.* 1956, **13,** 165
453. ASLAN *Medizinische* 1957, **52,** 1758
454. ASLAN *Therapiewoche* 1957, **8,** 10
455. ASLAN *Arzneimitt. Forsch.* 1958, **8,** 11
456. ASLAN *Minerva med.* 1958, **49,** 3570
457. EDITORIAL *Brit. med. J.* 1959, **2,** 1163
458. CHIU *J. Amer. med. Ass.* 1961, **175,** 502
459. BERRYMAN, FORBES and SIMPSON-WHITE *Brit. med. J.* 1961, **2,** 1683
460. FEE and CLARK *Brit. med. J.* 1961, **2,** 1680
461. GERICKE, LOBB and PARDOLL *J. clin. exper. Psychopathol.* 1961, **22,** 18
462. HIRSH *Brit. med. J.* 1961, **2,** 1684
463. VERZÁR *Gerontologia* 1959, **3,** 351
464. MÜLLER-DIETZ *Dtsch. med. Wschr.* 1956, **81,** 481
465. SHANG TE-YEN and HSIEH JUNG *Chung-hua Wai-ko Tsa-chih (Chinese J. Surg.)* 1959, **7,** 848. Abstracted in *Anesthesiology* 1961, **22,** 855
466. FOLDES, DAVIS and PLEKSS *Anesthosiology* 1956, **17,** 187
467. ANSBRO, PILLION, BLUNDELL and BODELL *N.Y. St. J. Med.* 1958, **58,** 3447
468. ANSBRO, BLUNDELL, FURLONG, PILLION and BODELL *Arch. Surg., Chicago* 1959, **78,** 75
469. ANSBRO, BLUNDELL, BODELL and PILLION *Anesth. Analg., Cleveland* 1960, **39,** 7
470. BONICA *Survey Anesthesiol.* 1960, **4,** 562
471. BONICA, NISHIMURA, LAWRENCE and GOODSON *Anesthesiology* 1960, **21,** 92
472. SWERDLOW and BROWN *Brit. J. Anaesthesia* 1961, **33,** 642
473. LUDUENA *Anesthesiology* 1955, **16,** 751
474. LUDUENA *J. dent. Res.* 1960, **39,** 947
475. SCHMIDT, MARTIN and POHLEY *J. Pharmacol.* 1955, **113,** 46
476. EPSTEIN, MEYER and GINSBERG *Curr. Res. Anesth.* 1955, **34,** 171
477. BROADBENT *Austral. dent. J.* 1957, **2,** 67
478. TRUANT *Arch. int. Pharmacodyn.* 1958, **115,** 483
479. PROFFT *Die Falicaine; Chemie, Pharmakologie und klinische Anwendung:* Verlag Technik, Berlin, 1954
480. HANNIG *Arzneimitt. Forsch.* 1955, **5,** 559
481. ARORA and SHARMA *J. Pharmacol.* 1955, **115,** 413
482. ABREU, RICHARDS, WEAVER, BURCH, BUNDE, BOCKSTAHLER and WRIGHT *J. Pharmacol.* 1955, **115,** 419
483. HUGHES, MOBLEY, BILLS, BURWELL and PATE *J. thorac. Surg.* 1957, **33,** 685
484. FLORESTANO and BAHLER *J. Amer. pharm. Ass., Sci. Ed.* 1956, **45,** 320
485. SOEHRING *Arch. int. Pharmacodyn.* 1951, **86,** 472
486. SOEHRING, SCRIBA, FRAHM and ZOELLNER *Arch. int. Pharmacodyn.* 1951, **87,** 301
487. SIEMS and SOEHRING *Arzneimitt. Forsch.* 1952, **2,** 109
488. SOEHRING, DASS and STAVE *Arch. int. Pharmacodyn.* 1952, **89,** 365
489. STELLMACH, SCHRÖDER and SOEHRING *Arch. int. Pharmacodyn.* 1952, **89,** 380
490. SOEHRING, FRAHM and MLETZKO *Arch. int. Pharmacodyn.* 1952, **91,** 112
491. SOEHRING and FRAHM *Arzneimitt. Forsch.* 1955, **5,** 655

492. SOEHRING *Arzneimitt. Forsch.* 1957, **7,** 282
493. ZIPF, WETZELS, LUDWIG and FRIEDRICH *Arzneimitt. Forsch.* 1957, **7,** 162
494. ZIPF and HANSEN *Arch. exp. Path. Pharmak.* 1961, **242,** 284
495. FRIBERG *Nord. med.* 1955, **54,** 1824
496. HORÁKOVÁ, HACH and SMOLKOVÁ *Čsl. Farm.* 1956, **5,** 430

# INDEX

Italicized page numbers indicate that the subject is referred to on subsequent pages.